AUTOMOTIVE ENGINEERING
Suspension & Steering Systems
(*Shop Manual*)

Don Knowles

CENGAGE Learning™

Australia • Brazil • Japan • Korea • Mexico • Singapore • Spain • United Kingdom • United States

Automotive Engineering: Suspension & Steering Systems (Shop Manual)
Don Knowles

ISBN-13: 978-81-315-1288-3

Cengage Learning India Private Limited
418, F.I.E. Patparganj
New Delhi-110092

Tel: 91-11-43641111
Fax: 91-11-43641100

Cengage Learning products are represented in Canada by Nelson Education, Ltd.

For product information, visit www.cengage.co.in

Printed in India
First Indian Reprint 2010

CONTENTS

Preface to the India Edition

Unlike yesterday's mechanic, the technician of today and for the future must know the underlying theory of all automotive systems and be able to service and maintain those systems. Dividing the material into two volumes provides the reader with the information needed to begin a successful career as an automotive technician without interrupting the learning process by mixing cognitive and performance learning objectives into one volume.

Each Classroom Manual contains the principles of operation for each system and subsystem. The Classroom Manual also contains discussions on design variations of key components used by the different vehicle manufacturers. This volume is organized to build on basic facts and theories. The primary objective of this volume is to allow the reader to gain an understanding of how each system and subsystem operates. This understanding is necessary to diagnose the complex automobiles of today and tomorrow. Although the basics contained in the Classroom Manual provide the knowledge needed for diagnostics, diagnostic procedures appear only in the Shop Manual. An understanding of the basics is also a requirement for competence in the skill areas covered in the Shop Manual.

This Shop Manual covers the "how-to's." This volume includes step-by-step instructions for diagnostic and repair procedures. Photo Sequences are used to illustrate some of the common service procedures. Other common procedures are listed and are accompanied with line drawings and photos that allow the reader to visualize and conceptualize the finest details of the procedure. This volume also contains the reasons for performing the procedures as well as when that particular service is appropriate.

The two volumes are designed to be used together and are arranged in corresponding chapters. Not only are the chapters in the volumes linked together, but also the contents of the chapters are linked.

Both volumes contain clear and thoughtfully selected illustrations, many of which are original drawings or photos specially prepared for inclusion in this series. This means that the art is a vital part of each textbook and not merely inserted to increase the numbers of illustrations.

REVIEWERS

The author and publisher would like to extend a special thanks to the following instructors who reviewed this text and offered their invaluable feedback.

Jim Addington
Lincoln Land Community College
Springfield, IL

Steve Bilger
Valdosta Technical College
Valdosta, GA

Dana Brewer
Wyoming Technical Institute
Laramie, WY

Roger Donovan
Illinois Central College
East Peoria, IL

C. Neel Flannagan
Aiken Technical College
Graniteville, SC

Eddie Shumate
Forsyth Technical Community College
Winston-Salem, NC

Randy Smith
Northeast Wisconsin Technical College
Green Bay, WI

John Wood
Ranken Technical College
St. Louis, MO

1

SAFETY

Upon completion and review of this chapter, you should be able to:

- Recognize shop hazards and take the necessary steps to avoid personal injury or property damage.
- Describe the general shop rules that must be followed in an automotive shop.
- Explain the purposes of the Occupational Safety and Health Act.
- Explain two reasons why batteries are a shop hazard.
- Describe how long hair may be a shop hazard.
- Explain how incandescent trouble lights may be a shop hazard.
- Describe the harmful effects of carbon monoxide on the human body.
- Explain why asbestos dust in the shop air is a hazard.
- Describe the requirements for the location of safety equipment in the shop.
- Explain four different types of fires, and the fire extinguisher required for each type of fire.
- Describe three pieces of shop safety equipment other than fire extinguishers.
- Describe the main purposes of the Right-to-Know laws.

- Describe the purpose of MSDSs and list the information that must be contained on these sheets.
- Explain the employer's responsibility regarding hazardous materials in the shop.
- Observe all general shop safety precautions.
- Demonstrate all precautions related to personal safety when working in the shop.
- Explain why smoking is dangerous in the shop.
- Explain why drug or alcohol use is dangerous in the shop.
- Describe basic electrical safety precautions.
- Explain gasoline safety precautions.
- Describe housekeeping safety precautions.
- Explain fire safety precautions.
- Describe the proper procedure for using a fire extinguisher.
- Describe the necessary precautions to maintain air bag safety.
- Describe the precautions to be observed when driving vehicles in the shop.
- Explain the proper procedure for lifting heavy objects.
- Describe the necessary steps for hand tool safety.
- Explain the necessary precautions when operating a vehicle lift.
- Describe hydraulic jack and safety stand safety precautions.
- Explain the necessary safety precautions when using power tools.
- Describe the precautions required to maintain compressed-air equipment safety.
- Explain the precautions and environmental concerns related to cleaning equipment safety.

INTRODUCTION

Safety is extremely important in the automotive shop! The knowledge and practice of safety precautions prevent serious personal injury and expensive property damage. Automotive students and technicians must be familiar with shop hazards and shop safety rules. The first step in providing a safe shop is learning about shop hazards and safety rules. The second, and most important, step in this process is applying your knowledge of shop hazards and safety rules while working in the shop. In other words, you must develop safe working habits in the shop from your understanding of shop hazards and safety rules. When shop employees have a careless attitude toward safety, accidents are more likely to occur; therefore, all shop personnel must develop a serious attitude toward safety. The result of this attitude is serious shop personnel who will learn and adopt all shop safety rules.

Shop personnel must be familiar with their rights regarding hazardous waste disposal. These rights are explained in the **Right-to-Know laws**. Shop personnel must also be familiar with the types of hazardous materials in the automotive shop and the proper disposal methods for these materials according to state and federal regulations.

OCCUPATIONAL SAFETY AND HEALTH ACT

The **Occupational Safety and Health Act** (**OSHA**) was passed by the U.S. government in 1970. The purposes of this legislation are:

1. to assist and encourage the citizens of the United States in their efforts to ensure safe and healthful working conditions by providing research, information, education, and training in the field of occupational safety and health.
2. to ensure safe and healthful working conditions for working men and women by authorizing enforcement of the standards developed under the Act.

Because approximately 25 percent of workers are exposed to health and safety hazards on the job, the OSHA is necessary to monitor, control, and educate workers regarding health and safety in the workplace.

SHOP HAZARDS

Service technicians and students encounter many hazards in an automotive shop. When these hazards are known, basic shop safety rules and procedures must be followed to avoid personal injury. Some of the hazards in an automotive shop include the following:

1. Flammable liquids, such as gasoline and paint, must be handled and stored properly in approved, closed containers to comply with safety regulations.
2. Flammable materials, such as oily rags, must be stored properly in closed containers to avoid a fire hazard.
3. Batteries contain a corrosive sulfuric acid solution and produce explosive hydrogen gas while charging.
4. Loose sewer and drain covers may cause foot or toe injuries.
5. Caustic liquids, such as those in hot cleaning tanks, are harmful to skin and eyes.
6. High-pressure air in the shop's compressed-air system can be very dangerous or fatal if it penetrates the skin and enters the bloodstream. High-pressure air released near the eyes may cause eye injury.
7. Frayed cords on electrical equipment and lights may result in severe electrical shock.
8. Hazardous waste material, such as batteries and caustic cleaning solutions, must be handled with adequate personal protection to avoid injury (Figure 1-1).
9. Carbon monoxide from vehicle exhaust is poisonous and potentially fatal.
10. Loose clothing or long hair may become entangled in rotating parts on equipment or vehicles, resulting in serious injury.
11. Dust and vapors generated during some repair jobs are harmful. Asbestos dust, which may be released during brake lining service and clutch service, is a contributor to lung cancer.

FIGURE 1-1 *Always wear recommended safety clothing and equipment when handling hazardous materials.*

12. High noise levels from shop equipment such as an air chisel may be harmful to the ears.
13. Oil, grease, water, or parts cleaning solutions on shop floors may cause someone to slip and fall, resulting in serious injury.
14. The incandescent bulbs used in some trouble lights may shatter if the light is dropped, igniting flammable materials in the area and causing a fire. Many insurance companies now require the use of trouble lights with fluorescent bulbs in the shop.

SHOP SAFETY RULES

Applying basic shop rules helps prevent serious, expensive accidents. Failure to comply with shop rules may cause personal injury or expensive damage to vehicles and shop facilities. It is the responsibility of the employer and all shop employees to make sure that shop rules are understood and followed until these rules become automatic habits. The following basic shop rules should be observed:

1. Always wear safety glasses and other protective equipment that is required by a service procedure (Figure 1-2). For example, a brake parts washer must be used to avoid breathing asbestos dust into the lungs. Asbestos dust is a known cause of lung cancer. This dust is encountered in manual transmission clutch facings and brake linings.
2. Tie long hair securely behind your head, and do not wear loose or torn clothing.
3. Do not wear rings, watches, or loose hanging jewelry. If jewelry such as a ring, metal watchband, or chain makes contact between an electrical terminal and ground, the jewelry becomes extremely hot, resulting in severe burns.

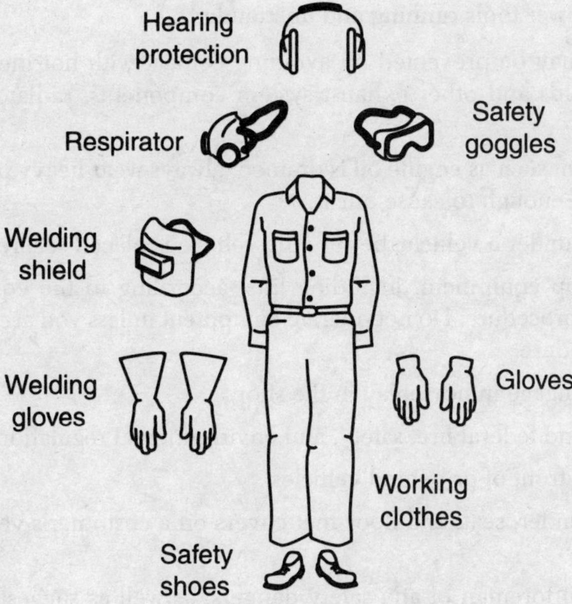

FIGURE 1-2 *Shop safety clothing and equipment, including safety goggles, respirator, welding shield, proper work clothes, ear protection, welding gloves, work gloves, and safety shoes.*

4. Do not work in the shop while under the influence of alcohol or drugs.
5. Set the parking brake when working on a vehicle. If the vehicle has an automatic transmission, place the gear selector in park unless a service procedure requires another selector position. When the vehicle is equipped with a manual transmission, position the gear selector in neutral with the engine running or in reverse with the engine stopped.
6. Always connect a shop exhaust hose to the vehicle tailpipe, and be sure the shop exhaust fan is running. If it is absolutely necessary to operate a vehicle without a shop exhaust pipe connected to the tailpipe, open the large shop door to provide adequate ventilation. Carbon monoxide in the vehicle exhaust may cause severe headaches and other medical problems. High concentrations of carbon monoxide may result in death!
7. Keep hands, clothing, and wrenches away from rotating parts such as cooling fans. Remember that electric-drive fans may start turning at any time, even with the ignition off.
8. Always leave the ignition switch off unless a service procedure requires another switch position.
9. Do not smoke in the shop. If the shop has designated smoking areas, smoke only in these areas.
10. Store oily rags and other discarded combustibles in covered metal containers designed for this purpose.
11. Always use the wrench or socket that fits properly on the bolt. Do not substitute metric for English wrenches, or vice versa.
12. Keep tools in good condition. For example, do not use a punch or chisel with a mushroomed end because when struck with a hammer, a piece of the mushroomed metal could break off, resulting in severe eye or other injury.

13. Do not leave power tools running and unattended.
14. Serious burns may be prevented by avoiding contact with hot metal components, such as exhaust manifolds and other exhaust system components, radiators, and some air-conditioning hoses.
15. When a lubricant such as engine oil is drained, always wear heavy plastic gloves because the oil could be hot enough to cause burns.
16. Prior to getting under a vehicle, be sure the vehicle is placed securely on safety stands.
17. Operate all shop equipment, including lifts, according to the equipment manufacturer's recommended procedure. Do not operate equipment unless you are familiar with the correct operating procedure.
18. Do not run or engage in horseplay in the shop.
19. Obey all state and federal fire, safety, and environmental regulations.
20. Do not stand in front of or behind vehicles.
21. Always place fender, seat, and floor mat covers on a customer's vehicle before working on the car.
22. Inform the shop foreman of any safety dangers, as well as suggestions for safety improvement.
23. Do not direct high-pressure air from an air gun toward human skin or near the eyes. High-pressure air may penetrate the skin and enter the bloodstream. Air in the bloodstream may be fatal! High-pressure air discharged near the eyes may cause serious eye damage.

AIR QUALITY

Vehicle exhaust contains small amounts of carbon monoxide, which is a poisonous gas. Weak concentrations of carbon monoxide in the shop air may cause nausea and headaches; strong concentrations may be fatal. All shop personnel are responsible for air quality in the shop. Shop management is responsible for providing an adequate exhaust system that can remove exhaust fumes from the maximum-allowable number of vehicles that may be running in the shop at one time. Technicians should never run a vehicle in the shop unless a shop exhaust hose is installed on the tailpipe of the vehicle. The exhaust fan must be switched on to remove exhaust fumes.

If shop heaters or furnaces have restricted chimneys, they release carbon monoxide emissions into the shop air. Therefore, chimneys should be checked periodically for restriction and proper ventilation. Diesel exhaust contains some carbon monoxide, but particulate emissions are also present in the exhaust from these engines. Particulates are small carbon particles that can be harmful to the lungs.

Monitors are available to measure the level of carbon monoxide in the shop. Some of these monitors read the amount of carbon monoxide present in the shop air; others provide an audible alarm if the concentration of carbon monoxide exceeds the danger level.

The sulfuric acid solution in car batteries is a corrosive, poisonous liquid. If a battery is charged with a fast charger at a high rate for a period of time, the battery becomes hot, and the sulfuric acid solution begins to boil. Under this condition, the battery may emit strong sulfuric acid fumes that may be harmful to the lungs. If this happens, the battery charger should be turned off or the charging rate should be reduced considerably.

Some automotive clutch facings and brake linings contain asbestos. Never use an air hose to blow dirt from these components, because this action disperses asbestos dust into the shop where it may be inhaled by technicians and other people in the shop. A brake parts washer or a vacuum cleaner with special attachments must be used to clean the dust from these components. Even though technicians take every precaution to maintain air quality in the shop, some undesirable gases may still get into the air. For example, exhaust manifolds may get oil on them during an engine overhaul. When the engine is started and these manifolds get hot, the oil burns off the manifolds and pollutes the shop air with oil smoke. Adequate shop ventilation must be provided to take care of this type of air contamination.

SHOP SAFETY EQUIPMENT

Fire Extinguishers

Fire extinguishers are one of the most important pieces of safety equipment. All shop personnel must know the location of each fire extinguisher in the shop. If you have to waste time looking for an extinguisher after a fire starts, the fire could get out of control before you get the extinguisher into operation. Fire extinguishers should be located where they are easily accessible at all times. A decal on each fire extinguisher identifies the type of chemical in the extinguisher and provides operating information (Figure 1-3). Shop personnel should be familiar with the following types of fires and fire extinguishers:

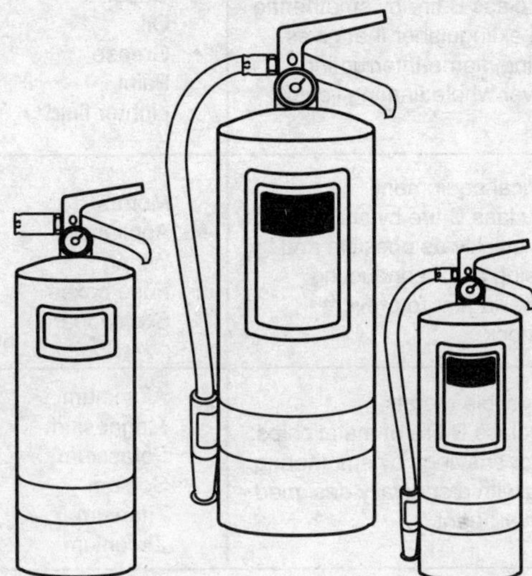

FIGURE 1-3 *Types of fire extinguishers.*

1. *Class A fires* are those involving ordinary combustible materials such as paper, wood, clothing, and textiles. **Multipurpose dry chemical fire extinguishers** are used on these fires.
2. *Class B fires* involve the burning of flammable liquids such as gasoline, oil, paint, solvents, and greases. These fires can also be extinguished with multipurpose dry chemical fire extinguishers. In addition, fire extinguishers containing halogen, or halon, may be used to extinguish class B fires. The chemicals in this type of extinguisher attach to the hydrogen, hydroxide, and oxygen molecules to stop the combustion process almost instantly. However, the resultant gases from the use of halogen-type extinguishers are very toxic and harmful to the operator of the extinguisher.

3. *Class C fires* involve the burning of electrical equipment such as wires, motors, and switches. These fires can be extinguished with multipurpose dry chemical fire extinguishers.
4. *Class D fires* involve the combustion of metal chips, turnings, and shavings. Dry chemical fire extinguishers are the only type of extinguisher recommended for these fires.

Some multipurpose dry chemical fire extinguishers may be used on Class A, B, C, or D fires. Additional information regarding which types of extinguishers are used for various types of fires is provided in Table 1-1.

TABLE 1-1 *Guide to Fire Extinguisher Selection*

	Class of fire	Typical fuel involved	Type of extinguisher
Class A Fires (green)	For ordinary combustibles Put out a class A fire by blowing its temperature or by coating the burning combustibles.	Wood Paper Cloth Rubber Plastics Rubbish Upholstery	Water* Foam* Multipurpose dry chemical
Class B Fires (red)	For flammable liquids Put out a class B fire by smothering it. Use an extinguisher that gives a blanketing, flame-interrupting effect; cover whole flaming liquid surface.	Gasoline Oil Grease Paint Lighter fluid	Foam* Carbon dioxide Halogenated agent Standard dry chemical Purple K dry chemical Multipurpose dry chemical
Class C Fires (blue)	For electrical equipment Put out a class C fire by shutting off power as quickly as possible and by always using a nonconducting extinguisher agent to prevent electric shock.	Motors Appliances Wiring Fuse boxes Switchboards	Carbon dioxide Halogenated agent Standard dry chemical Purple K dry chemical Multipurpose dry chemical
Class D Fires (yellow)	For combustible metals Put out a class D fire of metal chips, turnings, or shavings by smothering or coating with a specially designed extinguisher agent.	Aluminum Magnesium Potassium Sodium Titanium Zirconium	Dry power extinguisher and agents only

*Cartridge-operated water, foam, and soda-acid types of extinguishers are no longer manufactured. These extinguishers should be removed from service when they become due for their next hydrostatic pressure test.

Causes of Eye Injuries

Eye injuries can occur in various ways in the automotive shop. Some of the more common eye accidents are:

1. Thermal burns from excessive heat
2. Irradiation burns from excessive light such as from an arc welder
3. Chemical burns from strong liquids such as battery electrolyte

4. Foreign material in the eye
5. Penetration of the eye by a sharp object
6. A blow from a blunt object

Wearing safety glasses and observing shop safety rules will prevent most eye accidents

Eyewash Fountains

If a chemical gets in your eyes, it must be washed out immediately to prevent a chemical burn. An eyewash fountain is the most effective way to wash the eyes. An eyewash fountain is similar to a drinking water fountain, but the eyewash fountain has water jets placed throughout the fountain top. Every shop should be equipped with some type of eyewash facility (Figure 1-4). Be sure you know the location of the eyewash fountain in the shop.

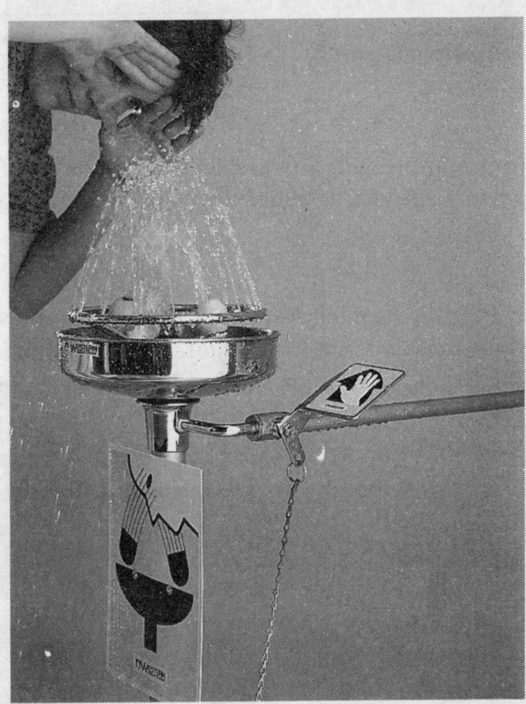

FIGURE 1-4 *Eyewash fountain.*

Safety Glasses and Face Shields

The mandatory use of eye protection, either safety glasses or a face shield, is one of the most important safety rules in an automotive shop. Face shields protect the face; safety glasses protect the eyes. When grinding, safety glasses must be worn, and a face shield can be worn. Many shop insurance policies require the use of eye protection in the shop. Some automotive technicians have been blinded in one or both eyes because they did not wear safety glasses. All safety glasses must be equipped with safety glass and should provide some type of side protection (Figure 1-5). When selecting a pair of safety glasses, they should feel comfortable on your face because if they are uncomfortable, you may

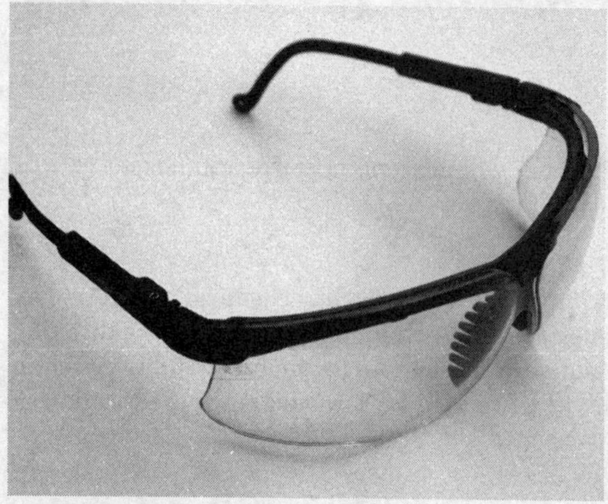

FIGURE 1-5 *Safety glasses with side protection must be worn in the automotive shop.*

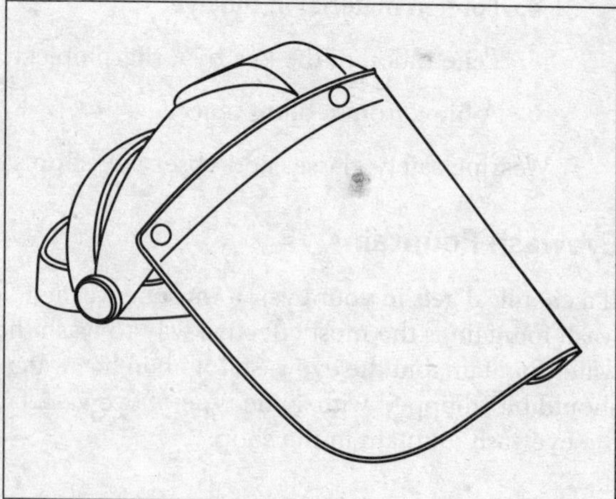

FIGURE 1-6 *Face shield.*

remove them, leaving your eyes unprotected. A face shield should be worn when handling hazardous chemicals or when using an electric grinder or buffer (Figure 1-6).

First-Aid Kits

First-aid kits should be clearly identified and conveniently located (Figure 1-7). These kits contain such items as bandages in a variety of sizes and ointment required for minor cuts. All shop personnel must be familiar with the location of first-aid kits. At least one of the shop personnel should have basic first-aid training. This person should be in charge of administering first aid and keeping first-aid kits filled.

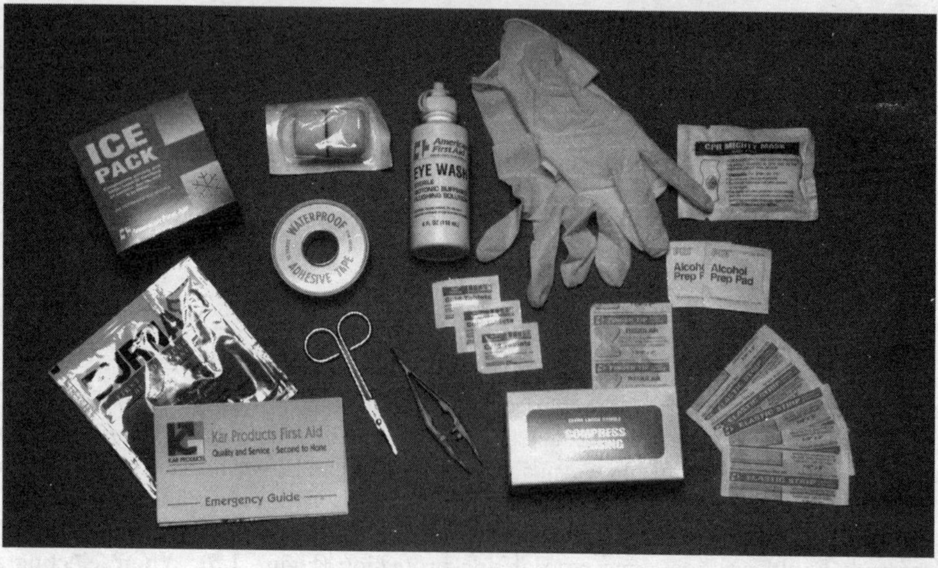

FIGURE 1-7 *First-aid kit.*

SHOP LAYOUT

There are many different types of shops in the automotive service industry, including:

- New car dealers
- Independent repair shops
- Specialty shops
- Service stations
- Fleet shops

In any shop, the layout is important to maintain shop efficiency and contribute to safety. Every shop employee must be familiar with the location of all safety equipment in the shop. Shop layout includes bays for various types of repairs, equipment storage areas, and office locations. Some specific types of bays are electrical repair, wheel alignment and tires, and machining bays (Figure 1-8). Safety equipment such as fire extinguishers, first-aid kits, and eyewash fountains must be in easily accessible locations, and the location of each piece of safety equipment must be clearly marked. Areas such as the parts department and the parts cleaning area must be located so they are easily accessible from all areas of the shop. The service manager's office should also be centrally located. All shop personnel should familiarize themselves with the shop layout, especially the location of safety equipment. If you know the exact fire extinguisher locations, you may get an extinguisher into operation a few seconds faster. Those few seconds could make the difference between a fire that is quickly extinguished and one that gets out of control, causing extensive damage and personal injury!

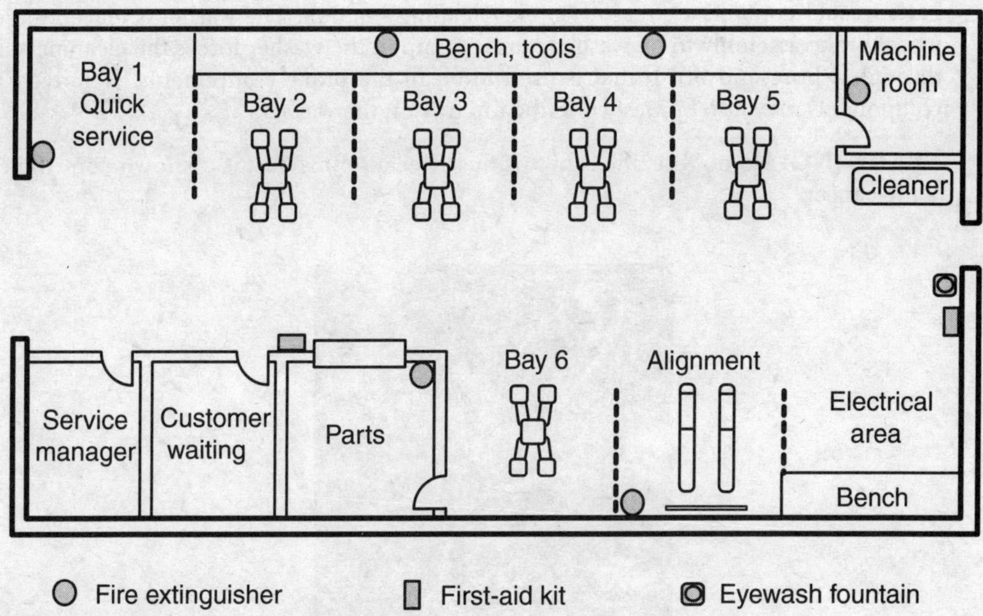

FIGURE 1-8 *Shop layout.*

The tools and equipment required for a certain type of work are stored in that specific bay. For example, the equipment for electrical and electronic service work is stored in the bay allotted to that type of repair. When certain bays are allotted to specific types of repair work, unnecessary equipment movement is eliminated. Each technician has his or her own tools on a portable roll cabinet that is moved to the vehicle being repaired. Special tools are provided by the shop, and these tools should be located on tool boards attached to the wall. Other shops may have a tool room where special tools are located. Adequate workbench space must be provided in those bays where bench work is required.

SAFETY IN THE AUTOMOTIVE SHOP

Each person in an automotive shop must follow certain basic shop safety rules to remove the danger from shop hazards and prevent personal injury, vehicle damage, and property damage.

Technicians must understand shop safety as it applies to these categories:

1. General shop safety
2. Personal safety

GENERAL SHOP SAFETY

When general shop safety rules are observed, personal injury and expensive property or vehicle damage may be avoided, and shop production is increased.

1. All sewer covers must fit properly and be kept securely in place.
2. When servicing brakes or clutches from manual transmissions, always clean asbestos dust from these components with an OSHA-approved brake parts washer (Figure 1-9). The brake parts washer contains a Greasoff® brake cleaning solution. The washer is placed under the wheel brake assembly to be washed, and a pump in the washer forces the cleaning solution through a hose and brush that is used to clean the brake components. Removed brake components may also be washed in the top tray on the washer.

WARNING: Do not breathe asbestos dust, because this dust is a known contributor to lung cancer.

FIGURE 1-9 *Brake parts cleaner.*

3. Always use the correct tool for the job. For example, never strike a hardened steel component, such as a piston pin, with a steel hammer. This type of component may shatter, and fragments can penetrate eyes or skin.
4. Follow the car manufacturer's recommended service procedures.
5. Avoid working on a vehicle parked on an incline.
6. Never work under a vehicle unless the vehicle chassis is supported securely on safety stands.
7. When one end of a vehicle is raised, place wheel chocks on both sides of the wheels remaining on the floor.
8. Be sure that you know the location of shop first-aid kits, eyewash fountains, and fire extinguishers.
9. Collect oil, fuel, brake fluid, and other liquids in the proper safety containers.
10. Use only approved cleaning fluids and equipment. Do not use gasoline to clean parts.
11. Do not leave running equipment unattended.
12. Be sure the safety shields are in place on rotating equipment.
13. All shop equipment must have regularly scheduled maintenance and adjustment.
14. Some shops have safety lines around equipment. Always work within these lines when operating equipment.
15. Be sure that shop heating equipment is well-ventilated.
16. Do not run in the shop or engage in horseplay.
17. Post emergency phone numbers near the phone. These numbers should include doctor, ambulance, fire department, hospital, and police.
18. Do not place hydraulic jack handles where someone can trip over them.
19. Keep aisles clear of debris.

PERSONAL SAFETY

Personal safety is the responsibility of each technician in the shop.

Always follow these safety practices:

1. Always use the correct tool for the job. If the wrong tool is used, it may slip and cause injury.
2. Follow the vehicle manufacturer's recommended service procedures.
3. Always wear eye protection, such as safety glasses with side protection or a face shield.
4. Wear protective gloves when cleaning parts in hot or cold tanks and when handling hot parts, such as exhaust manifolds.
5. Do not smoke when working in the shop. A spark from a cigarette or lighter may ignite flammable materials in the work area.
6. When working on a running engine, keep hands and tools away from rotating parts. Remember that electric-drive fans may start turning at any time.
7. Do not wear loose clothing, and keep long hair tied behind your head. Loose clothing or long hair is easily entangled in rotating parts.
8. Wear safety shoes or boots. Heavy-duty work boots or shoes with steel toe caps are best for working in the automotive shop. Footwear must protect against heavy falling objects, flying

sparks, and corrosive liquids. Soles on footwear must protect against punctures by sharp objects. Athletic shoes and street shoes are not recommended in the shop.

9. Be sure that the shop has adequate ventilation. Carbon monoxide is odorless; do not expect to be able to smell it.
10. Make sure the work area has adequate lighting.
11. When servicing a vehicle, always apply the parking brake. Place the transmission in park with an automatic transmission, or neutral with a manual transmission.
12. Avoid working on a vehicle parked on an incline.
13. Never work under a vehicle unless the vehicle chassis is supported securely on safety stands.
14. Do not use electrical equipment, including trouble lights, with frayed cords.
15. Be sure the safety shields are in place on rotating equipment.
16. Before operating electric equipment, be sure the power cord has a ground connection.
17. When working in an area where noise levels are extreme, wear earplugs or ear covers.
18. Wear a respirator to protect your lungs when working in dusty conditions.
19. Do not use **incandescent bulb-type trouble lights**. Use **fluorescent trouble lights** (Figure 1-10).

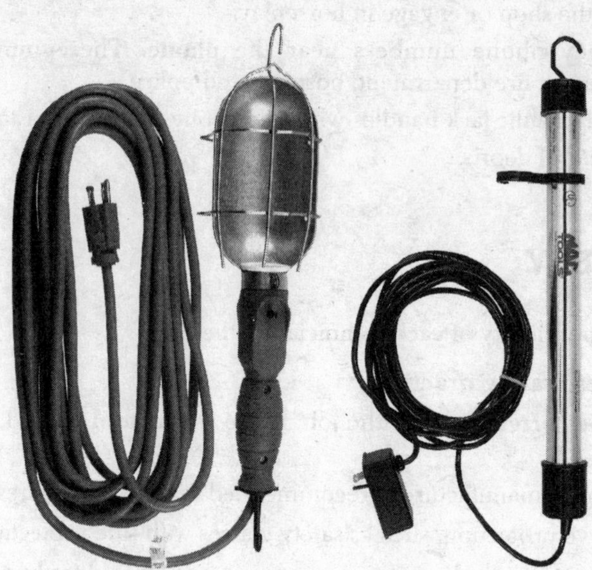

FIGURE 1-10 *Incandescent-type trouble light and fluorescent-type trouble light. (Courtesy of Mac Tools, Inc.)*

Smoking, Alcohol, and Drugs in the Shop

Do not smoke when working in the shop. If the shop has designated smoking areas, smoke only in these areas. Do not smoke in customers' cars. A nonsmoker will not appreciate cigarette odor in the car. A spark from a cigarette or lighter may ignite flammable materials in the workplace. The use of drugs or alcohol must be avoided while working in the shop. Even a small amount of drugs or alcohol affects reaction time. In an emergency situation, slow reaction time may cause personal injury. If a heavy object falls off the workbench, and your reaction time is slowed by drugs or alcohol, you may not get your foot out of the way in time to avoid a foot injury. When a fire starts in the workplace, and you are a few seconds slower getting a fire extinguisher into operation because of alcohol or drug use, it could make the difference between extinguishing a fire and having expensive fire damage.

ELECTRICAL SAFETY

In the automotive shop you will be using electric drills, shop lights, wheel balancers, and wheel aligners.

Observe the following electrical safety precautions on this equipment:

1. Frayed cords on electrical equipment must be replaced or repaired immediately.
2. All electrical cords from lights and electrical equipment must have a ground connection. The ground connector is the round terminal in a three-pronged electrical plug. Do not use a two-pronged adapter to plug in a three-pronged electrical cord. Three-pronged electrical outlets should be mandatory in all shops.
3. Do not leave electrical equipment running and unattended.

GASOLINE SAFETY

Gasoline is a very explosive liquid! One exploding gallon of gasoline has a force equal to 14 sticks of dynamite. The expanding vapors from gasoline are extremely dangerous. These vapors are present even in cold temperatures. Vapors formed in gasoline tanks on cars are controlled, but vapors from a gasoline storage can may escape from the can, resulting in a hazardous situation. Therefore, gasoline storage containers must be placed in a well-ventilated space.

Approved gasoline storage cans have a flash-arresting screen at the outlet (Figure 1-11). This screen prevents external ignition sources from igniting the gasoline within the can while the gasoline is being poured.

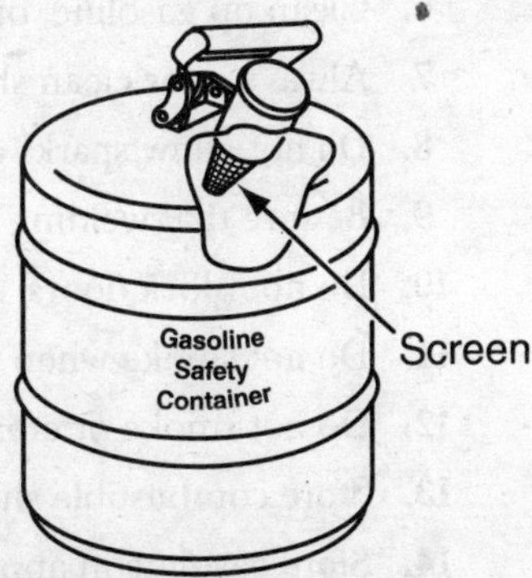

FIGURE 1-11 *Approved gasoline container.*

Follow these safety precautions regarding gasoline containers:

1. Always use approved gasoline containers that are painted red for proper identification.
2. Do not fill gasoline containers completely full. Always leave the level of gasoline at least one inch from the top of the container. This allows for expansion of the gasoline at higher temperatures. If gasoline containers are completely full, the gasoline will expand when the temperature increases. This expansion forces gasoline from the can and creates a dangerous spill.
3. If gasoline containers must be stored, place them in a well-ventilated area such as a storage shed. Do not store gasoline containers in your home or in the trunk of a vehicle.
4. When a gasoline container must be transported, be sure it is secured against upsets.
5. Do not store a partially filled gasoline container for long periods of time, because it may give off vapors and produce a potential danger.

6. Never leave gasoline containers open except while filling or pouring gasoline from the container.
7. Do not prime an engine with gasoline while cranking the engine.
8. Never use gasoline as a cleaning agent.

FIRE SAFETY

When fire safety rules are observed, personal injury and expensive fire damage to vehicles and property may be avoided. Follow these fire safety rules:

1. Familiarize yourself with the location and operation of all shop fire extinguishers.
2. If a fire extinguisher is used, report it to management so the extinguisher can be recharged.
3. Do not use any type of open-flame heater to heat the work area.
4. Do not turn on the ignition switch or crank the engine with a gasoline line disconnected.
5. Store all combustible materials such as gasoline, paint, and oily rags in approved safety containers.
6. Clean up gasoline, oil, or grease spills immediately.
7. Always wear clean shop clothes. Do not wear oil-soaked clothes.
8. Do not allow sparks and flames near batteries.
9. Be sure that welding tanks are securely fastened in an upright position.
10. Do not block doors, stairways, or exits.
11. Do not smoke when working on vehicles.
12. Do not smoke or create sparks near flammable materials or liquids.
13. Store combustible shop supplies such as paint in a closed steel cabinet.
14. Store gasoline in approved safety containers.
15. If a gasoline tank is removed from a vehicle, do not drag the tank on the shop floor.
16. Know the approved fire escape route from your classroom or shop to the outside of the building.
17. If a fire occurs, do not open doors or windows. This action creates extra draft, which makes the fire worse.
18. Do not put water on a gasoline fire, because the water will make the fire worse.
19. Call the fire department as soon as a fire begins, and then attempt to extinguish the fire.
20. If possible, stand 6 to 10 feet from the fire and aim the fire extinguisher nozzle at the base of the fire with a sweeping action.
21. If a fire produces a lot of smoke in the room, remain close to the floor to obtain oxygen and avoid breathing smoke.
22. If the fire is too hot or the smoke makes breathing difficult, get out of the building.
23. Do not re-enter a burning building.
24. Keep solvent containers covered except when pouring from one container to another. When flammable liquids are transferred from bulk storage, the bulk container should be

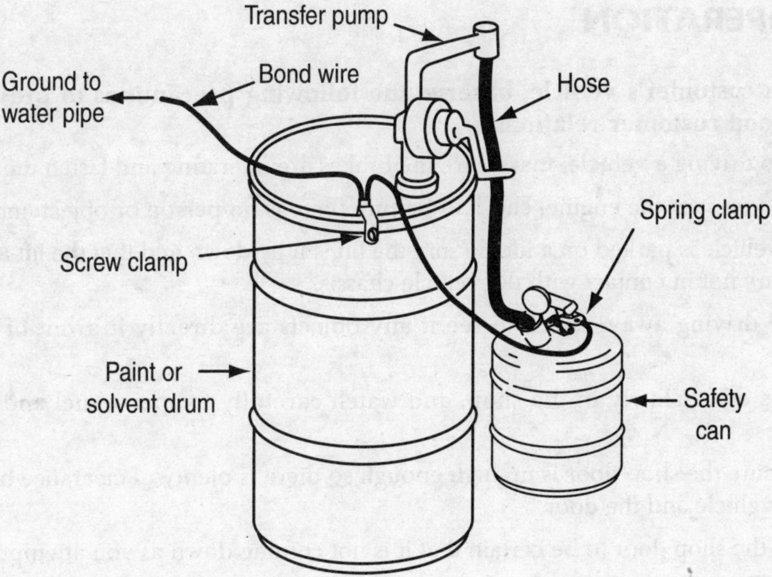

FIGURE 1-12 *Safe procedures for flammable liquid transfer.*

grounded to a permanent shop fixture, such as a metal pipe. During this transfer process, the bulk container should be grounded to the portable container (Figure 1-12). These ground wires prevent the buildup of a static electric charge, which could cause a spark and a disastrous explosion. Always discard or clean empty solvent containers, because fumes in these containers are a fire hazard.

25. Familiarize yourself with different types of fires and fire extinguishers, and know the type of extinguisher to use on each type of fire.

Using a Fire Extinguisher

Everyone working in the shop must know how to operate the fire extinguishers.

There are several different types of fire extinguishers, but their operation usually involves the following steps:

1. Get as close as possible to the fire without jeopardizing your safety.
2. Grasp the extinguisher firmly and aim the extinguisher at the fire.
3. Pull the pin from the extinguisher handle.
4. Squeeze the handle to dispense the contents of the extinguisher.
5. Direct the fire extinguisher nozzle at the base of the fire, and dispense the contents of the extinguisher with a sweeping action back and forth across the fire. Most extinguishers discharge their contents in 8 to 25 seconds.
6. Always be sure the fire is extinguished.
7. Always keep an escape route open behind you so a quick exit is possible if the fire gets out of control.

VEHICLE OPERATION

When driving a customer's vehicle, observe the following precautions to prevent accidents and maintain good customer relations:

1. Prior to driving a vehicle, make sure the brakes are operating and fasten the safety belt.
2. Before you start the engine, check to be sure there is no person or object under the car.
3. If the vehicle is parked on a lift, be sure the lift is fully down and that the lift arms or components are not in contact with the vehicle chassis.
4. Before driving away, check to see if any objects are directly in front of or behind the vehicle.
5. Always drive slowly in the shop, and watch carefully for personnel and other moving vehicles.
6. Make sure the shop door is up high enough so there is plenty of clearance between the top of the vehicle and the door.
7. Watch the shop door to be certain that it is not coming down as you attempt to drive under the door.
8. If a road test is necessary, wear your seat belt, obey all traffic laws, and never drive in a reckless manner.
9. Do not squeal tires when accelerating or turning corners.

If customers observe that service personnel take good care of their car by driving carefully and by installing fender, seat, and floor mat covers, the service department's image is greatly enhanced in their eyes. These procedures impress upon the customers that shop personnel respect their car. Conversely, if grease spots are found on the upholstery or fenders after service work is completed, the customers will probably think the shop is careless, not only in car care but also in service work quality.

HOUSEKEEPING SAFETY

Careful housekeeping habits prevent accidents and increase worker efficiency. Good housekeeping also helps impress upon the customer that quality work is a priority in this shop.

Follow these housekeeping rules:

1. Keep aisles and walkways clear of tools, equipment, and other items.
2. Be sure all sewer covers are securely in place.
3. Keep floor surfaces free of oil, grease, water, and loose material.
4. Sweep up under a vehicle before lowering the vehicle on the lift.
5. Proper trash containers must be conveniently located, and these containers should be emptied regularly.
6. Access to fire extinguishers must be unobstructed at all times, and fire extinguishers should be checked for proper charge at regular intervals.

7. Tools must be kept clean and in good condition.
8. When not in use, tools must be stored in their proper location.
9. Oily rags must be stored in approved, covered containers (Figure 1-13). A slow generation of heat occurs from the oxidation of oil on these rags. Heat may continue to be generated until the ignition temperature is reached. The oil and rags then begin to burn, causing a fire. This action is called spontaneous combustion. However, if the oily rags are in an airtight, approved container, there is not enough oxygen to cause burning.
10. Store paint, gasoline, and other flammable liquids in a closed steel cabinet (Figure 1-14).

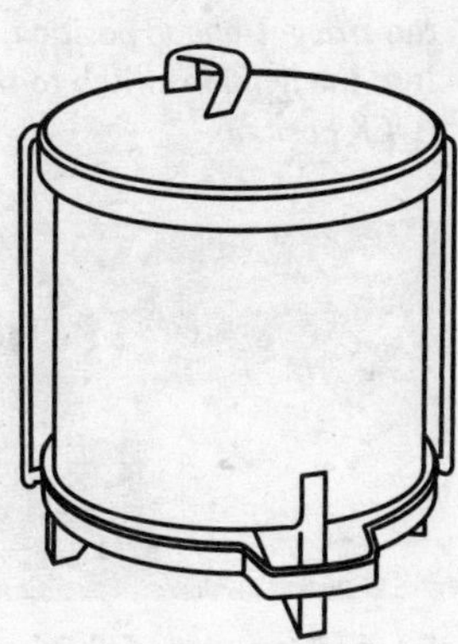

FIGURE 1-13 *Dirty shop towels or rags must be kept in an approved, closed container.*

FIGURE 1-14 *Store combustible materials in an approved safety cabinet.*

11. Rotating components on equipment and machinery must have guards, and all shop equipment should have regular service and adjustment schedules.
12. Keep the workbenches clean. Do not leave heavy objects, such as used parts, on the bench after you are finished with them.
13. Keep parts and materials in their proper location.
14. When not in use, creepers must not be left on the shop floor. Creepers should be stored in a specific location.
15. The shop should be well-lit, and all lights should be in working order.
16. Frayed electrical cords on lights or equipment must be replaced.
17. Walls and windows should be cleaned regularly.
18. Stairs must be clean, well-lit, and free of loose material.

AIR BAG SAFETY

1. When service is performed on any **air bag system** component, always disconnect the negative battery cable, isolate the cable end, and wait for the amount of time specified by the vehicle manufacturer before proceeding with the necessary diagnosis or service. The average waiting period is two minutes, but some vehicle manufacturers specify up to ten minutes. Photo Sequence 1 shows a typical procedure for removing an air bag module.

PHOTO SEQUENCE 1
TYPICAL PROCEDURE FOR REMOVING AIR BAG MODULE

P1-1 *Tools required to remove the air bag module: safety glasses, seat covers, screwdriver set, torx driver set, battery terminal pullers, battery pliers, assorted wrenches, ratchet and socket set, and service manual.*

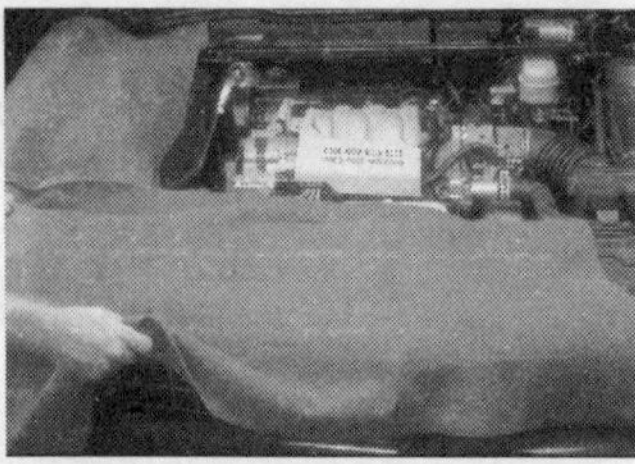

P1-2 *Place the seat and fender covers on the vehicle.*

P1-3 *Place the front wheels in the straight-ahead position, and turn the ignition switch to the LOCK position.*

P1-4 *Disconnect the negative battery cable.*

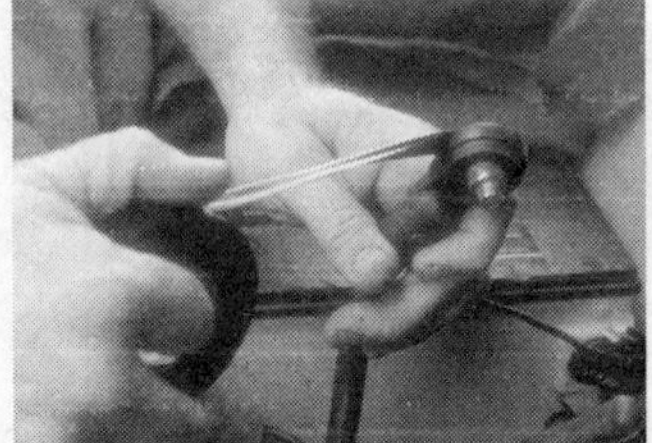

P1-5 *Tape the cable terminal to prevent accidental connection with the battery post. Note: A piece of rubber hose can be substituted for the tape.*

P1-6 *Remove the SIR fuse from the fuse box. Wait 10 minutes to allow the reserve energy to dissipate.*

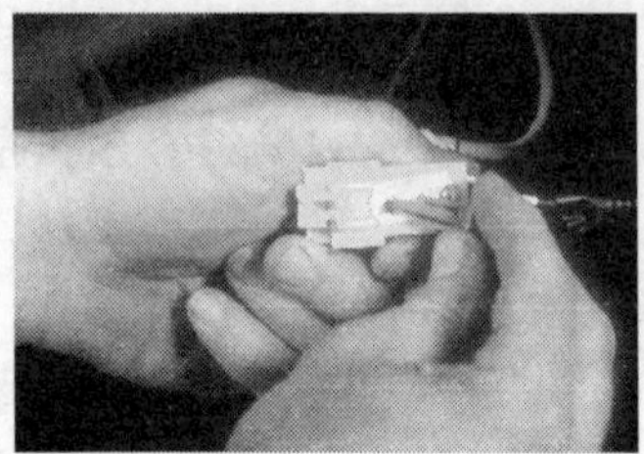

P1-7 *Remove the connector position assurance (CPA) from the yellow electrical connector at the base of the steering column.*

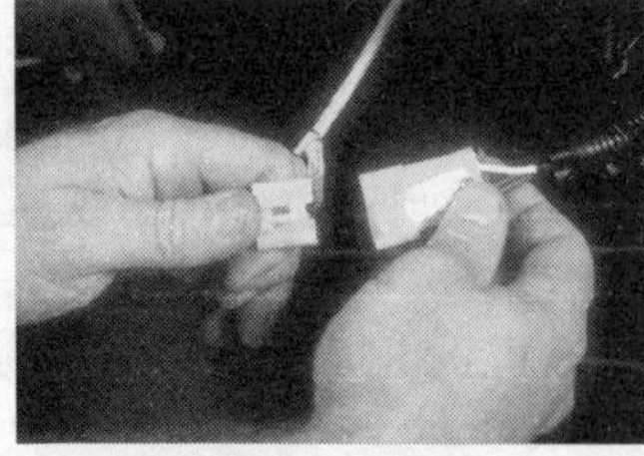

P1-8 *Disconnect the yellow two-way electrical connector.*

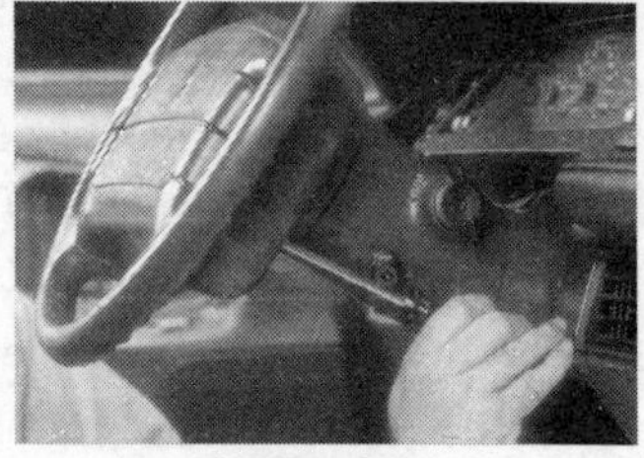

P1-9 *Remove the four bolts that secure the module from the rear of the steering wheel.*

P1-10 *Rotate the horn lead 1/4 turn and disconnect.*

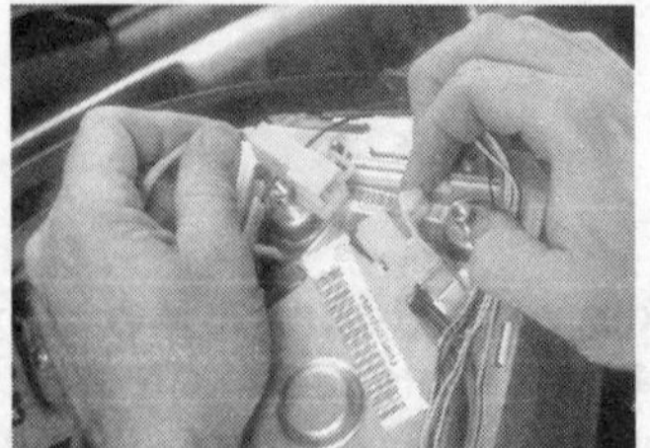

P1-11 *Disconnect the electrical connectors.*

P1-12 *Remove the module.*

On some recent-model vehicles, the air bag system is divided into different disabling and enabling zones for diagnostic and service purposes. When performing vehicle service on or near air bag system components, the vehicle manufacturer recommends disabling the air bag components, in the zone where the air bag components are located rather than disconnecting the vehicle battery (Figure 1-15). The air bag system components in each disabling zone are the following:

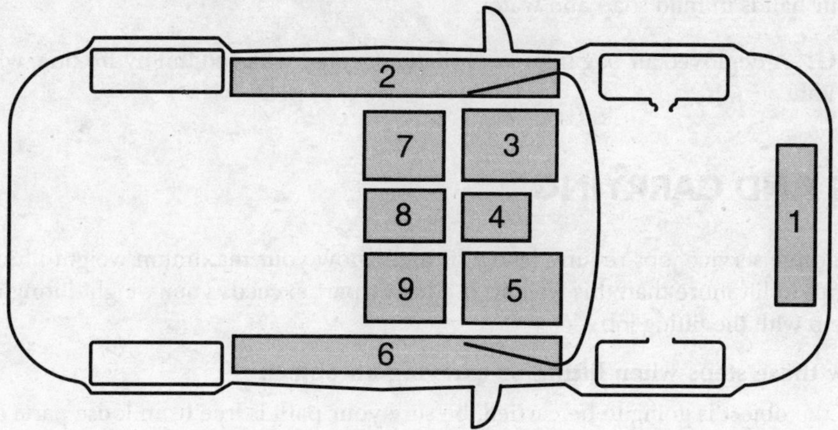

FIGURE 1-15 *Air bag system disabling and enabling zones.*

Zone 1–Front end air bag sensors

Zone 2–Driver/side impact sensor

Zone 3–Steering wheel air bag inflator module and coil

Zone 4–Air bag system sensing and diagnostic module (SDM)

Zone 5–Air bag system instrument panel module

Zone 6–Passenger/side impact sensor

Zone 7–Driver seat with L/F side impact module and seat belt pretensioner

Zone 8–Not used

Zone 9–Passenger seat with R/F side impact module and seat belt pretensioner

2. Replacement air bag system parts must have the same part number as the original part. Replacement parts of lesser or questionable quality must not be used. Improper or inferior components may result in inappropriate air bag deployment and injury to the vehicle occupants.
3. Do not strike or jar a sensor or an air bag system diagnostic monitor (ASDM). This may cause air bag deployment or make the sensor inoperative. Accidental air bag deployment may cause personal injury, and an inoperative sensor may result in air bag deployment failure, causing personal injury to vehicle occupants.
4. All sensors and mounting brackets must be properly torqued to ensure correct sensor operation before an air bag system is powered up. If sensor fasteners do not have the proper torque, improper air bag deployment may result in injury to vehicle occupants.

5. When working on the electrical system on an air-bag-equipped vehicle, use only the vehicle manufacturer's recommended tools and service procedures. The use of improper tools or service procedures may cause accidental air bag deployment and personal injury. For example, do not use 12V or self-powered test lights when servicing the electrical system on an air-bag-equipped vehicle.
6. When handling a deployed air bag always wear safety glasses and shop gloves. Dispose of the deployed air bag through the normal refuse channels. Remove the shop gloves and wash your hands in mild soap and water.

WARNING: A deployed air bag may be partially covered with sodium hydroxide, which is a skin and eye irritant.

LIFTING AND CARRYING

Many automotive service jobs require heavy lifting. Know your maximum weight-lifting ability, and do not attempt to lift more than this weight. If a heavy part exceeds your weight-lifting ability, have a coworker help with the lifting job.

Follow these steps when lifting or carrying an object:

1. If the object is going to be carried, be sure your path is free from loose parts or tools.
2. Position your feet close to the object; position your back reasonably straight for proper balance.
3. Your back and elbows should be kept as straight as possible. Continue to bend your knees until your hands reach the best lifting location on the object.
4. Be certain the container is in good condition. If a container falls apart during the lifting operation, parts may drop out of the container and result in foot injury or part damage.
5. Maintain a firm grip on the object; do not attempt to change your grip while lifting is in progress.
6. Straighten your legs to lift the object and keep the object close to your body. Use your leg muscles rather than your back muscles (Figure 1-16).
7. If you have to change the direction of travel, turn your whole body. Do not twist.
8. Do not bend forward to place an object on a workbench or table. Position the object on the front surface of the workbench and slide it back. Do not pinch your fingers under the object while setting it on the front of the bench.
9. If the object must be placed on the floor or a low surface, bend your legs to lower the object. Do not bend your back forward, because this movement strains back muscles.
10. When a heavy object must be placed on the floor, place suitable blocks under the object to prevent jamming your fingers.

HAND TOOL SAFETY

Many shop accidents are caused by improper use and care of hand tools.

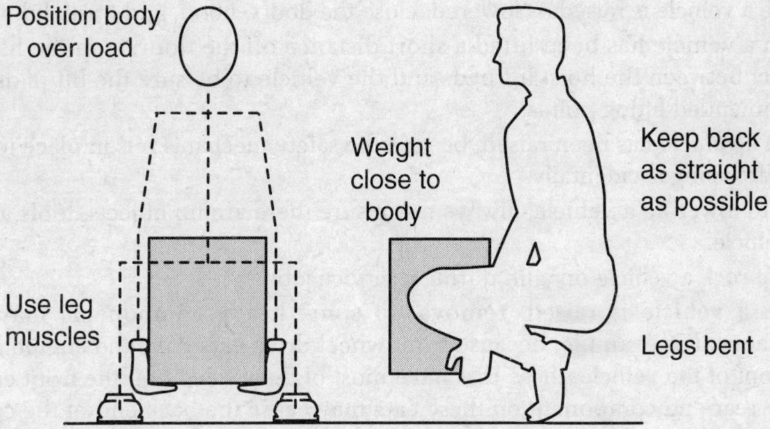

FIGURE 1-16 *Use your leg muscles, never your back, to lift heavy objects.*

Follow these safety steps when working with hand tools:

1. Maintain tools in good condition and keep them clean. Worn tools may slip and result in hand injury. If a hammer with a loose head is used, the head may fly off and cause personal injury or vehicle damage. If your hand slips off a greasy tool, it may cause some part of your body to hit the vehicle, causing injury.
2. Using the wrong tool for the job may damage the tool, fastener, or your hand if the tool slips. If you use a screwdriver as a chisel or pry bar, the blade may shatter, causing serious personal injury.
3. Use sharp-pointed tools with caution. Always check your pockets before sitting on the vehicle seat. A screwdriver, punch, or chisel in the back pocket may put an expensive tear in the upholstery. Do not lean over fenders with sharp tools in your pockets.
4. Tools that are intended to be sharp should be kept sharp. A sharp chisel, for example, will do the job faster with less effort.

LIFT SAFETY

CAUTION: When a vehicle is raised on a lift, the vehicle must be raised high enough to allow engagement of the lift locking mechanism.

Special precautions and procedures must be followed when a vehicle is raised on a lift.

Follow these steps for safe lift operation:

1. Always be sure the lift is completely lowered before driving a vehicle on or off the lift.
2. Do not hit or run over lift arms and adaptors when driving a vehicle on or off the lift. Have a coworker guide you when driving a vehicle onto the lift. Do not stand in front of a lift with the car coming toward you.
3. Be sure the lift pads contact the car manufacturer's recommended lifting points shown in the service manual. If the proper lifting points are not used, components under the vehicle such as brake lines or body parts may be damaged. Failure to use the recommended lifting points may cause the vehicle to slip off the lift, resulting in severe vehicle damage and personal injury.

4. Before a vehicle is raised or lowered, close the doors, hood, and trunk lid.
5. When a vehicle has been lifted a short distance off the floor, stop the lift and check the contact between the hoist lift pads and the vehicle to be sure the lift pads are still on the recommended lifting points.
6. When a vehicle has been raised, be sure the safety mechanism is in place to prevent the lift from dropping accidentally.
7. Prior to lowering a vehicle, always make sure there are no objects, tools, or people under the vehicle.
8. Do not rock a vehicle on a lift during a service job.
9. When a vehicle is raised, removal of some heavy components may cause vehicle imbalance. For example, because front-wheel-drive cars have the engine and transaxle at the front of the vehicle, these cars have most of their weight on the front end. Removing a heavy rear-end component on these cars may cause the back end of the car to rise off the lift. If this happens, the vehicle could fall off the lift!
10. Do not raise a vehicle on a lift with people in the vehicle.
11. When raising pickup trucks and vans on a lift, remember these vehicles are higher than a passenger car. Be sure there is adequate clearance between the top of the vehicle and the shop ceiling or components under the ceiling.
12. Do not raise a four-wheel drive vehicle with a frame contact lift unless proper adaptors are used. Lifting a vehicle on a frame contact lift without the proper adaptors may damage axle joints.
13. Do not operate a front-wheel drive vehicle that is raised on a frame contact lift. This may damage the front drive axles.

HYDRAULIC JACK AND SAFETY STAND SAFETY

WARNING: Always make sure the safety stand weight capacity rating exceeds the vehicle weight that you are planning to raise. A safety stand with insufficient weight capacity may collapse, resulting in vehicle damage and/or personal injury.

WARNING: Never lift a vehicle with a floor jack if the weight of the vehicle exceeds the rated capacity of the jack. If the vehicle weight exceeds the weight rating of the floor jack, the vehicle weight may collapse the floor jack, resulting in jack and vehicle damage and/or personal injury.

Accidents involving the use of floor jacks and safety stands may be avoided if these safety precautions are followed:

1. Never work under a vehicle unless safety stands are placed securely under the vehicle chassis and the vehicle is resting on these stands (Figure 1-17).
2. Prior to lifting a vehicle with a floor jack, be sure that the jack lift pad is positioned securely under a recommended lifting point on the vehicle. Lifting the front end of a vehicle with the jack placed under a radiator support may cause severe damage to the radiator and support.
3. Position the safety stands under a strong chassis member such as the frame or axle housing. The safety stands must contact the vehicle manufacturer's recommended lifting points.
4. Because the floor jack is on wheels, the vehicle and safety stands tend to move as the vehicle is lowered from a floor jack onto the safety stands. Always be sure the safety stands remain

FIGURE 1-17 *Safety stands.*

under the chassis member during this operation, and be sure the safety stands do not tip. All the safety stand legs must remain in contact with the shop floor.

5. When the vehicle is lowered from the floor jack onto the safety stands, remove the floor jack from under the vehicle. Never leave a jack handle sticking out from under a vehicle, which may trip someone and cause an injury.

POWER TOOL SAFETY

Power tools use electricity, shop air, or hydraulic pressure as a power source. Careless operation of power tools may cause personal injury or vehicle damage.

Follow these steps for safe power tool operation:

1. Do not operate power tools with frayed electrical cords.
2. Be sure the power tool cord has a proper ground connection.
3. Do not stand on a wet floor while operating an electric power tool.
4. Always unplug an electric power tool before servicing the tool.
5. Do not leave a power tool running and unattended.
6. When using a power tool on small parts, do not hold the part in your hand. The part must be secured in a bench vise or with locking pliers.
7. Do not use a power tool on a job where the maximum capacity of the tool is exceeded.
8. Be sure that all power tools are in good condition; always operate these tools according to the tool manufacturer's recommended procedure.
9. Make sure all protective shields and guards are in position.
10. Maintain proper body balance while using a power tool.
11. Always wear safety glasses or a face shield.
12. Wear ear protection.
13. Follow the equipment manufacturer's recommended maintenance schedule for all shop equipment.

14. Never operate a power tool unless you are familiar with the tool manufacturer's recommended operating procedure, because serious accidents can occur.
15. Always make sure that the wheels are securely attached and in good condition on the electric grinder.
16. Keep fingers and clothing away from grinding and buffing wheels. When grinding or buffing a small part, hold the part with a pair of locking pliers.
17. Always make sure the sanding or buffing disc is securely attached to the sander pad.
18. Special heavy-duty sockets must be used on impact wrenches. If ordinary sockets are used on an impact wrench, they may break and cause serious personal injury.

COMPRESSED-AIR EQUIPMENT SAFETY

The shop air supply contains high-pressure air in the shop compressor and air lines. Serious injury or property damage may result from careless operation of compressed-air equipment.

Follow these steps to improve safety:

1. Never operate an air chisel unless the tool is securely connected to the chisel with the proper retaining device.
2. Never direct a blast of air from an air gun toward any part of your body. If air penetrates the skin and enters the bloodstream, it may cause very serious health problems and even death.
3. Safety glasses or a face shield should be worn for all shop tasks, including those tasks involving the use of compressed-air equipment.
4. Wear ear protection when using compressed-air equipment.
5. Always maintain air hoses and fittings in good condition. If an end suddenly blows off an air hose, the hose will whip around, causing possible personal injury.
6. Do not direct compressed air against the skin, because it may penetrate the skin, especially through small cuts or scratches, and enter the bloodstream, causing death or serious health complications. Use only OSHA-approved air gun nozzles.
7. Do not use an air gun to blow debris off clothing or hair.
8. Do not clean the workbench or floor with compressed air. This action may blow very small parts toward your skin or into your eye. Small parts blown by compressed air may also cause vehicle damage. For example, if the car in the next stall has the air cleaner removed, a small part may find its way into the carburetor or throttle body. When the engine is started, this part will likely be pulled into a cylinder by engine vacuum, and the part will penetrate through the top of a piston.
9. Never spin bearings with compressed air because the bearing will rotate at extremely high speed. This may damage the bearing or cause it to disintegrate, causing personal injury.
10. All pneumatic tools must be operated according to the tool manufacturer's recommended operating procedure.
11. Follow the equipment manufacturer's recommended maintenance schedule for all compressed-air equipment.

CLEANING EQUIPMENT SAFETY AND ENVIRONMENTAL CONSIDERATIONS

Cleaning Equipment Safety

All technicians are required to clean parts during their normal work routines. Face shields and protective gloves must be worn while operating cleaning equipment. In most states, environmental regulations require that the runoff from steam cleaning must be contained in the steam cleaning system. This runoff cannot be dumped into the sewer system. Because it is expensive to contain this runoff in the steam cleaning system, the popularity of steam cleaning has decreased. The solution in hot and cold cleaning tanks may be caustic, and contact between this solution and skin or eyes must be avoided. Parts cleaning often creates a slippery floor, and care must be taken when walking in the parts cleaning area. The floor in this area should be cleaned frequently. When the cleaning solution in hot or cold cleaning tanks is replaced, environmental regulations require that the old solution be handled as hazardous waste. Use caution when placing aluminum or aluminum alloy parts in a cleaning solution. Some cleaning solutions will damage these components. Always follow the cleaning equipment manufacturer's recommendations.

Parts Washers with Electromechanical Agitation

Some parts washers provide electromechanical agitation of the parts to provide improved cleaning action (Figure 1-18). These parts washers may be heated with gas or electricity. Various water-based **hot cleaning tank** solutions are available, depending on the type of metals being cleaned. For example, Kleer-Flo Greasoff® No. 1 powdered detergent is available for cleaning iron and steel. Non-heated electromechanical parts washers are also available, and these washers use cold cleaning solutions such as Kleer-Flo Degreasol® formulas.

Many cleaning solutions, such as Kleer-Flo Degreasol® 99R, contain no ingredients listed as hazardous by the Environmental Protection Agency's Resource Conservation and Recovery Act (RCRA). This cleaning solution is a blend of sulfur-free hydrocarbons, wetting agents, and detergents. Degreasol® 99R does not contain aromatic or chlorinated solvents, and it conforms to California's Rule 66 for clean air. Always use the cleaning solution recommended by the equipment manufacturer.

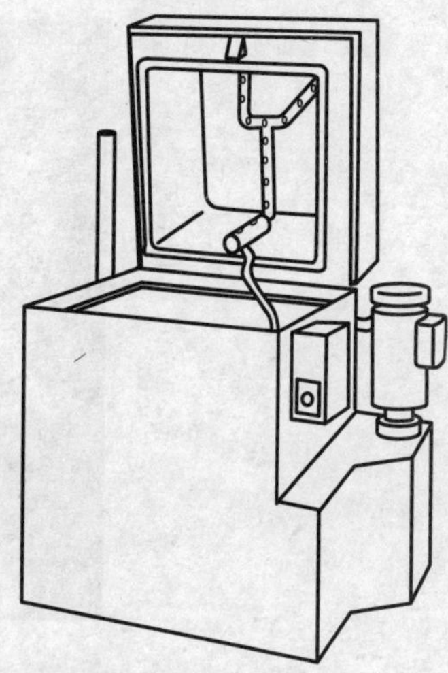

FIGURE 1-18 *Parts washer with electromechanical agitation.*

Cold Parts Washer with Agitation Immersion Tank

Some parts washers have an agitator immersion chamber under the shelves that provides thorougl parts cleaning. Folding work shelves provide a large upper cleaning area with a constant flow o solution from the dispensing hose (Figure 1-19). This **cold parts washer** operates on Degreasol® 99I cleaning solution.

Aqueous Parts Cleaning Tank

The **aqueous parts cleaning tank** uses a water-based, environmentally friendly cleaning solutioı such as Greasoff® 2, rather than traditional solvents. The immersion tank is heated and agitated fc

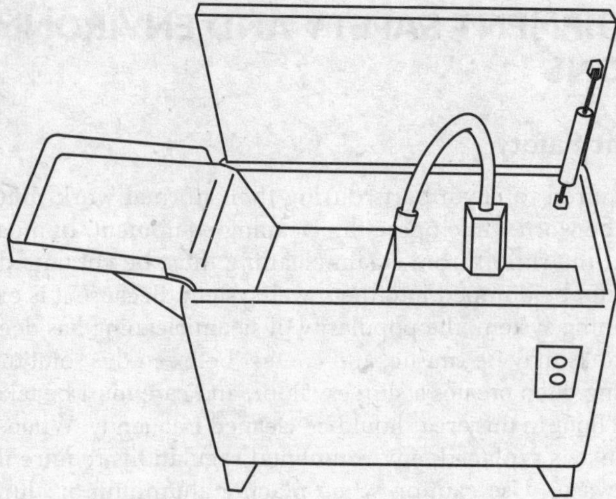

FIGURE 1-19 *Cold parts washer with agitated immersion tank.*

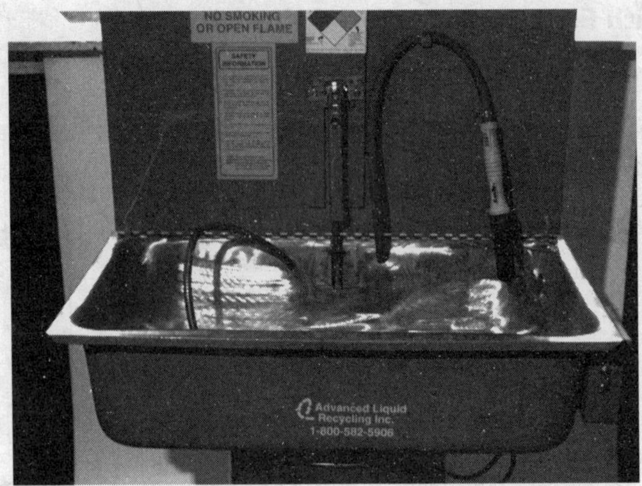

FIGURE 1-20 *Aqueous parts cleaning tank.*

effective parts cleaning (Figure 1-20). A sparger bar pumps a constant flow of cleaning solution across the surface to push floating oils away, and an integral skimmer removes these oils. This action prevents floating surface oils from redepositing on cleaned parts.

Handling Shop Wastes

The shop is responsible for hazardous waste until such waste is delivered to a hazardous waste site. Many shops contract a hazardous waste hauler to transport hazardous waste from the shop to government-approved recyclers or hazardous waste disposal sites. Always hire a properly licensed waste hauler, and have a written contract with them. Be sure you know how the waste hauler disposes of shop wastes. The hazardous waste hauler fills out the necessary forms related to waste disposal and communicates with state and federal agencies that are in charge of hazardous waste disposal regulations. Keep all shipping bills from your hazardous waste hauler to prove you have recycled or disposed of hazardous waste material.

Batteries

Batteries should be recycled by shipping them to a reclaimer or back to the battery distributor. When defective batteries are stored on-site, they should be kept in watertight, acid-resistant containers. Acid residue from batteries is hazardous because it is corrosive and may contain lead and other toxins. Inspect defective batteries for cracks and leaks. Cover spilled battery acid with baking soda or lime to neutralize it, then clean up and dispose of any other hazardous material.

Oil

Used oil is commonly hauled to an oil recycling facility. Place oil drip pans under a vehicle with oil leaks so oil does not drip onto the storage area. In some states it is legal to burn used oil in a commercial space heater. State and local authorities must be contacted regarding regulations and permits.

Oil Filters

Used oil filters should be allowed to drain into an appropriate drip pan for 24 hours. After the draining process, oil filters should be squashed and recycled.

Solvents

Parts cleaning equipment that uses hazardous cleaning chemicals should be replaced with cleaning equipment that uses water-based degreasers. If hazardous chemicals are used in cleaning equipment, these chemicals must be recycled or disposed of as hazardous waste. Evaporation from spent cleaning chemicals is a contributor to ozone depletion and smog formation. Spent cleaning chemicals should be placed in closed, labeled containers and stored in drip pans or in diked areas. The storage area for waste materials should be covered to prevent rain from washing contaminants from stored materials into the groundwater. This storage area may have to be fenced and locked if vandalism is a possibility.

Liquids

Engine coolant should be collected and recycled in an approved coolant recycling machine. Other liquids such as brake fluid and transmission fluid should be labeled and stored in the same area as solvents. Used brake fluid or transmission fluid should be recycled or disposed of as hazardous waste material.

Shop Towels

When dirty shop towels are stored on-site, they should be placed in closed containers that are clearly marked “Contaminated shop towels only.” Shop towels should be cleaned by a laundry service that has the capability to treat the wastewater generated by cleaning these towels.

Refrigerants

When servicing automotive air-conditioning systems, it is illegal to vent refrigerants to the atmosphere. Certified equipment must be used to recover and recycle the refrigerant and to recharge air-conditioning systems. This service work must be performed by an EPA-certified technician.

The EPA approves a Refrigerant Recovery and Recycling Review and Quiz supplied by the National Institute for Automotive Service Excellence (ASE). Upon successful completion of the ASE review and quiz, a technician is certified to service mobile A/C refrigerant systems. The ASE review and quiz meets Section 609 regulations in the Clean Air Act Amendments.

HAZARDOUS WASTE DISPOSAL

Hazardous waste materials in automotive shops are chemicals or components that the shop no longer needs. These materials pose a danger to the environment and to people if they are disposed of in ordinary trash cans or sewers. However, no material is considered hazardous waste until the shop has finished using it and is ready to dispose of it. The **Environmental Protection Agency (EPA)** publishes a list of hazardous materials, which is included in the Code of Federal Regulations. Waste is considered hazardous if it is included on the EPA list of hazardous materials, or if it has one or more of these characteristics:

1. **Reactive.** Any material that reacts violently with water or other chemicals is considered hazardous. If a material releases cyanide gas, hydrogen sulphide gas, or similar gases when exposed to low-pH acid solutions, it is hazardous.
2. **Corrosive.** If a material burns the skin or dissolves metals and other materials, it is considered hazardous.
3. **Toxic.** Materials are hazardous if they leach one or more of eight heavy metals in concentrations greater than 100 times the primary drinking water standard.
4. **Ignitable.** A liquid is hazardous if it has a flashpoint below 140°F (60°C). A solid is hazardous if it ignites spontaneously.

Federal and state laws control the disposal of hazardous waste materials. Every shop employee must be familiar with these laws. Hazardous waste disposal laws include the **Resource Conservation and Recovery Act (RCRA)**. This law states that hazardous material users are responsible for hazardous materials from the time they become waste until the proper waste disposal is completed. Many automotive shops hire an independent hazardous waste hauler to dispose of hazardous waste material (Figure 1-21). The shop owner or manager should have a written contract with the hazardous waste hauler. Rather than hauling hazardous waste material to an approved hazardous waste disposal site, a shop may choose to recycle the material in the shop; therefore, hazardous waste material must be properly and safely stored. The user is responsible for the transportation of this material until it arrives at an approved hazardous waste disposal site and is processed according to the law.

The RCRA controls these types of automotive waste:

1. Paint and body repair products waste
2. Solvents for parts and equipment cleaning
3. Batteries and battery acid
4. Mild acids used for metal cleaning and preparation
5. Waste oil, engine coolants, and antifreeze
6. Air-conditioning refrigerants
7. Engine oil filters

Never, under any circumstances, use these methods to dispose of hazardous waste material:

1. Pour hazardous wastes on weeds to kill them.

FIGURE 1-21 *Hazardous waste hauler.*

2. Pour hazardous wastes on gravel streets to prevent dust.
3. Throw hazardous wastes in a dumpster.
4. Dispose of hazardous wastes anywhere but an approved disposal site.
5. Pour hazardous wastes down sewers, toilets, sinks, or floor drains.

The Right-to-Know Laws state that employees have a right to know when the materials they use at work are hazardous. The Right-to-Know Laws started with the **Hazard Communication Standard** published by the Occupational Safety and Health Administration (OSHA) in 1983. This document was originally intended for chemical companies and manufacturers that required employees to handle hazardous materials in their work situation. Currently, most states have established their own Right-to-Know Laws. Meanwhile, federal courts have decided to apply these laws to all companies, including automotive service shops. Under the Right-to-Know Laws, the employer has three responsibilities regarding the handling of hazardous materials by its employees.

First, all employees must be trained about the types of hazardous materials they will encounter in the workplace. Employees must be informed about their rights under legislation regarding the handling of hazardous materials. All hazardous materials must be properly labeled, and information about each hazardous material must be posted on **material safety data sheets (MSDS)**, which are available from the manufacturer (Figure 1-22). In Canada, MSDSs may be called **workplace hazardous materials information systems (WHMIS).**

The employer has a responsibility to place MSDSs where they are easily accessible by all employees. The MSDSs provide extensive information about hazardous materials such as:

1. Chemical name.
2. Physical characteristics.
3. Protective equipment required for handling.
4. Explosion and fire hazards.

MATERIAL SAFETY DATA SHEET

PRODUCT NAME: KLEAN-A-KARB (aerosol) #- HPMS 102068

PRODUCT: 5078, 5931, 6047T

(page 1 of 2)

1. Ingredients	CAS #	ACGIH TLV	OSHA PEL	OTHER LIMITS	%
Acetone	67-64-1	750 ppm	750 ppm		2–5
Xylene	1330-20-7	100 ppm	100 ppm		68–75
2-Butoxy Ethanol	111-76-2	25 ppm	25 ppm	(skin)	3–5
Methanol	67-56-1	200 ppm	200 ppm		3–5
Detergent	-	NA	NA		0–1
Propane	74-98-6	NA	1000 ppm		10–20
Isobutane	75-28-5	NA	NA	1000 ppm	10–20

2. PHYSICAL DATA : (without propellent)

Specific Gravity : 0.865

Vapor Pressure : ND

% Volatile : >99

Boiling Point : 176F Initial

Evaporation Rate : Moderately Fast

Freezing Point : ND

Vapor Density : ND

Solubility: Partially soluable in water

pH :NA

Appearance and Odor: A clear colorless liquid, aromatic odor

3. FIRE AND EXPLOSION DATA

Flashpoint : -40°F

Method : TCC

Flammable Limits propellent

LEL: 1.8 UEL: 9.5

Extinguishing Media: CO_2, dry chemical, foam

Unusual Hazards : Aerosol cans may explode when heated above 120°F.

4. REACTIVITY AND STABILITY

Stability : Stable

Hazardous decomposition products: CO_2, carbon monoxide (thermal)

Materials to avoid: Strong oxidizing agents and sources of ignition

5. PROTECTION INFORMATION

Ventilation : Use mechanical means to ensure vapor concentration is below TLV.

Respiratory: Use self-contained breathing apparatus above TLV.

Gloves : Solvent resistant

Eye and Face: Safety Glasses

Other Protective Equipment: Not normally required for aerosol product usage

FIGURE 1-22 *Material safety data sheets (MSDS) inform employees about hazardous materials.*

5. Other incompatible materials.
6. Health hazards such as signs and symptoms of exposure, medical conditions aggravated by exposure, and emergency and first-aid procedures.
7. Safe handling precautions.
8. Spill and leak procedures.

Second, the employer has a responsibility to make sure that all hazardous materials are properly labeled. The label information must include health, fire, and reactivity hazards posed by the material and the protective equipment necessary to handle the material. The manufacturer must supply all warning and precautionary information about hazardous materials, and this information must be read and understood by the employee before handling the material.

Third, employers are responsible for maintaining permanent files regarding hazardous materials. These files must include information on hazardous materials in the shop, proof of employee training programs, and information about accidents such as spills or leaks of hazardous materials. The employer's files must also include proof that employees' requests for hazardous material information such as MSDSs have been met. A general right-to-know compliance procedure manual must be maintained by the employer.

CASE STUDY

A technician raised a Grand Marquis on a lift to perform an oil and filter change and a chassis lubrication. This lift was a twin-post-type with separate front and rear lift posts. On this type of lift, the rear wheels must be positioned in depressions in the floor to position the rear axle above the rear lift arm. Then the front lift post and arms must be moved forward or rearward to position the front lift arms under the front suspension. The front lift arms must also be moved inward or outward so they are lifting on the vehicle manufacturer's specified lifting points.

The technician carefully positioned the front lift post and arms properly, but forgot to check the position of the rear tires in the floor depressions. The car was raised on the lift, and the technician proceeded with the service work. Suddenly there was a loud thump, and the rear of the car bounced up and down! The rear lift arms were positioned against the floor of the trunk rather than on the rear axle, and the lift arms punched through the floor of the trunk, narrowly missing the fuel tank. The technician was extremely fortunate the car did not fall off the lift, resulting in more severe damage. If the rear lift arms had punctured the fuel tank, a disastrous fire could have occurred! Luckily, these things did not happen.

The technician learned a very important lesson about lift operation. Always follow all the recommended procedures in the lift operator's manual! The trunk floor was repaired at no cost to the customer, and fortunately, the shop and the vehicle escaped without major damage.

SERVICE TIPS

- When you are finished with a tool, never set it on the customer's car. After using a tool, the best place for it is in your tool box or on the workbench. Many tools have been lost by leaving them on customers' vehicles.
- After disconnecting battery voltage from an air bag system, failure to wait for the specified time period before servicing the system may cause accidental air bag deployment.

REVIEW QUESTIONS

1. Breathing carbon monoxide may cause:
   A. Arthritis
   B. Cancer
   C. Impaired vision
   D. Headaches
2. While discussing shop rules:
   Technician A says breathing asbestos dust may cause heart defects. *Technician B* says oily rags should be stored in uncovered trash containers.
   Who is correct?
   A. A only
   B. B only
   C. Both A and B
   D. Neither A nor B
3. All these shop rules are correct EXCEPT:
   A. USC tools may be substituted for metric tools.
   B. Foot injuries may be caused by loose sewer covers.
   C. Hands should be kept away from electric-drive cooling fans.
   D. Power tools should not be left running and unattended.
4. While discussing personal safety:
   Technician A says rings and jewelry may be worn in the automotive shop. *Technician B* says some electric-drive cooling fans may start turning at any time.
   Who is correct?
   A. A only
   B. B only
   C. Both A and B
   D. Neither A nor B
5. While lifting heavy objects in the automotive shop:
   A. Bend your back to pick up the heavy object.
   B. Place your feet as far as possible from the object.
   C. Bend forward to place the object on the workbench.
   D. Straighten your legs to lift an object off the floor.
6. While discussing power tool safety:
   Technician A says an electric power tool cord does not require a ground. *Technician B* says frayed electric cords should be replaced.
   Who is correct?
   A. A only
   B. B only
   C. Both A and B
   D. Neither A nor B
7. While operating hydraulic equipment safely in the automotive shop remember that:
   A. Safety stands have a maximum weight capacity.
   B. The driver's door should be open when raising a vehicle on a lift.
   C. A lift does not require a safety mechanism to prevent lift failure.
   D. Four-wheel drive vehicles should be lifted on a frame contact lift.
8. While discussing shop hazards:
   Technician A says high-pressure air from an air gun may penetrate the skin. *Technician B* says air in the bloodstream may be fatal.
   Who is correct?
   A. A only
   B. B only
   C. Both A and B
   D. Neither A nor B

9. While discussing hazardous material disposal:
Technician A says certain types of hazardous waste material can be poured down a floor drain. *Technician B* says a shop is responsible for hazardous waste materials from the time they become waste until the proper waste disposal is completed.
Who is correct?
A. A only
B. B only
C. Both A and B
D. Neither A nor B

10. When working in an automotive shop, hazardous conditions must be avoided by:
A. Storing oily rags in open containers.
B. Storing flammable liquids such as paint in metal cupboards.
C. Leaving sewer covers loose for quick access.
D. Cleaning brake parts with an air gun.

JOB SHEET 1

Name ______________________________ Date ______________

DEMONSTRATE PROPER LIFTING PROCEDURES

Upon completion of this job sheet, you should be able to follow the proper procedure when lifting heavy objects.

Tools and Materials

A heavy object with a weight that is within the weight-lifting capability of the technician.

Procedure

Have various members of the class demonstrate proper weight-lifting procedures by lifting an object off the shop floor and placing it on the workbench. Other class members are to observe and record any improper weight-lifting procedures.

Task Completed

1. If the object is to be carried, be sure your path is free from loose parts or tools. ☐
2. Position your feet close to the object, and position your back reasonably straight for proper balance. ☐
3. Your back and elbows should be kept as straight as possible. Continue to bend your knees until your hands reach the best lifting location on the object to be lifted. ☐
4. Be certain the container is in good condition. If a container falls apart during the lifting operation, parts may drop out of the container, resulting in foot injury or part damage. ☐
5. Maintain a firm grip on the object; do not attempt to change your grip while lifting is in progress. ☐
6. Straighten your legs to lift the object, keeping the object close to your body. Use leg muscles rather than back muscles. ☐
7. If you have to change direction of travel, turn your whole body. Do not twist. ☐
8. Do not bend forward to place an object on a workbench or table. Position the object on the front surface of the workbench and slide it back, watching your fingers under the object to avoid pinching them. ☐
9. If the object must be placed on the floor or a low surface, bend your legs to lower the object. Do not bend your back forward because this movement strains back muscles. ☐
10. When a heavy object must be placed on the floor, put suitable blocks under the object to prevent jamming your fingers under the object. ☐
11. List any improper weight-lifting procedures observed during the weight-lifting demonstrations.

    1. ______________________________
    2. ______________________________
    3. ______________________________
    4. ______________________________
    5. ______________________________
    6. ______________________________

Instructor's Response ____

____

____

JOB SHEET 2

Name ______________________________ Date ______________

LOCATE AND INSPECT SHOP SAFETY EQUIPMENT

Upon completion of this job sheet, you should be familiar with the location of shop safety equipment and know if this equipment is serviced properly.

Procedure

Task Completed

1. Fire extinguishers: Are the fire extinguishers tagged to indicate they have been checked or serviced recently? ☐ Yes ☐ No

   Draw a basic diagram of the shop layout in the space below, and mark the locations of the fire extinguishers and fire exits.

2. Eyewash fountain or shower: Is the eyewash fountain or shower operating properly? ☐ Yes ☐ No

   Mark the location of the eyewash fountain or shower on the shop layout diagram in step 1.

3. First-aid kits: Are the first-aid kits properly stocked with supplies? ☐ Yes ☐ No

   Mark the location of the first-aid kits on the shop layout diagram in step 1.

4. Electrical shut-off box: Mark the location of the shop electrical shut-off box on the shop layout diagram in step 1. ☐

5. Are the trash containers equipped with proper covers? ☐ Yes ☐ No

   Mark the location of the trash containers on the shop layout diagram in step 1.

6. Metal storage cabinet: Mark the location of metal storage cabinet(s) for combustible materials on the shop layout diagram in step 1. ☐

Instructor's Response ______________________________

____

____

JOB SHEET 3

Name ______________________________ Date ______________

SHOP HOUSEKEEPING INSPECTION

Upon completion of this job sheet, you should be able to apply shop housekeeping rules in your shop.

Procedure

Task Completed

When students from another class of Automotive Technology are working in the shop, evaluate their shop housekeeping procedures using the 16 shop housekeeping procedures. List all the improper shop housekeeping procedures that you observed in the space provided at the end of the job sheet.

1. Keep aisles and walkways clear of tools, equipment, and other items. ☐
2. Be sure all sewer covers are securely in place. ☐
3. Keep floor surfaces free of oil, grease, water, and loose material. ☐
4. Proper trash containers must be conveniently located, and these containers should be emptied regularly. ☐
5. Access to fire extinguishers must be unobstructed at all times; fire extinguishers should be checked for proper charge at regular intervals. ☐
6. Tools must be kept clean and in good condition. ☐
7. When not in use, tools must be stored in their proper location. ☐
8. Oily rags and other combustibles must be placed in proper, covered metal containers. ☐
9. Rotating components on equipment and machinery must have guards. All shop equipment should have regular service and adjustment schedules. ☐
10. Benches and seats must be kept clean. ☐
11. Keep parts and materials in their proper location. ☐
12. When not in use, creepers must not be left on the shop floor. Creepers should be stored in a specific location. ☐
13. The shop should be well-lit, and all lights should be in working order. ☐
14. Frayed electrical cords on lights or equipment must be replaced. ☐
15. Walls and windows should be cleaned regularly. ☐
16. Stairs must be clean, well-lit, and free of loose material. ☐

Observed improper shop housekeeping procedures:

1. ______________________________
2. ______________________________
3. ______________________________
4. ______________________________
5. ______________________________
6. ______________________________

Instructor's Response ____

____

____

Tools and Shop Procedures

2

Upon completion and review of this chapter, you should be able to:

- Diagnose steering and suspension problems using a basic diagnostic procedure.
- Raise a vehicle with a floor jack and lower the vehicle so it is supported on safety stands.
- Raise a vehicle with a lift.
- Test power steering pump pressure with an appropriate pressure gauge and valve assembly.
- Measure ball joint wear with a dial indicator designed for this purpose.
- Remove and replace a coil spring on a strut using a coil spring compressor tool.
- Use a tire changer to dismount and mount a tire.
- Use a scan tool to diagnose a computer-controlled suspension system.
- Balance tire-and-wheel assemblies with an electronic wheel balancer.
- Perform a four wheel alignment with a computer wheel aligner.
- Fulfill employee obligations when working in the shop.
- Accept job responsibility for each job completed in the shop.
- Describe the ASE automotive technician testing and certification process including the eight areas of certification.

USING SUSPENSION AND STEERING EQUIPMENT

Learn to use equipment properly the first time. When improper procedures are learned and become a habit, it is more difficult to break these wrong habits. Using service and test equipment will help you to work more safely and efficiently, and in the long term, this should improve your income. We will discuss the proper use of some of the most common service and test equipment used by suspension and steering technicians.

MEASURING SYSTEMS

Two systems of weights and measures are commonly used in the United States. One system is the **U. S. customary (USC) system**, which is commonly referred to as the English system. Well-known measurements for length in the USC system are the inch, foot, yard, and mile. In this system, the quart and gallon are measurements for volume; ounce, pound, and ton are measurements for weight. A second system of weights and measures is called the **international system (SI)**, also known as the metric system.

In the USC system, the basic linear measurement is the yard; in the metric system, it is the meter. Each unit of measurement in the metric system is related to the other metric units by a factor of 10. Thus, every metric unit can be multiplied or divided by 10 (or 100 or 1,000) to obtain larger units (multiples) or smaller units (submultiples). For example, the meter may be divided by 100 to obtain centimeters (1/100 meter) or by 1,000 to obtain millimeters (1/1,000 meter).

The U.S. government passed the Metric Conversion Act in 1975 in an attempt to move American industry and the general public to accept and adopt the metric system. The automotive industry has adopted the metric system, and in recent years most bolts, nuts, and fittings on vehicles have been changed to metric. During the early 1980s some vehicles had a mix of English and metric bolts. Imported vehicles have used the metric system for many years. Although the automotive industry has changed to the metric system, the general public in the United States has been slow to convert from the USC system to the metric system. One of the factors involved in this change is cost. What would it cost to change every highway distance and speed sign in the United States to read kilometers? Probably hundreds of millions, or even billions, of dollars.

Service technicians must be able to work with both the USC and the metric system. One meter (m) in the metric system is equal to 39.37 inches (in.) in the USC system. A metric tape measure may be graduated in millimeters, and 10 millimeters = 1 centimeter (Figure 2-1).

FIGURE 2-1 *Metric tape graduated in millimeters.*

Some common equivalents between the metric and USC systems are:

1 meter (m) = 39.378 inches

1 centimeter (cm) = 0.3937 inch

1 millimeter (mm) = 0.03937 inch

1 inch = 2.54 centimeter

1 inch = 25.4 millimeter

In the USC system, phrases such as 1/8 of an inch are used for measurements. The metric system uses a set of prefixes. For example, in the word kilometer the prefix kilo means 1,000, indicating that there are 1,000 meters in a kilometer. Common prefixes in the metric system include:

NAME	SYMBOL	MEANING
mega	M	one million
kilo	k	one thousand
hecto	h	one hundred
deca	da	ten
deci	d	one tenth of
centi	c	one hundredth of
milli	m	one thousandth of
micro	µ	one millionth of

Measurement of Mass

In the metric system mass is measured in grams, kilograms, or tonnes: 1,000 grams (g) = 1 kilogram (kg). In the USC system mass is measured in ounces, pounds, or tons. When converting pounds to kilograms, 1 pound = 0.453 kilograms.

Measurement of Length

In the metric system length is measured in millimeters, centimeters, meters, or kilometers: 10 millimeters (mm) = 1 centimeter (cm). In the USC system length is measured in inches, feet, yards, or miles.

When distance conversions are made between the two systems some of the following conversion factors are used:

1 inch = 25.4 millimeters

1 foot = 30.48 centimeters

1 yard = 0.91 meters

1 mile = 1.60 kilometers

Measurement of Volume

In the metric system volume is measured in milliliters, cubic centimeters, and liters: 1 cubic centimeter = 1 milliliter. If a cube has a length, depth, and height of 10 centimeters (cm), the volume of the cube is 10 cm x 10 cm x 10 cm = 1,000 cm^3 = 1 liter. When volume conversions are made between the two systems, 1 cubic inch = 16.38 cubic centimeters. If an engine has a displacement of 350 cubic inches, 350 x 16.38 = 5,733 cubic centimeters, and 5,733 ÷ 1,000 = 5.7 liters.

BASIC DIAGNOSTIC PROCEDURE

One of the most important parts of a technician's job is diagnosing automotive problems. Each year more vehicle systems are controlled by increasingly sophisticated electronic systems, and this makes accurate diagnosis even more important.

The following basic diagnostic procedure may be used to diagnose various automotive problems:

1. Be absolutely sure the problem is identified. Obtain all the information you can from the customer; for example, politely ask the customer to describe the exact symptoms of the problem. Ask the customer at what vehicle speed, engine temperature, and atmospheric temperature the problem occurs. From your discussion, find out when, where, and how the problem occurs.
2. Verify the problem. If necessary, road test the vehicle under the same conditions as the customer described to verify the problem.
3. Think of the possible causes of the problem based on your own experience in diagnosing similar problems on other vehicles.
4. Consult original equipment manufacturer (OEM) or generic technical service bulletin (TSB) information regarding service procedures, parts replacement, or computer reprogramming that are designed to correct the problem.
5. Perform the necessary diagnostic tests to locate the exact cause of the complaint. Always begin the diagnostic tests with the quickest, easiest test, and if the problem is not located, proceed with the more complicated, time-consuming tests. During your diagnosis watch for other problems with the vehicle that may give trouble in the near future. If there are any other potential problems such as worn belts and radiator hoses, advise the customer about them and attempt to obtain the customer's approval to repair these problems. If the customer does not approve the repair of these potential problems, describe them on the work order. If we repair a car based on a complaint on a customer's vehicle, and two weeks later the customer brings the vehicle back with another serious complaint, the customer may assume that the repairs were not completed thoroughly.
6. After the cause of the complaint is definitely located, advise the customer about the extent and cost of the repairs. After the customer approves the necessary repairs, perform the appropriate service work on the vehicle.
7. Road test the vehicle if necessary to be sure the customer's complaint is eliminated.

SUSPENSION AND STEERING TOOLS

Seal Drivers

WARNING: When using any suspension and steering tools, the vehicle manufacturer's recommended procedure in the service manual must be followed. Improper use of tools may lead to personal injury.

CAUTION: Do not hit the seal case with a hammer. This action will damage the seal.

CAUTION: Always be sure the seal goes into the housing squarely and evenly. If the seal does not go squarely into the housing, the outer seal case may be distorted, and this condition may cause an oil leak around the seal housing.

Seal drivers are designed to fit squarely against the seal case and inside the seal lip. A soft hammer is used to tap the seal driver and drive the seal straight into the housing. Some tool manufacturers market a seal driver kit with drivers to fit many common seals (Figure 2-2).

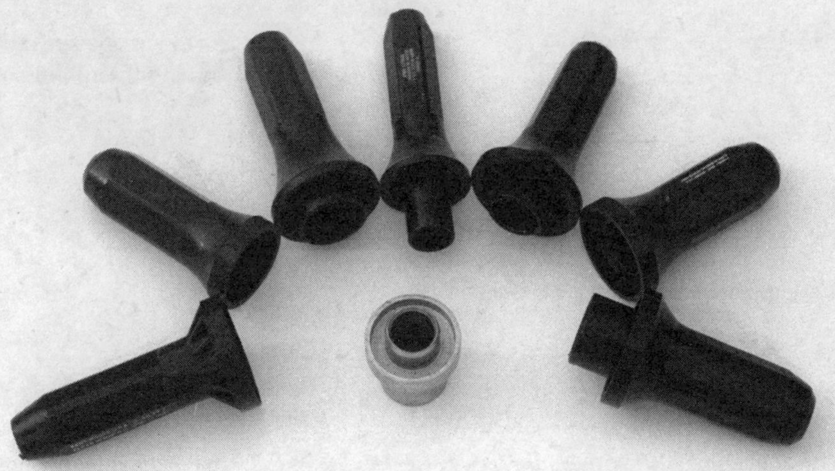

FIGURE 2-2 *Seal drivers.*

Bearing Pullers

A variety of **bearing pullers** are available to pull different sizes of bearings in various locations (Figure 2-3). Some bearing pullers are slide-hammer-type, whereas others are screw-type.

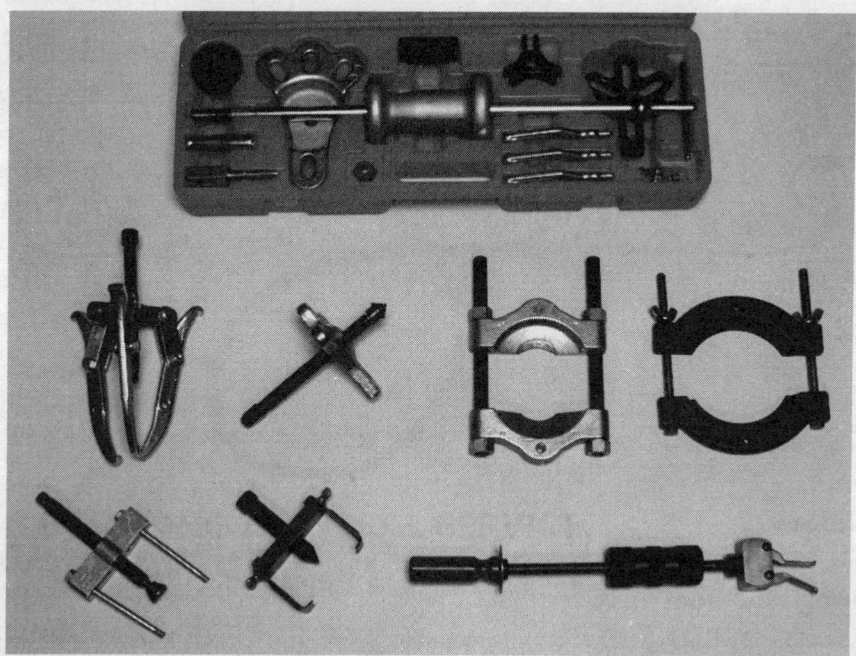

FIGURE 2-3 *Bearing pullers.*

Axle Pullers

Axle pullers are used to pull rear axle shafts in rear-wheel-drive vehicles. Most rear axle pullers are slide-hammer-type (Figure 2-4).

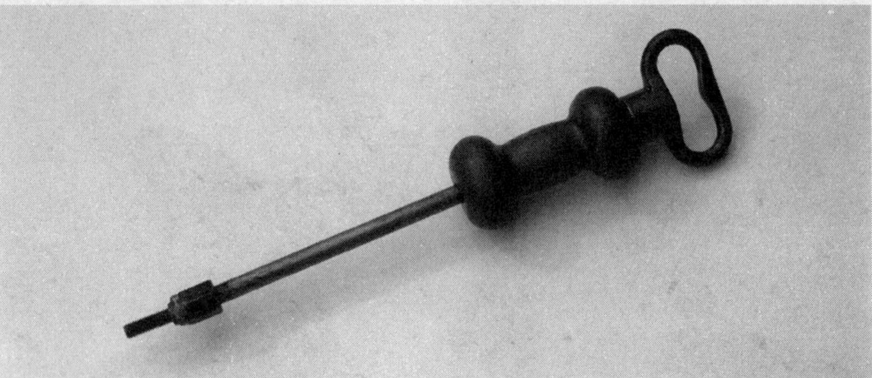

FIGURE 2-4 *Axle puller.*

Stethoscope

A **stethoscope** is a mechanical device that amplifies sound and diagnoses the source of noises such as bearing noise. The stethoscope pickup is placed on the suspected noise source, and the ends of the two arms are placed in the technician's ears (Figure 2-5). Electronic stethoscopes provide improved sound amplification compared with mechanical stethoscopes and can locate the causes of mechanical noises, air leaks, and wind whistles.

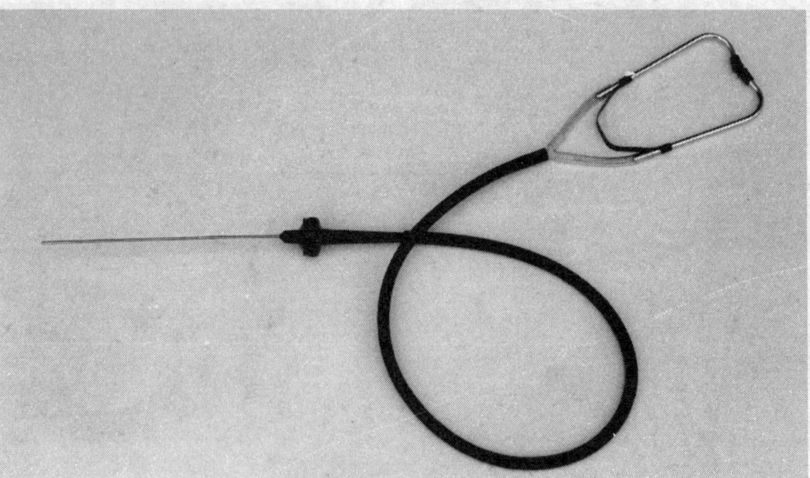

FIGURE 2-5 *Stethoscope.*

Front Bearing Hub Tool

Front bearing hub tools are designed to remove and install front wheel bearings on front-wheel-drive cars (Figure 2-6). These bearing hub tools are usually designed for a specific make of vehicle.

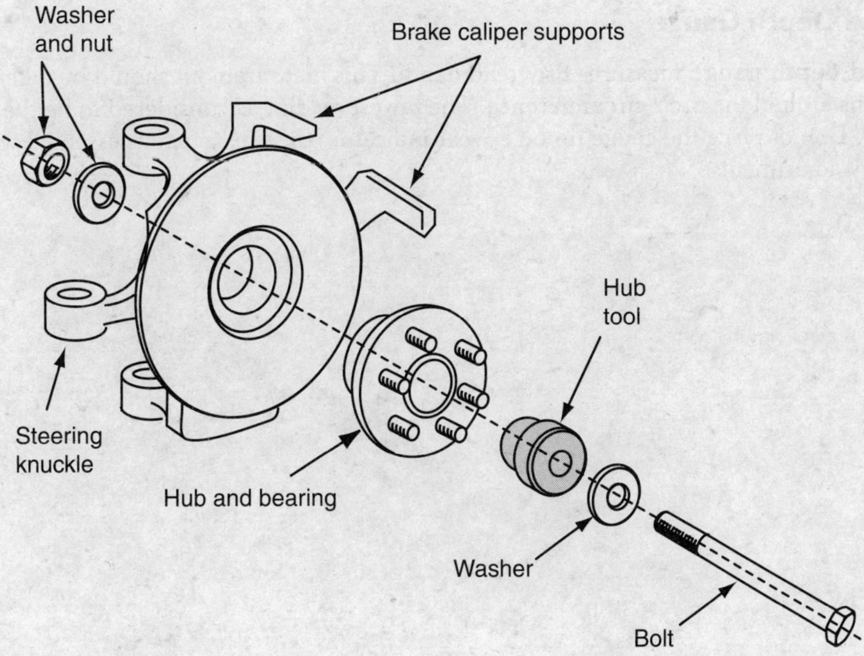

FIGURE 2-6 *Front bearing hub tool.*

Dial Indicator

Dial indicators are used for measuring in many different locations. In the suspension and steering area, dial indicators are used for measurements, such as tire runout and ball joint movement (Figure 2-7). Dial indicators have many different attaching devices to connect the indicator to the component to be measured.

FIGURE 2-7 *Dial indicator designed for ball joint measurement. (Courtesy of Moog Automotive)*

Tire Tread Depth Gauge

A **tire tread depth gauge** measures tire tread depth. This measurement should be taken at three or four locations around the tire's circumference. The lowest reading is considered to be the tread depth (Figure 2-8). Do not place the gauge tip on a wear indicator bar. This gauge is essential when making tire warranty adjustments.

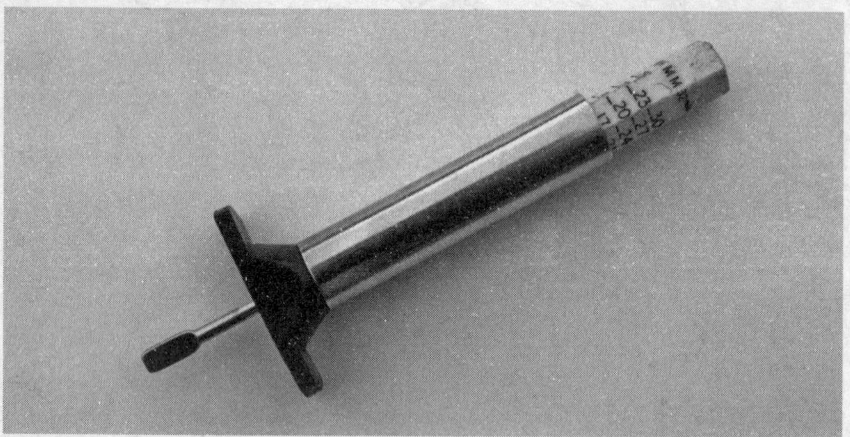

FIGURE 2-8 *Tire tread depth gauge. (Courtesy of Mac Tools, Inc.)*

Tire Changer

WARNING: Never operate a **tire changer** until you are familiar with its operation because this may lead to serious personal injury. Your instructor will explain and demonstrate the operation of this equipment. You should read the equipment operator's manual and use this equipment under the instructor's supervision until you are familiar with it.

Tire changers are used to dismount and mount tires (Figure 2-9). These changers may be used on most common tire sizes. A wide variety of tire changers are available, and each one operates differently. Always follow the procedure in the equipment operator's manual and the directions provided by your instructor.

Wheel Balancer

WARNING: Using a wheel balancer before you are familiar with its operation may result in serious personal injury and property damage.

Electronic wheel balancers are used in most automotive repair shops (Figure 2-10). Do not attempt to use this equipment until you have studied wheel balance theory. Your instructor will explain and demonstrate the use of this equipment before you attempt to use it. This equipment should be used under the supervision of your instructor until you are familiar with it.

FIGURE 2-9 *Typical tire changer.*

FIGURE 2-10 *Typical electronic wheel balancer.*

Machinist's Rule

A **machinist's rule** performs many accurate measurements in the shop. Most machinist's rules are graduated in inches and millimeters (Figure 2-11).

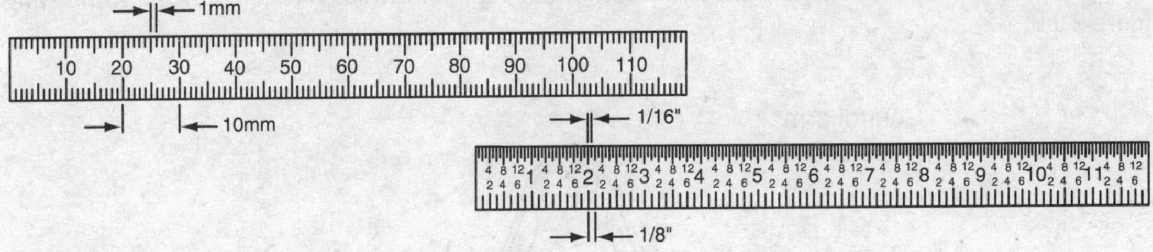

FIGURE 2-11 *Graduations on a typical machinist's rule.*

Ball Joint Removal and Installation Tools

Ball joint removal and installation tools remove and install pressed-in ball joints on front suspension systems (Figure 2-12). The size of the removal and pressing tool adapter must match the size of the ball joint.

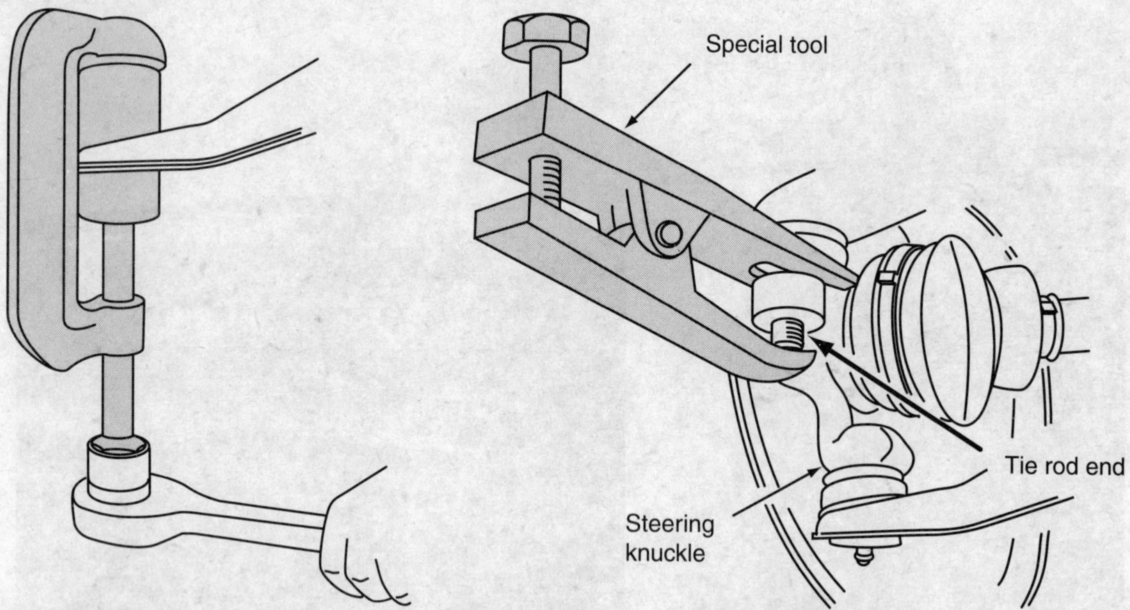

FIGURE 2-12 *Ball joint removal and installation tool.*

FIGURE 2-13 *Tie rod end and ball joint puller.*

Tie Rod End and Ball Joint Puller

Some car manufacturers recommend a **tie rod end and ball joint puller** to remove tie rod ends and pull ball joint studs from the steering knuckle (Figure 2-13).

Control Arm Bushing Tools

A variety of **control arm bushing tools** are available to remove and replace control arm bushings. The bushing removal and installation tool must match the size of the control arm bushing (Figure 2-14).

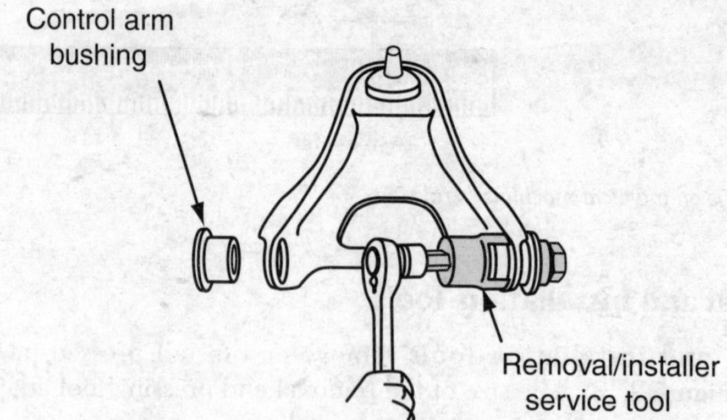

FIGURE 2-14 *Control arm bushing removal and replacement tools.*

Coil Spring Compressor Tool

WARNING: There is a tremendous amount of energy in a compressed coil spring. Never disconnect any suspension component that will suddenly release this tension because this may result in serious personal injury and vehicle or property damage.

CAUTION: The vehicle manufacturer's and equipment manufacturer's recommended procedures must be followed for each type of spring compressor tool.

Many types of **coil spring compressor tools** are available to the automotive service industry (Figure 2-15). These tools compress the coil spring and hold it in the compressed position while removing the strut from the coil spring or performing other suspension work. Each type of front suspension system requires a different type of spring compressor tool. The vehicle manufacturer's and equipment manufacturer's recommended procedure must be followed.

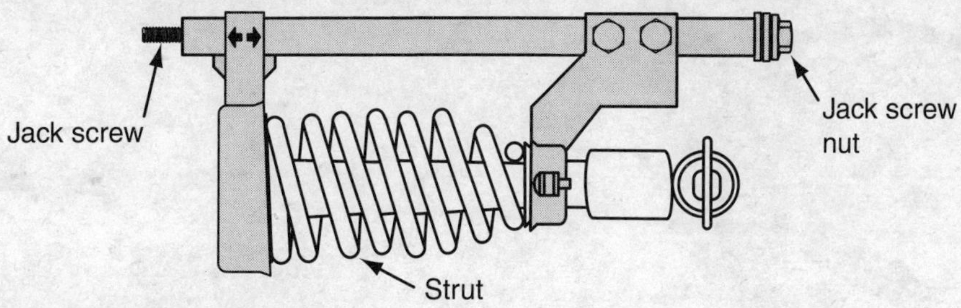

FIGURE 2-15 *MacPherson strut coil spring compressor tool.*

Power Steering Pressure Gauge

WARNING: The power steering pump delivers extremely high pressure during the pump pressure test. Always follow the recommended test procedure in the vehicle manufacturer's service manual to avoid personal injury during this test.

A **power steering pressure gauge** is used to test the power steering pump pressure (Figure 2-16). Because the power steering pump delivers extremely high pressure during this test, the recommended procedure in the vehicle manufacturer's service manual must be followed.

Pitman Arm Puller

WARNING: Never strike a puller with a hammer when it is installed and tightened because this may result in personal injury.

A **pitman arm puller** is a heavy-duty puller that removes the pitman arm from the pitman shaft (Figure 2-17).

Vacuum Hand Pump

A **vacuum hand pump** creates a vacuum to test vacuum-operated components and hoses (Figure 2-18).

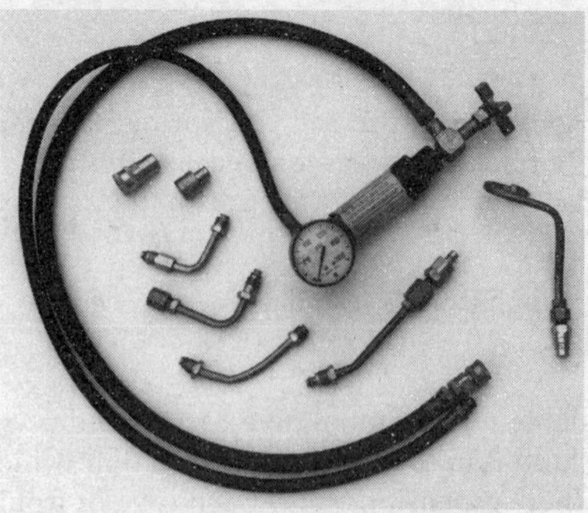

FIGURE 2-16 *Power steering pressure gauge.*

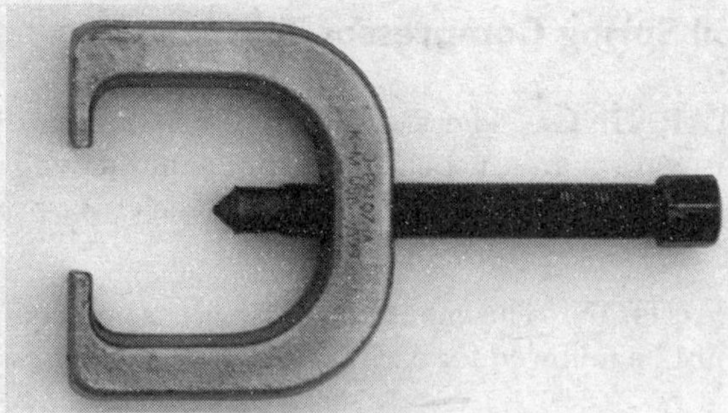

FIGURE 2-17 *Pitman arm puller.*

FIGURE 2-18 *Vacuum hand pump.*

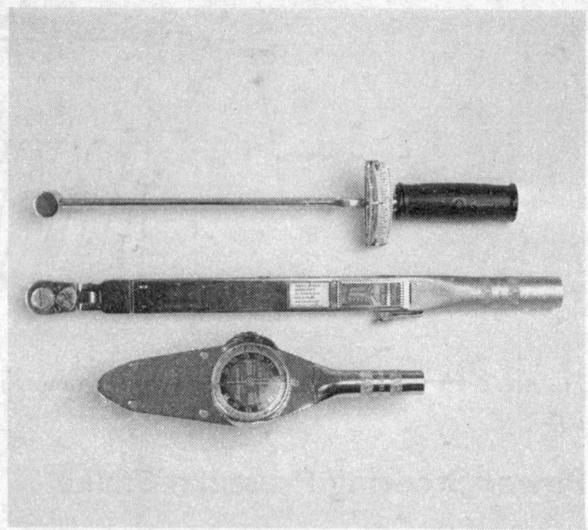

FIGURE 2-19 *Various types of torque wrenches.*

Torque Wrenches and Torque Sticks

A torque wrench is required to tighten fasteners to a specified torque. Tightening fasteners to the specified torque is extremely important. If fastener torque is less than tightened, the component retained by the fastener(s) may loosen, resulting in severe component or vehicle damage. When fasteners are tightened to a torque above the specified value, the component may become warped, resulting in improper component operation. Torque wrenches can be beam, click, or dial-type (Figure 2-19). A beam-type torque wrench bends as torque is applied, and a beam on the wrench points to the torque applied on a scale attached to the wrench handle. On a click-type torque wrench, the handle is rotated to set the specified torque on a scale adjacent to the handle. When the fastener is tightened to the torque setting, the torque wrench provides an audible click. On a dial-type torque wrench, the torque applied to the fastener is indicated on the dial. Digital-type torque wrenches that indicate the torque reading on a digital display are also available.

Some tool manufactures provide torque sticks for tightening fasteners to the specified torque with an impact wrench. One end of the torque stick has a $^{11}/_{42}$ in. drive opening, and a socket is attached to the opposite end. A spring steel, heat-treated shaft is connected between the $^{11}/_{42}$ in. drive opening and the socket end of the torque stick. Torque sticks are calibrated to twist at a specific torque with each blow of an impact wrench, and thus prevent further tightening of the fastener. Torque sticks are available in various USC and metric sizes and are usually sold in color-coded sets. The torque stick color indicates the specified torque at which they twist. For example, a yellow torque stick twists at 65 ft. lbs. Some torque sticks are a $^{11}/_{42}$ in. extension that fits between the impact wrench drive and a thin-wall impact socket (Figure 2-20).

FIGURE 2-20 *Torque stick.*

FIGURE 2-21 *Turning radius gauge.*

Turning Radius Gauge

Turning radius gauge turntables are placed under the front wheels during a wheel alignment. The top plate in the turning radius gauge rotates on the bottom plate to allow the front wheels to be turned during a wheel alignment. A degree scale and a pointer on the gauge indicate the number of degrees the front wheels are turned (Figure 2-21). If the car has four-wheel steering (4WS), the turning radius gauges are also placed under the rear wheels during a wheel alignment.

Plumb Bob

A **plumb bob** is a metal weight with a tapered end (Figure 2-22). This weight is suspended on a string. Plumbers use a plumb bob to locate pipe openings directly below each other at the top and bottom of partitions. Some vehicle manufacturers recommend checking vehicle frame measurements with a plumb bob.

Tram Gauge

A **tram gauge** is a long, straight graduated bar with an adjustable pointer at each end (Figure 2-23). The tram gauge performs frame and body measurements.

Magnetic Wheel Alignment Gauge

Each **magnetic wheel alignment gauge** contains a strong magnet that holds the gauge securely on the front wheel hubs. The magnetic wheel alignment gauge measures some of the front suspension alignment angles (Figure 2-24).

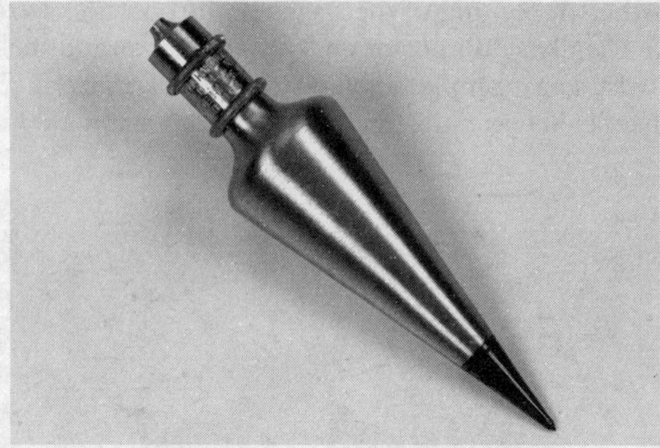

FIGURE 2-22 *Plumb bob.*

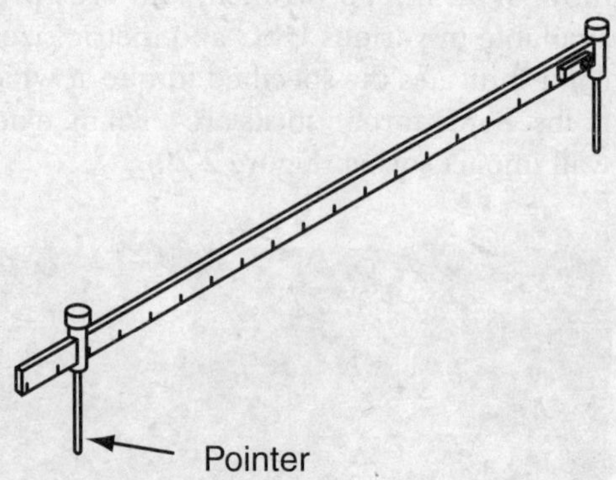

FIGURE 2-23 *Tram gauge.*

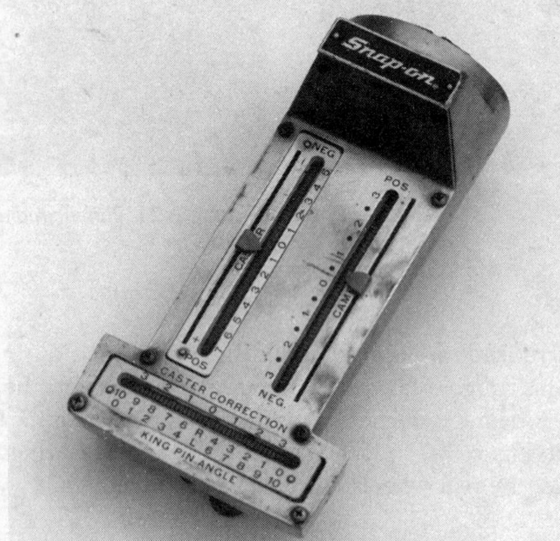

FIGURE 2-24 *Magnetic wheel alignment gauge.*

Rim Clamps

When the wheel hub is inaccessible to the magnetic alignment gauge, an adjustable **rim clamp** may be attached to each front wheel. The magnetic gauges may be attached to the rim clamp (Figure 2-25). Rim clamps are also used on computer wheel aligners.

Brake Pedal Jack

A **brake pedal jack** must be installed between the front seat and the brake pedal to apply the brakes while checking some front wheel alignment angles (Figure 2-26).

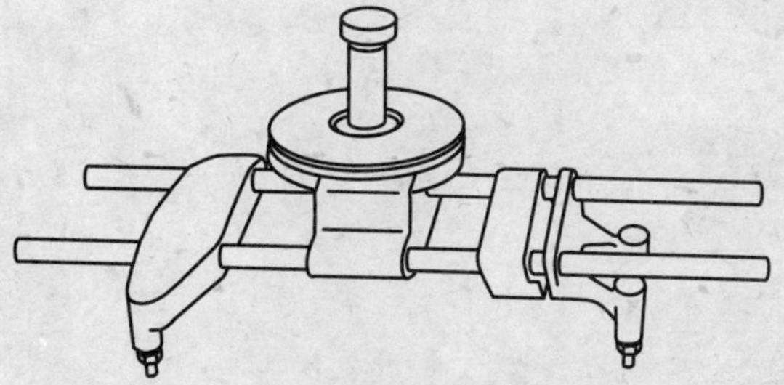

FIGURE 2-25 *Rim clamps.*

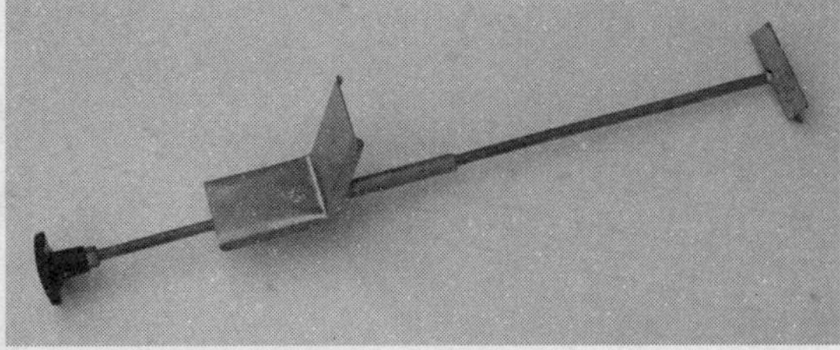

FIGURE 2-26 *Brake pedal jack.*

Tie Rod Sleeve Adjusting Tool

CAUTION: Do not use anything except a tie rod adjusting tool to adjust the tie rod sleeves. Tools, such as a pipe wrench, will damage the sleeves.

A **tie rod sleeve adjusting tool** rotates the tie rod sleeves and performs some front wheel adjustments (Figure 2-27).

Steering Wheel Locking Tool

A **steering wheel locking tool** locks the steering wheel while performing some front suspension service (Figure 2-28).

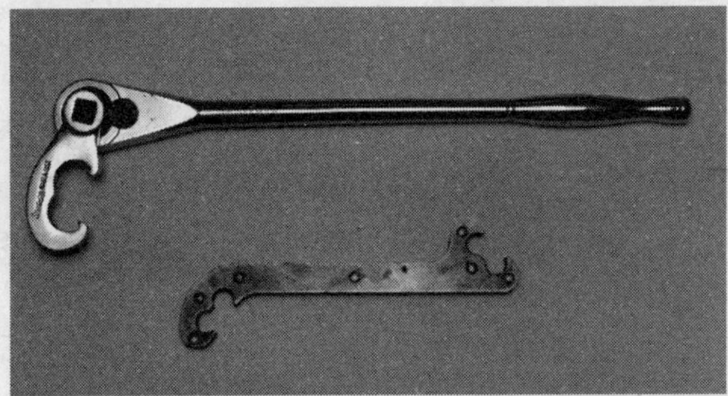

FIGURE 2-27 *Tie rod sleeve adjusting tool.*

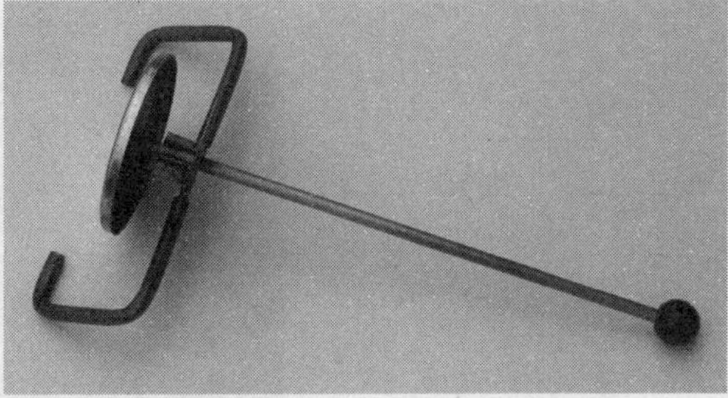

FIGURE 2-28 *Steering wheel locking tool.*

Toe Gauge

A **toe gauge** is a long, straight, graduated bar that measures front wheel toe (Figure 2-29).

Track Gauge

Some **track gauges** use a fiber-optic alignment system to measure front wheel toe and to determine if the rear wheels are tracking directly behind the front wheels. The front and rear fiber-optic gauges may be connected to the wheel hubs or to rim clamps attached to the wheel rims (Figure 2-30). A remote light source in the main control is sent through fiber-optic cables to the wheel gauges. A strong light beam between the front and rear wheel units informs the technician if the rear wheel tracking is correct.

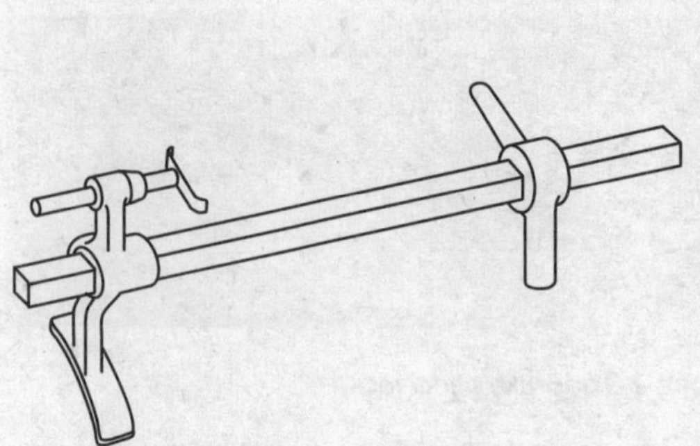

FIGURE 2-29 *Toe gauge.*

FIGURE 2-30 *Fiber optic track and toe gauge.*

Computer Four Wheel Aligner

Many automotive shops are equipped with a **computer four wheel aligner** (Figure 2-31). These wheel aligners perform all front and rear wheel alignment angles quickly and accurately.

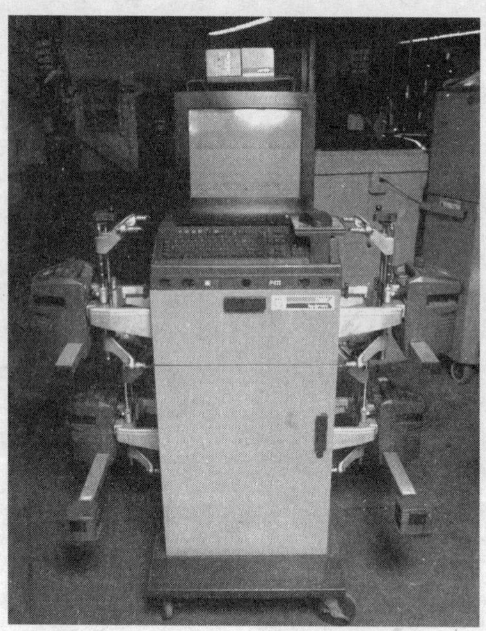

FIGURE 2-31 *Computer wheel aligner.*

Scan Tool

A variety of **scan tools** are available for diagnosing automotive computer systems (Figure 2-32). These testers obtain fault codes and perform other diagnostic functions on computer-controlled suspension systems.

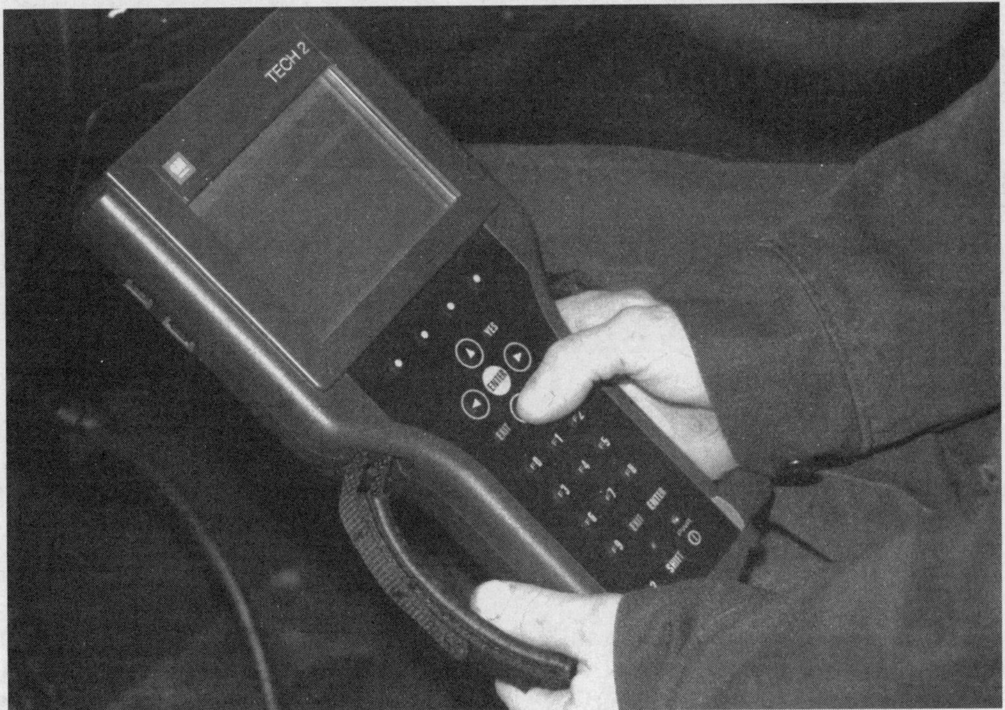

FIGURE 2-32 *Scan tool for diagnosing computer-controlled suspension systems.*

Bench Grinder

WARNING: Always wear a face shield when using a bench grinder. Failure to observe this precaution may cause personal injury.

WARNING: When grinding small components on a grinding wheel, wire brush wheel, or buffing wheel, always hold these components with a pair of vise grips to avoid injury to fingers and hands.

WARNING: Grinding and buffing wheels on bench grinders must be mounted on the grinder according to the manufacturer's instructions. Grinding and buffing wheels must be retained with the manufacturer's specified washers and nuts, and the retaining nuts must be tightened to the specified torque. Personal injury may occur if grinding and buffing wheels are not properly attached to the bench grinder.

Bench grinders usually have a grinding wheel and a wire wheel brush driven by an electric motor (Figure 2-33). The grinding wheel may be replaced with a grinding disc containing several layers of synthetic material (Figure 2-34). A buffing wheel may be used in place of the wire wheel brush. The grinding wheel may be used for various grinding jobs and deburring. A buffing wheel is most commonly used for polishing. Most bench grinders have grinding wheels and wire brush wheels that are 6 to 10 in. (15.24 to 25.4 cm) in diameter. Bench grinders must be securely bolted to the workbench.

FIGURE 2-33 *Bench grinder.*

FIGURE 2-34 *Bench grinder accessories.*

HYDRAULIC PRESSING AND LIFTING EQUIPMENT

Hydraulic Press

WARNING: When operating a **hydraulic press**, always be sure that the components being pressed are supported properly on the press bed with steel supports. Improperly supported components may slip, resulting in personal injury.

WARNING: When using a hydraulic press, never operate the pump handle if the pressure gauge exceeds the maximum pressure rating of the press. If this pressure maximum is exceeded, some part of the press may suddenly break, causing severe personal injury.

WARNING: Be sure the safety cage is in place around the press to prevent personal injury.

When two components have a tight precision fit between them, a hydraulic press is used to either separate these components or press them together. The hydraulic press rests on the shop floor, and an adjustable steel-beam bed is retained to the lower press frame with heavy steel pins. A hydraulic cylinder and ram is mounted on the top part of the press with the ram facing downward toward the press bed (Figure 2-35). The component being pressed is placed on the press bed with appropriate steel supports. A hand-operated hydraulic pump is mounted on the side of the press. When the handle is pumped, hydraulic fluid is forced into the cylinder, and the ram is extended against the component on the press bed to complete the pressing operation. A pressure gauge on the press indicates the pressure applied from the hand pump to the cylinder. The press frame is designed for a certain maximum pressure, and this pressure must not be exceeded during hand pump operation.

Floor Jack

WARNING: The maximum lifting capacity of the **floor jack** is usually written on the jack decal. Never lift a vehicle that exceeds the jack lifting capacity. This action may cause the jack to break or collapse, resulting in vehicle damage or personal injury.

A floor jack is a portable unit mounted on wheels. The lifting pad on the jack is placed under the chassis of the vehicle, and the jack handle is operated with a pumping action (Figure 2-36), forcing

FIGURE 2-35 *Hydraulic press.*

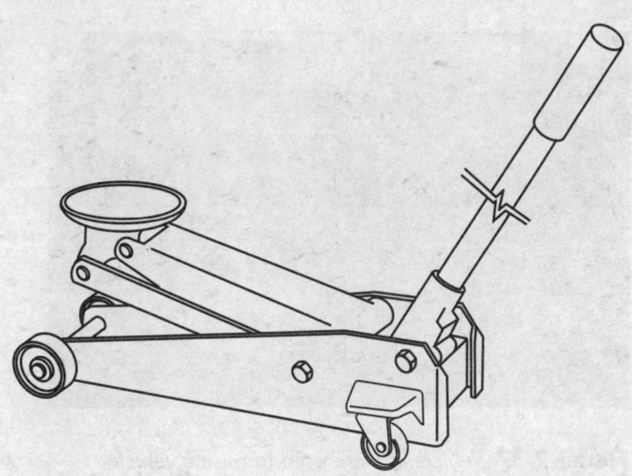

FIGURE 2-36 *Hydraulic floor jack.*

fluid into a hydraulic cylinder in the jack. Then this cylinder extends to force the jack lift pad upward and lift the vehicle. Always be sure that the lift pad is positioned securely under one of the car manufacturer's recommended lifting points. To release the hydraulic pressure and lower the vehicle, the handle or release lever must be turned slowly. Do not leave the jack handle where someone can trip over it.

Vehicle Lift (Hoist)

CAUTION: Always be sure that the lift arms are securely positioned under the car manufacturer's recommended lifting points before raising the vehicle. These lifting points are shown in the service manual. If the lift arms are not positioned on the proper lift points, chassis components may be damaged, or the vehicle may slide off the lift, resulting in vehicle damage and/or personal injury.

CAUTION: The maximum capacity of the vehicle lift is placed on an identification plate. Never lift a vehicle that is heavier than the maximum capacity of the lift. Lifting a vehicle with a weight greater than the lift weight rating may bend the lift or cause the vehicle to slip off the lift, resulting in vehicle damage and/or personal injury.

A **vehicle lift** raises a vehicle so the technician can work under it. The lift arms must be placed under the car manufacturer's recommended lifting points prior to raising a vehicle. Twin posts are used on some lifts, whereas other lifts have a single post (Figure 2-37). Some lifts have an electric motor, which drives a hydraulic pump to create fluid pressure and force the lift upward. Other lifts use air pressure from the shop air supply to force the lift upward. If shop air pressure is used, it is applied to fluid in the lift cylinder. A control lever or switch is placed near the lift, which supplies shop air pressure to the lift cylinder and turns on the lift pump motor. Always be sure that the safety lock is engaged after the lift is raised. When the safety lock is released, a release lever is operated slowly to lower the vehicle.

FIGURE 2-37 *Vehicle lifts are used to raise a vehicle.*

FIGURE 2-38 *Typical safety stands.*

Using a Floor Jack and Safety Stands

A floor jack is often used to raise a vehicle off the floor. The vehicle is then lowered onto **safety stands** to allow service work to be performed under the vehicle (Figure 2-38).

Follow this procedure to lift a vehicle with a floor jack and then support it on safety stands:

1. Check the weight ratings of the floor jack and the safety stands; be sure these ratings exceed the weight to be lifted and supported.

WARNING: If the vehicle weight to be lifted and supported exceeds the weight rating of the floor jack or safety stands, the floor jack or safety stands may collapse, allowing the vehicle to drop suddenly, which may cause personal injury and/or vehicle damage.

2. Be sure the vehicle is parked on a level surface. Place wheel blocks behind the rear wheels of the vehicle if you are lifting the front end. Place these wheel blocks in front of the front wheels if you are lifting the rear end.
3. Determine the vehicle manufacturer's specified lift point from the vehicle service manual, and position the floor jack lift pad under this lift point. Pump the floor jack handle until the lift pad contacts the lift point on the vehicle.

CAUTION: Lifting or supporting a vehicle at a location other than the vehicle manufacturer's specified lift point may cause damage to the vehicle chassis and other components.

4. Look under the vehicle and be sure the floor jack lift pad is contacting the specified lift point. If necessary, lower the lift pad and move it so it contacts the lift point properly.
5. Pump the floor jack handle until the vehicle is at the desired height. Place jack stands adjusted to the appropriate height under the vehicle manufacturer's lift points. These lift points will be a strong chassis member such as the frame or axle housing.

6. Because the floor jack is on casters, the vehicle and floor jack tend to move slightly as the vehicle is lowered onto safety stands. Slowly operate the hydraulic pressure release on the floor jack to lower the vehicle onto the safety stands. As the vehicle is lowered, be sure the safety stands do not tip. All four legs on both safety stands must remain in contact with the floor surface. Be sure the safety stands are contacting the vehicle lift points properly, and double-check to be sure the safety stand legs are all contacting the floor.

WARNING: Never work under a vehicle unless it is securely supported on safety stands. If a vehicle is supported only by a floor jack, the jack may allow the vehicle to drop, resulting in personal injury.

7. After the vehicle is supported properly on safety stands, lower and remove the floor jack to allow more room for under-car service.

WARNING: Never under any condition leave a floor jack handle down so it is near the floor surface; someone may trip over the handle, resulting in personal injury.

Using a Vehicle Lift

A vehicle lift raises a vehicle to allow a technician to perform under-car repairs.

Follow this procedure to raise a vehicle on a lift:

CAUTION: When driving a vehicle on a lift, do not run over lift arms, adapters, or axle supports. This action may damage the lift, tires, or vehicle chassis components.

1. Determine both the weight rating of the lift and the vehicle weight to be lifted. Be sure the weight rating of the lift exceeds the vehicle's weight.
2. Before driving a vehicle on a lift, be sure the lift arms are positioned properly out of the path of the vehicle. The lift arms must also be positioned to provide unobstructed clearance between the lift and the vehicle chassis.
3. After driving the vehicle on the lift, be sure the vehicle is properly positioned in relation to the lift. Make sure the vehicle doors, hood, and trunk lid are closed. Do not raise a vehicle with any person inside the vehicle.
4. Determine the specified vehicle lift points from the vehicle service manual (Figure 2-39).

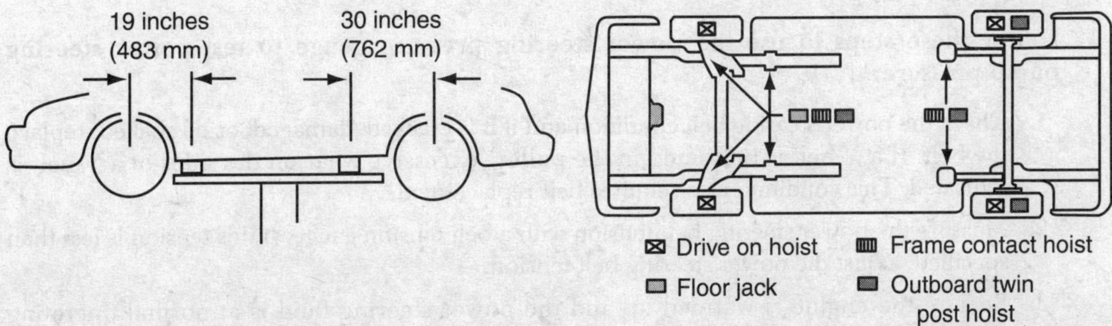

FIGURE 2-39 *Lift points for a typical unibody vehicle.*

5. Position the lift supports so they are directly under the specified vehicle lift points. Operate the lift so the lift supports contact the specified lift points.

CAUTION: If the lift supports are not in proper contact with the specified vehicle lift points, chassis components such as brake lines may be damaged.

WARNING: If the lift supports are not in proper contact with the specified vehicle lift points, the vehicle may slip off the lift, resulting in personal injury and vehicle damage.

6. Operate the lift a short distance off the shop floor and stop the lift. Look under the vehicle to be sure the lift supports are in full contact with the specified lift points. If the lift supports are not in full contact with the specified lift points, lower the vehicle onto the floor and reposition the lift supports.
7. Raise the vehicle to the desired height. Be sure the lift safety mechanism is engaged.

WARNING: If heavy components are removed from one end of a vehicle, the vehicle may become unstable on the lift. Therefore, to prevent this action, chain a strong chassis component to the lift on the opposite end of the vehicle before removing heavy components from the other end.

8. Before lowering the lift, remove all tools, toolboxes, and equipment from under the vehicle, and sweep up discarded parts from under the vehicle.
9. Be sure nobody is standing under the vehicle before lowering it.
10. Lower the vehicle slowly until it is resting on the shop floor and be sure the lift is completely lowered.
11. Before driving the vehicle off the lift, be sure there is proper clearance between all parts of the lift and the vehicle chassis.

SUSPENSION AND STEERING SERVICE, DIAGNOSTIC, AND MEASUREMENT TOOLS

Using a Power Steering Pressure Gauge

The power steering pump pressure test is one of the most important indications of power steering pump condition.

Follow these steps to use the power steering pressure gauge to test power steering pump pressure:

1. Check the power steering belt condition and if it is cracked, damaged, or oil soaked, replace the belt. If a V-belt is bottomed in the pulley, excessive wear on the sides of a V-belt is indicated. This condition also requires belt replacement.
2. Measure the power steering belt tension with a belt tension gauge. If this tension is less than specified, adjust the power steering belt tension.
3. Be sure the engine is warmed up and the power steering fluid is at normal operating temperature.

4. With the engine shut off, check the fluid level in the power steering pump reservoir. If necessary, add the vehicle manufacturer's specified fluid until the proper level is obtained.
5. Listen to the power steering pump with the engine idling. A growling noise from the pump may indicate aeration of the power steering fluid in the reservoir or air in the power steering system. If air is indicated in the system, turn the steering wheel several times fully in each direction to bleed air from the system before proceeding with the power steering pump pressure test.
6. Shut the engine off and remove the high-pressure hose from the power steering pump. Connect the power steering pressure gauge and valve assembly to the fitting on the end of the high-pressure hose and to the fitting on the pump from which the high-pressure hose was removed (Figure 2-40). Be sure the valve on the power steering pressure gauge is fully open.

FIGURE 2-40 *Pressure gauge connections to power steering.*

7. With the engine idling, close the power steering gauge valve for no more than 10 seconds and observe the power steering pump pressure on the gauge. Turn the gauge valve fully open. If the power steering pump pressure is less than the vehicle manufacturer's specified pressure, replace the power steering pump.

WARNING: Wear a face shield and protective gloves during the power steering pressure test. Power steering fluid and components become hot during this test.

WARNING: If the gauge valve is closed for more than 10 seconds during the power steering pressure test, excessive power steering pump pressure may rupture power steering hoses. Hot fluid spraying from a ruptured hose may burn anyone near the vehicle.

CAUTION: Do not allow the power steering fluid to become too hot during the pump pressure test. Excessive fluid temperature reduces pump pressure, resulting in false test results.

8. Shut the engine off and remove the power steering pressure gauge. Tighten the high-pressure hose fitting to the specified torque. Start the engine and check for leaks at this fitting. Be sure the power steering reservoir is filled to the proper level.

Using a Dial Indicator

A dial indicator performs precision measurements on some suspension components such as ball joints. A special dial indicator with a stiff, flexible attaching bracket is available for measuring ball joint wear. When measuring ball joint wear, the end of this flexible bracket is clamped to a stable suspension component with a pair of vise grips. The dial indicator must be mounted so there is no movement in the indicator mounting. A dial indicator contains a movable plunger that is positioned against the component to be measured. The pointer on the dial indicator registers the amount of plunger movement. Each rotation of the pointer represents 0.100 in. (2.54 mm) of plunger movement (Figure 2-41). The dial indicator plunger must be positioned against the component to be measured so the dial indicator is preloaded approximately 0.250 in. (6.35 mm). When the dial indicator is preloaded properly, about one-half of the plunger should be outside the dial indicator. After the preload procedure is completed, the dial indicator face must be rotated until the zero position on the scale is aligned with the pointer. Always look squarely at the indicator face. Looking at the dial indicator face from an angle may provide an inaccurate reading.

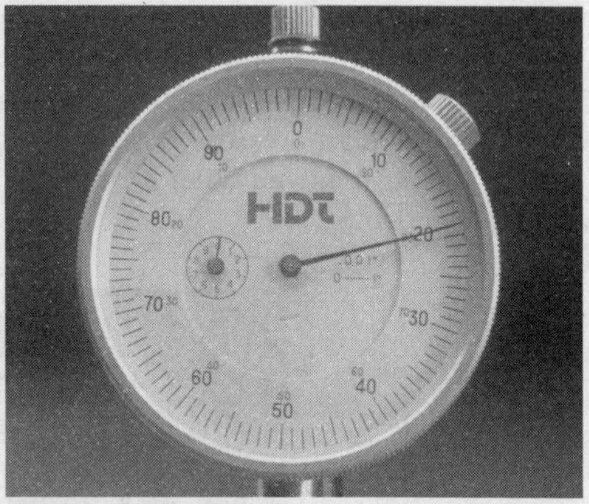

FIGURE 2-41 *The dial indicator pointer rotation indicates the amount of plunger movement.*

The following is a typical procedure for measuring ball joint wear on a short-and-long arm suspension system with the coil spring positioned between the lower control arm and the chassis:

1. Lift the front of the vehicle with a floor jack positioned under the manufacturer's specified lift point, and position a safety stand under the lower control arm. Lower the vehicle so the lower control arm and vehicle weight rests on the safety stand. The tire must remain several inches off the floor.
2. Clamp the end of the dial indicator's flexible bracket onto the lower control arm.
3. Position the dial indicator plunger against the lower side of the steering knuckle next to the nut on the ball joint stud. The dial indicator plunger should be positioned at a 90° angle with the ball joint stud (Figure 2-42).
4. Preload and zero the dial indicator. Be sure the dial indicator is clamped securely to the lower control arm without any movement in the indicator mounting.
5. Position a long steel bar under the tire, and lift upward on the bar while an assistant observes the movement on the dial indicator pointer. If the dial indicator pointer movement exceeds the maximum-specified ball joint vertical movement, the ball joint must be replaced.

FIGURE 2-42 *Dial indicator installed to measure vertical ball joint movement.*

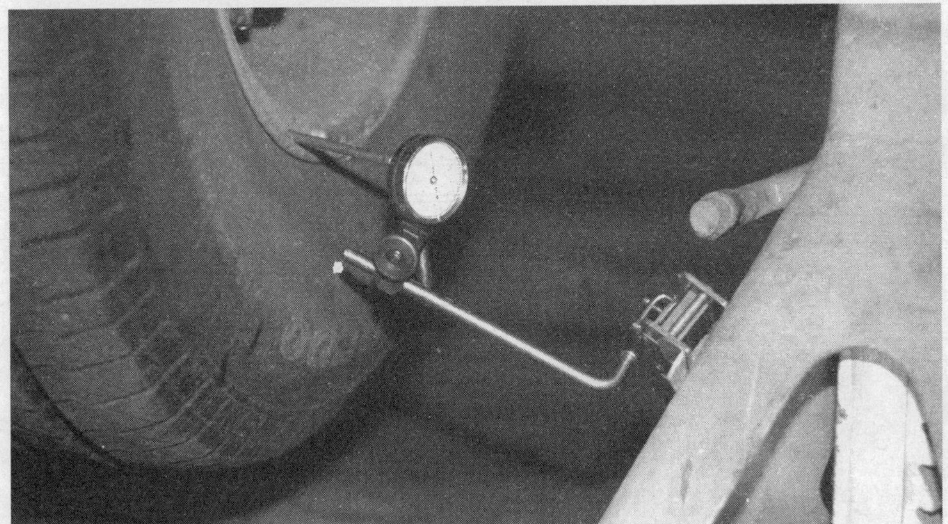

FIGURE 2-43 *Dial indicator installed to measure horizontal joint movement.*

6. Be sure the front wheel bearings are adjusted properly. Position the dial indicator plunger against the inner edge of the wheel rim (Figure 2-43). Preload and zero the dial indicator. Grasp the top and bottom of the tire, and attempt to tip the tire out at the bottom and in at the top. Release the tire, and repeat this procedure several times while an assistant observes the dial indicator. If the dial indicator pointer movement exceeds the maximum-specified ball joint horizontal movement, the ball joint must be replaced.

Using a Coil Spring Compressing Tool

A coil spring compressing tool is required to compress the coil spring before removing the spring from the strut on a MacPherson strut suspension system.

Follow this procedure for using a coil spring compressing tool to remove a spring from a strut:

1. With the strut-and-coil-spring assembly removed from the vehicle, install the coil spring in the compressing tool according to the tool manufacturer's or vehicle manufacturer's recommended procedure.

CAUTION: If the coil spring has an enamel-type coating, tape the spring in the areas where the compressor tool contacts the spring. If the compressor tool chips this coating, the spring may break prematurely.

WARNING: Unless the coil spring is compressed, never loosen the nut on the strut rod that retains the upper strut mount on the strut and coil spring. Loosening this nut will suddenly release the coil spring tension, resulting in personal injury.

2. Adjust the compressing arms on the spring compressing tool so the arms contact the coils farthest away from the center of the spring (Figure 2-44).

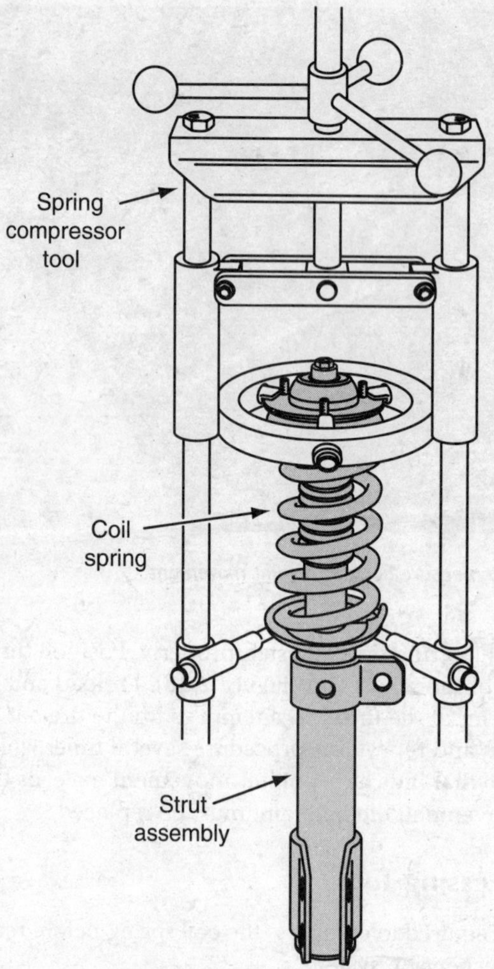

FIGURE 2-44 *Coil spring and strut assembly mounted in a spring compressing tool.*

WARNING: Always use the coil spring compressor tool recommended by the vehicle manufacturer. Some compressor tools are designed to work only on specific strut-and-coil-spring assemblies. If the compressor tool does not fit properly on the coil spring, the tool may slip off the spring, suddenly releasing the coil spring tension, which may result in personal injury.

CAUTION: Never clamp the lower end of the strut in a vise, which may cause internal strut damage.

3. Turn the handle on top of the compressor tool until all the spring tension is removed from the upper strut mount.
4. Loosen and remove the strut rod nut in the center of the upper strut mount (Figure 2-45). Be sure all the spring tension is removed from the upper strut mount before loosening this nut.
5. Remove the upper strut mount assembly, mount bearing, and then remove the upper spring seat and insulator.
6. Rotate the handle on the spring compressing tool to release all the tension on the coil spring, and then remove the spring.
7. Remove the dust shield and jounce bumper from the strut rod, and then remove the lower spring insulator (Figure 2-46).

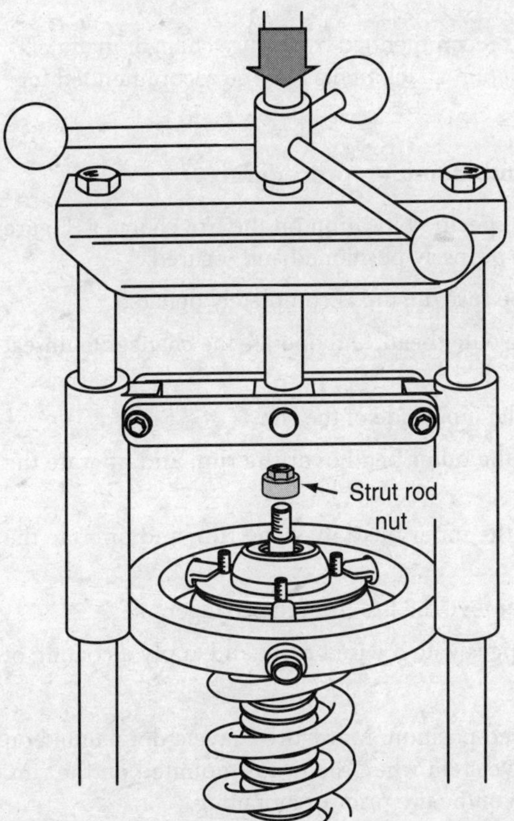

FIGURE 2-45 *After the compressing tool is operated to remove all the spring tension, remove the strut rod nut.*

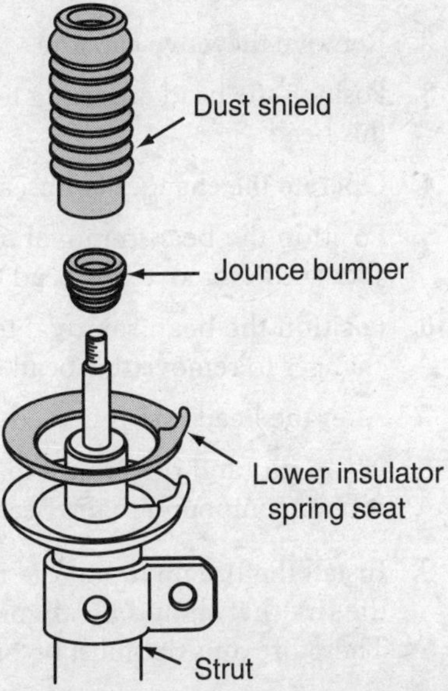

FIGURE 2-46 *Removal of the dust shield, jounce bumper, and lower spring insulator.*

8. Replace all worn or defective parts, and be sure the strut rod is fully extended. Install the lower insulator on the lower strut spring seat, and be sure the insulator is properly positioned on the seat.
9. Install the spring bumper on the strut rod.
10. Place the coil spring properly in the spring compressing tool, and rotate the handle on the spring compressing tool to compress the coil spring.
11. Install the strut into the coil spring, and be sure the lower insulator is properly positioned on the coil spring.
12. Install the upper spring insulator and upper strut mount, and be sure these components are properly positioned.
13. Install the strut rod nut and tighten this nut to the specified torque.
14. Rotate the handle on the spring compressing tool to slowly release all the spring tension, and remove the strut and spring assembly from the tool.

Using a Tire Changer

A tire changer dismounts and mounts tires on wheel rims without damaging the rims. Most tire changers are operated by shop air pressure.

WARNING: If the tire changer manufacturer's recommended procedure for dismounting and mounting tires is not followed, personal injury and/or rim damage may occur.

CAUTION: Always use the tire changer attachments recommended by the tire changer manufacturer. For example, specific bead removal and installation attachments may be recommended for certain types of wheel rims.

The following is a typical tire dismounting and mounting procedure:

1. Position the tire-and-wheel assembly in the specified location on the tire changer (Figure 2-47). Be sure the tire-and-wheel assembly is properly positioned and secured.
2. Remove the valve cap and valve core, and be sure the tire is completely deflated.
3. Position the bead unseating tool to unseat the outer bead, and operate the changer to unseat this bead.
4. Operate the changer to unseat the bead on the inner side of the rim.
5. Position the bead removal tool to remove the outer bead over the rim, and operate the changer to remove this bead over the rim.
6. Position the bead removal tool to remove the inner bead over the rim, and operate the changer to remove this bead over the rim.
7. After the beads are removed over the rim, remove the tire from the changer.
8. Clean dirt and rust from the rim sealing flanges with a wire brush, and apply a coating of rubber compound to the bead area of the tire.
9. Install the tire on top of the rim in the desired position. Many tires have a dot painted on the tire that should be aligned with the valve stem when the tire is mounted on the rim. Therefore, this dot must be on the outer side of the tire prior to mounting.
10. Position the bead installation tool to install the inner bead over the rim, and operate the changer to install this bead over the rim.

FIGURE 2-47 *Typical tire changer.*

11. Position the bead installation tool to install the outer bead over the rim, and operate the changer to install this bead over the rim.
12. Rotate the tire on the rim to align the painted dot with the valve stem, and install the valve core. Be sure the tire is centered properly on the rim.
13. Inflate the tire to the specified tire pressure, install the valve cap, and remove the tire and wheel from the tire changer.

Using a Scan Tool

A **scan tool** performs an electronic diagnosis of computer-controlled suspension systems and other electronic systems. Various test modules may be plugged into the scan tool, depending on the vehicle and system being diagnosed (Figure 2-48). The scan tool cable is connected to the data link connector (DLC) under the dash. On 1996 and newer vehicles with on-board diagnostic II (OBD II) systems, the scan tool is powered from a terminal in the DLC. On most pre-1996 vehicles, a power cable on the scan tool has to be connected to a 12V power source such as the cigarette lighter.

CAUTION: Never connect or disconnect the scan tool data cable with the ignition switch on. This action may damage expensive electronic components on the vehicle or the scan tool.

After the scan tool is connected, the vehicle make, model year, and engine size usually has to be selected on the scan tool display. On vehicles with several different computer systems, the technician must select the computer system to be diagnosed from the list of computer systems on the vehicle. For

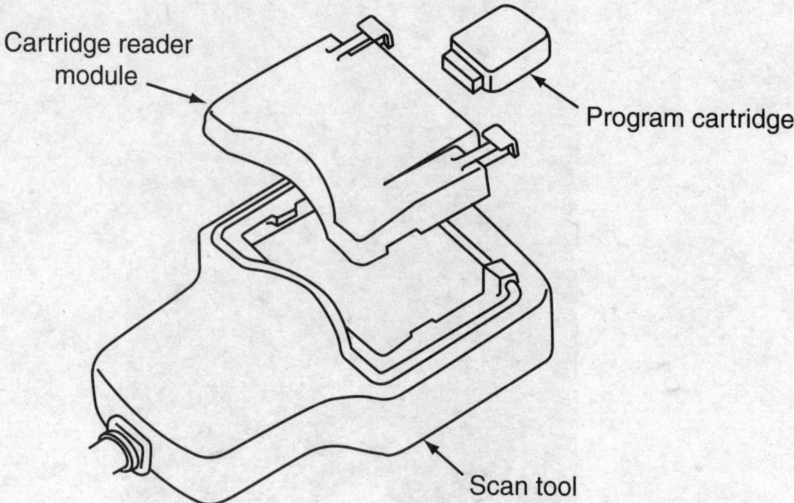

FIGURE 2-48 *Scan tool and related modules.*

example, if the technician wants to diagnose the continuously variable road sensing suspension system (CVRSS), then RSS must be selected from the list of computer systems displayed on the scan tool display. After the RSS selection, the scan tool display will ask the technician to select diagnostic trouble codes (DTCs), data, inputs, outputs, or clear codes.

On OBD II vehicles, the DTCs contain five digits. A typical DTC from a CVRSS is C1712. The "C" indicates this DTC is in the chassis group, and the "1" informs the technician this is a manufacturer specific code. A common DTC dictated by Society of Automotive Engineers (SAE) standards is indicated if the second digit is a "0." The digits 712 in the DTC indicate an open circuit in the left front (LF) damper actuator circuit. On a CVRSS, the damper actuators are solenoids in each shock absorber or strut. Diagnostic trouble codes (DTCs) indicate a defect in a certain electrical area, but they do not indicate a defect in a specific component. For example, the C1712 DTC indicates there is an open circuit in the LF damper actuator solenoid or in the connecting wires between this solenoid and the suspension computer. The technician usually has to use a volt-ohm meter to locate the exact cause of the DTC. Diagnostic trouble codes (DTCs) may be identified on the scan tool display as CURRENT or HISTORY. A CURRENT DTC is one that is present at the time of testing. A HISTORY DTC represents an intermittent defect that occurred in the past, which has since disappeared.

If "data" is selected, the scan tool display indicates data related to the CVRSS. This data includes readings from the input sensors and readings such as battery voltage or vehicle speed. When "inputs" is selected, the scan tool displays readings from the input sensors in the CVRSS. In the "output" parameter the scan tool displays readings from the outputs in the CVRSS. The output displays may be a voltage reading or solenoids displayed as being "on" or "off." If "clear codes" is selected on the scan tool display, the DTCs are erased from the computer memory.

Depending on the computer-controlled suspension system being diagnosed, the scan tool may be used to perform different functions. For example, on some computer-controlled air suspension systems, the scan tool may be used to command the suspension computer to fill and vent each air spring. This test mode may be used to check the operation of system components. The scan tool may be used to flash program the suspension computer memory. This mode installs new software in the computer as directed by service bulletins from the original equipment manufacturer (OEM). On some computer-controlled suspension systems, such as the system on the 2002 Lincoln Blackwood, the scan tool is used to adjust the suspension ride height.

Using an Electronic Wheel Balancer

The most popular type of wheel balancer in automotive service shops is the electronic balancer. Most electronic wheel balancers have an electric motor that spins the tire-and-wheel assembly at moderate speed during the balance procedure. On some electronic wheel balancers, the tire-and-wheel assembly is spun by hand for balance purposes. Certain preliminary checks must be performed on the tire-and-wheel assembly before installing this assembly on an electronic wheel balancer.

These preliminary checks include the following:

1. Clean all mud and debris from the tire-and-wheel assembly.
2. Remove all old wheel weights from the rim.

WARNING: Improperly installed wheel weights may fly off the rim when the wheel is spun on the balancer, resulting in personal injury.

3. Remove objects such as stones from the tire tread.

WARNING: Stones or other objects in the tire tread may fly out when the wheel is spun on the balancer, resulting in personal injury.

4. Inspect the tire tread and sidewall for defects, such as splits, cuts, chunks out of the tread or sidewall, and bulges indicating ply separation. Replace tires with these defects.
5. Inflate the tire to the specified pressure.

The tire-and-wheel assembly must be installed on the wheel balancer according to the instructions of the wheel balancer manufacturer. After the tire-and-wheel assembly is installed securely on the balancer, slowly rotate the tire by hand and listen for objects such as balls of rubber rolling inside the tire. Objects inside the tire must be removed, because they make wheel balancing difficult or impossible.

WARNING: If the tire-and-wheel assembly is not securely installed on the wheel balancer, the wheel may come loose and fly off the balancer during the balance procedure, resulting in personal injury.

Use a dial indicator to measure vertical and lateral tire and wheel runout. If tire and wheel runout is excessive, wheel balancing may be difficult. Enter the wheel diameter, width, and offset in the wheel balancer. The balancer must have this information to calculate the required amount of wheel weight and the weight position. Lower the safety hood on the wheel balancer, and activate the balancer to spin the wheel. Apply the brake on the balancer to stop the wheel. Install the indicated amount of wheel weight in the proper position as indicated on the wheel balancer display. Be sure the weight(s) are securely attached to the wheel rim.

Using a Computer Four Wheel Aligner

If a vehicle has a frame and a live-axle rear suspension system, it is not as likely to require rear wheel alignment as a unibody vehicle with a semi-independent or independent rear suspension system. Because of increased four wheel alignment requirements on unibody cars, most shops that offer wheel alignment service are equipped with a computer four wheel aligner. Before performing a wheel alignment, the technician must complete a preliminary vehicle inspection. The purpose of the preliminary inspection is to locate any defective or worn components that would make wheel alignment inaccurate.

A preliminary wheel alignment inspection includes these checks:

1. Be sure the vehicle has the normal curb weight that it has when the driver is operating the vehicle. Make sure the gas tank is full, and check for excessive mud adhered to the underside of the chassis.
2. Be sure the tires are inflated to the specified tire pressure, and inspect the tires for excessive wear, bulges, cuts, and splits. Be sure the tires are all the same size.
3. Check for the specified front and rear suspension height. Because the suspension height affects many of the wheel alignment angles, this height must be corrected before performing a wheel alignment if it is not within specifications.
4. Check the steering wheel free play. If this free play is more than specified, inspect the steering linkages and tie rod ends for excessive wear. The excessive steering wheel free play must be corrected before a wheel alignment, because this problem affects front wheel toe and steering quality.
5. Be sure the shock absorbers and struts are in satisfactory condition.
6. Check the front and rear wheel bearing adjustments, and correct these adjustments as necessary. Loose wheel bearing adjustments affect some of the wheel alignment angles.
7. Check the ball joints for excessive wear. Worn ball joints affect some of the wheel alignment angles.
8. Inspect the front and rear, upper and lower control arms for damage, and inspect all the control arm bushings for wear. Bent control arms or worn control arm bushings affect wheel alignment angles.
9. Inspect the front and rear stabilizer bars and bushings. Worn stabilizer bushings affect ride quality and vehicle handling.

After the preliminary inspection is completed, and all the necessary components have been replaced or adjusted, drive the vehicle onto the wheel alignment rack.

Then follow this procedure to complete the four wheel alignment with a computer wheel aligner:

1. Follow all instructions provided in the wheel aligner operator's manual.
2. Be sure the front wheels are centered on the wheel aligner turntables.
3. Be sure the rear wheels are positioned properly on the slip plates.
4. Mount the wheel sensor units on each wheel.
5. Select the vehicle make and model year on the wheel aligner screen.
6. On the wheel aligner preliminary inspection screen, check the condition of each item. Most of these items are mentioned in the previous preliminary inspection procedure.
7. Display the ride height screen on the wheel aligner, and be sure the front and rear ride height is within specifications.
8. Display the wheel runout screen of the wheel aligner, and compensate for wheel runout as directed.
9. Display the turning angle screen on the wheel aligner. Apply the brakes with a brake pedal depressor as directed on the screen, and perform the turning angle check.
10. Display the front and rear wheel alignment angles on the screen. Most computer four wheel aligners mark the alignment angles that are not within specifications.
11. Display the adjustment screen on the wheel aligner, and perform the necessary front and rear suspension adjustments to bring all the alignment angles within specifications. Photo Sequence 2 illustrates a typical procedure for performing a four wheel alignment with a computer wheel aligner.

PHOTO SEQUENCE 2
TYPICAL PROCEDURE FOR PERFORMING FOUR WHEEL ALIGNMENT WITH A COMPUTER WHEEL ALIGNER

P2-1 Position the vehicle on the alignment rack.

P2-2 Make sure the front tires are positioned properly on the turntables.

P2-3 Position the rear wheels on the slip plates.

P2-4 Attach the wheel units.

P2-5 Select the vehicle make and model year.

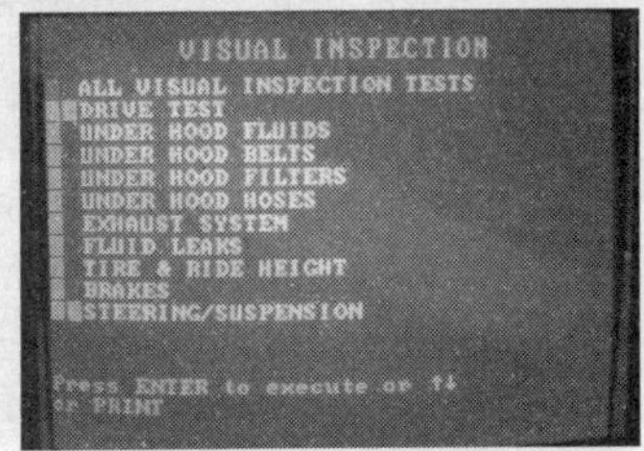

P2-6 Check the items on the screen during the preliminary inspection.

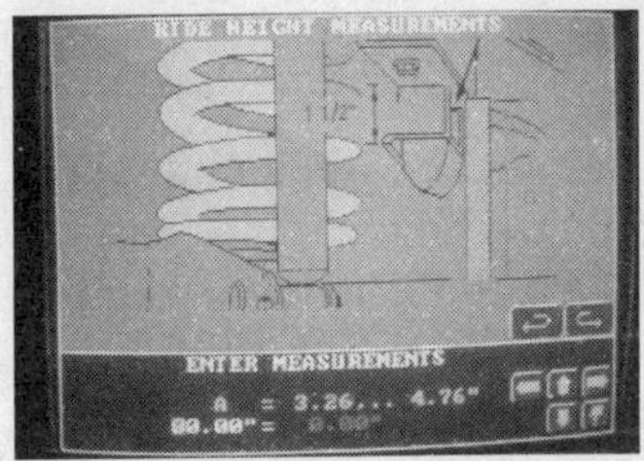

P2-7 Display the ride height screen. Check the tire condition for each tire on the tire condition screen.

P2-8 Display the wheel runout compensation screen.

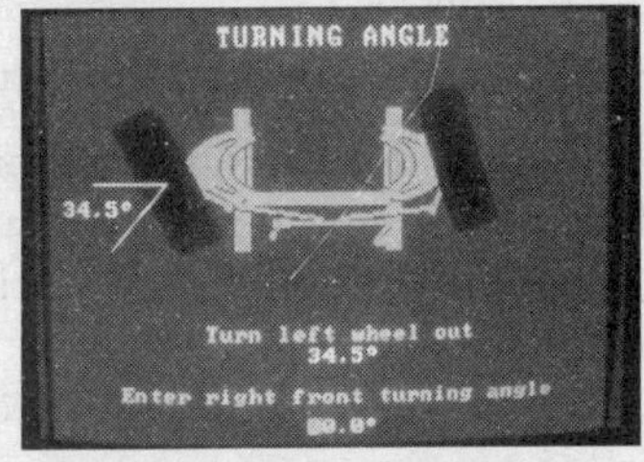

P2-9 Display the turning angle screen and perform the turning angle check.

P2-10 Display the front and rear wheel alignment angle screen.

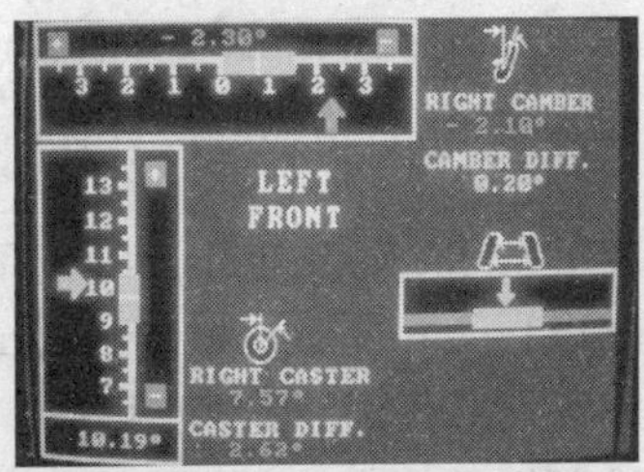

P2-11 Display the adjustment screen.

EMPLOYER AND EMPLOYEE OBLIGATIONS

The ever increasing electronics content on today's vehicles also requires that technicians are familiar with the latest electronics technology. To be a successful automotive technician, you must be committed to lifelong training. There are many different ways to obtain this training, but it is absolutely essential.

Automotive training may be obtained by these methods:

1. Obtain bulletins, service manuals, and training information from original equipment manufacturers (OEMs); independent parts and component manufacturers; and independent suppliers of service manuals and training books. After the information is obtained, it is essential that you read and study it.
2. Join an organization dedicated to supplying information to automotive service technicians such as the International Automotive Technician's Association (IATA).
3. Join an Internet organization such as the International Automotive Technicians Network where you can communicate with other technicians and obtain answers to service problems.
4. Download information available on the Internet from automotive equipment manufacturers. Many of these manufacturers provide operator's manuals and other information on their equipment for downloading purposes.
5. Attend satellite training seminars available from some independent automotive training organizations and OEMs.
6. Attend training seminars in your location sponsored by equipment and parts manufacturers or OEMs.
7. Attend training seminars sponsored by the automotive department at your local college.
8. Attend National Institute for Automotive Service Excellence (ASE) certification classes.

Successful automotive technicians must be committed to lifelong training, but their employers must also be committed to assisting them in obtaining the necessary training. This assistance may be financial, providing time off work to attend training seminars or arranging the necessary training programs.

When you begin employment, you enter into a business agreement with your employer. A business agreement involves an exchange of goods or services that have value. Although the automotive technician may not have a written agreement with his or her employer, the technician exchanges time, skills, and effort for money paid by the employer. Both the employee and the employer have obligations.

The automotive technician's obligations include the following:

1. Productivity: As an automotive technician you have a responsibility to your employer to make the best possible use of time on the job. Each job should be done in a reasonable length of time. Employees are paid for their skills, effort, and time.
2. Quality: Each repair job should be a quality job! Work should never be done in a careless manner. Nothing improves customer relations like quality workmanship.
3. Teamwork: The shop staff are a team, and everyone including technicians and management personnel is a team member. You should cooperate with and care about other team members. Each member of the team should strive for harmonious relations with fellow

workers. Cooperative teamwork helps improve shop efficiency, productivity, and customer relations. Customers may be "turned off" by bickering between shop personnel.

4. Honesty: Employers and customers expect and deserve honesty from automotive technicians. Honesty creates a feeling of trust among technicians, employers, and customers.
5. Loyalty: As an employee, you are obliged to act in the best interests of your employer, both on and off the job.
6. Attitude: Employees should maintain a positive attitude at all times. As in other professions, automotive technicians have days when it may be difficult to maintain a positive attitude. For example, there will be days when the technical problems on a certain vehicle are difficult to solve. However, a negative attitude certainly will not help the situation! A positive attitude has a positive effect on the job situation as well as on the customer and employer.
7. Responsibility: You are responsible for your conduct on the job and your work-related obligations. These obligations include always maintaining good workmanship and customer relations. Attention to details such as always placing fender, seat, and floor mat covers on customer vehicles prior to driving or working on the vehicle greatly improve customer relations.
8. Following directions: All of us like to do things "our way." Such action, however, may not be in the best interests of the shop; as an employee, you have an obligation to follow the supervisor's directions.
9. Punctuality and regular attendance: Employees have an obligation to be on time for work and to be regular in attendance on the job. It is very difficult for a business to operate successfully if it cannot count on its employees to be on the job at the appointed time.
10. Regulations: Automotive technicians should be familiar with all state and federal regulations pertaining to their job situation, such as the Occupational Safety and Health Act (OSHA) and hazardous waste disposal laws. In Canada, employees should be familiar with workplace hazardous materials information systems (WHMIS).

Employer to employee obligations include:

1. Wages: The employer has a responsibility to inform the employee regarding the exact amount of financial remuneration they will receive and when they will be paid.
2. Fringe benefits: A detailed description of all fringe benefits should be provided by the employer. These benefits may include holiday pay, pension plans, and sickness and accident insurance.
3. Working conditions: A clean, safe workplace must be provided by the employer. The shop must have adequate safety equipment and first-aid supplies. Employers must be certain that all shop personnel maintain the shop area and equipment to provide adequate safety and a healthy workplace atmosphere.
4. Employee instruction: Employers must provide employees with clear job descriptions and be sure that each worker is aware of his or her obligations.
5. Employee supervision: Employers should inform their workers regarding the responsibilities of their immediate supervisors and other management personnel.
6. Employee training: Employers must make sure that each employee is familiar with the safe operation of all the equipment that they are required to use in their job situation. Since automotive technology is changing rapidly, employers should provide regular update training for their technicians. Under the Right-to-Know Laws, employers are required to

inform all employees about hazardous materials in the shop. Employees should be familiar with material safety data sheets (MSDSs), which detail the labeling and handling of hazardous waste, and the health problems if exposed to hazardous waste.

Job Responsibilities

An automotive technician has specific responsibilities regarding each job performed on a customer's vehicle.

These job responsibilities include:

1. Do every job to the best of your ability. There is no place in the automotive service industry for careless workmanship! Automotive technicians and students must realize they have a very responsible job. During many repair jobs you, as a student or technician working on a customer's vehicle, actually have the customer's life and vehicle safety in your hands. For example, if you are doing a brake job and leave the wheel nuts loose on one wheel, that wheel may fall off the vehicle at high speed. This could result in serious personal injury for the customer and others, plus extensive vehicle damage. If this type of disaster occurs, the individual who worked on the vehicle and the shop may be involved in a very expensive legal action. As a student or technician working on customer vehicles, you are responsible for the safety of every vehicle that you work on! Even when careless work does not create a safety hazard, it leads to dissatisfied customers, who often take their business to another shop. Nobody benefits when that happens.
2. Treat customers fairly and honestly on every repair job. Do not install parts that are unnecessary to complete the repair job.
3. Use published specifications; do not guess at adjustments.
4. Follow the service procedures in the service manual provided by the vehicle manufacturer or an independent manual publisher.
5. When the repair job is completed, always be sure the customer's complaint has been corrected.
6. Do not be too concerned with work speed when you begin working as an automotive technician. Speed comes with experience.

NATIONAL INSTITUTE FOR AUTOMOTIVE SERVICE EXCELLENCE (ASE) CERTIFICATION

The National Institute for Automotive Service Excellence (ASE) has provided voluntary testing and certification of automotive technicians on a national basis for many years. The image of the automotive service industry has been enhanced by the ASE certification program. More than 415,000 technicians now have current certifications and work in a wide variety of automotive service shops.

ASE provides certification in eight areas of automotive repair:

1. Engine repair
2. Automatic transmissions/transaxles
3. Manual drivetrain and axles
4. Suspension and steering

5. Brakes
6. Electrical systems
7. Heating and air conditioning
8. Engine performance

A technician may take the ASE test and become certified in any or all of the eight areas. When a technician passes an ASE test in one of the eight areas, an Automotive Technician's shoulder patch is issued by ASE. Technicians who pass all eight tests receive a Master Technician's shoulder patch (Figure 2-49). Retesting at five-year intervals is required to remain certified. The certification test in each of the eight areas contains 40 to 80 multiple-choice questions. The test questions are written by a panel of automotive service experts from various areas of automotive service, including automotive instructors, service managers, automotive manufacturers' representatives, test equipment representatives, and certified technicians. The test questions are pretested and checked for quality by a national sample of technicians. On an ASE certification test, approximately 45 to 50 percent of the questions are Technician A and Technician B format, and the multiple-choice format is used in 40 to 45 percent of the questions. Less than 10 percent of ASE certification questions are an EXCEPT format in which the technician selects one incorrect answer out of four possible answers. ASE regulations demand that each technician must have two years of working experience in the automotive service industry prior to taking a certification test or tests. However, relevant formal training may be substituted for one year of working experience. Contact ASE for details regarding this substitution. The contents of the suspension and steering test are listed in Table 2-1.

FIGURE 2-49 *ASE certification shoulder patches worn by Automotive Technicians and Master Technicians.*

ASE also provides certification tests in automotive specialty areas, such as Parts Specialist; Advanced Engine Performance Specialist; Alternate Fuels, Light Vehicle–Compressed Natural Gas; Machinist, Cylinder Head Specialist; Machinist, Cylinder Block Specialist; and Machinist, Assembly Specialist.

Shops that employ ASE-certified technicians display an official **ASE blue seal of excellence**. This blue seal increases the customer's awareness of both the shop's commitment to quality service and the competency of its certified technicians.

SERVICE MANUALS

The service manual is one of the most important tools for today's technician. It provides information concerning component identification, service procedures, specifications, and diagnostic information. In addition, the service manual provides information concerning wiring harness connections and

TABLE 2-1 *Suspension and Steering Test Summary*

CONTENT AREA	QUESTIONS IN TEST	PERCENTAGE OF TEST
A. Steering systems diagnosis and repair	10	25%
1. Steering columns and manual steering gears (3)		
2. Power-assisted steering units (4)		
3. Steering linkage (3)		
B. Suspension systems diagnosis and repair	13	33%
1. Front suspensions (6)		
2. Rear suspensions (5)		
3. Miscellaneous service (2)		
C. Wheel alignment diagnosis, adjustment, and repair	12	30%
D. Wheel and tire diagnosis and repair	5	12%
TOTAL	**40**	**100%**

FIGURE 2-50 *Uniform service manual layout.*

Ball Joint Boot Replacement

NOTE: The upper control arm ball joint, lower control arm ball joint, and knuckle upper ball joint are attached with the boot retainer to improve the sealing efficiency of the boot.

1. Remove the set ring and boot.

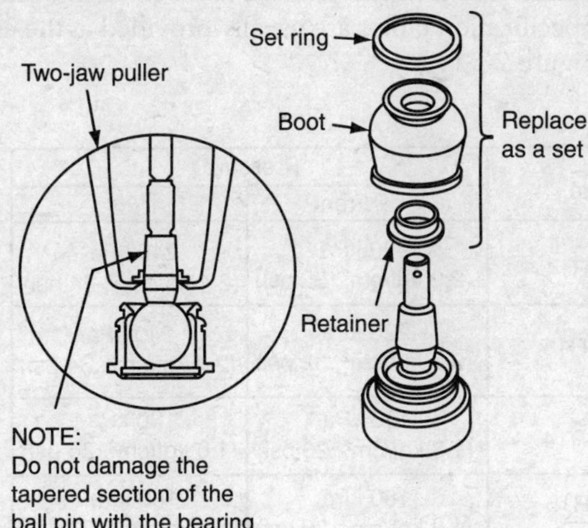

NOTE:
Do not damage the tapered section of the ball pin with the bearing puller.

2. Remove the retainer.

NOTE: The knuckle lower ball joint does not have a retainer.

3. Pack the interior of the boot and lip with grease.

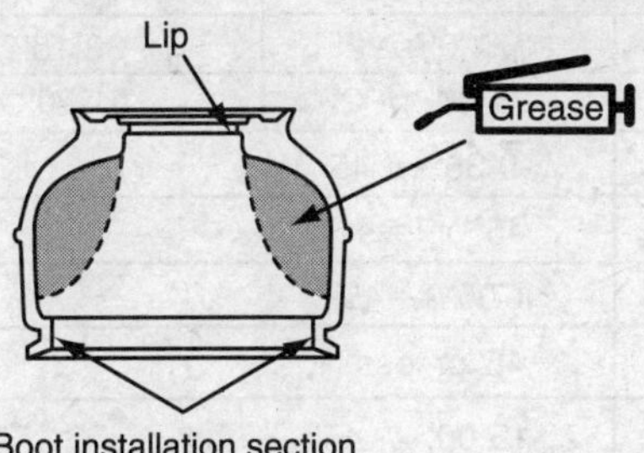

CAUTION: Do not contaminate the boot installation section with grease.

4. Wipe the grease off the sliding surface of the ball pin, and pack with fresh grease.

5. Insert the new retainer lightly into the ball joint pin.

NOTE: When installing the ball joint, press the retainer into the ball joint pin.

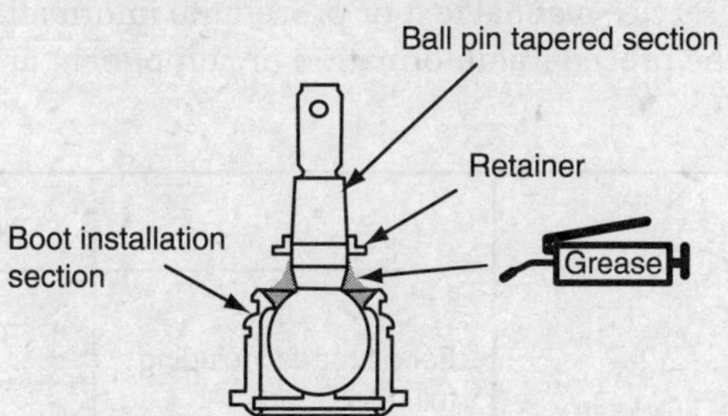

CAUTION:

Keep grease off the boot installation section and the tapered section of the ball pin.

Do not allow dust, dirt, or other foreign materials to enter the boot.

6. Install the boot in the groove of the boot installation section securely, then bleed air.

7. Adjust the special tool with the adjusting bolt until the end of the tool aligns with the groove on the boot.

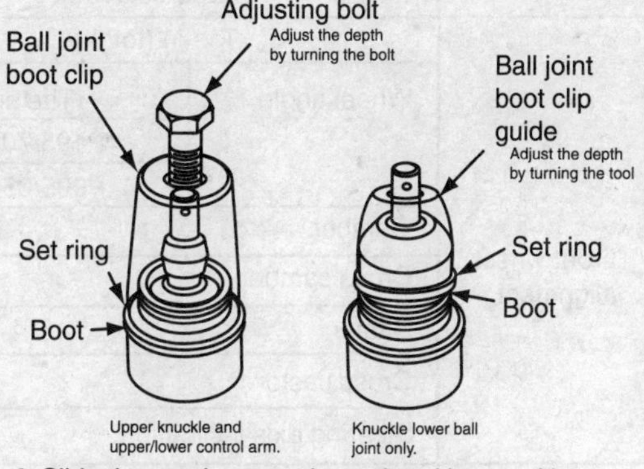

8. Slide the set ring over the tool and into position.

CAUTION: After installing the boot, check the ball pin tapered section and threads for grease contamination and wipe them if necessary.

FIGURE 2-51 *Illustrations in the service manual that guide the technician through service procedures.*

routing, component location, and fluid capacities. Service manuals can be supplied by the vehicle manufacturer or through aftermarket suppliers.

The service manual provides an explanation of the vehicle identification number (VIN). The VIN information is essential when ordering parts. Most service manuals published by vehicle manufacturers now have a standard format (Figure 2-50). The service manual usually provides illustrations to guide the technician through the service operation (Figure 2-51). Always use the correct manual for the vehicle and system being serviced. Follow each step in the service procedure. Do not skip steps! Measurements such as torque, end play, and clearance specifications are located in or near the service manual text or procedural information. Specification tables are usually provided at the end of the procedural information or component area (Figure 2-52).

		Tire size	Pressure	
			Front	Rear
Cold tire inflation pressure	For all roads including full rated loads	P195/70R14	220 kPa (2.2 kgf/cm^2, 32 psi)	240 kPa (2.4 kgf/cm^2, 34 psi)
		P205/65R15	220 kPa (2.2 kgf/cm^2, 32 psi)	240 kPa (2.4 kgf/cm^2, 34 psi)
	Optional inflation for reduced loads (1 to 4 passengers)	P195/70R14	180 kPa (1.8 kgf/cm^2, 26 psi)	180 kPa (1.8 kgf/cm^2, 26 psi)
		P205/65R15	180 kPa (1.8 kgf/cm^2, 26 psi)	180 kPa (1.8 kgf/cm^2, 26 psi)
Vehicle height	Tire size		Height	
			Front	Rear
	P195/70R14		210 mm (8.27 in.)	270 mm (10.63 in.)
	P205/65R15		213 mm (8.39 in.)	276 mm (10.87 in.)
Front wheel alignment	Toe-in (total)		0° +/- 0.2° (0 +/- 2mm, 0 +/- 0.08 in.)	
	Wheel angle	Tire size	Inside wheel	Outside wheel
		P195/70R14	37°20' +/- 2°	32°15'
		P205/65R15	36°00' +/- 2°	31°20'
	Camber		-0°35' +/- 45'	
	Cross camber		45' or less	
	Caster		1°05' +/- 45'	
	Cross caster		45' or less	
	Steering axis inclination		13°00' +/- 45'	
Rear wheel alignment	Toe-in (total)		0.4° +/- 0.2° (4 +/- 2mm, 0.16 +/- 0.08in.)	
	Camber		-0°15' +/- 45'	
	Cross camber		45' or less	

FIGURE 2-52 *Specification table.*

Because the service manual is divided into a number of main component and system areas, a table of contents is provided at the front of the manual to provide quick access to the desired information. Each component area or system is covered in a section of the service manual (Figure 2-53). At

TABLE OF CONTENTS	SECTION NUMBER
GENERAL INFO. AND LUBE	
General Information	0A
Maintenance and Lubrication	0B
HEATING AND AIR COND.	
Heating and Vent. (nonA/C)	1A
Air-Conditioning System	1B
V-5 A/C Compressor Overhaul	1D3
BUMPERS AND FRONT BODY PANELS	
Bumpers (See 10-4)	
Fr. End Body Panels (See 10-5)	
STEERING, SUSPENSION, TIRES, AND WHEELS	
Diagnosis	3
Wheel Alignment	3A
Power Steering Gear & Pump	3B1
Front Suspension	3C
Rear Suspension	3D
Tires and Wheels	3E
Steering Col. On-Vehicle Service	3F
Steering Col. – Std. Unit Repair	3F1
Steering Col. – Tilt, Unit Repair	3F2
DRIVE AXLES	
Drive Axles	4D
BRAKES	
General Info. – Diagnosis and On-Car Service	5
Compact Master Cylinder	5A1
Disc Brake Caliper	5B2
Drum Brake - Anchor Plate	5C2
Power Brake Booster Assembly	5D2
ENGINES	
General Information	6
2.0 Liter I-4 Engine	6A1
3.1 Liter V6 Engine	6A3
Cooling System	6B
Fuel System	6C
Engine Electrical – General	6D
Battery	6D1
Cranking System	6D2
Charging System	6D3
Ignition System	6D4
Engine Wiring	6D5
Driveability & Emissions – Gen.	6E
Driveability & Emissions – TBI	6E2
Driveability & Emissions – PFI	6E3
Exhaust System	6F

TABLE OF CONTENTS	SECTION NUMBER
TRANSAXLE	
Auto.Transaxel On-Car Serv.	7A
Auto. Trans. – Hydraulic Diagnosis	3T40-HD
Auto. Trans. – Unit Repair	3T40
Man. Trans. On-Car Service	7B
5-Sp. 5TM40 Man. Trans. Unit Repair	7B1
5-Sp. Isuzu Man. Trans. Unit Repair	7B2
Clutch	7C
CHASSIS ELECTRICAL, INSTRUMENT PANEL & WIPER/WASHER	
Electrical Diagnosis	8A
Lighting and Horns	8B
Instrument Panel and Console	8C
Windshield Wiper/Washer	8E5
ACCESSORIES	
Audio System	9A
Cruise Control	9B
Engine Block Heater	9C
BODY SERVICE	
General Body Service	10-1
Stationary Glass	10-2
Underbody	10-3
Bumpers	10-4
Body Front End	10-5
Doors	10-6
Rear Quarters	10-7
Body Rear End	10-8
Roof & Convertible Top	10-9
Seats	10-10
Safety Belts	10-11
Body Wiring	10-12
Unibody Collision Repair	11-1
Welded Panel Replacement	11-2
INDEX	
Alphabetical Index	

FIGURE 2-53 *The table of contents directs you to the major systems and component areas in the service manual.*

the beginning of each section in the service manual, a smaller table of contents guides the technician to the information regarding the specific system or component being serviced. The service manual may be divided into several volumes, because of the extensive amount of information required to service today's vehicles. Diagnostic information in each section of the service manual is usually provided in **diagnostic procedure charts** (Figure 2-54). The test results obtained in a specific diagnostic step guide the technician to the next appropriate step.

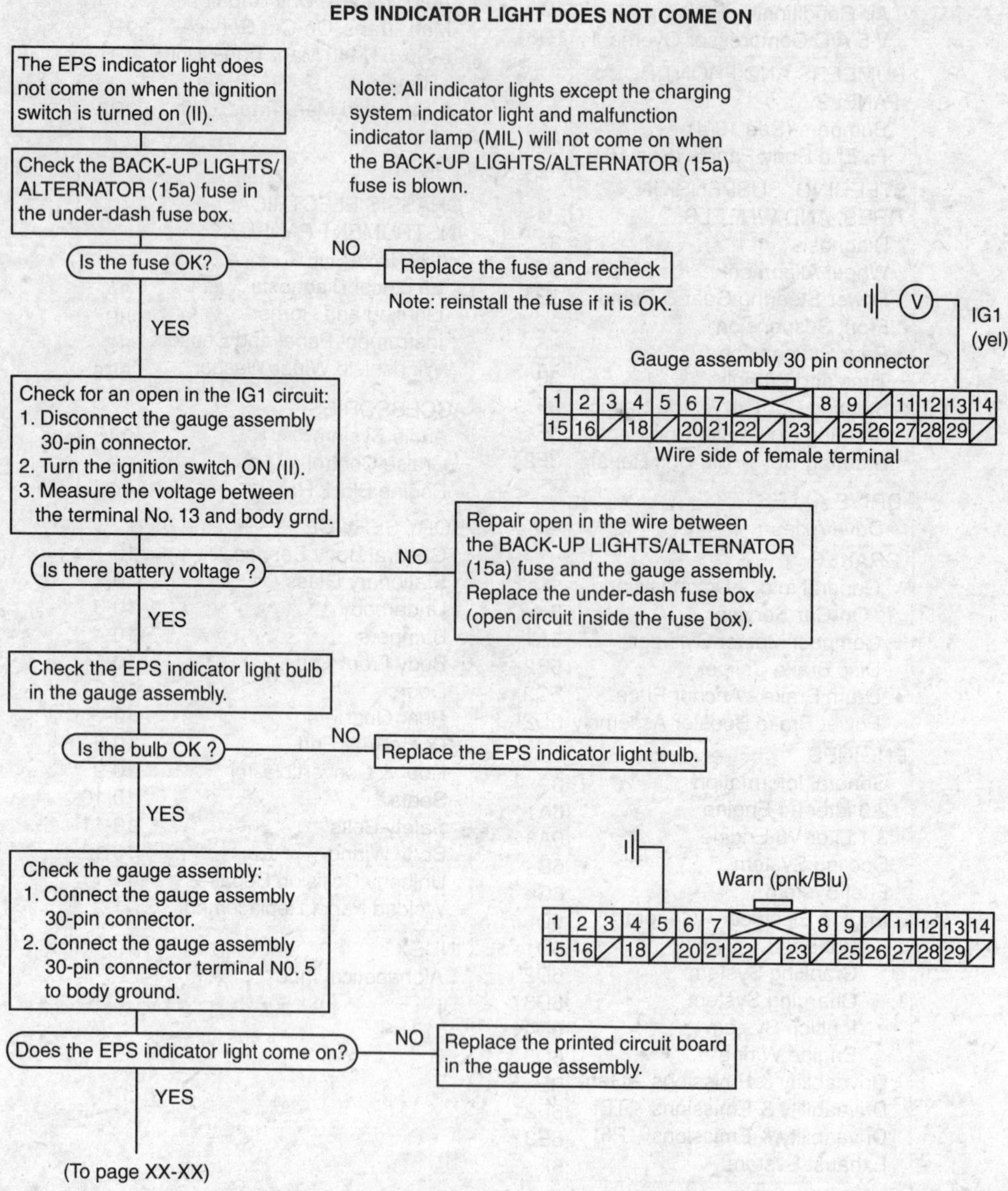

FIGURE 2-54 *Typical diagnostic chart.*

FIGURE 2-55 *Computers are replacing printed service manuals in many shops.*

Service and parts information can also be provided through computer services (Figure 2-55). Computerized service information may be provided on computer disks or compact disks (CDs), which are easier to store and access. Computers may also be connected to a central database to obtain service information. Using the mouse, light pen, computer keyboard, or touch-sensitive screen, the technician selects choices from a series of menus on the computer monitor. When the desired information is accessed, it may be printed out for detailed study. Modern automotive service information is presently computer or Web-based.

Service procedures may be modified by the vehicle manufacturer at any time. Service bulletins provide up-to-date corrections for the service manuals. If a significant number of corrections are required, a second edition of the manual may be published. When service information is provided on CDs, the CDs are updated frequently to provide the latest information.

CASE STUDY

A technician was removing and replacing the alternator of a General Motors car. After installing the replacement alternator and connecting the alternator battery wire, she proceeded to install the alternator belt. The rubber boot was still removed from the alternator battery terminal. While installing this belt, her wristwatch expansion bracelet made electrical contact from the alternator battery terminal to ground on the alternator housing. Even though the alternator battery wire is protected with a fuse link, which melted, a high current flowed through the wristwatch bracelet. This heated the bracelet to a very high temperature and severely burned the technician's arm.

The technician forgot two safety rules:

1. Never wear jewelry, such as watches and rings, while working in an automotive shop.
2. Before performing electrical work on a vehicle, disconnect the negative battery cable. If the vehicle is equipped with an air bag, wait the specified time after this cable is disconnected.

CASE STUDY

A customer brought a 1998 Cavalier into the shop with a rough idle complaint. The customer informed the service salesman that he had this problem since the car was purchased new, and the problem was always caused by an open exhaust gas recirculation (EGR) valve. The customer said the

(EGR) valve had been replaced three times under warranty, and he had also paid for an EGR valve replacement, and one EGR valve cleaning, after the warranty had expired.

The technician connected a scan tool to the DLC, and verified that a diagnostic trouble code (DTC) was present indicating the EGR valve was stuck open. Next the technician checked for technical service bulletins (TSBs) related to this problem in the shop database. One TSB indicated that the vehicle manufacturer had revised powertrain control module (PCM) software that caused the PCM to pulse the EGR valve briefly each time the PCM closed the EGR valve to remove carbon buildup on the EGR valve pintle. Using the appropriate equipment the technician installed the updated software in the PCM, and this permanently corrected the problem.

Previous technicians who serviced this vehicle had forgotten, or neglected, to check the TSB database for the cause of this problem. As a result, both the vehicle manufacturer and the customer spent a considerable amount of money for EGR valve replacements, when computer reprogramming was required to correct the problem.

Case Study

A technician had just replaced the engine in a Ford vehicle and was performing final adjustments such as timing and air-fuel mixture. In this shop, the cars were parked in the work bays at an angle on both sides of the shop. With the engine running at fast idle, the automatic transmission suddenly slipped into reverse. The car went backward across the shop and collided with a car in one of the electrical repair bays. Both vehicles were damaged to a considerable extent. Fortunately, no personnel were injured.

This technician forgot to apply the parking brake while working on the vehicle!

Service Tips

- When installing a seal, the garter spring must face toward the flow of lubricant.
- Dial indicators must be kept clean and dry for accuracy and long life.
- Using a torque stick allows the use of an impact wrench when tightening fasteners, and this speeds up the service operation. However, the use of torque sticks may not be as accurate as using a torque wrench. It is a good practice to double check the accuracy of a torque stick by checking the fastener torque with a torque wrench after it is tightened with a torque stick.
- Magnetic wheel alignment gauge mounting surfaces must be clean with no metal burrs.
- The procedure for measuring ball joint wear varies depending on the type of suspension system and the type of ball joint mounting. Always consult the vehicle manufacturer's service manual.
- The tire dismounting and mounting procedure varies depending on the type of tire changer. Always follow the dismounting and mounting procedure recommended by the tire changer manufacturer.
- Many shops have a policy of always installing a new valve stem when repairing or replacing a tire, which prevents problems with cracked or defective valve stems.
- Aligning the painted dot on the tire sidewall ensures proper tire balancing with a minimum amount of balance weight.
- The valve core may be left out of the valve stem and the tire partially inflated. This action allows the air pressure to enter the tire quicker and seat the beads against the rim flanges. After the beads are seated, allow most of the air to escape from the tire, and then install the valve core.
- The wheel runout compensation procedure varies, depending on the make and year of the wheel aligner.

Review Questions

1. While discussing systems of weights and measures:
Technician A says the international system (SI) is called the metric system. *Technician B* says every unit in the metric system can be divided or multiplied by 10.
Who is correct?
A. A only **C.** Both A and B
B. B only **D.** Neither A nor B

2. While discussing the metric system:
Technician A says that 1 inch is equal to 2.54 millimeters. *Technician B* says that 1 meter is equal to 36.37 inches.
Who is correct?
A. A only **C.** Both A and B
B. B only **D.** Neither A nor B

3. When diagnosing a vehicle operational problem, the first step is to:
A. Think of the possible causes of the problem.
B. Perform diagnostic tests to locate the exact cause of the problem.
C. Consult TSB information to find the cause of the problem.
D. Identify the complaint.

4. When testing power steering pump pressure, the power steering gauge valve should be closed for a maximum of:
A. 10 seconds. **C.** 25 seconds.
B. 20 seconds. **D.** 35 seconds.

5. While discussing employer and employee responsibilities:
Technician A says employers are required to inform their employees about hazardous materials in the shop. *Technician B* says that employers have no obligation to inform their employees about the safe operation of shop equipment.
Who is correct?
A. A only **C.** Both A and B
B. B only **D.** Neither A nor B

6. When connecting a scan tool to diagnose a computer-controlled suspension system on a 1998 vehicle:
A. The scan tool power cord is connected to the cigarette lighter socket.
B. The scan tool is connected to the DLC located under the dash.
C. The ignition switch should be on when disconnecting the scan tool.
D. On OBD II vehicles the 7-digit DTCs are displayed on the scan tool.

7. All these statements about suspension and steering tools are true EXCEPT:
A. A plumb bob may be used for frame measurement.
B. A tram gauge may be used to measure front wheel alignment.
C. A scan tool may be used to diagnose electronically controlled suspension systems.
D. A brake pedal jack may be used to apply the brakes during a wheel alignment.

8. When using a vehicle lift:
A. The lift arms may be positioned on any strong chassis member.
B. The safety catch must be engaged after the vehicle is raised on a lift.

C. The vehicle hood should be open when raising a vehicle on a lift.
D. The vehicle weight may exceed the maximum capacity of the lift.

9. When taking ASE certification tests:
A. A technician must pass four of the eight ASE certification tests to receive a Master Technician's shoulder patch.
B. Each ASE certification test contains 35 to 45 questions.
C. An ASE specialty test is available in Advanced Engine Performance Specialist.
D. Retesting at three-year intervals is required to maintain ASE certification.

10. When taking ASE certification tests:
A. A technician must have four years of automotive repair experience before taking an ASE certification test.
B. ASE may allow relevant training to be substituted for one year of work experience.
C. On any ASE certification test, 90 percent of the questions are Technician A and Technician B type.
D. Employers who employ ASE-certified technicians may display a green ASE seal of excellence.

JOB SHEET 4

Name ______________________________ Date ______________

RAISE A CAR WITH A FLOOR JACK AND SUPPORT IT ON SAFETY STANDS

Upon completion of this job sheet, you should be able to raise the front and rear of a vehicle with a floor jack and support the vehicle on safety stands.

Tools and Materials

A car
Hydraulic floor jack
Four safety stands

Describe the Vehicle Being Worked On:

Year __________ Make ______________ Model ______________
VIN ______________________ Engine type and size ______________

This job sheet must be completed under the supervision of your instructor!

Procedure

Task Completed

1. Determine the proper vehicle floor jack lifting points in the car manufacturer's service manual. Proper front lifting point ______________ Proper rear lifting point ______________________
2. Be sure the car is parked on a level shop floor surface with the parking brake applied. ☐
3. Place the floor jack under the proper lifting point on the front of the vehicle, and raise the floor jack pad until it contacts the lifting point. ☐
4. Release the parking brake and be sure the transmission is in neutral. Is the parking brake released? ☐ Yes ☐ No

   Is the transmission in neutral? ☐ Yes ☐ No

   Instructor check ______________________
5. Operate the floor jack and raise the vehicle to the desired height. Place safety stands under the proper support points on the vehicle chassis or suspension. ☐
6. Very slowly operate the release lever on the hydraulic floor jack to slowly lower the vehicle until the support points lightly contact the safety stands. Stop lowering the floor jack. ☐
7. Be sure the safety stands contact the proper support points on the vehicle, and check to be sure all the safety stand legs contact the shop floor evenly.

   Are the safety stands contacting the proper support points on the vehicle?
   ☐ Yes ☐ No

   Are all safety stand legs contacting the floor evenly? ☐ Yes ☐ No

   Instructor check ______________________

Task Completed

☐ **8.** If the answer to both questions in step 7 is yes, very slowly operate the release lever on the hydraulic floor jack to slowly lower the vehicle until the vehicle weight is completely supported on the safety stands. Be sure all the safety stand legs are contacting the shop floor evenly, and then remove the floor jack.

☐ **9.** Place the floor jack under the proper lifting point on the rear of the vehicle, and raise the floor jack pad until it contacts the lifting point.

10. Operate the floor jack, and raise the vehicle to the desired height. Place safety stands under the proper support points on the rear of the vehicle chassis or suspension.

Are the safety stands properly positioned? ☐ Yes ☐ No

Instructor check ______________________________

☐ **11.** Very slowly operate the release lever on the hydraulic floor jack to slowly lower the vehicle until the rear support points lightly contact the safety stands. Stop lowering the floor jack.

12. Be sure the safety stands contact the proper rear support points on the vehicle, and check to be sure all the safety stand legs contact the shop floor evenly.

Are the safety stands contacting the proper support points on the vehicle?
☐ Yes ☐ No

Are all the safety stand legs contacting the floor evenly? ☐ Yes ☐ No

Instructor check ______________________________

☐ **13.** If the answer to both questions in step 12 is yes, very slowly operate the release lever on the hydraulic floor jack to slowly lower the rear of the vehicle until the vehicle weight is completely supported on the safety stands. Be sure all the safety stand legs are contacting the shop floor evenly; then remove the floor jack.

Instructor's Response ______________________________

____

____

JOB SHEET 5

Name ______________________________ Date ______________

FOLLOW THE PROPER PROCEDURE TO HOIST A CAR

Upon completion of this job sheet, you should be able to raise and lower a car on a hoist.

Tools and Materials

Car
Lift with enough capacity to hoist the car

Describe the Vehicle Being Worked On:

Year __________ Make ____________________ Model ______________
VIN ____________________ Engine type and size ______________

Procedure

Task Completed

1. Always be sure the lift is completely lowered before driving the car onto the lift. ☐

CAUTION: Do not raise a four-wheel-drive vehicle with a frame contact lift because this may damage axle joints. ☐

2. Do not hit or run over lift arms and adaptors when driving a car onto the lift. ☐
3. Have a coworker guide you when driving a car onto the lift.

WARNING: Do not stand in front of a lift with the car coming toward you. This action may result in personal injury.

4. Be sure the lift pads on the lift are contacting the car manufacturer's recommended lifting points shown in the service manual.

   Is the vehicle properly positioned on lift? ☐ Yes ☐ No

   Recommended front lifting points: ☐ Right side ☐ Left side

   Recommended rear lifting points: ☐ Right side ☐ Left side

   Are all four lift pads contacting the recommended lifting points? ☐ Yes ☐ No

   Instructor check ______________________________

CAUTION: If the proper lifting points are not used, components under the vehicle such as brake lines or body parts may be damaged. Failure to use the recommended lifting points may cause the car to slip off the lift, resulting in severe vehicle damage and personal injury. ☐

5. Be sure the doors and hood are closed, and be sure there are no people in the car. ☐
6. When a car is lifted a short distance off the floor, stop the lift and check the contact between the lift pads and the car chassis to be sure the lift pads are still on the recommended lifting points. ☐
7. Be sure there is adequate clearance between the top of the vehicle and the shop ceiling or components under the ceiling.

Task Completed

☐ **8.** When a car is raised on a lift, be sure the safety mechanism is in place to prevent the lift from dropping accidentally.

Is the lift safety mechanism in place? ☐ Yes ☐ No

Instructor check ______________________________

List one precaution that must be observed when a front-wheel-drive vehicle is raised on a lift, and explain the reason for this precaution.

____

____

☐ **9.** Prior to lowering a car on a lift, always make sure there are no tools, objects, or people under the vehicle.

WARNING: Do not rock a car on a lift during a service job. This action may cause the car to fall off the lift, resulting in personal injury and vehicle damage.

WARNING: When a car is raised on a lift, removal of some heavy components may cause car imbalance on the lift, which may cause the car to fall off the lift, resulting in personal injury and vehicle damage.

☐ **10.** Be sure the lift is lowered completely and no lift components are contacting the vehicle before backing the vehicle off the lift.

Instructor's Response ______________________________

____

____

JOB SHEET 6

Name ______________________________ Date ______________

DETERMINE THE AVAILABILITY AND PURPOSE OF SUSPENSION AND STEERING TOOLS

Procedure

Locate the following tools in your shop or tool room, and explain the purpose of each tool.

1. Stethoscope: available? ☐ Yes ☐ No

Location ______________________________

Purpose ______________________________

2. Dial indicator for measuring ball joint wear: available? ☐ Yes ☐ No

Location ______________________________

Purpose ______________________________

3. Ball joint removal and installing tools: available? ☐ Yes ☐ No

Location ______________________________

Purpose ______________________________

4. Coil spring compressing tool: available? ☐ Yes ☐ No

Location ______________________________

Purpose ______________________________

5. Power steering pressure gauge: available? ☐ Yes ☐ No

Location ______________________________

Purpose ______________________________

6. Vacuum hand pump: available? ☐ Yes ☐ No

Location ______________________________

Purpose ______________________________

7. Turning radius gauge: available? ☐ Yes ☐ No

Location ______________________________

Purpose ______________________________

8. Brake pedal jack: available? ☐ Yes ☐ No

Location ______________________________

Purpose ______________________________

9. Steering wheel locking tool: available? ☐ Yes ☐ No

Location ______________________________

Purpose ______________________________

10. Scan tool: available? ☐ Yes ☐ No

Location ____

Purpose ____

Instructor's Response ____

____

____

WHEEL BEARING AND SEAL SERVICE

3

Upon completion and review of this chapter, you should be able to:

- Diagnose bearing defects.
- Clean and repack wheel bearings.
- Reassemble and adjust wheel bearings.
- Remove and replace wheel bearing seals.
- Diagnose wheel bearing problems.
- Diagnose problems in wheel bearing hub units.
- Remove and replace front drive axles.
- Remove and replace wheel bearing hub units.
- Remove and replace rear-axle bearings on rear-wheel-drive cars.

Technicians must accurately diagnose wheel bearing problems to avoid repeat bearing failures, and thus provide customer satisfaction. Accurate wheel bearing service procedures are essential to maintain vehicle safety! Improper wheel bearing service may cause brake problems, steering complaints, and premature bearing failure. Improper wheel bearing service may even cause a wheel to fly off a vehicle, resulting in personal injury and vehicle damage. A knowledge of drive axle removal is necessary to service the front wheel bearings on front-wheel-drive vehicles, because the drive axle must be removed from the front hub to service the wheel bearings. Similarly, technicians must also understand rear-axle bearing service procedures on rear-wheel-drive vehicles.

DIAGNOSIS OF BEARING DEFECTS

Bearings are designed to provide long life, but there are many causes of premature bearing failure. If a bearing fails, the technician must decide if the bearing failure was caused by normal wear or if the bearing failed prematurely. For example, if a front wheel bearing fails on a car that is one year old with an original odometer reading of 15,000 miles (24,000 kilometers), experience tells us the bearing failure is premature, because front wheel bearings normally last for a much longer mileage period. Always listen to the customer's complaints, and obtain as much information as possible from the customer. Ask the customer specific questions about abnormal or unusual vehicle noises and operation. If a bearing fails prematurely, there must be some cause for the failure.

The causes of premature bearing failure are:

1. Lack of lubrication
2. Improper type of lubrication
3. Incorrect endplay adjustment (where applicable)
4. Misalignment of related components, such as shafts or housings
5. Excessive bearing load
6. Improper installation or service procedures
7. Excessive heat
8. Dirt or contamination

When a bearing fails prematurely, the technician must correct the cause of this failure to prevent the new bearing from failing. The types of bearing failures and the necessary corrective service procedures are provided in Figure 3-1 (see page 105) and Figure 3-2 (see page 106). **Bearing fatigue spalling** appears as flaking of surface metal on bearing rollers and races. **Bearing brinelling** shows up as straight-line indentations on the races and rollers. **Bearing smears** appear as metal loss in a circular, blotched pattern around the bearing races and rollers. **Bearing frettage** shows up as a fine, corrosive wear pattern around the bearing races and rollers. This wear pattern is circular on the races.

The first indication of bearing failure is usually a howling noise while the bearing is rotating. The howling noise will likely vary depending on the bearing load. A front wheel bearing usually provides a more noticeable howl when the vehicle is turning a corner, because this places additional thrust load on the bearing. A defective rear-axle bearing usually provides a howling noise that is more noticeable at lower speeds. The howling noise is more noticeable when driving on a narrow street with buildings on each side, because the noise vibrates off the nearby buildings. A rear-axle bearing noise is present during acceleration and deceleration, because the vehicle weight places a load on the bearing regardless of the operating condition. The rear-axle bearing noise may be somewhat more noticeable during deceleration because there is less engine noise at that time.

TAPERED ROLLER BEARING DIAGNOSIS

Consider the following factors when diagnosing bearing condition:

1. General condition of all parts during disassembly and inspection.
2. Classify the failure with the aid of the illustrations.
3. Determine the cause.
4. Make all repairs following recommended procedures.

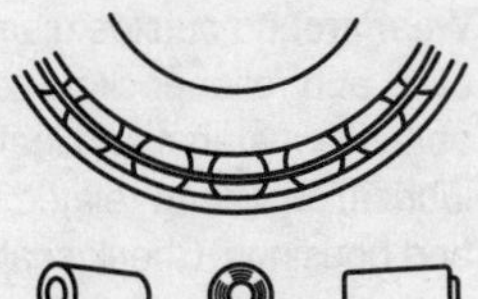

ABRASIVE STEP WEAR

Pattern on roller ends caused by fine abrasives. Clean all parts and housings, check seals and bearings, and replace if leaking, rough, or noisy.

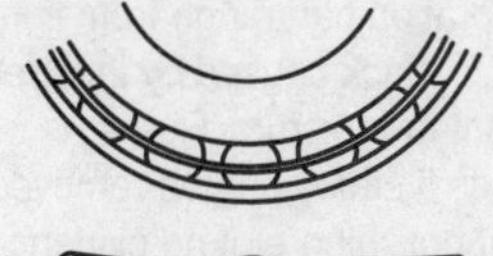

GALLING

Metal smears on roller ends due to overheating, lubricant failure, or overload. Replace bearing, check seals, and check for proper lubrication.

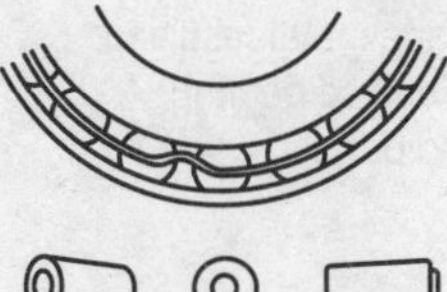

BENT CAGE

Cage damaged due to improper handling or tool usage. Replace bearing.

ABRASIVE ROLLER WEAR

Pattern on races and rollers caused by fine abrasives. Clean all parts and housings, check seals and bearings, and replace if leaking, rough, or noisy.

ETCHING

Bearing surfaces appear gray or grayish black in color with related etching away of material usually at roller spacing. Replace bearings, check seals, and check for proper lubrication.

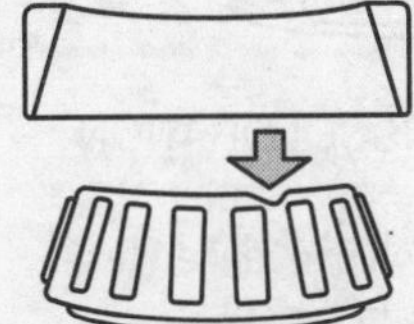

BENT CAGE

Cage damaged due to improper handling or tool usage. Replace bearing.

INDENTATIONS

Surface depressions on race and rollers caused by hard particles of foreign material. Clean all parts and housings. Check seals, and replace bearings if rough or noisy.

MISALIGNMENT

Outer race misalignment due to foreign object. Clean related parts and replace bearing. Make sure races are properly sealed.

FIGURE 3-1 *Bearing failures and corrective procedures.*

FATIGUE SPALLING

Flaking of surface metal resulting from fatigue. Replace bearing, clean all related parts.

STAIN DISCOLORATION

Discoloration can range from light brown to black caused by incorrect lubricant or moisture. Re-use bearings if stains can be removed by light polishing or if no evidence of overheating is observed. Check seals and related parts for damage.

CAGE WEAR

Wear around outside diameter of cage and roller pockets caused by abrasive material and inefficient lubrication. Clean related parts and housings. Check seals and replace bearings.

HEAT DISCOLORATION

Heat discoloration can range from faint yellow to dark blue, resulting from overload or incorrect lubricant. Excessive heat can cause softening of races or rollers. To check for loss of temper on races or rollers, a simple file test may be made. A file drawn over a tempered part will grab and cut metal, whereas, a file drawn over a hard part will glide readily with no metal cutting. Replace bearings if overheating damage is indicated. Check seals and other parts.

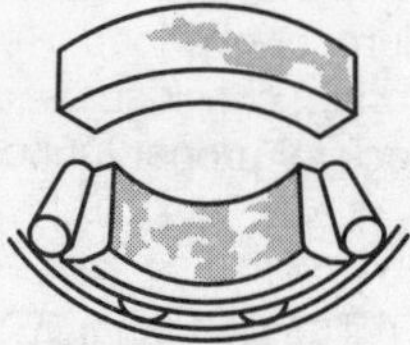

FRETTAGE

Corrosion set up by small relative movement of parts with no lubrication. Replace bearings. Clean related parts. Check seals and check for proper lubrication.

BRINELLING

Surface indentations in raceway caused by rollers either under impact loading or vibration while the bearing is not rotating. Replace bearing if rough or noisy.

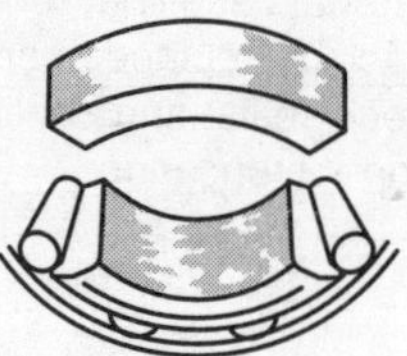

SMEARS

Smearing of metal due to slippage. Slippage can be caused by poor fits, lubrication, overheating, overloads, or handling damage. Replace bearings, clean related parts, and check for proper fit and lubrication.

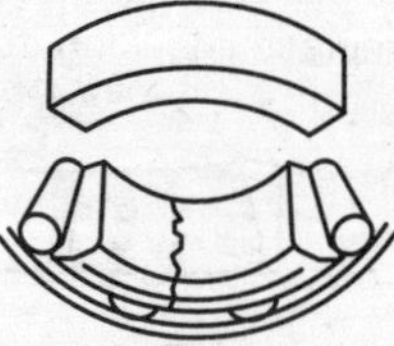

CRACKED INNER RACE

Race cracked due to improper fit, cocking, or poor bearing seats. Replace bearing and correct bearing seats.

FIGURE 3-2 *Bearing failures and corrective procedures, continued.*

SERVICE AND ADJUSTMENT OF TAPERED ROLLER BEARING-TYPE WHEEL BEARINGS

Cleaning Bearings

WARNING: Always wear safety goggles when working in the shop.

WARNING: Do not aim compressed air directly toward any part of your body. Compressed air can penetrate human flesh and enter the blood stream with very serious consequences.

WARNING: Do not spin the bearing at high speed with compressed air. Bearing damage or disintegration may result. Bearing disintegration may cause serious personal injury.

WARNING: Never strike a bearing with a ball peen hammer. This action will damage the bearing and the bearing may shatter, causing severe personal injury.

CAUTION: Never wash a sealed bearing or a bearing that is shielded on both sides because solvent may enter the bearing and destroy the lubricant in the bearing, resulting in very short bearing life.

Two separate tapered roller bearings are used in the front wheel hubs of many rear-wheel-drive cars. The rear wheel hubs on some front-wheel-drive cars have the same type of bearings. Similar service and adjustment procedures apply to these tapered roller bearings.

These bearings should be cleaned, inspected, and packed with wheel bearing grease at the vehicle manufacturer's recommended service intervals. Pry the grease seal out of the inner hub opening with a seal removal tool, and discard the seal. This seal should always be replaced when the bearings are serviced. Do not attempt to wash sealed bearings or bearings that are shielded on both sides. If a bearing is sealed on one side, it may be washed in solvent and repacked with grease.

Bearings may be placed in a tray and lowered into a container of clean solvent. A brush may be used to remove old grease from the bearing (Figure 3-3). The bearings may be dried with compressed air after the cleaning operation. Be sure the shop air supply is free from moisture, which causes rust formation in the bearing. After all the old grease has been cleaned from the bearing, rinse the bearing in clean solvent and dry it thoroughly with compressed air.

When bearing cleaning is completed, bearings should be inspected for the defects illustrated in Figures 3-1 and 3-2. If any of these conditions are present on the bearing, replacement is necessary. Tapered roller bearings and their matching outer races must be replaced as a set. If the bearing installation is not done immediately, cover the bearings with a protective lubricant and wrap them in waterproof paper (Figure 3-4). Be sure to identify the bearings, or lay them in order, so you reinstall them in their original location. Do not clean bearings or races with paper towels. If you are using a shop towel for this purpose, be sure it is lint free. Lint from shop towels or paper towels may contaminate the bearing. Bearing races and the inner part of the wheel hub should be thoroughly cleaned with solvent and dried with compressed air. Inspect the seal mounting area in the hub for metal burrs. Remove any burrs with a fine round file.

Bearing races must be replaced if any of the defects described in Figures 3-1 and 3-2 are found. The proper bearing race driving tool must be used to remove the bearing races (Figure 3-5). If a driver is not available for the bearing races, a long brass punch and hammer may be used to drive the races from the hub. When a hammer and punch are used for this purpose, be careful not to damage the hub inner surface with the punch.

FIGURE 3-3 *Cleaning a bearing with solvent.*

FIGURE 3-4 *Wrapping a bearing in waterproof paper.*

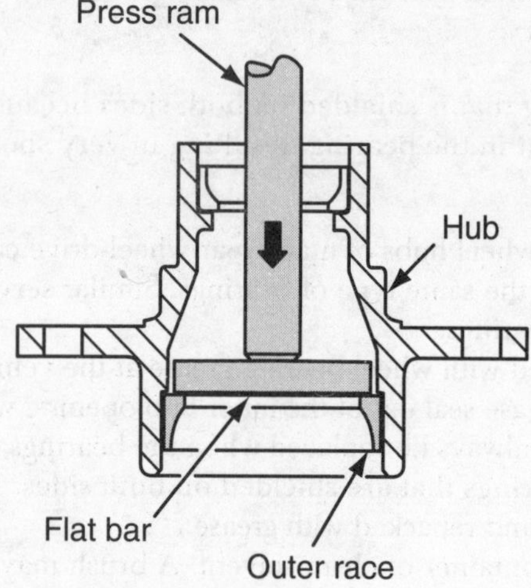

FIGURE 3-5 *Bearing race removal.*

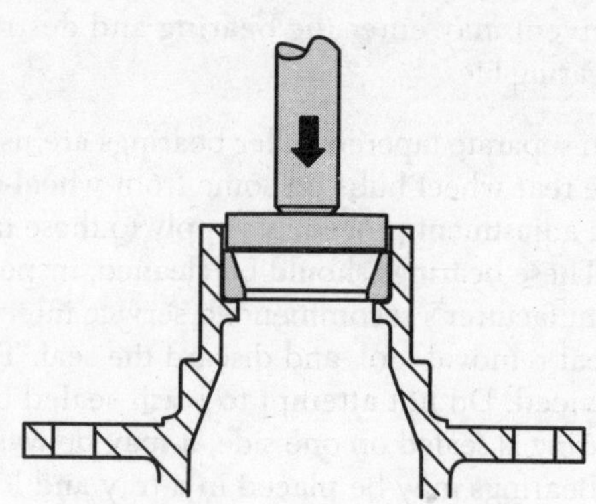

FIGURE 3-6 *Bearing race installation.*

The new bearing races should be installed in the hub with the correct bearing race driving tool (Figure 3-6). When bearings and races are replaced, be sure they are the same as the original bearings. The part numbers should be the same on the old bearings and the replacement bearings.

Inspect the bearing and seal mounting surfaces on the spindle. Small metal burrs may be removed from the spindle with a fine-toothed file. If the spindle is severely scored in the bearing or seal mounting areas, spindle replacement is necessary.

Bearing Lubrication and Assembly

CAUTION: Cleanliness is very important during wheel bearing service. Always maintain cleanliness of hands, tools, work area, and all related bearing components. One small piece of dirt in a bearing will cause bearing failure.

CAUTION: Always keep grease containers covered when not in use. Uncovered grease containers are easily contaminated with dirt and moisture.

After the bearings and races have been cleaned and inspected, the bearings should be packed with grease. Always use the vehicle manufacturer's specified wheel bearing grease. Vehicle manufacturers usually recommend a lithium-based wheel bearing grease. Place a lump of grease in the palm of one hand and grasp the bearing in the other hand. Force the widest edge of the bearing into the lump of grease, and squeeze the grease into the bearing. Continue this process until grease is forced into the bearing around the entire bearing circumference. Place a coating of grease around the outside of the rollers, and apply a light coating of grease to the races. A bearing packing tool may be used to force grease into the bearings rather than using the hand method (Figure 3-7).

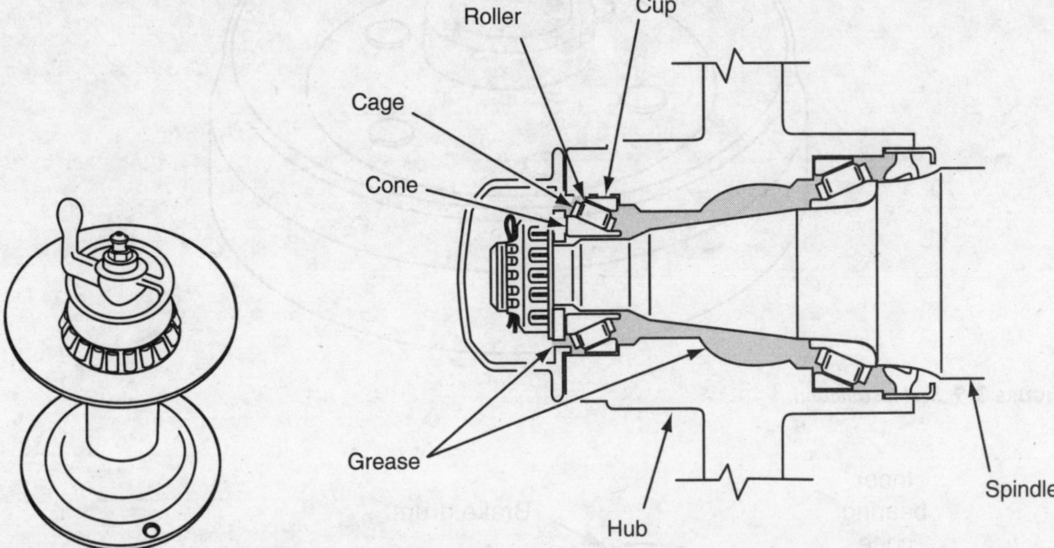

FIGURE 3-7 *Mechanical wheel bearing packer.*

FIGURE 3-8 *Wheel bearing lubrication.*

Place some grease in the wheel hub cavity and position the inner bearing in the hub (Figure 3-8). Check the fit of the new bearing seal on the spindle and in the hub. The seal lip must fit snugly on the spindle, and the seal case must fit properly in the hub opening. The part number on the old seal and the replacement seal should be the same. Be sure the seal is installed in the proper direction with the garter spring and higher part of the lip toward the lubricant in the hub. The new inner bearing seal must be installed in the hub with a suitable seal driver (Figure 3-9). Place a light coating of wheel bearing grease on the spindle and slide the hub assembly onto the spindle. Install the outer wheel bearing and be sure there is adequate lubrication on the bearing and race. Be sure the washer and nut are clean and install these components on the spindle (Figure 3-10). Tighten the nut until it is finger tight.

Photo Sequence 3 shows a typical procedure for adjusting rear wheel bearings on a front-wheel-drive car.

Wheel Bearing Adjustment with Two Separate Tapered Roller Bearings in the Wheel Hub

Wheel bearing endplay is the amount of horizontal wheel bearing hub movement. If a bearing has a preload condition, a slight tension is placed on the bearing. Loose front wheel bearing adjustment

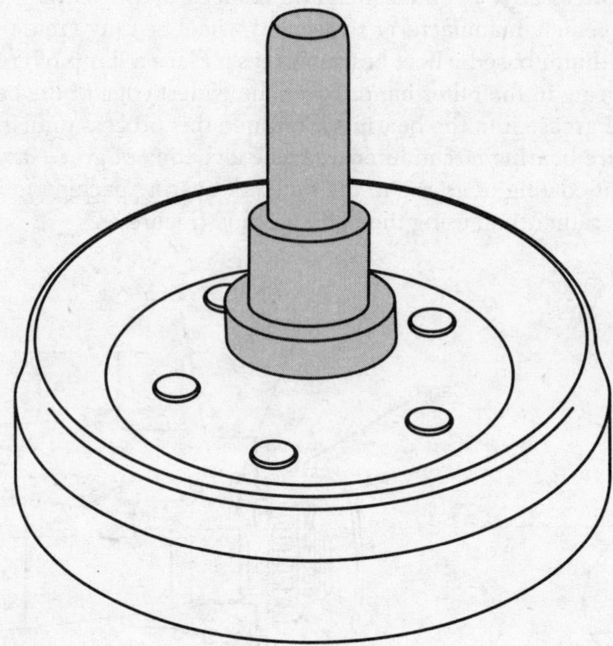

FIGURE 3-9 *Seal installation.*

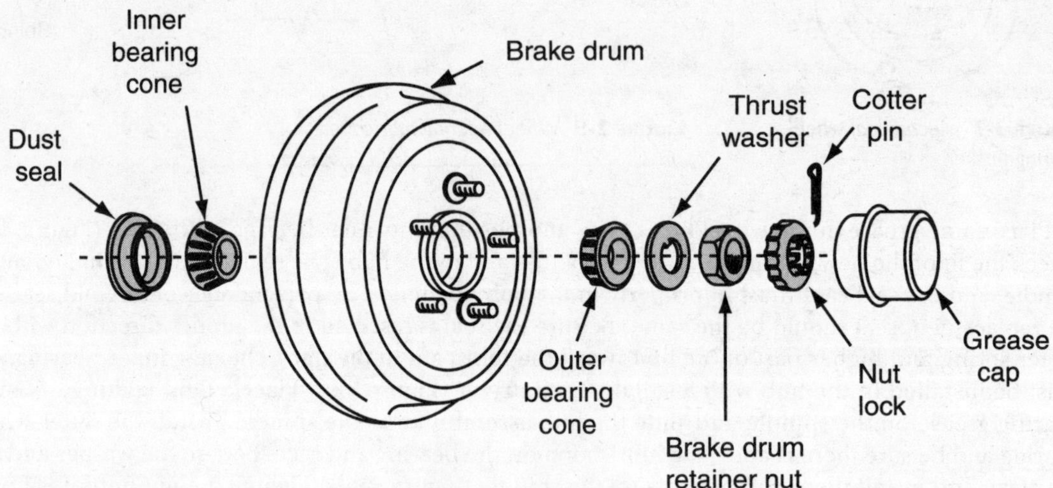

FIGURE 3-10 *Installation of wheel bearings and related components.*

results in lateral front wheel movement and reduced directional stability. If the wheel bearing adjusting nut is tightened excessively, the bearings may overheat, resulting in premature bearing failure. The bearing adjustment procedure may vary depending on the make of vehicle. Always follow the procedure in the vehicle manufacturer's service manual.

PHOTO SEQUENCE 3
TYPICAL PROCEDURE FOR ADJUSTING REAR WHEEL BEARINGS ON A FRONT-WHEEL-DRIVE CAR

P3-1 *Always make sure the car is positioned safely on a lift before working on the vehicle.*

P3-2 *Remove the dust cap from the wheel hub.*

P3-3 *Remove the cotter pin and nut retainer from the bearing adjusting nut.*

P3-4 *Tighten the bearing adjusting nut to 17 to 25 ft-lb.*

P3-5 *Loosen the bearing adjusting nut one-half turn.*

P3-6 *Tighten the bearing adjusting nut to 10 to 15 in-lb.*

P3-7 *Position the adjusting nut retainer over the adjusting nut so the slots are aligned with the holes in the nut and spindle.*

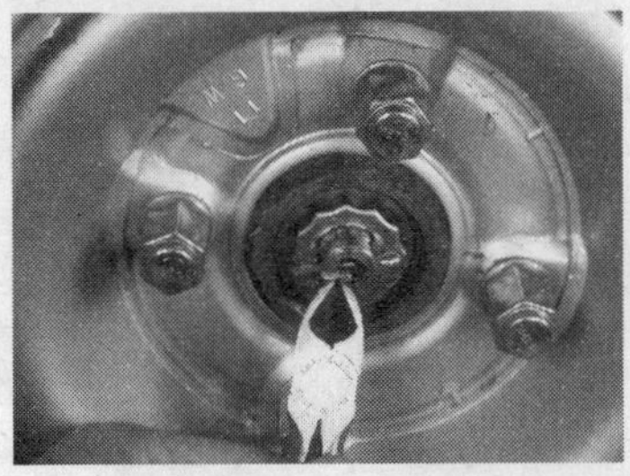

P3-8 *Install a new cotter pin and bend the ends around the retainer flange.*

P3-9 *Install the dust cap and be sure the hub rotates freely.*

A typical bearing adjustment procedure follows:

1. With the hub and bearings assembled on the spindle, tighten the adjusting nut to 17 to 25 ft.-lb. (23 to 34 Nm) while the hub is rotated in the forward direction.
2. Loosen the adjusting nut 1/2 turn and retighten it to 10 to 15 in.-lb. (1.0 to 1.7 Nm). This specification varies depending on the make of vehicle. Always use the manufacturer's specifications.
3. Position the adjusting nut retainer over the nut so the retainer slots are aligned with the cotter pin hole in the spindle.
4. Install a new cotter pin, and bend the ends around the retainer flange.
5. Install the grease cap, and make sure the hub and drum rotate freely.

After a wheel bearing adjustment is performed, the hub must have an endplay of 0.001 in. to 0.005 in. (0.0254 mm to 0.127 mm). A dial indicator may be mounted with the stem positioned against the outer edge of the hub to perform this measurement. When the hub is pulled outward and pushed inward, the specified endplay must be displayed on the dial indicator. If the endplay is not correct, the wheel bearing adjustment must be repeated.

WHEEL HUB UNIT DIAGNOSIS

When wheel bearings and hubs are an integral assembly, the bearing endplay should be measured with a dial indicator stem mounted against the hub. If the endplay exceeds 0.005 in. (0.127 mm) as the hub is moved in and out, the hub and bearing assembly should be replaced. This specification is typical, but the vehicle manufacturer's specifications must be used. Hub and bearing replacement is also necessary if the bearing is rough or noisy. Integral-type bearing and hub assemblies are used on the front and rear wheels on some front-wheel-drive cars.

When the front wheel bearings are mounted in the steering knuckle, the wheel bearings may be checked with the vehicle raised on the hoist and a dial indicator positioned against the outer wheel rim lip as shown in Figure 3-11.

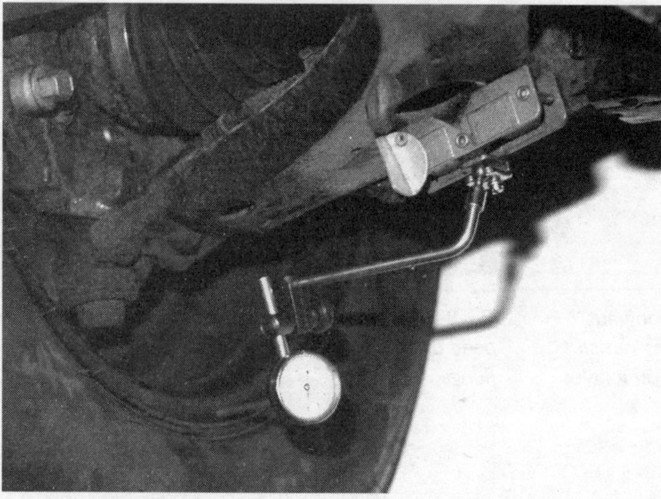

FIGURE 3-11 *Wheel bearing diagnosis on vehicle.*

When the wheel is moved in and out, the maximum bearing movement on the dial indicator should be as follows:

0.020 in. (0.508 mm) for 13-in. (33-cm) wheels
0.023 in. (0.584 mm) for 14-in. (35.5-cm) wheels
0.025 in. (0.635 mm) for 15-in. (38-cm) wheels

If the bearing movement is excessive, check the hub nut torque before replacing the bearing. When this torque is correct and bearing movement is excessive, the bearing should be replaced.

When a wheel is removed to service the wheel bearings, proper balance must be maintained between the wheel and tire and the hub. Therefore, the tire, wheel, and hub stud should be chalk marked prior to removal (Figure 3-12).

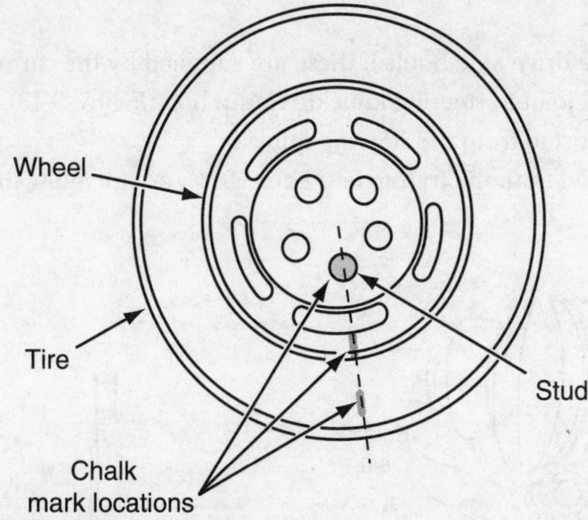

FIGURE 3-12 *Chalk marking on wheel, tire, and stud.*

FRONT DRIVE AXLE DIAGNOSIS

On many front-wheel-drive vehicles, the front drive axles must be removed before the wheel hub unit or steering knuckle and bearing can be detached. Therefore, we will discuss front drive axle diagnosis and removal. Because drive axle noises may be confused with front wheel bearing noise, a brief discussion of drive axle noises and problems may be helpful. A defective inner drive axle joint usually causes a vibration when the vehicle is decelerating at 35 to 45 miles per hour (mph), or 56 to 72 kilometers per hour (km/h). When an outer drive axle joint is worn, a clicking noise is heard during a hard turn below 20 mph (32 km/h). To determine which drive axle has the defective joint, lift the vehicle on a hoist, and allow the front wheels to drop down. This action will position the axle joints at a different angle than when the car is driven on the road. Lift the lower control arms one at a time with a floor jack, and place the transmission in drive to simulate the driving conditions that provided the vibration or noise. If the vibration or noise occurs with one lower control arm lifted, that side has the defective drive axle joint.

DRIVE AXLE REMOVAL

Many drive axles have a **circlip** on the inner joint extension that holds the inner joint into the differential side gear. Drive axle systems vary depending on the vehicle. Follow the drive axle removal procedure in the vehicle manufacturer's service manual.

A general front drive axle removal procedure follows:

1. Loosen the front wheel nuts and hub nuts.
2. Lift the vehicle on a hoist and be sure the hoist safety mechanism is in place; then remove the front wheels and tires.
3. Remove the brake calipers and rotors. Connect a piece of wire from the calipers to a suspension or chassis component. Do not allow the calipers to hang on the end of the brake line.
4. Install protective drive axle boots if these are supplied by the car manufacturer.
5. Remove the ball joint to steering knuckle clamp bolt (Figure 3-13).
6. Pry the ball joint stud from the steering knuckle.
7. Pull the inner axle from the transaxle (Figure 3-14); do not allow the axle to drop down at a severe angle.

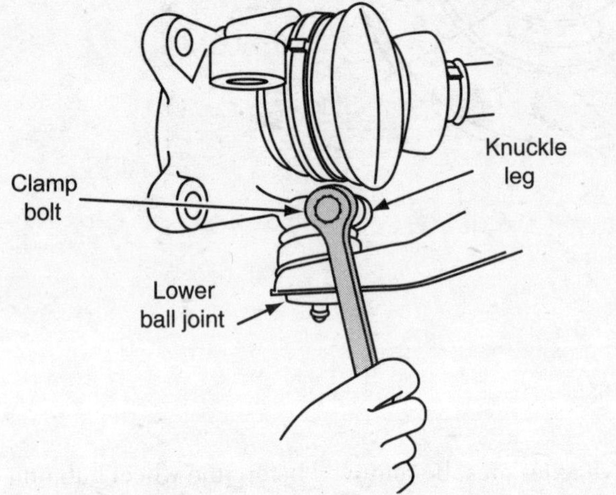

FIGURE 3-13 *Removal of ball joint to steering knuckle clamp bolt.*

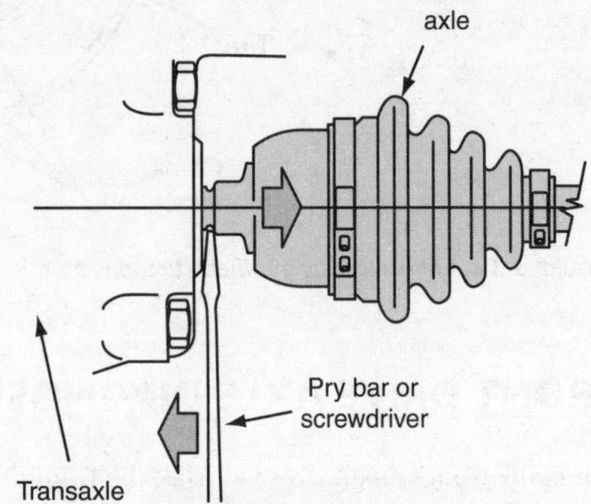

FIGURE 3-14 *Removal of inner axle joint from transaxle.*

8. Remove the hub nut and washer, and separate the outer axle joint from the wheel hub. Some outer axle joint splines, such as those used on early model Ford Escorts or Lynxes, are slightly spiraled. On this type of outer axle joint, a special puller is required to separate the axle joint from the wheel (Figure 3-15).
9. Remove the drive axle from the chassis.

Reverse the drive axle removal procedure for front drive axle installation.

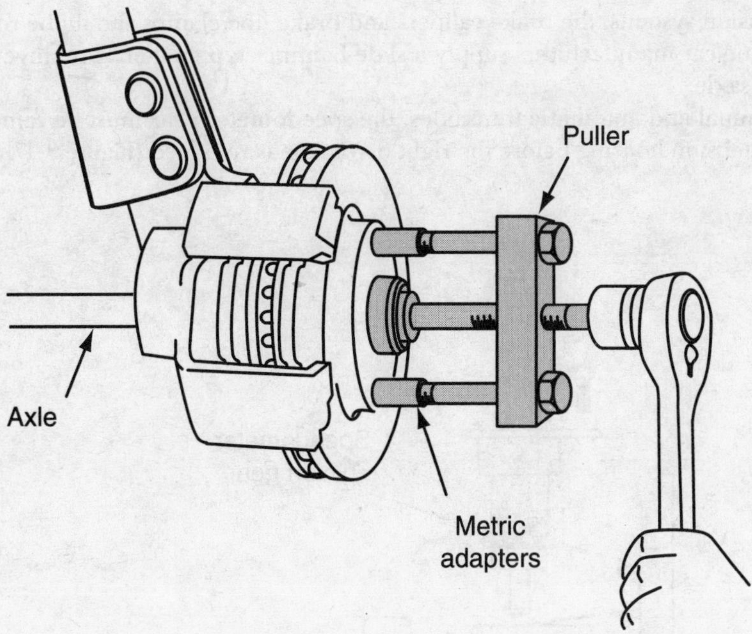

FIGURE 3-15 *Removal of outer axle joint from front wheel hub.*

SPECIAL PROCEDURES FOR DRIVE AXLE REMOVAL

Some car manufacturers recommend removal of the strut from the steering knuckle rather than removal of the ball joint when the drive axles are removed. This type of suspension system has a threaded nut on the ball joint stem to hold the ball joint into the steering knuckle. If an eccentric camber adjustment bolt is positioned in the strut, the bolt head position should be marked in relation to the strut before the bolt is removed (Figure 3-16).

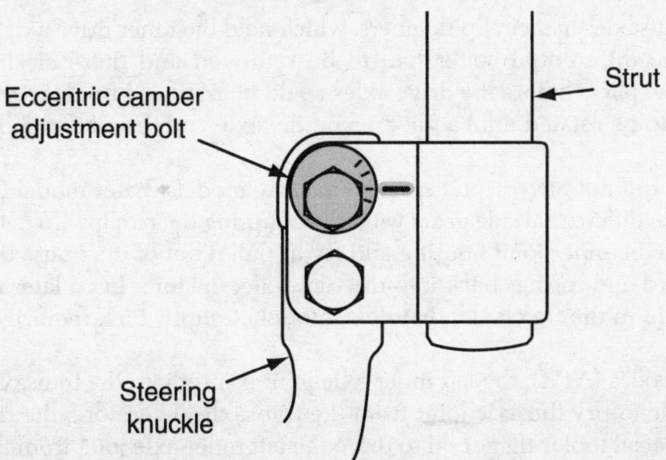

FIGURE 3-16 *Marking eccentric strut bolt before removal.*

On these suspension systems, the brake calipers and brake line clamps should be removed before the drive axles. Some car manufacturers supply a slide-hammer-type puller to remove the inner axle joints from the transaxle.

On Chrysler manual and automatic transaxles, the speedometer gear must be removed from the right differential extension housing before the right drive axle is removed (Figure 3-17).

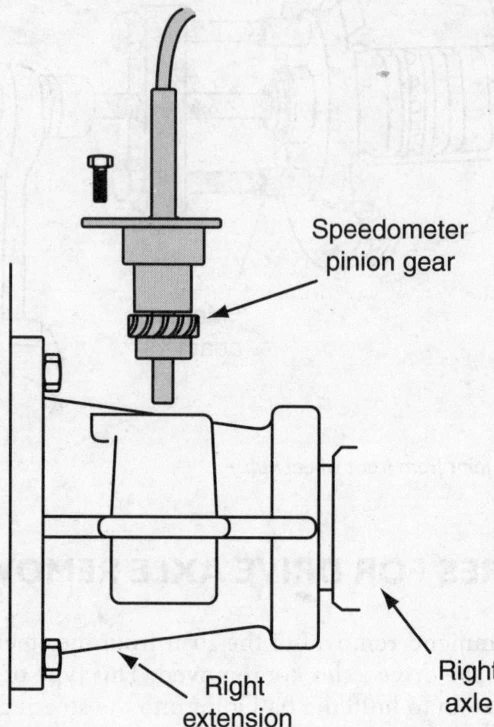

FIGURE 3-17 *Speedometer drive gear removal before right axle removal.*

Early model Chrysler transaxles had circlip retainers, which held the inner drive axle joints into the differential side gears. The differential cover had to be removed and these circlips had to be compressed with needle nose pliers before the drive axles could be removed from the differential side gears. The drive axles had to be rotated until a flat area on the axle and the circlip ends were visible (Figure 3-18).

The inner joint housings did not have tripod springs on early models. Later model Chrysler drive axles may be pulled from the differential side gears without collapsing the circlips. To determine which type of circlip is used, grasp the inner joint housing and try to pull it out of the transaxle. If the inner joint housing moves outward and springs back into the transaxle, the joint has a later model circlip. When the inner joint is solid in the transaxle, the older model circlip, which requires compressing before removal, is used.

On Ford automatic transaxles (ATX), the left inner axle joint is inset into the transaxle housing. In this location, it is impossible to pry the axle joint from the transaxle. Therefore, the right axle joint must be removed first. A special tool is then used to drive the left inner axle joint from the differential side gear (Figure 3-19).

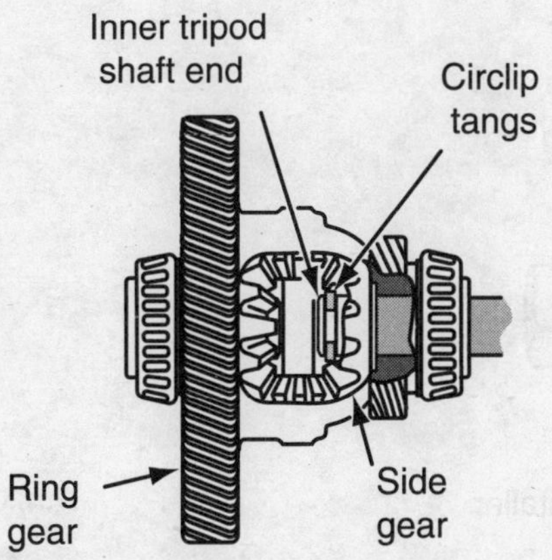

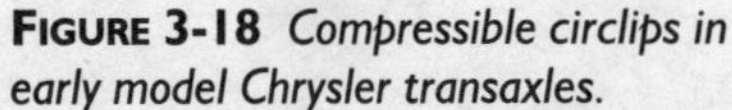

FIGURE 3-18 *Compressible circlips in early model Chrysler transaxles.*

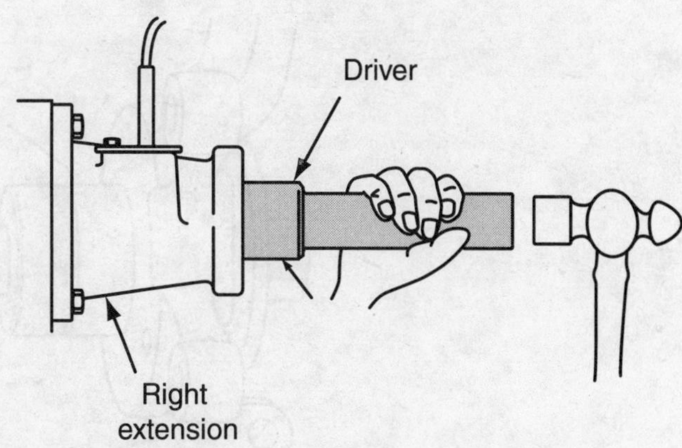

FIGURE 3-19 *Removal of left inner drive axle joint on Ford automatic transaxles.*

If both left and right drive axles are removed at the same time on Ford transaxles, the differential side gears may become dislocated. When this occurs, the differential must be removed to realign the side gears. The special tool for driving out the left inner axle joint may be left in place to support the side gears on ATX models. On manual transaxles (MTX), shipping plugs T81P-1177-B should be installed in each side gear when the drive axles are removed.

FRONT WHEEL BEARING HUB UNIT REMOVAL AND REPLACEMENT

The front wheel bearing removal and replacement procedure varies depending on the vehicle and the type of front wheel bearing. Always follow the front wheel bearing removal and replacement procedure in the manufacturer's service manual. The following procedure applies to front wheel bearing units that are pressed into the steering knuckle.

When front wheel bearing replacement is necessary, the steering knuckle must be removed and the wheel hub must be pressed from the bearing with a special tool (Figure 3-20).

A special puller is used to remove and replace the wheel bearing in the knuckle (Figure 3-21 and Figure 3-22).

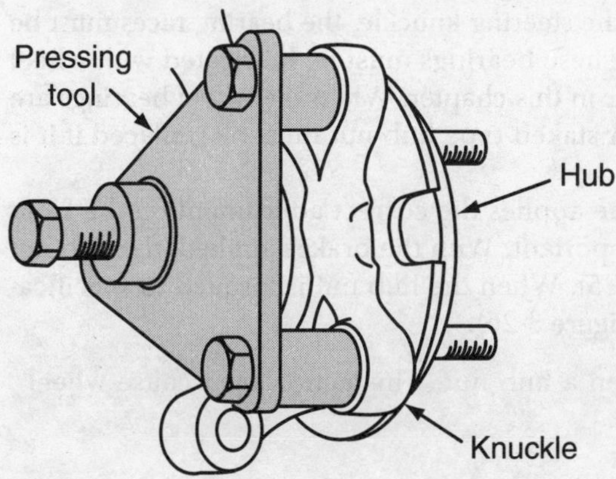

FIGURE 3-20 *Wheel hub removal from bearing.*

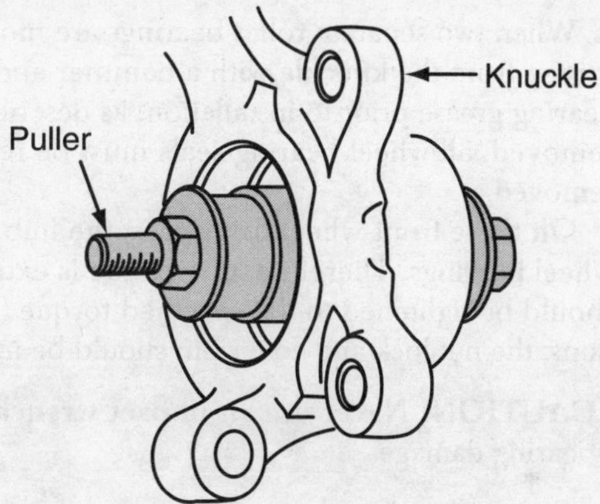

FIGURE 3-21 *Wheel bearing removal from knuckle.*

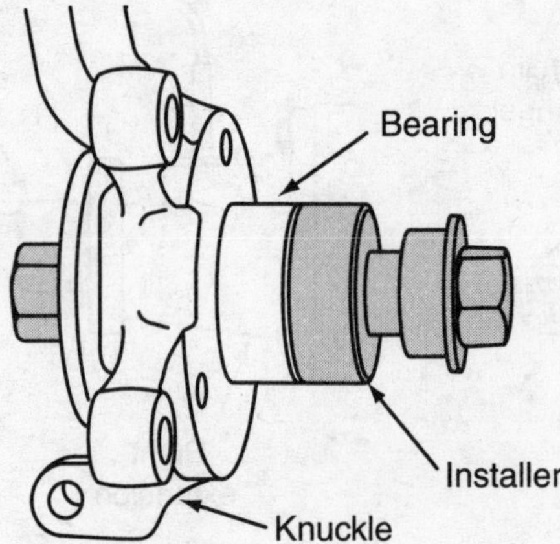

FIGURE 3-22 *Wheel bearing installation in knuckle.*

The wheel hub must be pulled into the wheel bearing with a special tool (Figure 3-23). The proper driving tool is used to install the seal behind the bearing in the knuckle (Figure 3-24).

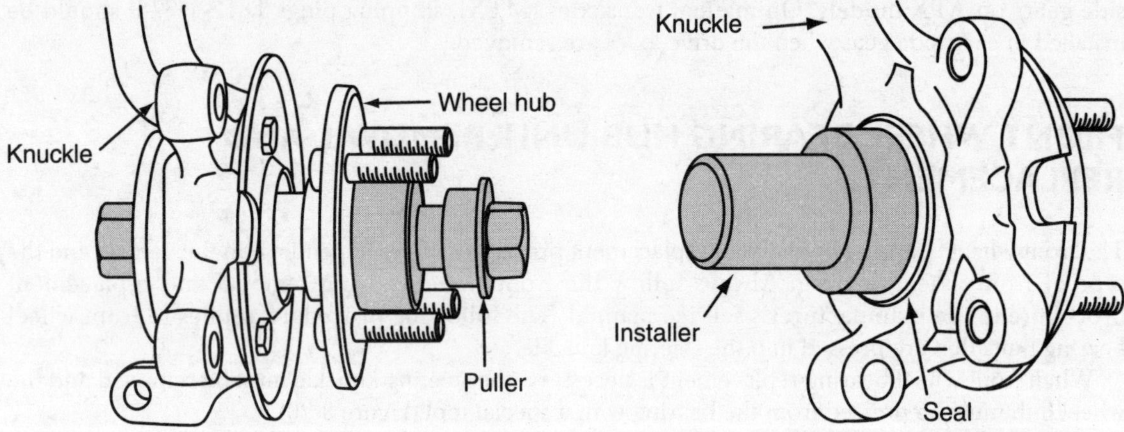

FIGURE 3-23 *Wheel hub installation in wheel bearing.*

FIGURE 3-24 *Seal installation in steering knuckle.*

When two separate roller bearings are mounted in the steering knuckle, the bearing races must be driven from the knuckle with a hammer and punch. These bearings must be lubricated with wheel bearing grease prior to installation, as described earlier in this chapter. When the wheel bearings are removed, all wheel bearing seals must be replaced. A staked-type hub nut must be replaced if it is removed.

On these front-wheel-drive cars, the hub nut torque applies the correct adjustment on the front wheel bearings. Therefore, this torque is extremely important. With the brakes applied, the hub nut should be tightened to the specified torque (Figure 3-25). When the hub nut is torqued to specifications, the nut lock and cotter pin should be installed (Figure 3-26).

CAUTION: Never use an impact wrench to tighten a hub nut. This action may cause wheel bearing damage.

FIGURE 3-25 *Hub nut torquing.*

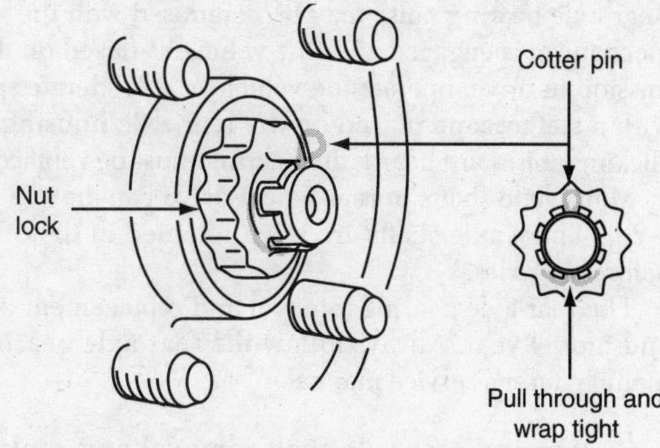

FIGURE 3-26 *Nut lock and cotter pin installation.*

WARNING: Never reuse a cotter pin. A used cotter pin may break, allowing the hub nut to loosen. This may allow the wheel and hub to come off.

After the wheel is installed, the wheel nuts should be tightened in sequence to the specified torque (Figure 3-27). On cars with the front wheel bearings mounted in the steering knuckles, never move a car unless the front hub nuts are torqued to specifications. Lack of bearing preload could damage the bearings if the hub nuts are not tightened to specifications. If the car must be moved when the drive axles are removed, place a large bolt and nut with suitable washers through the front wheel bearing and tighten the nut to specifications.

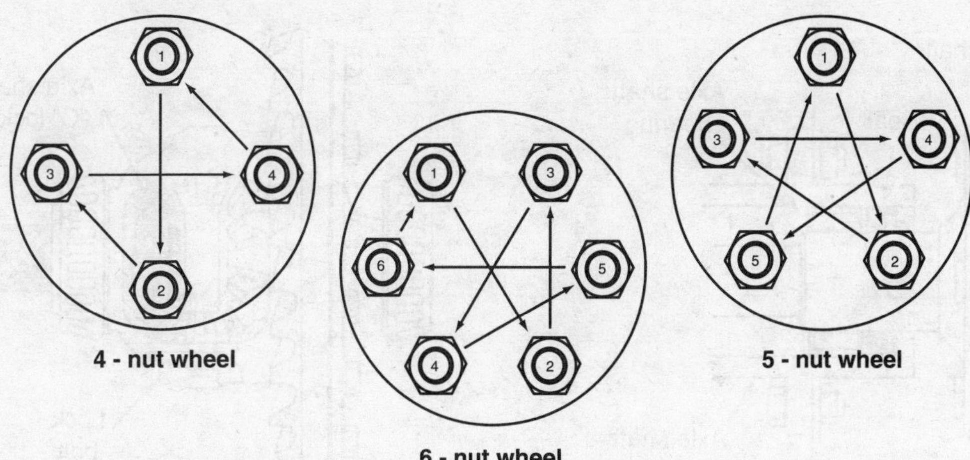

FIGURE 3-27 *Wheel nut tightening sequence.*

REAR-AXLE BEARING AND SEAL SERVICE, REAR-WHEEL-DRIVE CARS

WARNING: Use extreme caution when diagnosing problems with a vehicle raised on a hoist and the engine running with the transmission in drive. Keep away from rotating wheels, drive shafts, or drive axles.

Rear-axle bearing noise may be diagnosed with the vehicle raised on a hoist. Be sure the hoist safety mechanism is engaged after the vehicle is raised on the hoist. With the engine running and the transmission in drive, operate the vehicle at a moderate speed of 35 to 45 mph (56 to 72 km/h) and listen with a **stethoscope** placed on the rear axle housing directly over the axle bearings. If grinding or clicking noises are heard, the bearing must be replaced.

Many axle shafts in rear-wheel-drive cars have a roller bearing and seal at the outer end (Figure 3-28). These axle shafts are often retained in the differential with **"C" locks** that must be removed before the axles.

The rear-axle bearing removal and replacement procedure varies depending on the vehicle make and model year. Always follow the rear-axle bearing removal and replacement procedure in the manufacturer's service manual.

A typical rear axle shaft removal and replacement procedure on a rear-wheel-drive car with "C" lock axle retainers is as follows:

1. Loosen the rear wheel nuts and chalk mark the rear wheel position in relation to the rear axle studs.
2. Raise the vehicle on a hoist and make sure the hoist safety mechanism is in place.
3. Remove the rear wheels and brake drums, or calipers and rotors.
4. Place a drain pan under the differential and remove the differential cover. Discard the old lubricant.
5. Remove the differential lock bolt, pin, pinion gears, and shaft (Figure 3-29).
6. Push the axle shaft inward and remove the axle "C" lock.
7. Pull the axle from the differential housing.

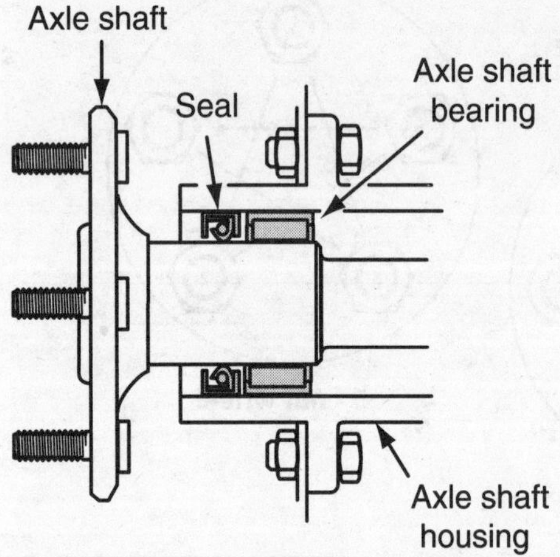

FIGURE 3-28 *Rear axle roller bearing and seal, rear-wheel-drive car.*

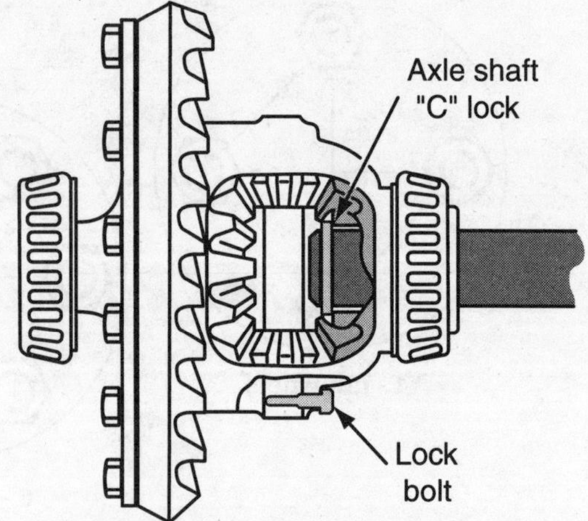

FIGURE 3-29 *Rear axle "C" lock, lock bolt, and pinion gears.*

Reverse the axle removal procedure to reinstall the axle. Always use a new differential cover gasket, and fill the differential to the bottom of the filler plug opening with the manufacturer's recommended lubricant. Be sure all fasteners, including the wheel nuts, are tightened to the specified torque.

A typical axle bearing and seal removal procedure follows:

1. Remove the axle seal with a seal puller.
2. Use the proper bearing puller to remove the axle bearing (Figure 3-30).
3. Clean the axle housing seal and bearing mounting area with solvent and a brush. Clean this area with compressed air.
4. Check the seal and bearing mounting area in the housing for metal burrs and scratches. Remove any burrs or irregularities with a fine-toothed round file.
5. Wash the axle shaft with solvent and blow it dry with compressed air.
6. Check the bearing contact area on the axle for roughness, pits, and scratches. If any of these conditions are present, the axle must be replaced.
7. Be sure the new bearing fits properly on the axle and in the housing. Install the new bearing with the proper bearing driver (Figure 3-31). The bearing driver must apply pressure to the outer race that is pressed into the housing.

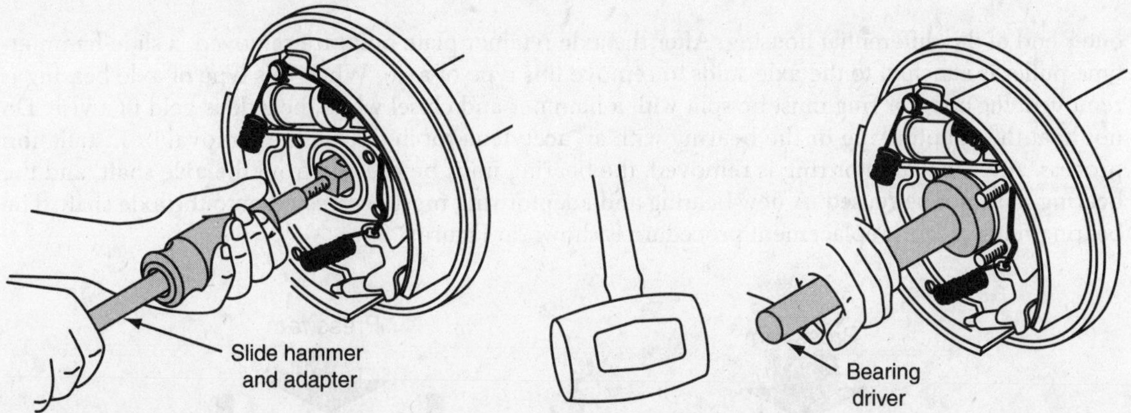

FIGURE 3-30 *Rear-axle bearing puller.*

FIGURE 3-31 *Rear-axle bearing driver.*

8. Be sure the new seal fits properly on the axle shaft and in the housing. Make sure the garter spring on the seal faces toward the differential. Use the proper seal driver to install the new seal in the housing (Figure 3-32).
9. Lubricate the bearing, seal, and bearing surface on the axle with the manufacturer's specified differential lubricant.
10. Reverse the rear axle removal procedure to reinstall the rear axle.
11. Be sure all fasteners are tightened to the specified torque.

WARNING: Never use an acetylene torch to heat axle bearings or adaptor rings during the removal and replacement procedure. The heat may cause fatigue in the steel axle and the axle may break suddenly, causing the rear wheel to fall off. This action will likely result in severe vehicle damage and personal injury.

Some rear axles have a sealed bearing that is pressed onto the axle shaft and held in place with a retainer ring. These rear axles usually do not have "C" locks in the differential. A retainer plate is mounted on the axle between the bearing and the outer end of the axle. This plate is bolted to the

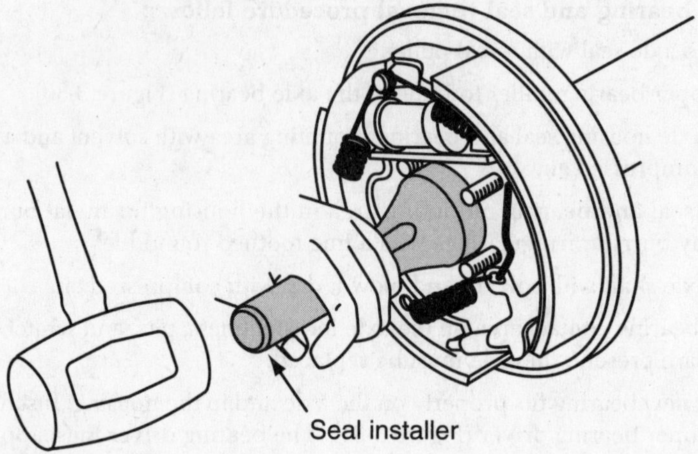

FIGURE 3-32 *Installing rear axle seal.*

outer end of the differential housing. After the axle retainer plate bolts are removed, a slide-hammer-type puller is attached to the axle studs to remove this type of axle. When this type of axle bearing is removed, the adaptor ring must be split with a hammer and chisel while the axle is held in a vise. Do not heat the adaptor ring or the bearing with an acetylene torch during the removal or installation process. After the adaptor ring is removed, the bearing must be pressed from the axle shaft, and the bearing must not be reused. A new bearing and adaptor ring must be pressed onto the axle shaft. The bearing removal and replacement procedure is shown in Figure 3-33.

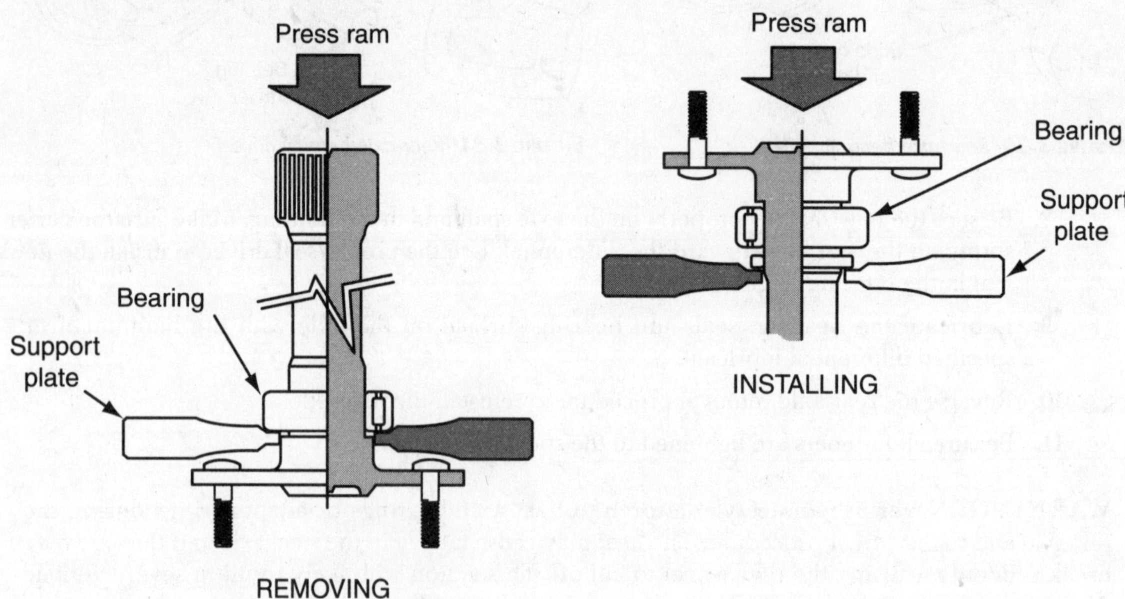

FIGURE 3-33 *Axle bearing and adaptor ring removal and replacement.*

DIAGNOSTIC TABLE

PROBLEM	SYMPTOMS	POSSIBLE CAUSES
Noise in drive train, front-wheel-drive car.	Clicking noise while turning a corner at low speeds.	Worn outer front drive axle joint.
Vibration in front drive train, front-wheel-drive car.	Vibration while decelerating at 35 to 45 mph, 56 to 72 km/h.	Worn inner drive axle joint.
Noise in front suspension.	Growling noise in front suspension, most noticeable when turning a corner or driving at low speeds.	Worn wheel bearings.
Lack of directional stability.	Steering wanders to either side when driving straight ahead.	Excessive front wheel bearing endplay, improper wheel bearing adjustment.
Noise in drive train, rear-wheel-drive car.	Constant growling or clicking noise in rear axle, most noticeable when driving at low speeds or down a narrow street.	Worn rear-axle bearing.

CASE STUDY

A customer complains of a bearing noise in the right front wheel of his full-size Ford wagon. He says the right front outer wheel bearing has been replaced twice in the last year, and this is the third failure. The technician asks the customer about the mileage intervals between bearing replacements, and the customer indicates that the wheel bearing has lasted about 8,000 miles (12,800 kilometers) each time it has been replaced. The technician finds out from the customer that no other work was done on the car each time the bearing was replaced.

When the technician removes the right front wheel and hub, the outer bearing rollers and races are badly scored. After cleaning both bearings, races, and hub, the technician closely examines the outer bearing race. It shows an uneven wear pattern, which indicates misalignment. The technician removes the outer bearing race and finds a small metal burr behind the bearing race. This burr caused race misalignment and excessive wear on the race and rollers. The technician removes the burr with a fine-toothed file. The inner bearing and race have indentation wear because metal particles from the outer bearing contaminated the lubricant in the hub. The technician removes the inner bearing race and cleans the hub and spindle thoroughly. He replaces both bearings and the inner seal and repacks the bearings and hub with grease. After reinstalling the hub, the technician carefully adjusts the bearings to the manufacturer's specifications and tightens the wheel nuts to the specified torque. A road test indicates that the bearing noise has been eliminated.

One small metal burr caused this customer a considerable amount of unnecessary expense. This experience proves that a technician's diagnostic capability is extremely important!

SERVICE TIPS

- When a lip seal is installed, the garter spring should always face toward the flow of lubricant.
- Do not remove the tool until the left inner axle joint is reinstalled in the Ford ATX. If the tool is removed without installing the left inner axle joint, the side gears may fall out of place. If this action occurs, the Ford ATX may have to be disassembled to install the side gears properly.

REVIEW QUESTIONS

1. While discussing defective bearings:
Technician A says brinelling appears as indentations across the bearing races. *Technician B* says brinelling occurs while the bearing is rotating.
Who is correct?

A. A only **C.** Both A and B
B. B only **D.** Neither A nor B

2. While discussing bearing defects:
Technician A says misalignment wear on a front wheel bearing could be caused by a metal burr behind one of the bearing races. *Technician B* says misalignment wear on a front wheel bearing could be caused by a bent front spindle.
Who is correct?

A. A only **C.** Both A and B
B. B only **D.** Neither A nor B

3. While discussing front wheel bearing service on a vehicle with the bearing hub unit pressed into the steering knuckle:
Technician A says the front wheel bearings may be damaged if this front-wheel-drive vehicle is moved without the hub nuts torqued to specifications. *Technician B* says the hub nut torque supplies the correct wheel bearing adjustment.
Who is correct?

A. A only **C.** Both A and B
B. B only **D.** Neither A nor B

4. While discussing front wheel bearing service on a front-wheel-drive car with two separate tapered roller bearings mounted in the front steering knuckles:
Technician A says the hub nut torque supplies the correct bearing adjustment. *Technician B* says that the brake should be applied while the front hub nuts are torqued.
Who is correct?

A. A only **C.** Both A and B
B. B only **D.** Neither A nor B

5. A front-wheel-drive vehicle has 14-in (35.5-cm) rims and front wheel bearings mounted in the steering knuckles. The vehicle is lifted on a hoist, and a dial indicator is positioned against the outer rim lip. The total inward and outward rim movement is 0.035 in (0.889 mm).
Technician A says that the wheel bearing may require replacement. *Technician B* says that the hub nut torque should be checked prior to bearing replacement.
Who is correct?

A. A only **C.** Both A and B
B. B only **D.** Neither A nor B

6. When cleaning and inspecting wheel bearings:
A. Sealed bearings should be washed in solvent.
B. High-pressure air may be used to spin the bearings.
C. A bent bearing cage may be caused by improper tool use.
D. Bearing overload may cause bearing cage wear.

7. All these statements about hub seal service are true EXCEPT:
A. The garter spring must face toward the flow of lubricant.
B. A ball peen hammer should be used to install the seal.
C. Seal contact area on the spindle must be clean and free from metal burrs.
D. The outer edge of the seal case should be coated with sealant.

8. When servicing press-in rear-axle bearings on a rear-wheel-drive car:
A. These bearing may be reused after they are removed from the axle shaft.
B. The bearing adaptor ring should be removed by splitting it with a hammer and chisel.
C. A cutting torch may be used to cut the bearing off the axle shaft.
D. An acetylene torch may be used to heat the new adaptor ring prior to installation.

9. A front-wheel-drive vehicle has two tapered roller bearings in each rear wheel hub. When adjusting these wheel bearings:
A. The adjusting nut should be tightened to 17 to 25 ft-lb (23 to 24 Nm), backed off 1/2 turn, and then tightened to 10 to 15 in-lb (1.0 to 1.7 Nm).
B. The adjusting nut should be tightened to 40 ft-lb (54 Nm), backed off 1 turn, and then tightened to 10 ft-lb (13.5 Nm).
C. The adjusting nut should be tightened to 50 ft-lb (67.5 Nm), backed off 3/4 turn, and then tightened to 10 to 15 in-lb (1.0 to 1.7 Nm).
D. The wheel and hub should not be rotated while adjusting the wheel bearings.

10. A unitized front wheel bearing hub that is bolted to the steering knuckle has 0.010 in (0.254 mm) of hub endplay. The proper repair procedure is to:
A. Repack and readjust the wheel bearings in the hub.
B. Tighten the hub nut to the specified torque.
C. Inspect the drive axle and hub splines, and replace the worn components.
D. Replace the wheel bearing hub assembly.

CHALLENGE QUESTIONS

1. The customer says her front-wheel-drive car makes "a moaning noise" in a turn. Which of the following could cause this problem?
A. Outer front wheel bearing.
B. Rear-axle bearing.
C. Differential gear noise.
D. Transaxle output shaft bearing.

2. The customer complains of a "whining noise" in the back of her rear-wheel-drive car when driving between 30 and 40 miles per hour.
Technician A says a good way to diagnose this problem is on a hoist with a stethoscope.
Technician B says a good way to diagnose this problem is on the road with a microphone.
Who is correct?
A. A only
B. B only
C. Both A and B
D. Neither A nor B

3. Upon inspecting a noisy front wheel bearing from a 4WD sport utility vehicle, brinelling damage to the outer bearing race was noticed.
Technician A says the damage was probably caused by tightening the bearing nut with an impact wrench. *Technician B* says the damage was probably caused by driving the vehicle through deep, muddy water.
Who is correct?

A. A only **C.** Both A and B
B. B only **D.** Neither A nor B

4. While discussing the cause of overheating damage of a front wheel bearing:
Technician A says overheating may be caused by insufficient or incorrect bearing lubricant. *Technician B* says overheating may be caused by overtightening the wheel bearing nut on installation.
Who is correct?

A. A only **C.** Both A and B
B. B only **D.** Neither A nor B

5. The customer says her front-wheel-drive car has a noise and vibration when decelerating and is most noticeable under 50 miles per hour. Which would be the most probable cause of this problem?

A. Defective outer front wheel bearing.
B. Defective inner front wheel bearing.
C. Defective outer drive axle joint.
D. Defective inner drive axle joint.

JOB SHEET 7

Name ______________________________ Date ______________

SERVICE INTEGRAL WHEEL BEARING HUBS

Upon completion of this job sheet, you should be able to measure integral wheel bearing hub endplay, and remove and replace integral wheel bearing hubs.

ASE Correlation

This job sheet is related to the ASE Suspension and Steering Task: Diagnose, service, and adjust front and rear wheel bearings.

Tools and Materials

A front-wheel-drive vehicle with integral-type front wheel bearing hubs
A floor jack and safety stands, or a lift for raising the vehicle
Dial indicator
Integral wheel bearing hub puller
Torque wrench

Describe the Vehicle Being Worked On:

Year __________ Make ______________ Model ______________
VIN ______________ Engine type and size ______________

Procedure

Task Completed

1. Road test the vehicle and listen for any abnormal wheel bearing noises; check for steering looseness or wander that may be caused by loose wheel bearings.

   Type of abnormal noise — Possible causes

   a. ______________ **a.** ______________
   b. ______________ **b.** ______________
   c. ______________ **c.** ______________

   Steering wander and looseness

   ☐ Yes ☐ No

2. Use a dial indicator to measure the endplay on the front wheel bearing hubs with the wheel installed on the hub.

   Endplay left side ________ Endplay right side ________

   Specified endplay ________

   Necessary repairs ______________________________

3. Loosen and remove the cotter pin, lock nut, and drive axle nut before raising the vehicle. ☐

4. Raise the vehicle on a lift and remove the front wheels. ☐

5. Remove the brake calipers and brake rotors. Use a length of wire to tie the calipers to the chassis. ☐

Task Completed

6. Use a dial indicator to measure the endplay directly on the front wheel bearing hubs.

   Endplay left side __________ Endplay right side __________

   Specified endplay __________

   Necessary repairs ______________________________

7. If a wheel speed sensor for the antilock brake system (ABS) is integral in the front wheel hubs, disconnect the wheel speed sensor connectors. ☐

8. Remove the hub-to-knuckle bolts, and place the transaxle in park. ☐

9. Use the proper puller to remove the wheel bearing hub from the drive axle. ☐

10. Install the new hub and bearing assembly on the drive axle splines, and install a new drive axle nut. Tighten the drive axle nut to pull the hub onto the splines. Do not tighten this nut to the specified torque at this time. ☐

11. Place the transaxle in neutral and install the wheel bearing hub bolts. Tighten these bolts to the specified torque.

    Specified wheel bearing hub bolt torque ______________________________

    Actual wheel bearing hub bolt torque ______________________________

12. Install the wheel sensor connectors, rotors, and calipers. Tighten the caliper mounting bolts to the specified torque. Place a large punch between the rotor fins and the caliper, and tighten the drive axle nut to the specified torque.

    Specified caliper bolt torque ______________________________

    Actual caliper bolt torque ______________________________

    Specified drive axle nut torque ______________________________

    Actual drive axle nut torque ______________________________

13. Install the wheels in their original positions, and tighten the wheel nuts to the specified torque.

    Specified wheel nut torque ______________________________

    Actual wheel nut torque ______________________________

14. Lower the vehicle onto the shop floor, and tighten the drive axle nut to the specified torque. Install the lock nut and a new cotter pin.

    Specified drive axle nut torque ______________________________

    Actual drive axle nut torque ______________________________

    Are the lock nut and cotter pin properly installed and tightened?

    Instructor check ______________________________

15. Road test the car and listen for abnormal wheel bearing noises.

    Wheel bearing noise: ☐ Satisfactory ☐ Unsatisfactory

Instructor's Response ______________________________

____

____

JOB SHEET 8

Name ______________________________ Date ______________

DIAGNOSE WHEEL BEARINGS

Upon completion of this job sheet, you should be able to diagnose wheel bearings.

ASE Correlation

This job sheet is related to the ASE Suspension and Steering Task: Diagnose, service, and adjust front and rear wheel bearings.

Tools and Materials

A vehicle with wheel bearing noise or bearing noise from another source

Describe the Vehicle Being Worked On:

Year __________ Make ____________________ Model ______________
VIN ______________________ Engine type and size ______________

Procedure

Task Completed

1. Road test the vehicle, listen for any abnormal wheel noises, and check for steering looseness and wander that may be caused by loose wheel bearings. ☐
2. Wheel bearing noise: ☐ Satisfactory ☐ Unsatisfactory
3. Is the bearing noise coming from the front or rear of the vehicle?
   ☐ Front ☐ Rear
4. Is this noise more noticeable when turning a corner at low speeds?
   ☐ Yes ☐ No
5. Is this noise more noticeable during acceleration? ☐ Yes ☐ No
6. Is this noise more noticeable during deceleration? ☐ Yes ☐ No
7. Is this noise more noticeable when driving at a steady speed? ☐ Yes ☐ No
   If the answer to this question is yes, state the speed when the bearing noise is most noticeable. ____________________
8. Is this noise most noticeable when driving down a narrow street at a steady low speed?
   ☐ Yes ☐ No
9. State the exact cause of the bearing noise, and explain the reason for your diagnosis.
   ____
   ____
   ____

Instructor's Response ____

____

JOB SHEET 9

Name ______________________________ Date ______________

CLEAN, LUBRICATE, INSTALL, AND ADJUST NONSEALED WHEEL BEARINGS

Upon completion of this job sheet, you should be able to clean, lubricate, install, and adjust nonsealed wheel bearings.

ASE Correlation

This job sheet is related to the ASE Suspension and Steering Task List: Diagnose, service, and adjust front and rear wheel bearings.

Tools and Materials

A vehicle with tapered roller-type front wheel bearings or a front-wheel-drive car with tapered roller-type rear wheel bearings
A floor jack and safety stands, or a lift for raising the vehicle
Wheel bearing grease
Cleaning solution
Seal drivers
Torque wrench

Describe the Vehicle Being Worked On:

Year __________ Make ______________ Model ______________
VIN ______________________ Engine type and size ______________

Procedure

Task Completed

1. Raise the vehicle on a lift with the chassis supported on the lift. ☐
2. Chalk mark the wheels in relation to the studs; remove the wheels, wheel hubs, and brake drums or rotors. ☐
3. Remove the inner hub seal and wheel bearings from the hub. ☐
4. Clean the hub and bearings with an approved cleaning solvent.

   Are the hub and bearings properly cleaned? ☐ Yes ☐ No

   Instructor check ______________________________
5. Inspect the wheel bearings, bearing cones, and hubs.

Type of defects	Necessary replacement parts
a. ______________	a. ______________
b. ______________	b. ______________
c. ______________	c. ______________

6. Inspect all bearing-related conditions such as lubrication, alignment, spindle condition, and hub condition. State the cause(s) of the bearing defects listed in step 5.

   a. ______________________________

   b. ______________________________

   c. ______________________________

7. Repack the wheel bearings and hub with the car manufacturer's specified wheel bearing grease.

   Are the wheel bearings and hub repacked with the manufacturer's recommended grease? ☐ Yes ☐ No

   Instructor check ______________________________

8. Install a new inner hub seal with the proper seal driver. Lubricate the seal lips with a light coating of the car manufacturer's recommended wheel bearing grease.

   Is the new inner hub seal properly installed? ☐ Yes ☐ No

   Instructor check ______________________________

9. Inspect, clean, and lubricate the spindles and seal contact area.

   Spindle and seal contact condition: ☐ Satisfactory ☐ Unsatisfactory

   If unsatisfactory, state necessary repairs. ______________________________

   ____

   Is the spindle and seal contact area properly cleaned and lubricated?
   ☐ Yes ☐ No

   Instructor check ______________________________

10. Install the wheel hubs, wheel bearings, washer, and retaining nut. Adjust the wheel bearing retaining nut to the specified initial torque.

    Specified initial wheel bearing torque ______________________________

    Actual initial wheel bearing torque ______________________________

11. Back off the wheel bearing retaining nut the specified amount.

    Specified portion of a turn to back off the wheel bearing retaining nut ______________

    Actual portion of a turn the wheel bearing retaining nut is backed off ______________

12. Tighten the wheel bearing retaining nut to the final specified torque.

    Specified final wheel bearing retaining nut torque ______________________________

    Actual final wheel bearing retaining nut torque ______________________________

13. Install a new cotter pin through the wheel bearing retaining nut and spindle opening.

    Is the new cotter pin properly installed? ☐ Yes ☐ No

    Instructor check ______________________________

14. Install the wheel bearing dust covers. Install the wheels in their original position, and tighten the wheel nuts to the specified torque.

    Specified wheel nut torque ______________________________

    Actual wheel nut torque ______________________________

15. Road test the car and listen for abnormal wheel bearing noises.

    Wheel bearing noise: ☐ Satisfactory ☐ Unsatisfactory

Instructor's Response ________________________________

____

____

TIRE AND WHEEL SERVICING AND BALANCING

4

Upon completion and review of this chapter, you should be able to:

- Diagnose tire thump and vibration problems.
- Diagnose steering pull problems related to tire condition.
- Rotate tires according to the vehicle manufacturer's recommended procedure.
- Remove and replace tire-and-wheel assemblies.
- Dismount, inspect, repair, and remount tires.
- Inspect wheel rims.
- Diagnose and service tire pressure monitoring systems.
- Measure tire and wheel radial and lateral runout.
- Diagnose problems caused by excessive radial or lateral tire-and-wheel runout.
- Measure tire tread wear.
- Perform off-car static wheel balance procedures.
- Perform off-car dynamic wheel balance procedures.
- Diagnose tire wear problems caused by tire and wheel imbalance.
- Perform on-car balance procedures.

Proper servicing of tires and wheels is extremely important to maintain vehicle safety and provide normal tire life. Improperly serviced and/or balanced tires and wheels cause wheel vibration and shimmy problems, resulting in excessive tire tread wear, increased wear on suspension and steering components, and decreased vehicle stability and steering control.

TIRE NOISES AND STEERING PROBLEMS

Diagnosis of Tire Noises

Uneven tread surfaces may cause tire noises that seem to originate elsewhere in the vehicle. These noises may be confused with differential noise. Differential noise usually varies with acceleration and deceleration, whereas tire noise remains more constant in relation to these forces. Tire noise is most pronounced on smooth asphalt road surfaces at speeds of 15 to 45 mph (24 to 72 km/h).

Tire Thump and Vibration

When tire thump and tire vibration are present, check these items:

1. Cupped tire treads
2. Excessive tire **radial runout**
3. Manufacturing defects such as heavy spots, weak spots, or tread chunking
4. Incorrect wheel balance

Steering Pull

A vehicle should maintain the straight-ahead forward direction on smooth, straight road surfaces without excessive steering wheel correction by the driver. If the steering gradually pulls to one side on a smooth, straight road surface, a tire, steering, or suspension defect is present. Tires of different types, sizes, designs, or inflation pressures on opposite sides of a vehicle cause **steering pull.** Sometimes a tire manufacturing defect occurs in which the belts are wound off center on the tire. This condition is referred to as **tire conicity.** A cone-shaped object rolls in the direction of its smaller diameter. Similarly, a tire with conicity tends to lead, or pull, to one side, which causes the vehicle to follow the action of the tire (Figure 4-1).

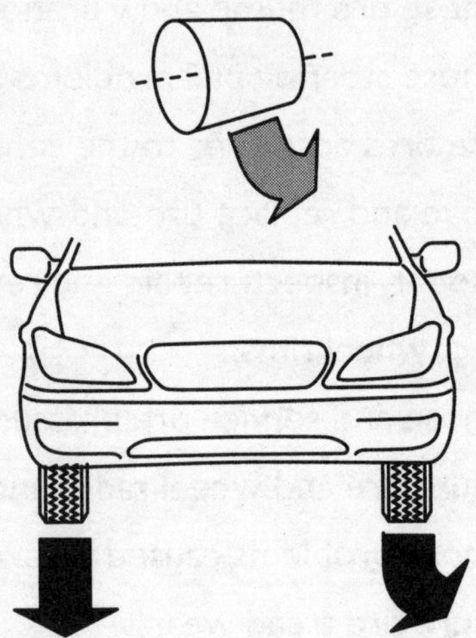

FIGURE 4-1 *Tire conicity.*

Because tire conicity cannot be diagnosed by a visual inspection, it must be diagnosed by switching the two front tires and reversing the front and rear tires (Figure 4-2). Incorrect front suspension alignment angles also cause steering pull.

Some wheel balancers with force variation capabilities sense and indicate tire conicity defects. These wheel balancers have a roller that presses against the tire tread during the wheel balance procedure, and this roller senses tire conicity.

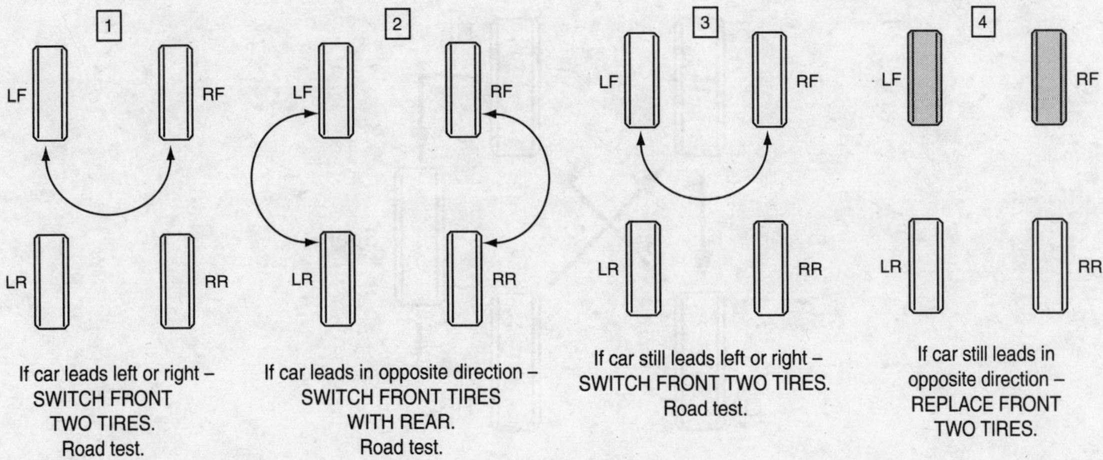

FIGURE 4-2 *Tire conicity diagnosis.*

TIRE ROTATION

Driving habits determine tire life to a large extent. Severe brake applications, high-speed driving, turning at high speeds, rapid acceleration and deceleration, and striking curbs are just a few driving habits that shorten tire life. Most car manufacturers recommend **tire rotation** at specified intervals to obtain maximum tire life. The exact tire rotation procedure depends on the model year, the type of tires, and whether the vehicle has a conventional spare or a compact spare (Figure 4-3). Tire rotation

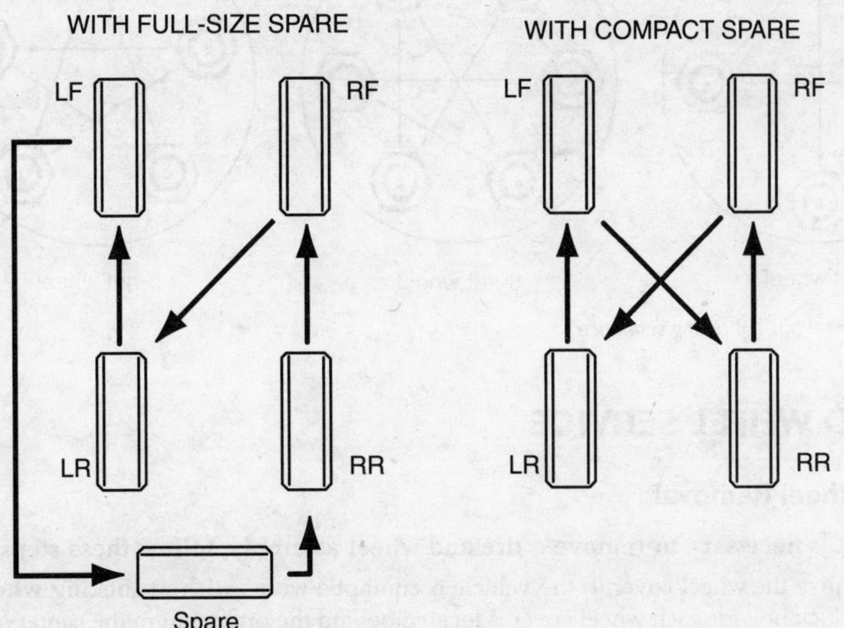

FIGURE 4-3 *Radial tire rotation procedure.*

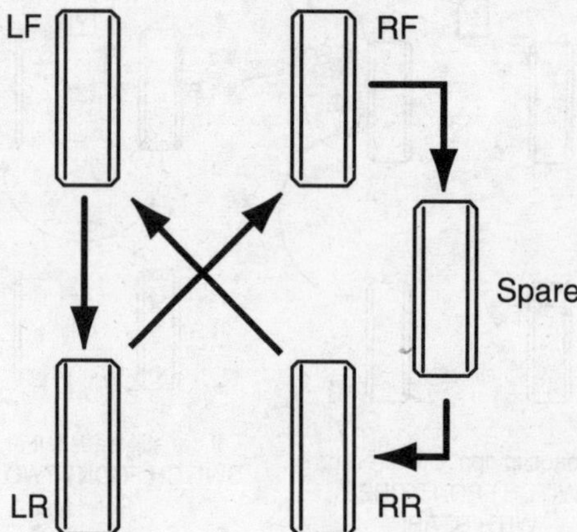

FIGURE 4-4 *Bias-ply tire rotation procedure.*

procedures do not include the compact spare. The vehicle manufacturer provides tire rotation information in the owner's manual and service manual. Vehicle manufacturers usually recommend different tire rotation procedures for bias-ply tires than for radial tires (Figure 4-4).

When tires and wheels are installed on a vehicle, it is very important that the wheel nuts are torqued to manufacturer's specifications in the proper sequence (Figure 4-5). Do not use an impact wrench when tightening wheel nuts to the specified torque.

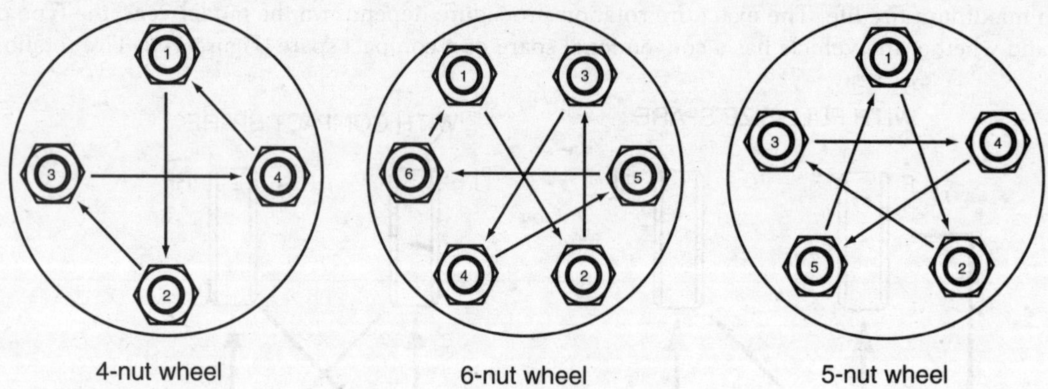

FIGURE 4-5 *Wheel nut tightening sequence.*

TIRE AND WHEEL SERVICE

Tire and Wheel Removal

When it is necessary to remove a tire-and-wheel assembly, follow these steps:

1. Remove the wheel cover. If the vehicle is equipped with **antitheft locking wheel covers,** the lock bolt for each wheel cover is located behind the ornament in the center of the wheel cover. A special key wrench is supplied to the owner for ornament and lock bolt removal. If the customer's key wrench has been lost, a master key is available from the vehicle dealer.

2. Loosen the wheel lug nuts about one-half turn, but do not remove the wheel nuts. Some vehicles are equipped with **antitheft wheel nuts**. A special lug nut key is supplied to the vehicle owner. This lug nut key has a hex nut on the outer end and a special internal projection that fits in the wheel nut opening. Install the lug nut key on the lug nuts, and connect the lug nut wrench on the key hex nut to loosen the lug nuts.

WARNING: Before the vehicle is raised on a hoist, be sure that the hoist is lifting on the car manufacturer's recommended lifting points. If the hoist is not lifting on the car manufacturer's recommended lift points, chassis components may be damaged, and the vehicle may slip off the hoist, resulting in personal injury.

WARNING: If the vehicle is lifted with a floor jack, place safety stands under the suspension or frame, and lower the vehicle onto the safety stands. Then remove the floor jack from under the vehicle. If the vehicle is not supported properly on safety stands, the vehicle may suddenly drop, resulting in personal injury.

3. Raise the vehicle on a hoist or with a floor jack to a convenient working level.
4. Chalk mark the tire, wheel, and one of the lug nuts so the tire and wheel can be reinstalled in the same position.

CAUTION: If heat is used to loosen a rusted wheel, the wheel and/or wheel bearings may be damaged.

5. Remove the lug nuts and the tire-and-wheel assembly. If the wheel is rusted and will not come off, hit the inside of the wheel with a large rubber mallet. Do not hit the wheel with a steel hammer, because this action could damage the wheel. Do not heat the wheel.

TIRE AND WHEEL SERVICE PRECAUTIONS

There are many different types of tire changing equipment in the automotive service industry. However, specific precautions apply to the use of any tire changing equipment.

These precautions include the following:

1. Before you operate any tire changing equipment, always be absolutely certain that you are familiar with the operation of the equipment.
2. When operating tire changing equipment, always follow the equipment manufacturer's recommended procedure.
3. Always deflate a tire completely before attempting to dismount the tire.
4. Clean the bead seats on the wheel rim before mounting the tire on the wheel rim.
5. Lubricate the outer surface of the tire beads with rubber lubricant before mounting the tire on the wheel rim.
6. When the tire is mounted on the wheel rim, be sure the tire is positioned evenly on the wheel rim.
7. While inflating a tire, do not stand directly over the tire. An air hose extension allows the technician to stand back from the tire during the inflation process.
8. Do not overinflate tires.
9. When mounting tires on cast aluminum alloy wheel rims or cast magnesium alloy wheel rims, always use the tire changing equipment manufacturer's recommended tools and procedures.

10. When mounting or dismounting run-flat tires, be sure the tire changing equipment is compatible with these tires and wheels.

Tire Dismounting

CAUTION: If hand tools or tire irons are used to dismount tires, tire bead and wheel rim damage may occur.

Always use a tire changer to dismount tires. Do not use hand tools or tire irons for this purpose. Various types of tire changers are available. When servicing tires it is very important that the tire changing equipment will mount and dismount run-flat tires, low-profile tires, and tires mounted on alloy wheels without damaging the wheel rims or tires. Some tire changers have the features illustrated in Figure 4-6 and described in the following explanation:

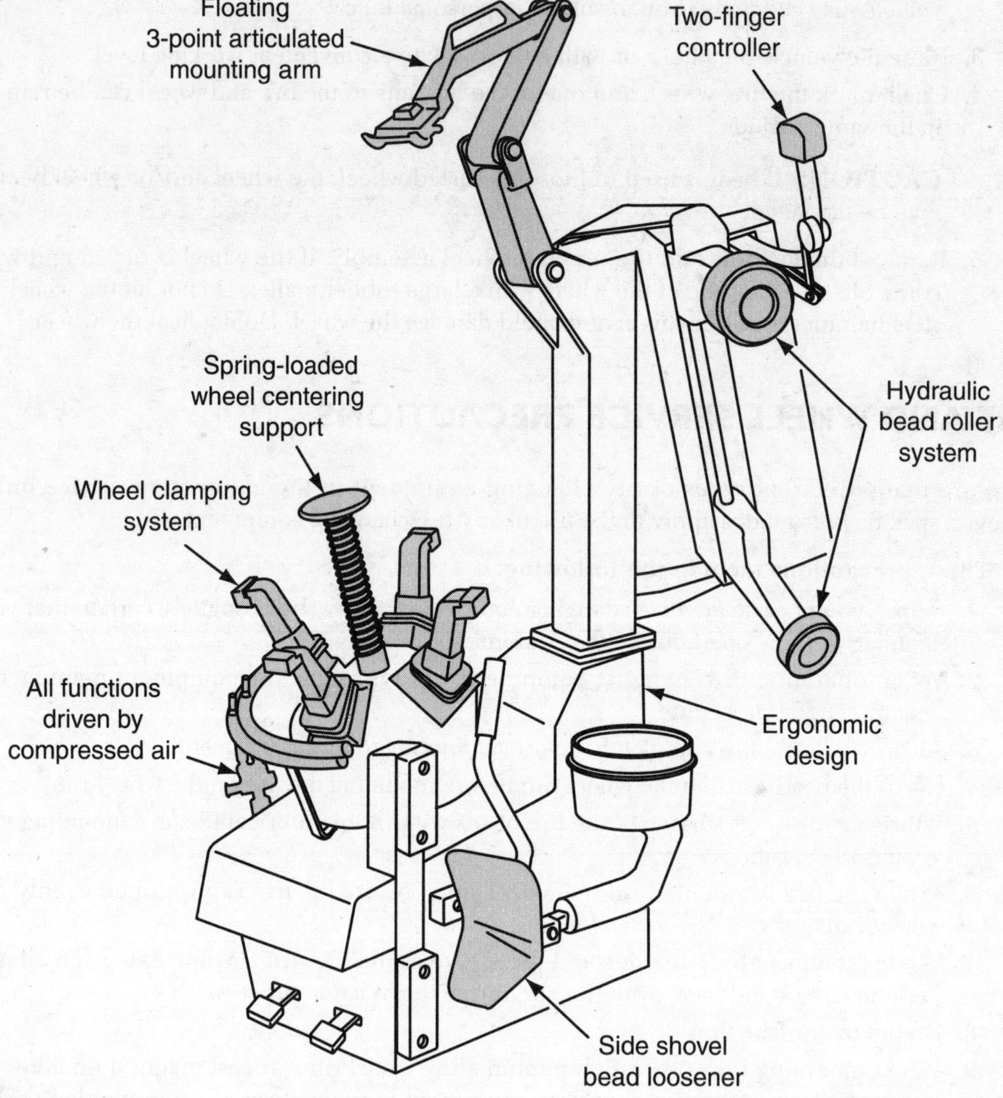

FIGURE 4-6 *Tire changer.*

1. A floating 3-point articulated arm has a polymer mount/dismount head on the end of the arm. This type of mount/dismount head goes between the tire bead and the rim when dismounting or mounting the tire (Figure 4-7). The polymer head will not damage alloy wheel rims. A mechanical bead pusher with a nylon roller facilitates handling stiff, low-profile tires.
2. A spring-loaded wheel centering support centers the wheel rim in the clamping system.
3. A rubber-pad clamping system eliminates steel-jaw clamping and wheel rim damage. The rim clamping system easily adjusts for internal or external rim clamping (Figure 4-8).

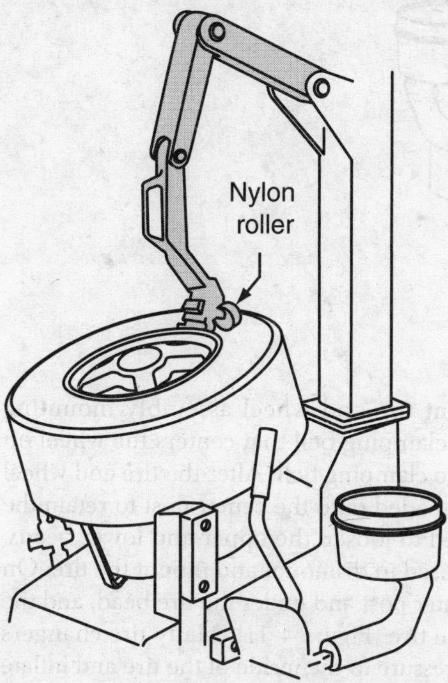

FIGURE 4-7 *Articulating arm with polymer head and mechanical bead pusher.*

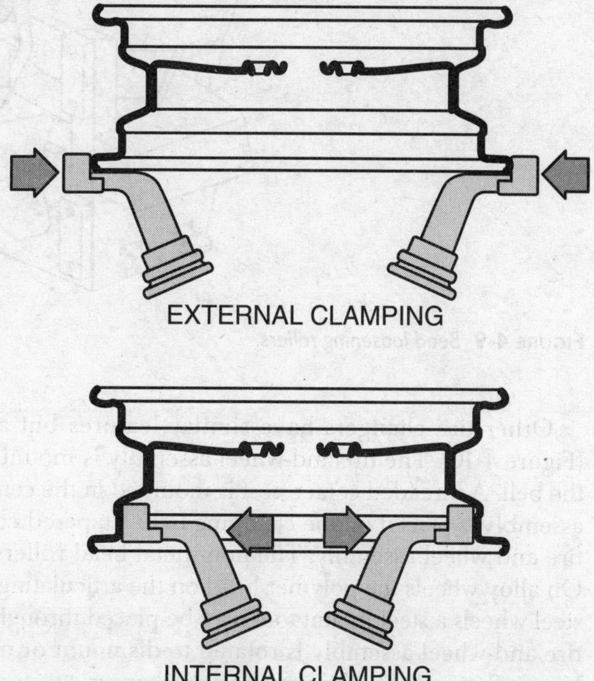

FIGURE 4-8 *Rim clamping system provides internal or external rim clamping action.*

4. A multi-piston air motor in the tire changer drives the clamp assembly and wheel rim in either direction up to 15 revolutions per minute (rpm). The technician controls the clamp and wheel rim rotation by foot-operated pedals on the front of the tire changer. This type of clamping system allows the technician to rotate the wheel rim inside the tire to correct excessive wheel and tire runout conditions.
5. The technician uses two fingers to operate control switches that control the upper and lower bead rollers by air-over-hydraulic pressure.
6. The non-metal bead rollers are placed against the tire next to the rim, and the technician uses the control switches to supply pressure to the rollers (Figure 4-9). The clamp and wheel assembly is rotated to loosen the upper and lower beads.
7. The tire changer is designed so the complete bead loosening, tire dismounting, and tire mounting operation can be performed from one position, which saves time and physical energy.
8. A side shovel bead-loosening tool is an optional feature that facilitates dismounting and mounting tires on special applications such as motorcycles and all-terrain vehicles (ATVs).

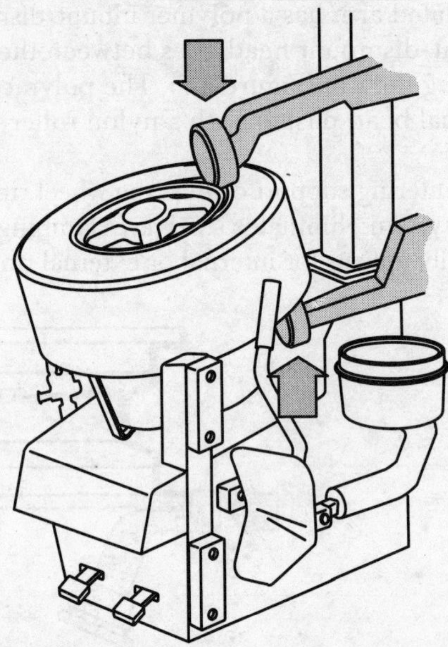

FIGURE 4-9 *Bead loosening rollers.*

Other tire changers have similar features but a different tire and wheel assembly mounting (Figure 4-10). The tire and wheel assembly is mounted on a clamping bell that centers the wheel on the bell. A threaded center post is mounted in the center of the clamping bell. After the tire and wheel assembly is placed on the clamping bell, a tapered cone is threaded onto the center post to retain the tire and wheel assembly. The non-metal bead rollers are used to loosen the upper and lower beads. On alloy wheels the polymer head on the articulating arm is used to dismount and mount the tire. On steel wheels a steel mount tool may be placed through the center post and under the tire bead, and the tire and wheel assembly is rotated to dismount or mount the tire (Figure 4-11). Many tire changers have inflation jets in the clamping mechanism to supply air pressure to the inside of the tire and inflate the tire after the tire is mounted properly.

A typical tire dismounting procedure follows:

1. Remove the valve core and be sure the tire is completely deflated.
2. Place the wheel and tire on the tire changer with the narrow bead ledge facing upward.
3. Follow the operating procedure recommended by the manufacturer of the tire changer to force the tire bead inward and separate it from the rim on both sides.
4. Push one edge of the top bead into the drop center of the rim.
5. Place the tire changer's head or lever between the bead and the rim on the opposite side of the rim from where the bead is in the drop center.
6. Operate the tire changer to rotate the head or lever and move the bead over the top of the rim.
7. Repeat steps 4, 5, and 6 to move the lower bead over the top of the rim.

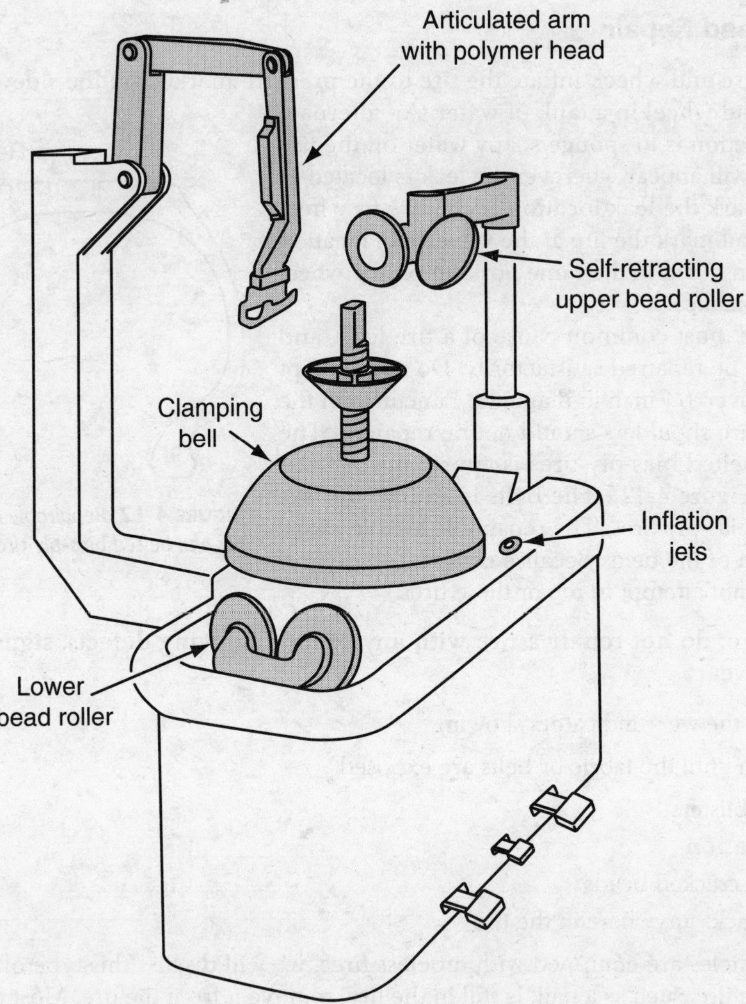

FIGURE 4-10 *Tire changer with horizontal clamping mechanism.*

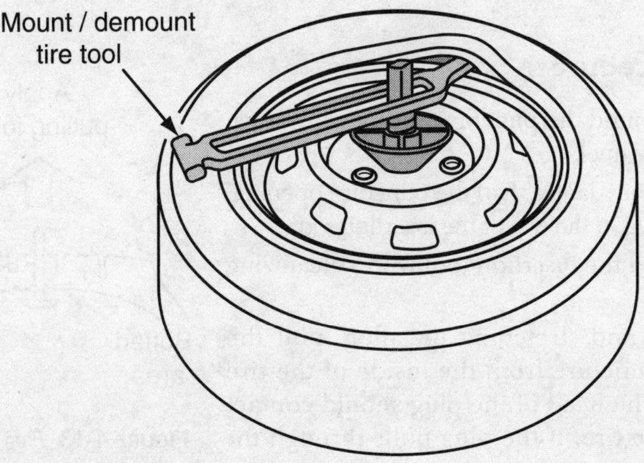

FIGURE 4-11 *Steel mount/demount tool for steel rims.*

Tire Inspection and Repair

To find a leak in a tire and wheel, inflate the tire to the pressure marked on the sidewall, and then submerge the tire and wheel in a tank of water. An alternate method of leak detection is to sponge soapy water on the tire and wheel. Bubbles will appear wherever the leak is located in the tire or wheel. Mark the leak location in the tire or wheel rim with a crayon, and mark the tire at the valve stem location so the tire can be reinstalled in the same position on the wheel to maintain proper balance.

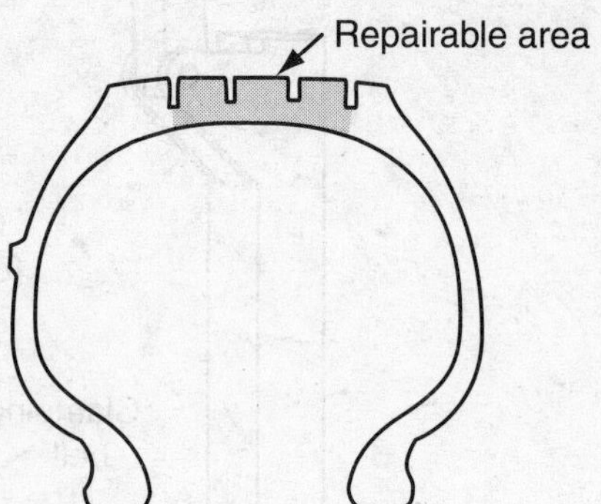

FIGURE 4-12 *Repairable area on bias-ply and belted bias-ply tires.*

A puncture is the most common cause of a tire leak, and many punctures can be repaired satisfactorily. Do not attempt to repair punctures over 1/4 inch in diameter. Punctures in the sidewalls or on the tire shoulders should not be repaired. The repairable area in belted bias-ply tires is approximately the width of the belts (Figure 4-12). The belts in radial tires are wider than those in bias-ply tires. The repairable area in radial tires is also the width of the belts. Because compact spare tires have thin treads, do not attempt to repair these tires.

Inspect the tire; do not repair a tire with any of the following defects, signs of damage, or excessive wear:

1. Tires with the wear indicators showing
2. Tires worn until the fabric or belts are exposed
3. Bulges or blisters
4. **Ply separation**
5. Broken or cracked beads
6. Cuts or cracks anywhere in the tire

Because most vehicles are equipped with tubeless tires, we will discuss this type of tire repair. If the cause of the puncture, such as a nail, is still in the tire, remove it from the tire. Most punctures can be repaired from inside the tire with a service plug or vulcanized patch service kit. The instructions of the tire service kit manufacturer should be followed, but we will discuss three common tire repair procedures.

Plug Installation Procedure

1. Buff the area around the puncture with a wire brush or wire buffing wheel.
2. Select a plug slightly larger than the puncture opening, and insert the plug in the eye of the insertion tool.
3. Wet the plug and the insertion tool with vulcanizing fluid.
4. While holding and stretching the plug, pull the plug into the puncture from the inside of the tire (Figure 4-13). The head of the plug should contact the inside of the tire. If the plug pulls through the tire, repeat the procedure.
5. Cut the plug off 1/32 inch from the tread surface. Do not stretch the plug while cutting.

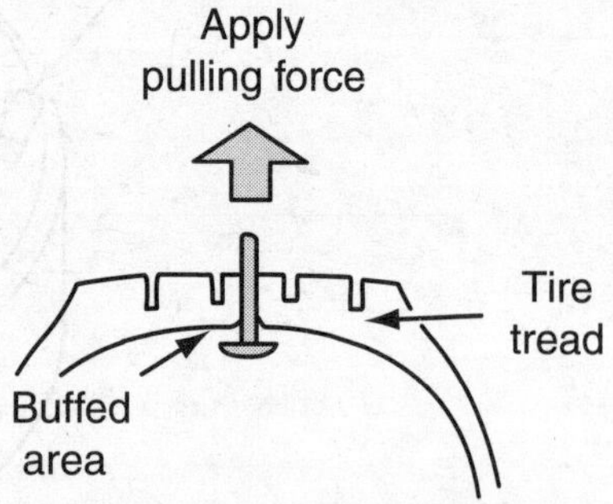

FIGURE 4-13 *Plug installation procedure.*

Cold Patch Installation Procedure

CAUTION: Radial tire patches should have arrows that must be positioned parallel to the radial plies to provide proper adhesion.

1. Buff the area around the puncture with a wire brush or buffing wheel.
2. Apply vulcanizing fluid to the buffed area and allow it to dry until it is tacky.
3. Peel the backing from the patch, and apply the patch over the puncture. Center the patch over the puncture.
4. Run a stitching tool back and forth over the patch to improve bonding.

Hot Patch Installation Procedure

1. Buff the area around the puncture with a wire brush or buffing wheel.
2. Apply vulcanizing fluid to the buffed area, if required.
3. Peel the backing from the patch and install the patch so it is centered over the puncture on the inside of the tire. Many hot patches are heated with an electric heating element clamped over the patch. This element should be clamped in place for the amount of time recommended by the equipment or patch manufacturer.
4. After the heating element is removed, allow the patch to cool for a few minutes and be sure the patch is properly bonded to the tire.

WHEEL RIM SERVICE

CAUTION: The use of abrasive cleaners, alkaline-base detergents, or caustic agents on aluminum or magnesium wheel rims may cause discoloration or damage to the protective coating.

Steel rims should be spray cleaned with a water hose. Aluminum or magnesium wheel rims should be cleaned with a mild soap and water solution, and rinsed with clean water. The use of abrasive cleaners, alkaline-base detergents, or caustic agents may damage aluminum or magnesium wheel rims. Clean the rim bead seats on these wheel rims thoroughly with the mild soap and water solution. The rim bead seats on steel wheel rims should be cleaned with a wire brush or coarse steel wool.

CAUTION: Steel wheel rims must not be welded, heated, or peened with a ball-peen hammer. These procedures may weaken the rim and create a safety hazard.

CAUTION: Installing an inner tube to correct leaks in a tubeless tire or wheel rim is not an approved procedure.

Steel wheel rims should be inspected for excessive rust and corrosion, cracks, loose rivets or welds, bent or damaged bead seats, and elongated lug nut holes. Aluminum or magnesium wheel rims should be inspected for damaged bead seats, elongated lug nut holes, cracks, and porosity. If any of these conditions are present on either type of wheel rim, replace the wheel rim.

Many shops always replace the tire valve assembly when a tire is repaired or replaced. This policy helps prevent future problems with tire valve leaks. The inner end of the valve may be cut off with a pair of diagonal pliers, and then the outer end may be pulled from the rim. Coat the new valve with rubber tire lubricant and pull it into the rim opening with a special puller screwed onto the valve threads.

Wheel Rim Leak Repair

A wheel rim leak may be repaired if the leak is not caused by excessive rust on a steel rim, and the rim is in satisfactory condition.

Follow these steps for wheel rim leak repair:

1. Use #80-grit sandpaper to thoroughly clean the area around the leak on the tire side of the rim.
2. Use a shop towel to remove any grit from the leak area.
3. Be sure the wheel rim is at room temperature, and apply a heavy coating of silicone rubber sealer over the leak area.
4. Spread the sealer over the entire sanded area with a putty knife.
5. Allow the sealer to cure for six hours before remounting the tire.

TIRE REMOUNTING PROCEDURE

1. Be sure the wheel rim bead seats are thoroughly cleaned.
2. Coat the tire beads and the wheel rim bead seats with rubber tire lubricant.
3. Secure the wheel rim on the tire changer with the narrow bead ledge facing upward, and place the tire on top of the wheel rim with the bead on the lower side of the tire in the drop center of the wheel rim.
4. Use the tire changer head or lever under the tire bead to install the tire bead over the wheel rim. Always operate the tire changer with the manufacturer's recommended procedure.
5. Repeat steps 3 and 4 to install the upper bead over the wheel rim.
6. Rotate the tire on the wheel rim until the crayon mark is aligned with the valve stem. This mark was placed on the tire prior to dismounting.

WARNING: When a bead expander is installed around the tire, never exceed 10 psi (69 kPa) pressure in the tire. A higher pressure may cause the expander to break and fly off the tire, causing serious personal injury or property damage.

WARNING: When a bead expander is not used, never exceed 40 psi (276 kPa) tire pressure to move the tire beads out tightly against the wheel rim. A higher pressure may blow the tire bead against the rim with excessive force, and this action could burst the rim or tire, resulting in serious personal injury or property damage.

WARNING: While inflating a tire, do not stand directly over the tire. In this position, serious injury could occur if the tire or wheel rim flies apart.

7. Follow the recommended procedure supplied by the manufacturer of the tire changer to inflate the tire. This procedure may involve the use of a bead expander installed around the center of the tire tread to expand the tire beads against the wheel rim. If a bead expander is used, inflate the tire to 10 psi (69 kPa) to move the beads out tightly against the wheel rim.

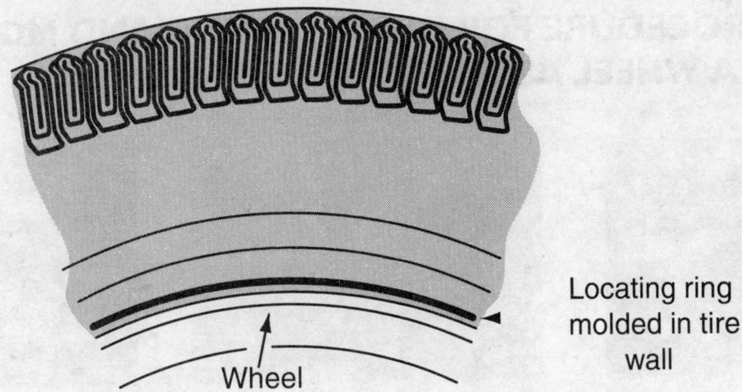

FIGURE 4-14 *The circular ring around the tire bead must be centered on the wheel rim.*

Never exceed this pressure with a bead expander installed on the tire. Always observe the circular marking around the tire bead as the tire is inflated. This mark should be centered around the wheel rim (Figure 4-14). Always observe both beads while a tire is inflated. If the circular mark around the tire bead is not centered on the rim, deflate the tire and center it on the wheel rim. If a bead expander is not used, never exceed 40 psi (276 kPa) when moving tire beads out tightly against the rim. When either tire bead will not move out tightly against the wheel rim with 40 psi (276 kPa) tire pressure, deflate the tire and center it on the wheel rim again.

Photo Sequence 4 shows a typical procedure for dismounting and mounting a tire on a wheel assembly.

DIAGNOSING AND SERVICING TIRE PRESSURE MONITORING SYSTEMS

If the tire pressure monitoring system (TPMS) warning light is illuminated and/or a warning message is displayed in the message center, the first step in diagnosing the system is a visual inspection. During this inspection be sure each tire is inflated to the specified pressure. Make sure all fours tires are the size specified by the vehicle manufacturer, and that each wheel contains a tire pressure sensor. Inspect the wiring harness connection to the TPMS module for loose or corroded connections and damaged wires.

If the visual inspection does not locate any problems, connect a scan tool to the data link connector (DLC) under the left side of the instrument panel. Select TPMS on the scan tool and check for TPMS diagnostic trouble codes. Defects in the TPMS may result in these DTCs:

1. B1342 – TPMS module is defective
2. B2477 – Module configuration failure/mismatch
3. B2849 – Horn output relay circuit open
4. B2872 – Tire pressure sensor fault
5. C2780 – Module in the manufacturing mode
6. U0073 – Controller area network (CAN) bus off, transmission error
7. U1900 – CAN communications bus fault receiver error

PHOTO SEQUENCE 4
TYPICAL PROCEDURE FOR DISMOUNTING AND MOUNTING A TIRE ON A WHEEL ASSEMBLY

P4-1 *Dismounting the tire from the wheel begins with releasing the air, removing the valve stem core, and unseating the tire from its rim. The machine does the unseating. The technician merely guides the operating lever.*

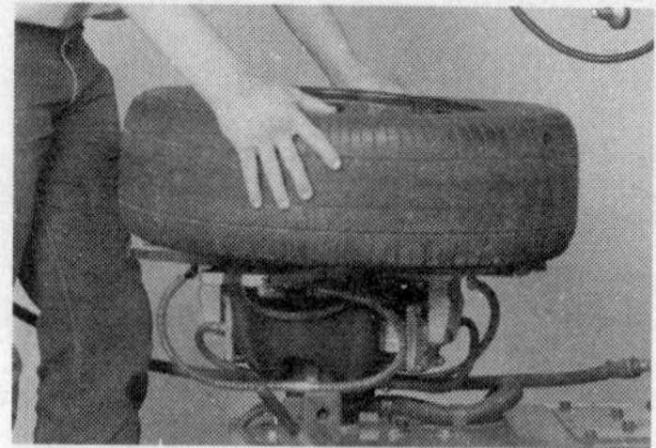

P4-2 *Once both sides of the tire are unseated, place the tire and wheel onto the machine. Then depress the pedal that clamps the wheel to the tire machine.*

P4-3 *Lower the machine's arm, into position on the tire-and-wheel assembly.*

P4-4 *Insert the tire iron between the upper bead of the tire and the wheel. Depress the pedal that causes the wheel to rotate. Do the same with the lower bead.*

P4-5 *After the tire is totally free from the rim, remove the tire.*

P4-6 *Prepare the wheel for the mounting of the tire by using a wire brush to remove all dirt and rust from the sealing surface. Apply rubber compound to the bead area of the tire.*

P4-7 *Place the tire onto the wheel and lower the arm into place. As the machine rotates the wheel, the arm will force the tire over the rim. After the tire is completely over the rim, install the air ring over the tire. Activate it to seat the tire against the wheel.*

P4-8 *Reinstall the valve stem core and inflate the tire to the recommended inflation.*

Vehicles with a TPMS may require a tire pressure adjustment in relation to atmospheric temperature. For example, if the atmospheric temperature decreases 30°F when a vehicle is parked outside overnight, the tire pressure decreases 3 psi. This pressure decrease may activate the TPMS warning system. Refer to the vehicle manufacturer's specifications for tire inflation pressure at various atmospheric temperatures.

CAUTION: Do not remove the valve stem core to relieve the tire pressure. If the valve stem core is inadvertently removed from the valve stem, a new nickel-plated valve core must be installed. Failure to use a nickel-plated valve core will result in corrosion and possible loss of tire pressure.

CAUTION: The tire pressure sensors are not serviceable. If a sensor is defective, it must be replaced.

CAUTION: Tire pressure sealing products may render the TPMS sensor inoperative. If this occurs, remove all of the tire sealing material and replace the sensor.

Proper valve stem and sensor removal procedures must be followed to avoid damage to the sensor: To remove a valve stem and sensor, follow these steps:

1. Before removing the tire and wheel assembly from the vehicle, mark the wheel rim in relation to one of the wheel studs.
2. Position the tire and wheel assembly with the valve stem at the 6 o'clock position.
3. Remove the sensor retention nut and push the valve stem and sensor into the tire.
4. Place the wheel and tire on the turntable of the tire changer so the valve stem is positioned 270° from the mounting/demounting arm on the tire changer (Figure 4-15).

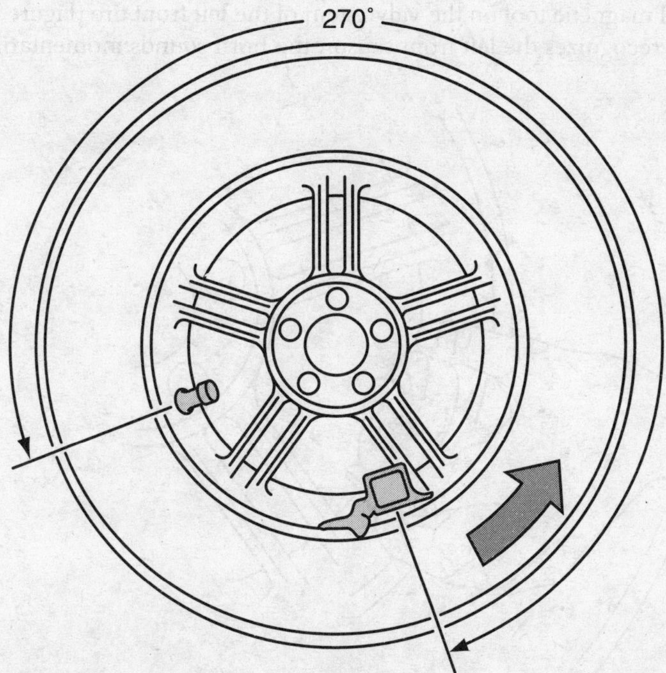

FIGURE 4-15 *Proper tire and wheel position on a tire changer.*

5. Loosen both tire beads away from the wheel rim.
6. Place index marks on the tire beside the valve stem opening and the wheel weight positions.
7. Lubricate the outer tire bead, and dismount the outer bead over the wheel rim.
8. Lift up on the outer tire bead, and remove the TPMS sensor and valve stem assembly.
9. Install the new sensor in the valve stem opening, and install a new grommet and retention nut.

CAUTION: Each time a TPMS sensor is removed, a new grommet, retention nut, and valve cap must be installed. Replace the valve core if it has been removed or damaged.

10. Tighten the retention nut to 71 in.-lbs. (8 Nm).
11. Lubricate and mount the outer tire bead.
12. Inflate the tire to the specified pressure.
13. Remove the tire and wheel from the tire changer and install this assembly in the proper position on the wheel studs. Tighten the wheel retaining nuts in the proper sequence to the specified torque.

When a TPMS sensor or component is serviced, a sensor training procedure must be performed. Follow these steps to complete the sensor training procedure:

1. Starting with the ignition switch off, cycle the ignition switch on and off three times, and on the third cycle leave the ignition switch in the on position. Do not wait more than two seconds between switch cycles.
2. Press and release the brake pedal.
3. Repeat the ignition switch cycling procedure as explained in step 1. Upon completion of this procedure, the horn should sound once to indicate successful entry to the learn mode.
4. After the horn sounds, a TRAIN LEFT FRONT TIRE message should appear in the instrument panel message center.
5. Place the special magnetic tool on the valve stem of the left front tire (Figure 4-16). When the TPMS module recognizes the left front sensor, the horn sounds momentarily.

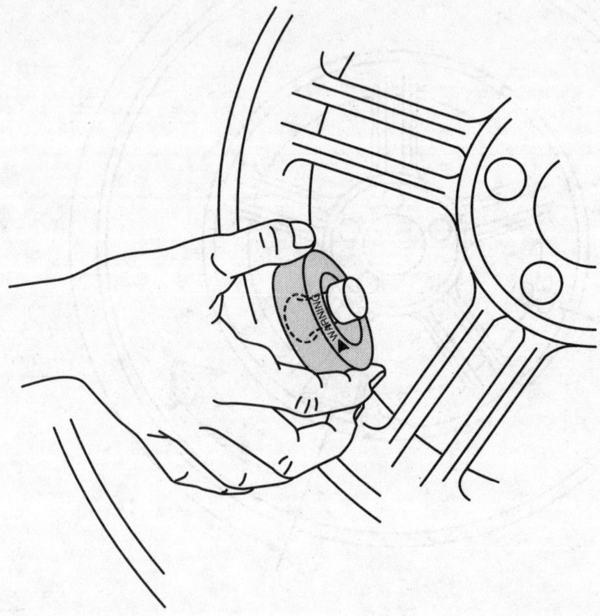

FIGURE 4-16 *Magnetic learning tool for TPMS sensors.*

WARNING: The special magnetic tool may adversely affect magnetically sensitive devices such as heart pacers, and this action may result in personal injury!

6. Repeat step 5 at the right front, right rear, left rear, and spare wheels.
7. If the learn procedure fails on any wheel, the horn sounds twice, and a TIRES NOT LEARNED-REPEAT message appears in the message center. If this action occurs, the learn procedure must be repeated from step 1.

TIRE AND WHEEL RUNOUT MEASUREMENT

Ideally, a tire-and-wheel assembly should be perfectly round. However, this condition is rarely achieved. A tire-and-wheel assembly that is out-of-round is said to have radial runout. If the radial runout exceeds manufacturer's specifications, a vibration may occur because the radial runout causes the spindle to move up and down (Figure 4-17). A defective tire with a variation in stiffness may also cause this up-and-down spindle action.

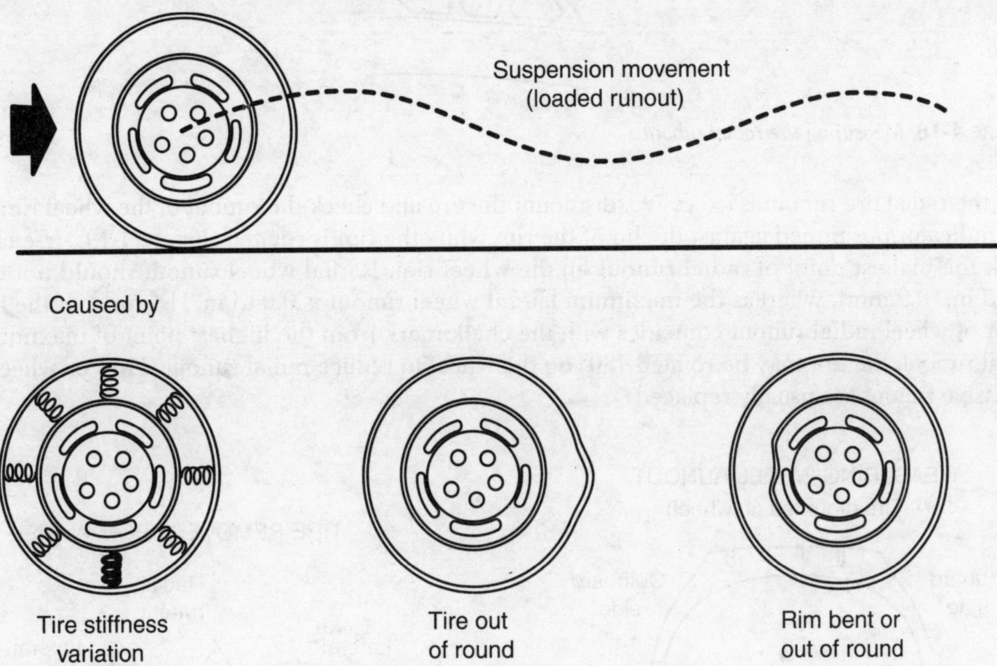

FIGURE 4-17 *Vertical tire and wheel vibrations caused by radial tire or wheel runout, or variation in tire stiffness.*

Wheel balancers with force variation capabilities have a roller that is pressed against the tire tread during the wheel balance procedure. This roller senses and indicates stiffness variation in a tire.

A dial indicator gauge may be positioned against the center of the tire tread as the tire is rotated slowly to measure radial runout (Figure 4-18). Radial runout of more than 0.060 in. (1.5 mm) will cause vehicle shake. If the radial runout is between 0.045 in. to 0.060 in. (1.1 mm to 1.5 mm), vehicle shake may occur. These are typical radial runout specifications. Always consult the vehicle manufacturer's specifications. Mark the highest point of radial runout on the tire with chalk, and mark the valve stem position on the tire.

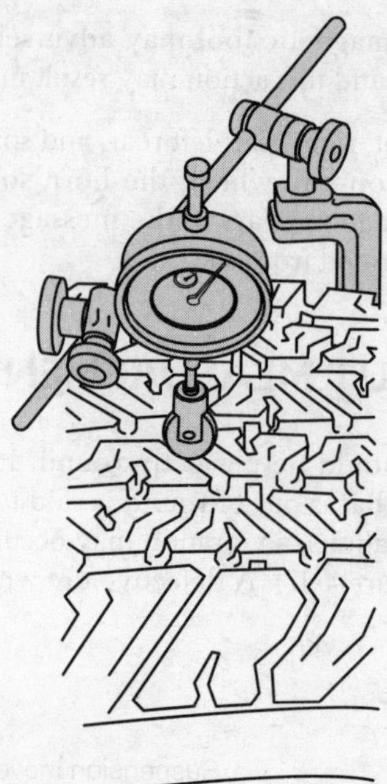

FIGURE 4-18 *Measuring tire radial runout.*

If the radial tire runout is excessive, dismount the tire and check the runout of the wheel rim with a dial indicator positioned against the lip of the rim while the rim is rotated (Figure 4-19). Use chalk to mark the highest point of radial runout on the wheel rim. Radial wheel runout should not exceed 0.035 in. (0.9 mm), whereas the maximum lateral wheel runout is 0.045 in. (1.1 mm). If the highest point of wheel radial runout coincides with the chalk mark from the highest point of maximum tire radial runout, the tire may be rotated 180° on the wheel to reduce radial runout. Tires or wheels with excessive runout are usually replaced.

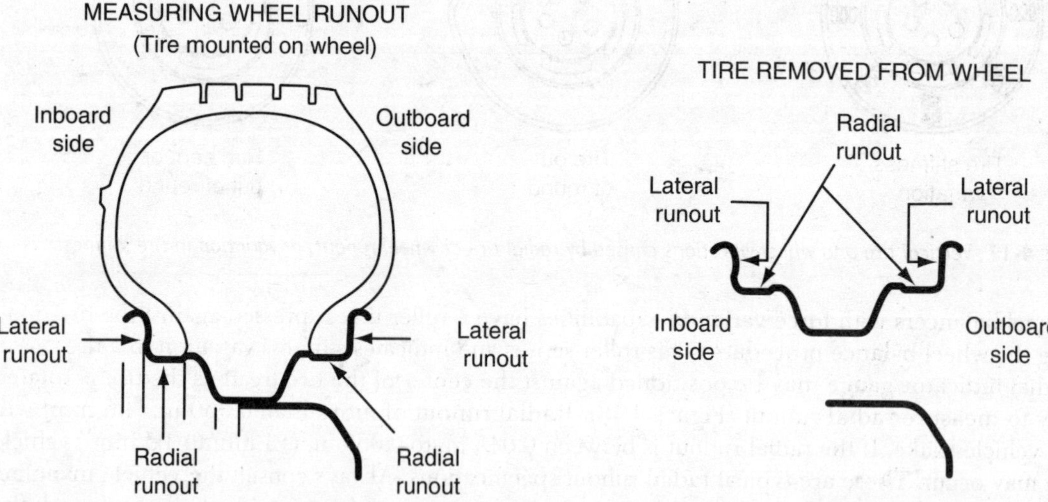

FIGURE 4-19 *Measuring wheel radial and lateral runout.*

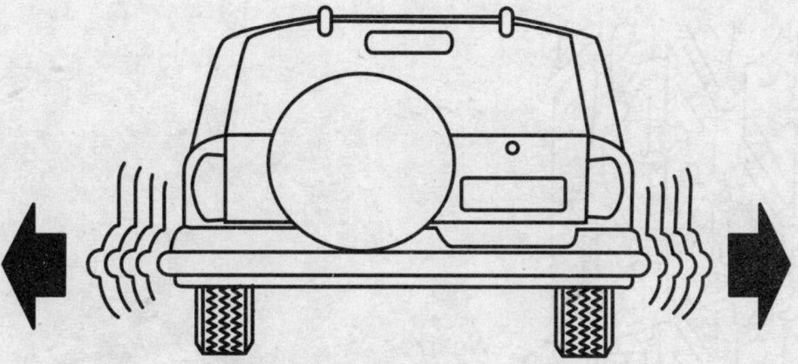

FIGURE 4-20 *Chassis waddling action caused by lateral tire or wheel runout, or a defective tire with a belt that is not straight.*

Lateral tire runout may be measured with a dial indicator located against the sidewall of the tire. Excessive lateral runout causes the tire to waddle as it turns, and this waddling sensation may be transmitted to the passenger compartment (Figure 4-20). A chassis waddling action may also be caused by a defective tire in which the belt is not straight. If the lateral runout exceeds 0.080 in. (2.0 mm), wheel shake problems will occur on the vehicle. Chalk mark the tire and wheel at the highest point of lateral runout. When the tire runout is excessive, the tire should be removed from the wheel, and the wheel lateral runout should be measured with a dial indicator positioned against the edge of the wheel as the wheel is rotated. Tires or wheels with excessive lateral runout should be replaced.

TREAD WEAR MEASUREMENT

On most tires, the **tread wear indicators** appear as wide bands across the tread when tread depth is worn to 1/16 in. (1.6 mm). Most tire manufacturers recommend tire replacement when the tread wear indicators appear across two or more tread grooves at three locations around the tire (Figure 4-21). If tires do not have wear indicators, a tread depth gauge may be used to measure the tread depth (Figure 4-22). The tread depth gauge reads in 32nds of an inch. Tires with 2/32 inch of tread depth or less should be replaced.

PRELIMINARY WHEEL BALANCING CHECKS

These preliminary checks should be completed before a tire and wheel are balanced:

1. Check for objects in the tire tread.
2. Check for objects inside the tire.
3. Inspect the tread and sidewall.
4. Check the inflation pressure.
5. Measure the tire and wheel runout.
6. Check the wheel bearing adjustment.

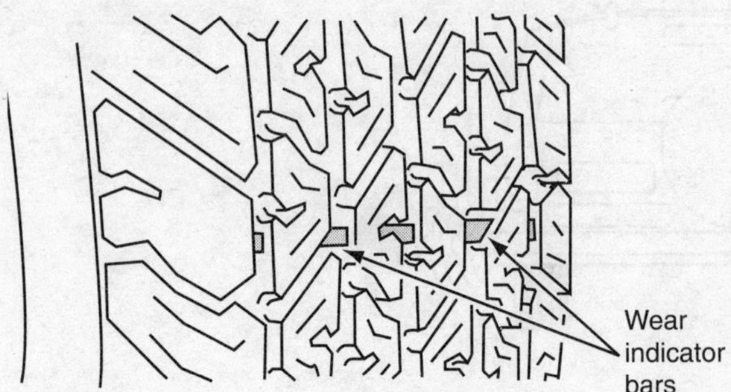

FIGURE 4-21 *Tire tread wear indicators.*

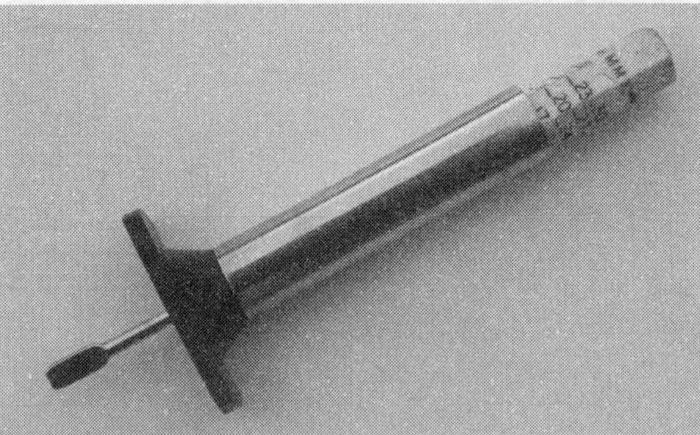

FIGURE 4-22 *Tread depth gauge.*

7. Check for mud collected on the inside of the wheel and wash the tire and wheel assembly.
8. Inspect the wheel rim for damage and excessive rust.

WARNING: On many wheel balancers, the tire and wheel are spun at high speed during the dynamic balance procedure. Be sure that all wheel weights are attached securely, and check for other loose objects on the tire and wheel, such as stones in the tread. If loose objects are detached from the tire or wheel at high speed, they may cause serious personal injury or property damage.

WARNING: On the type of wheel balancer that spins the tire and wheel at high speed during the dynamic balance procedure, always attach the tire-and-wheel assembly securely to the balancer. Follow the equipment manufacturer's recommended wheel mounting procedure. If the tire-and-wheel assembly becomes loose on the balancer at high speed, serious personal injury or property damage may result.

WARNING: Prior to spinning a tire and wheel at high speed on a wheel balancer, always lower the protection shield over the tire. This shield provides protection in case anything flies off the tire or wheel.

All of the items on the preliminary check list influence wheel balance or safety. Therefore, it is extremely important that the preliminary checks be completed. Since a tire-and-wheel assembly is rotated at high speed during the dynamic balance procedure, it is very important that objects such as stones be removed from the treads. Centrifugal force may dislodge objects from the treads and cause serious personal injury. For this reason, it is also extremely important that the old wheel weights be removed from the wheel prior to balancing and the new weights attached securely to the wheel during the balance procedure.

Follow these preliminary steps before attempting to balance a wheel and tire:

1. When off-car wheel balancers are used, the tire and wheel must be removed from the vehicle and installed on the balancer. All mud, dust, and debris must be washed from the wheel after it is removed.
2. Objects inside a tire, such as balls of rubber, make balance impossible. When the tire-and-wheel assembly is mounted on the balancer, be absolutely sure that the wheel is securely tightened on the balancer. As the tire is rotated slowly, listen for objects rolling inside the tire. If such objects are present, they must be removed prior to wheel balancing.

3. The tire should be inspected for tread and sidewall defects before the balance procedure. These defects create safety hazards, and they may influence wheel balance. For example, tread chunking makes the wheel balancing difficult.

TIRE INFLATION PRESSURE

A tire depends on correct inflation pressure to maintain its correct shape and support the vehicle weight.

Excessive inflation pressure causes the following problems:

1. Excessive center tread wear (Figure 4-23)
2. Hard ride
3. Damage to tire carcass

When tires are underinflated, the following problems will be evident:

1. Excessive wear on each side of the tread (Figure 4-23)

Condition	Rapid wear at center	Rapid wear at shoulders	Cracked treads
Effect			
Cause	Over inflation or lack of rotation Contact patch area	Under inflation or lack of rotation Contact patch area	Under inflation or excessive speed
Correction	Adjust pressure to specifications. When tires are cool, rotate tires.		

FIGURE 4-23 *Tire tread wear caused by underinflation or overinflation.*

2. Hard steering
3. Wheel damage
4. Excessive heat buildup in the tire and possible severe tire damage with resultant hazardous driving

The tires should be inflated to the car manufacturer's recommended pressure prior to the balance procedure. Loose wheel bearings allow lateral wheel shaking and simulate an imbalanced wheel condition when the vehicle is in motion. Therefore, wheel bearing adjustments should be checked when wheel balance conditions are diagnosed.

STATIC AND DYNAMIC WHEEL BALANCE PROCEDURE

The off-vehicle electronic wheel balancer is presently the most common type in use (Figure 4-24). When using this type of wheel balancer, each tire and wheel assembly is removed from the vehicle and installed on the wheel balancer. A special cone centers the wheel rim on the balancer shaft, and a large nut retains the wheel and tire assembly on the balancer. Tire and wheel assemblies must always be mounted on the balancer using the service procedures recommended by the balancer manufacturer. Most electronic wheel balancers have an electric motor that spins the tire and wheel assembly at moderate speed during the balance procedure. A safety cover on the balancer must be lowered over the tire and wheel assembly when the tire and wheel assembly is spun on the balancer. This hood protects the technician from any debris that might be dislodged from the tire tread. On some electronic wheel balancers, the tire and wheel assembly is spun by hand during the balance procedure.

FIGURE 4-24 *Electronic wheel balancer.*

After the tire and wheel assembly is mounted properly on the balancer, the technician must enter the wheel diameter, wheel width, and rim offset in the balancer computer. A special caliper may be used to measure the wheel width. A special tool on the balancer may be extended so it contacts the flange on the side of the wheel rim next to the balancer. This tool provides the required wheel offset measurement that indicates the position of the wheel on the balancer shaft. An electronic wheel balancer performs **static balance** and **dynamic wheel balance** calculations simultaneously. The following is a typical wheel balance procedure:

1. Complete all the preliminary balance checks mentioned previously in this chapter.
2. Be sure the tire and wheel assembly is mounted on the balancer using the balancer manufacturer's recommended mounting procedure.
3. Use a pair of wheel weight pliers to remove all the old wheel weights from the wheel rim (Figure 4-25).

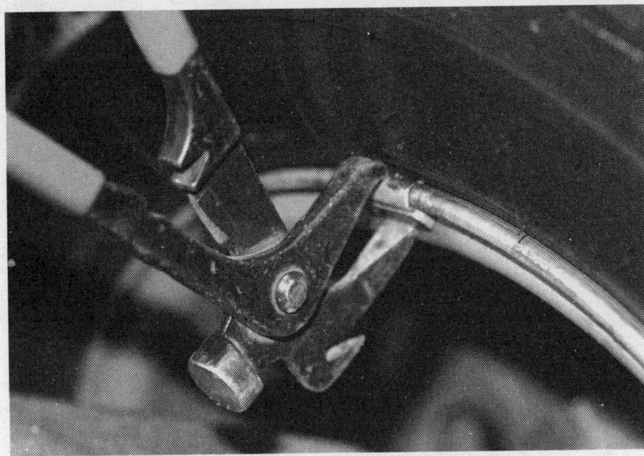

FIGURE 4-25 *Wheel weights are removed and installed with special wheel weight pliers.*

4. Enter the wheel diameter, width, and offset in the balancer computer.
5. Be sure the safety hood is lowered over the tire and wheel assembly, and activate the balancer control to spin the wheel and tire assembly.
6. Operate the balancer brake to slow and stop the wheel, and observe the balancer display screen to determine the size and location of wheel weight(s) required on the wheel rim.
7. Install the correct wheel weights in the locations indicated on the balancer screen. Use that hammer head on the wheel weight pliers to install the weights.
8. Spin the wheel again on the balancer; the balancer screen should indicate a balanced tire and wheel assembly.
9. Remove the wheel and tire assembly from the balancer, and install this assembly on the vehicle using the alignment marks placed on the tire wheel and hub stud prior to wheel removal.
10. Tighten the wheel lug nuts to the specified torque in the proper sequence.

On some pre-electronic wheel balancers, a static balance procedure is performed by allowing the wheel and tire assembly to rotate by gravity on the wheel balancer. A **heavy spot** in the tire rotates the tire and wheel assembly until the heavy spot is at the bottom. The necessary wheel balance weights were then added at the top of the wheel 180° from the heavy spot. Equal wheel weights were installed on each side of the wheel (Figure 4-26). If a wheel has dynamic unbalance, and the heavy spot is on the outside edge of the tire tread, the correct size of wheel weight is installed on the rim 180° from the heavy spot (Figure 4-27). Improper static or dynamic wheel balance causes cupped tire tread wear and bald spots on the tread (Figure 4-28). Incorrect static wheel balance results in wheel tramp, and improper dynamic wheel balance causes wheel shimmy. When using an electronic wheel

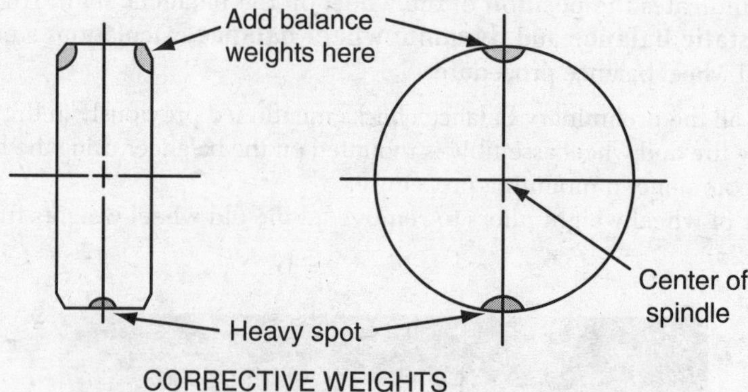

FIGURE 4-26 *Static wheel balance procedure.*

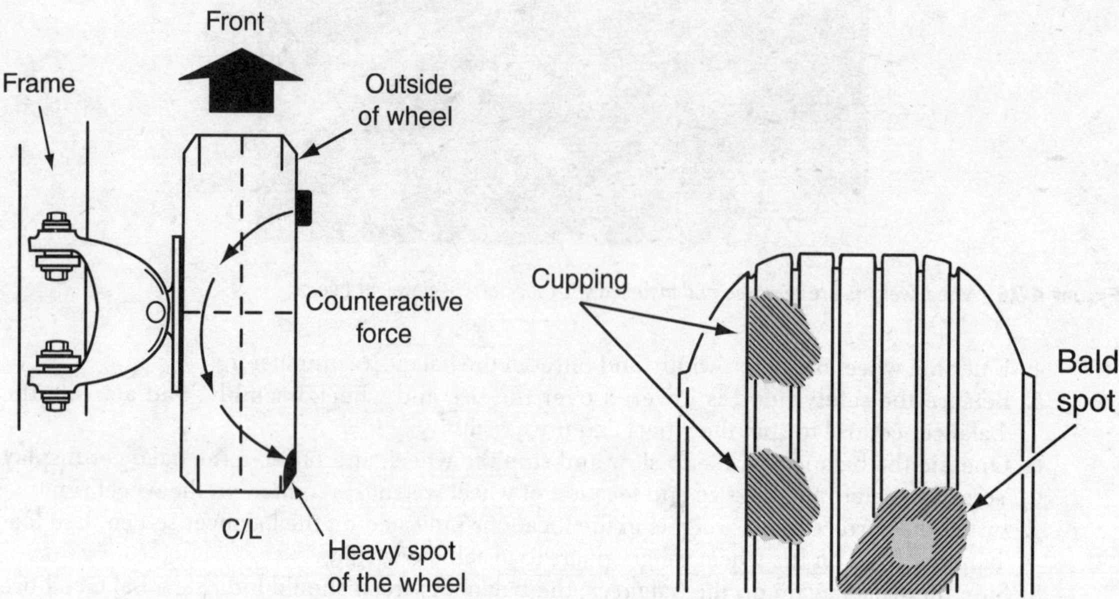

FIGURE 4-27 *Dynamic wheel balance procedure with heavy spot on the outside edge of the tread.*

FIGURE 4-28 *Cupped tire tread wear with bald spots on the tread caused by improper static or dynamic wheel balance.*

balancer, the technician does not have to determine the wheel weight size or location because the balancer provides this information to the technician.

ELECTRONIC WHEEL BALANCERS WITH LATERAL FORCE MEASUREMENT (LFM) AND RADIAL FORCE VARIATION CAPABILITIES

Improper wheel balance is only one cause of wheel vibration. Wheel vibration may also be caused by tire and/or wheel runout or stiffness variation in the tire sidewalls. Some wheel balancers now have the capability to measure wheel and tire runout and stiffness or force variation in the tire sidewalls. Tire and wheel rim runout may be measured with a dial indicator, but this operation is very time consuming. Many tires marketed today have a paint dot or mark on the sidewall that indicates either the high side or low side of the force variation in the tire. This paint dot is aligned with the valve stem when the tire is mounted on the wheel rim. Using this system, the technician is assuming the paint dot is placed at the high point of radial force, and the valve stem hole is at the low point of runout on the rim. However, this is not always true, and a tire mounted with this tire position in relation to the wheel rim may cause vibration even though it is properly balanced. Other tires may have a slight conicity problem that causes steering pull on the vehicle.

An electronic wheel balancer with radial force variation capabilities has a roller that is forced against the tire tread with considerable force during the balance procedure. This type of balancer provides wheel balance following the usual procedure. The roller forced against the tire allows the balancer to measure tire conicity that results in lateral force and steering pull (Figure 4-29). As each tire and wheel assembly is balanced, the balancer display indicates a number for each assembly (Figure 4-30). The balancer display also indicates the position on the vehicle where each numbered tire and wheel assembly should be installed to provide the least amount of steering pull and the best straight-ahead steering stability (Figure 4-31). The wheel balancer with LFM capabilities provides a much faster and more accurate method for diagnosing and correcting steering pull caused by tire conicity compared to the previous method of rotating tires to try and correct this problem.

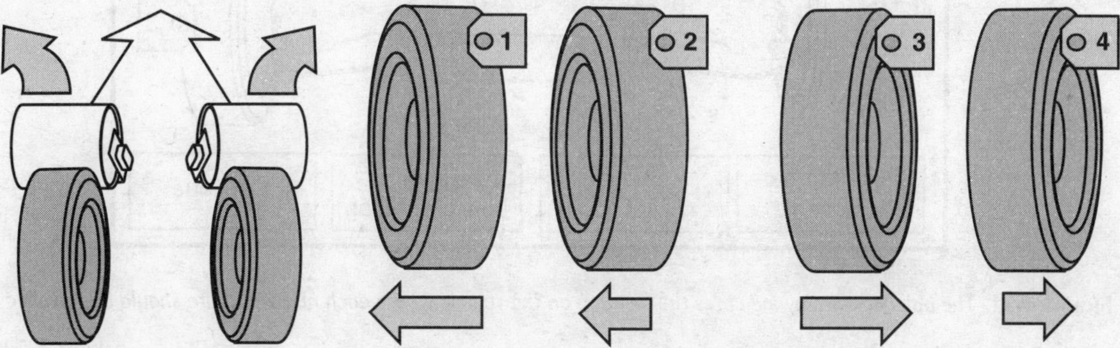

FIGURE 4-29 *Tire conicity sensed by the roller on the balancer causes lateral force and steering pull.*

FIGURE 4-30 *The balancer assigns a number to each tire and wheel assembly.*

The balancer also measures lateral and radial tire and wheel runout, and indicates if the runout is rim or tire related. This type of balancer also measures force variation in the tire (Figure 4-32). The balancer display indicates the amount of tire and tire and wheel assembly road force. The display also indicates the necessary tire and wheel service to correct the excessive road force. Using the balancer display, a chalk mark may be placed on the tire at the location of the high force variation, and a second chalk mark on the rim 180° away from the first chalk mark (Figure 4-33). The tire and wheel assembly may be installed on a tire changer, and the rim may be rotated in relation to the tire to correct the force variation.

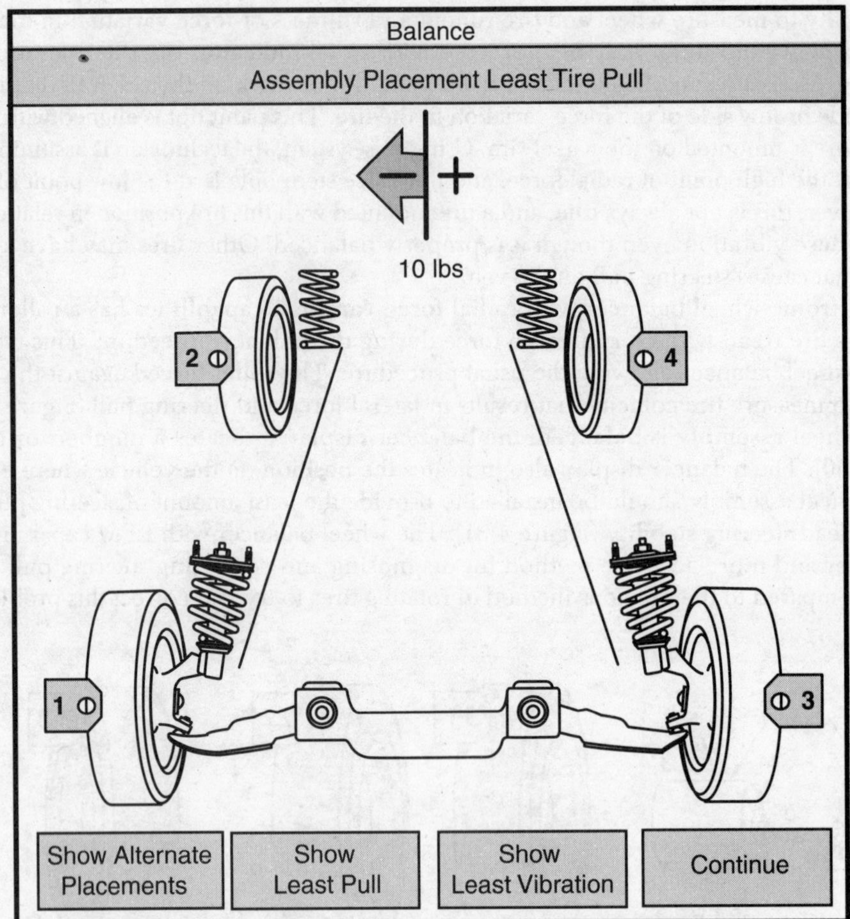

FIGURE 4-31 *The balancer display indicates the location on the vehicle where each numbered tire should be installed.*

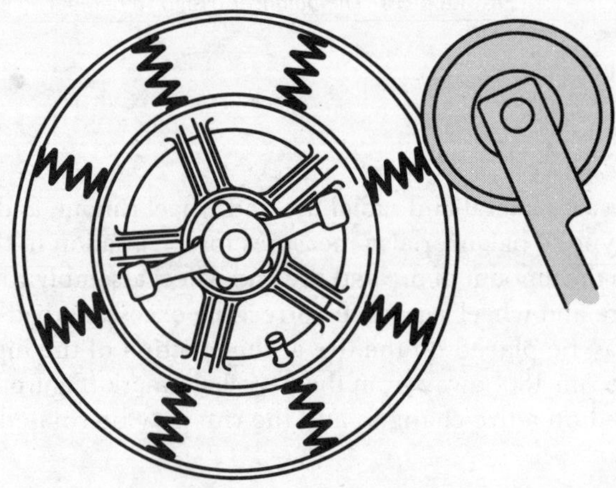

FIGURE 4-32 *The roller on the balancer senses force variation in the tire.*

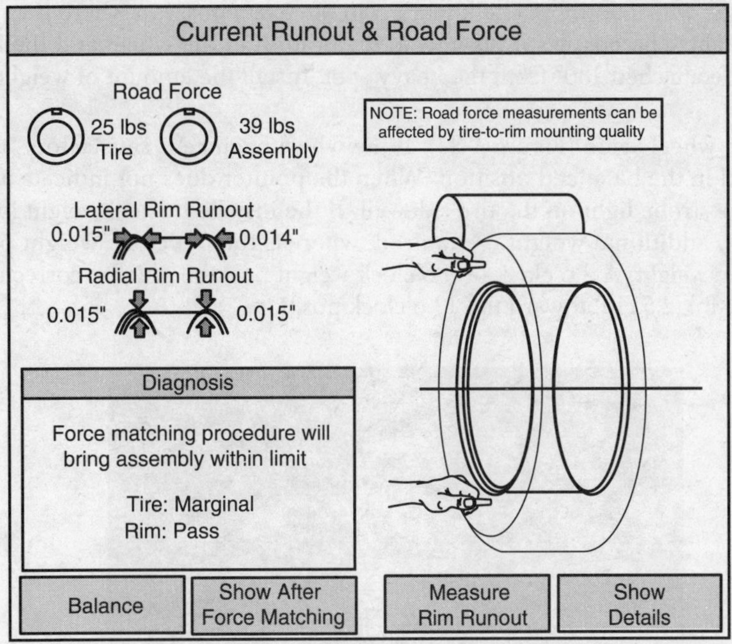

FIGURE 4-33 *The balancer display indicates the necessary correction for excessive force variation.*

ON-CAR WHEEL BALANCING

On-car wheel balancers contain a drum driven by an electric motor. This drum is positioned against the tire on the vehicle, which allows the electric motor to rotate the wheel. Many on-car balancers have a strobe light with a meter and an electronic vibration sensor. Off-car wheel balancing and on-car wheel balancing are a complementary combination for fine-tuning wheel balance. For example, a wheel vibration problem may still exist after an off-car balance procedure. If this problem occurs, the on-car balancer may be used to correct the problem. The on-car balance procedure corrects imbalance problems in all rotating components, including brake drums or rotors.

When a front wheel on a rear-wheel-drive car is balanced, use this procedure:

1. Perform the preliminary checks listed previously in this chapter.
2. Raise the wheel being balanced 5 in. (12 cm) off the floor and be sure the chassis is supported on safety stands so the wheel drops downward.
3. Install the electronic vibration sensor between the lower control arm and the floor.
4. Chalk mark a reference mark on the outer sidewall of the tire.
5. Spin the wheel just fast enough to produce vibration on the front bumper.
6. When vibration causes strobe light flashing, move the balancer drum away from the tire and allow the tire to spin freely.
7. Shine the strobe light around the tire sidewall and note the chalk-mark position.
8. Note the pointer position on the meter.
9. Use the balancer's brake plate to slow and stop the wheel.

10. Rotate the wheel until the chalk mark is in the exact position where it appeared under the strobe light. The heavy spot is now at the bottom of the wheel and the balancing weight should be attached 180° from the heavy spot. Install the amount of weight indicated on the meter.
11. Spin the wheel again (Figure 4-34). If the wheel balance is satisfactory, the meter pointer will read in the balanced position. When the pointer does not indicate a balanced wheel, shine the strobe light on the tire sidewall. If the installed wheel weight is at the 12 o'clock position, additional weight is required, whereas the 6 o'clock weight position indicates excessive weight. A 3 o'clock or 9 o'clock weight position may be corrected by moving the weight 1 in. (2.5 cm) toward the 12 o'clock position.

FIGURE 4-34 *On-car wheel balancer.*

Additional on-car wheel balancer precautions include:

1. Do not spin the wheel at excessive speeds.
2. Do not spin the front wheels on a front-wheel-drive vehicle with the floor jack under the chassis and the suspension dropped downward. Under this condition, severe angles exist in the front drive axle joints, and these joints may be damaged if the wheels are rotated with the balancer. Place the floor jack under the lower control arm to raise the wheel.

Rear Wheel Balancing

If an on-car balancer is used on the rear wheels of a rear-wheel-drive car, the technician must determine if the vehicle has a conventional or a limited slip differential. With the transmission in park, or in gear with a manual transmission, rotate one rear wheel by hand. If the vehicle has a limited slip differential, the rear wheels will not rotate, whereas a free-turning wheel indicates a conventional differential.

CAUTION: On a rear-wheel-drive vehicle when a rear wheel is rotated with an on-car balancer, do not allow the speed indicated on the speedometer to exceed 35 mph (56 km/h), because the wheel speed is much faster than the speed indicated on the speedometer.

When the vehicle has a conventional differential, use the same front wheel balance procedure on the rear wheels. Raise only the wheel to be balanced from the floor, and do not allow the speed indicated on the speedometer to exceed 35 mph (56 km/h). When the other rear tire is resting on the floor, the speed of the wheel being balanced is 70 mph (112 km/h).

If the vehicle has a limited slip differential, proceed as follows for on-car rear wheel balancing:

1. Raise the vehicle and place safety stands under the frame to support the vehicle weight.
2. Lift the rear axle housing with a floor jack to reduce the universal joint angles, but do not take the vehicle weight off the safety stands.
3. Remove the wheel that is not being balanced. Install and torque the wheel nuts on the brake drum to hold the drum in place.
4. Balance the opposite wheel using the same procedure as for the front wheels.
5. Leave the balanced wheel on the vehicle and install and balance the other wheel. Be sure to torque the wheel nuts properly. Do not allow rear wheel speed to exceed 55 mph (90 km/h) on the speedometer.

TABLE 4-1 *Tire and Wheel Diagnosis*

PROBLEM	SYMPTOMS	POSSIBLE CAUSES
Tire thump	Thumping noise while driving	Cupped tire treads Excessive radial tire or wheel runout Tire defects Improper wheel balance Variation in tire stiffness
Chassis waddling	Lateral rear chassis oscillations while driving	Excessive rear tire or wheel lateral runout
Steering pull	Steering pulls to one side while driving straight ahead	Tire conicity Unmatched tires side-to-side Improper wheel alignment angles
Wheel vibration	A vibration that occurs at certain speeds and may be felt on the steering wheel or throughout the chassis	Improper wheel balance Excessive lateral tire runout Variation in tire stiffness Tire defects
Excessive wear on tire treads	Cupped tire treads Wear on tread center Equal wear on tread edges	Improper wheel balance Overinflation Underinflation

CASE STUDY

A customer complains about severe front end waddling on a 2005 Cadillac STS equipped with steel-belted radial tires. The technician questions the customer further regarding this problem and learns that the problem occurs only after the car has sat overnight, and it lasts only for approximately six blocks when the customer starts driving the car.

The technician carefully checks all steering and suspension components, wheel bearing adjustment, and tire runout. No problems are found during these checks, and the technician asks the customer to leave the car in the shop overnight. The technician installs the front tires on the rear of the car and rotates the rear tires to the front, and the car is left in the shop overnight. A road test the next morning indicates rear end waddling, which proves the problem must be caused by a tire problem such as an improperly installed steel belt, since the tires were the only thing changed on the car. The technician installs and balances two new tires on the rear wheel rims, and installs these tires and wheels on the front of the car. The front tires and wheels were moved to the rear wheels. The customer reports later that the problem has been completely corrected.

SERVICE TIPS

- Tire noise varies with road surface conditions, whereas differential noise is not affected when various road surfaces are encountered.
- Tire conicity is not visible. It can be diagnosed only by changing the tire and wheel position.
- On some current vehicles, such as the 2004 Cadillac SRX, the front and rear tires have dissimilar widths. For example, if one of these cars has a V8 engine, the vehicle is equipped with 18 in. wheels, and the front tire size is P235/60R18 while the rear tire size is P255/55R18. These tires must not be rotated from front to rear, but they can be rotated from side-to-side.
- Some wheel covers have fake plastic lug nuts that must be removed to access the lug nuts. Be careful not to break the fake lug nuts.
- Some wheel rims such as magnesium rims require the use of stick-on wheel weights.
- Wheel weights are rated in ounces or grams.

REVIEW QUESTIONS

1. While discussing a tire thumping problem:
   Technician A says this problem may be caused by cupped tire treads. *Technician B* says a heavy spot in the tire may cause this complaint.
   Who is correct?
   A. A only **C.** Both A and B
   B. B only **D.** Neither A nor B

2. While discussing a vehicle that pulls to one side:
   Technician A says that excessive radial runout on the right front tire may cause this problem. *Technician B* says that tire conicity may be the cause of this complaint.
   Who is correct?
   A. A only **C.** Both A and B
   B. B only **D.** Neither A nor B

3. While discussing tire noise:
   Technician A says that tire noise varies with road surface conditions. *Technician B* says that tire noise remains constant when the vehicle is accelerated and decelerated.
   Who is correct?
   A. A only **C.** Both A and B
   B. B only **D.** Neither A nor B

4. While discussing tire wear:
   Technician A says that static imbalance causes feathered tread wear. *Technician B* says that dynamic imbalance causes cupped wear and bald spots on the tire tread.

Who is correct?

A. A only **C.** Both A and B
B. B only **D.** Neither A nor B

5. While discussing on-car wheel balancing:
Technician A says that during an on-car wheel balancing procedure on a rear wheel of a rear-wheel-drive car, the speed indicated on the speedometer should not exceed 65 mph (105 km/h). *Technician B* says that the speed indicated on the speedometer on this car must not exceed 35 mph (56 km/h).
Who is correct?
A. A only **C.** Both A and B
B. B only **D.** Neither A nor B

6. A front tire has excessive wear on both edges of the tire tread. The most likely cause of this problem is:
A. Overinflation.
B. Underinflation.
C. Improper static balance.
D. Improper dynamic balance.

7. When measuring radial tire and wheel runout, the maximum runout on most automotive tire-and-wheel assemblies should be:
A. 0.015 in. (0.038 mm). **C.** 0.045 in. (1.143 mm).
B. 0.025 in. (0.635 mm). **D.** 0.070 in. (1.77 mm).

8. When measuring lateral wheel runout with the tire demounted from the wheel, the maximum runout on most automotive wheels is:
A. 0.020 in. (0.508 mm). **C.** 0.045 in. (1.143 mm).
B. 0.030 in. (0.762 mm). **D.** 0.055 in. (1.397 mm).

9. All of these statements about improper wheel balance are true EXCEPT:
A. Dynamic imbalance may cause wheel shimmy.
B. Dynamic imbalance may cause steering pull in either direction.
C. Static imbalance causes wheel tramp.
D. Static imbalance causes rapid wear on suspension components.

10. When diagnosing wheel balance problems:
A. Balls of rubber inside the tire have no effect on wheel balance.
B. Loose wheel bearing adjustment may simulate improper static wheel balance.
C. Improper dynamic wheel balance may be caused by a heavy spot in the center of the tire tread.
D. After a tire patch is installed, the tire and wheel may be improperly balanced.

Challenge Questions

1. The owner of a rear-wheel-drive car with aftermarket alloy wheels says he has replaced the wheel bearings three times in the past two years. He wants to know why the bearings fail.
Technician A says excessive radial runout of the wheel may be the cause of the problem. *Technician B* says excessive offset of the wheel may be the cause of the problem.

Who is correct?

A. A only **C.** Both A and B

B. B only **D.** Neither A nor B

2. A customer returns with recently purchased radial tires saying that the rear of the car feels like "it's riding on Jello™." All of the following could cause this problem EXCEPT:
   A. The radial belt of a rear tire is not straight.
   B. The wheel is improperly mounted.
   C. Excessive lateral wheel runout.
   D. Excessive radial tire runout.

3. A customer says the new tires he just purchased vibrate. The installer says he balanced the wheels and tires with a conventional electronic balancer before placing them on the car. *Technician A* says one of the tires may have a conicity problem. *Technician B* says one of the tires may have a force variation problem.
   Who is correct?
   A. A only **C.** Both A and B
   B. B only **D.** Neither A nor B

4. After a set of radial tires is rotated, the customer returns saying he feels vibration and steering shimmy. To correct this problem, you should:
   A. Measure the lateral run out on each tire.
   B. Return the tires and wheels to their original positions.
   C. Check the wheel bearings.
   D. Balance the tires and wheels with an on-car balancer.

5. A customer says there is a "thumping" vibration in the wheels and an inspection of the tires shows the two front wheels have flat spots on the tire treads.
   Technician A says heavy spots in the tires may have caused this condition. *Technician B* says locking the wheels and skidding on pavement caused this condition.
   Who is correct?
   A. A only **C.** Both A and B
   B. B only **D.** Neither A nor B

JOB SHEET 10

Name ______________________________ Date ______________

TIRE DISMOUNTING AND MOUNTING

Upon completion of this job sheet, you should be able to demount and mount tires.

ASE Correlation

This job sheet is related to the ASE Suspension and Steering Task: Dismount and mount tire on wheel.

Tools and Materials

Tire changer

Tire-and-wheel assembly

Procedure

Task Completed ______

1. Remove the valve core to release all the air pressure from the tire. Chalk mark the tire at the valve stem opening in the wheel so the tire may be re-installed in the same position to maintain proper wheel balance.

Is all the air pressure released from the tire? ☐ Yes ☐ No

Is the tire chalk marked at the valve stem location in the wheel?

Instructor check ______________________________

SERVICE TIP: The following is a generic tire demounting and mounting procedure.

2. Position the tire and wheel on the tire changer with the narrow bead ledge facing upward. Follow the tire changer manufacturer's recommended procedure to attach the wheel to the tire changer.

Are the tire and wheel securely attached to the tire changer according to the tire changer manufacturer's recommended procedure? ☐ Yes ☐ No

Instructor check ______________________________

WARNING: Do not proceed to demount the tire unless the tire and wheel are securely attached to the tire changer. This action may cause personal injury.

3. Position the top bead breaker on the tire changer properly to loosen the top tire bead from the wheel. Is the top bead breaker properly positioned to loosen the top bead?
☐ Yes ☐ No

4. Operate the upper bead breaker on the tire changer to loosen the top tire bead. Is the top tire bead loosened from the wheel? ☐ Yes ☐ No

5. Position the lower bead breaker on the tire changer to loosen the lower bead from the wheel. Is the lower bead breaker properly positioned to loosen the lower bead?
☐ Yes ☐ No

6. Operate the lower bead breaker on the tire changer to loosen the lower tire bead from the wheel. Is the lower tire bead loosened from the wheel? ☐ Yes ☐ No

Instructor Response ______________________________

Task Completed

SERVICE TIP: Some tire changers rotate a bar or lever to move the tire beads over the wheel. Other tire changers rotate the tire and wheel to perform this function.

7. Push one part of the upper tire bead into the drop center in the wheel. Position the tire changer bar, lever, or tool under the opposite side of the upper bead from the part of the bead in the drop center of the wheel.

Is the tire changer bar, lever, or tool properly positioned to remove the upper tire bead over the top edge of the wheel? ☐ Yes ☐ No

8. Operate the tire changer bar, lever, or tool to remove the upper tire bead over the top edge of the wheel. Is the upper tire bead over the top edge of the wheel?
☐ Yes ☐ No

9. Push one part of the lower tire bead into the drop center in the wheel. Position the tire changer bar, lever, or tool under the opposite side of the lower bead from the part of the bead in the drop center of the wheel.

Is the tire changer bar, lever, or tool properly positioned to remove the lower tire bead over the top edge of the wheel? ☐ Yes ☐ No

10. Operate the tire changer bar, lever, or tool to remove the lower tire bead over the top of the wheel. Is the lower tire bead over the top edge of the wheel?
☐ Yes ☐ No

Instructor check ____________________

☐ **11.** Remove the tire from the wheel and remove the wheel from the tire changer.

12. Thoroughly clean the wheel-to-tire bead sealing surfaces with a wire brush. Inspect the wheel for rust or damage.

Wheel condition: ☐ Satisfactory ☐ Unsatisfactory

If the wheel condition is unsatisfactory, state the defective condition(s) and the necessary corrective action.

____

Wheel-to-tire bead sealing surfaces cleaned: ☐ Yes ☐ No

☐ **13.** Coat the tire beads with tire lubricant.

14. Position the wheel-on-the tire changer with the narrow bead ledge facing upward. Follow the tire changer manufacturer's recommended procedure to attach the wheel to the tire changer.

Is the wheel securely attached to the tire changer according to the tire changer manufacturer's recommended procedure? ☐ Yes ☐ No

Instructor check ____________________

WARNING: Do not proceed to mount the tire unless the wheel is securely attached to the tire changer. This action may cause personal injury.

15. Push one part of the lower tire bead into the drop center in the wheel. Position the tire changer bar, lever, or tool under the opposite side of the lower bead from the part of the bead in the drop center of the wheel.

Is the tire changer bar, lever, or tool properly positioned to install the lower tire bead over the top edge of the wheel? ☐ Yes ☐ No

Task Completed

16. Operate the tire changer bar, lever, or tool to install the lower tire bead over the top edge of the wheel. Is the lower tire bead over the top edge of the wheel?
☐ Yes ☐ No

17. Push one part of the upper tire bead into the drop center in the wheel. Position the tire changer bar, lever, or tool under the opposite side of the upper bead from the part of the bead in the drop center of the wheel.

Is the tire changer bar, lever, or tool properly positioned to install the upper tire bead over the top edge of the wheel? ☐ Yes ☐ No

18. Operate the tire changer bar, lever, or tool to install the upper tire bead over the top edge of the wheel. Is the upper tire bead over the top edge of the wheel?
☐ Yes ☐ No

Instructor check ______________________________

19. Rotate the tire on the wheel so the chalk mark placed on the tire in step 8 is aligned with the valve stem opening in the wheel.

Is the chalk mark on the tire aligned with the valve stem position?
☐ Yes ☐ No

Instructor check ______________________________

20. Install and tighten the valve core in the valve stem. ☐

SERVICE TIP: Different makes of tire changers have various ways of tire bead seating on the wheel. Some tire changers have an air inflation ring that is positioned on top of the wheel and tire. Other tire changers have air jets in each clamping jaw that hold the wheel on the tire changer. Air pressure from these jets helps force the tire beads against the wheel sealing surfaces.

SERVICE TIP: Some tire changers have an air hose and air pressure gauge designed into the tire changer. On other tire changers a shop air hose must be used to inflate the tire.

WARNING: When inflating a tire, do not stand or lean over the tire and wheel. If the tire bead comes off the rim or the rim cracks, personal injury may occur. When using a shop air hose to inflate the tire, install an extension on the air hose.

21. Supply air to the air ring or air jets on the tire changer to move the tire beads outward against the wheel. Are the tire beads moved outward against the wheel?
☐ Yes ☐ No

Instructor check ______________________________

22. Connect an air supply hose to the tire valve stem. When using a shop air hose, connect an extension to the air hose. Inflate the tire to the specified pressure.

Specified tire pressure ______________________________

Actual tire pressure ______________________________

Instructor's Response ______________________________

____

____

JOB SHEET 11

Name ______________________________ Date ______________

TIRE AND WHEEL RUNOUT MEASUREMENT

Upon completion of this job sheet, you should be able to measure radial and lateral tire and wheel runout.

ASE Correlation

This job sheet is related to the ASE Suspension and Steering Task: Measure wheel, tire, axle flange, and hub runout (radial and lateral); determine needed repairs.

Tools and Materials

Dial indicator
Wheel balancer
Tire-and-wheel assembly

Wheel diameter ______________________________
Manufacturer and type of tire ______________________________

Procedure

Task Completed

SERVICE TIP: The tire and wheel may be installed on an off-car wheel balancer to measure tire and wheel runout.

1. Mount the tire-and-wheel assembly properly on the wheel balancer and position a dial indicator against the center of the tire tread as the tire is rotated slowly to measure radial runout.

Radial runout ____________

Specified radial runout ____________

2. Mark the highest point of radial runout on the tire with chalk, and mark the valve stem position on the tire. ☐

3. If the radial tire runout is excessive, demount the tire, and check the runout of the wheel rim with a dial indicator positioned against the lip of the rim while the rim is rotated.

Wheel radial runout ____________

Specified wheel radial runout ____________

4. Use chalk to mark the highest point of radial runout on the wheel rim. ☐

5. If the highest point of wheel radial runout coincides with the chalk mark from the highest point of maximum tire radial runout, the tire may be rotated 180° on the wheel to reduce radial runout. Tires or wheels with excessive runout are usually replaced.

Does the highest point of tire radial runout coincide with the highest point of wheel radial runout? ☐ Yes ☐ No

Instructor Response ______________________________

Task Completed

State the required action to correct excessive radial runout and the reason for this action.

____

____

6. Position a dial indicator located against the sidewall of the tire to measure lateral runout.

   Tire lateral runout ______________

   Specified tire lateral runout ______________

☐ 7. Chalk mark the tire and wheel at the highest point of lateral runout.

☐ 8. If the tire runout is excessive, the tire should be demounted from the wheel and the wheel lateral runout measured.

9. If the tire runout was excessive, measure the wheel lateral runout with a dial indicator positioned against the edge of the wheel as the wheel is rotated.

   Wheel lateral runout ______________

   Specified wheel lateral runout ______________

   State the required action to correct excessive wheel lateral runout and the reason for this action. ______________________________

   ____

Instructor's Response ______________________________

____

____

JOB SHEET 12

Name ______________________________ Date ______________

OFF-CAR WHEEL BALANCING

Upon completion of this job sheet, you should be able to perform off-car wheel balancing procedures.

ASE Correlation

This job sheet is related to the ASE Suspension and Steering Task: Balance tire-and-wheel assembly (static and/or dynamic).

Tools and Materials

Electronic off-car wheel balancer
Wheel weights
Tire and wheel

Wheel diameter ______________________________

Manufacturer and type of tire ______________________________

Describe the Vehicle Being Worked On:

Year __________ Make ______________ Model ______________
VIN ______________ Engine type and size ______________

Procedure

Task Completed

1. Wash mud and debris from the tire and wheel. ☐
2. Mount the tire-and-wheel assembly on the wheel balancer with the wheel balancer manufacturer's recommended mounting components.
3. Tighten the tire and wheel retaining nut on the wheel balancer to the specified torque.

   Tire and wheel retaining nut on the wheel balancer tightened to the specified torque?
   ☐ Yes ☐ No

   Instructor check ______________________________
4. Remove stones and other objects from the tire tread.

   Are stones and other objects removed from the tire tread? ☐ Yes ☐ No

   Instructor check ______________________________
5. Check for objects inside tire.

   Are there objects inside the tire? ☐ Yes ☐ No

   Instructor check ______________________________
6. Remove all the old wheel weights from the wheel.

   Are the old wheel weights removed? ☐ Yes ☐ No

   Instructor check ______________________________

Task Completed

7. Inspect the tread and sidewall.

List defective tread and sidewall conditions. ______________________________

____

List the types of tire tread wear and state the causes of this wear.

____

____

Based on your inspection of the tire, list the required tire service.

____

____

8. Check tire inflation pressure.

Tire inflation pressure ____________

Specified tire inflation pressure ____________

9. Measure tire and wheel runout.

Radial tire and wheel runout ____________

Specified tire and wheel radial runout ____________

Lateral tire and wheel runout ____________

Specified lateral tire and lateral wheel runout ____________

Recommended tire and wheel service. ______________________________

____

10. Lower the safety hood on the wheel balancer.

Is the safety hood lowered? ☐ Yes ☐ No

11. Enter the required information on wheel balancer keypad, such as wheel diameter, wheel width, and wheel offset or distance.

Is the required wheel information entered in the wheel balancer? ☐ Yes ☐ No

Instructor check ______________________________

12. If the wheel balancer has a mode selector, select the desired balance mode.

Balance mode selected ____________

13. Spin the wheel on the balancer, then apply the balancer brake to stop the wheel.

☐ **14.** Observe the balancer display indicating the necessary amount of wheel weights and the required location of these weights. Install the required wheel weights in the locations indicated on the balancer. Be sure the wheel weights are securely attached to the rim.

Are the wheel weight(s) securely attached to the rim at the locations indicated by the wheel balancer? ☐ Yes ☐ No

Instructor check ______________________________

15. Spin the tire-and-wheel assembly on the the balancer again to be sure this assembly is properly balanced.

Does the wheel balancer indicate proper wheel balance? ☐ Yes ☐ No

If the answer to this question is no, repeat the balance procedure.

Instructor's Response ______________________________

____

JOB SHEET 13

Name ______________________________ Date ______________

ON-CAR WHEEL BALANCING

Upon completion of this job sheet, you should be able to perform on-car wheel balancing procedures.

ASE Correlation

This job sheet is related to the ASE Suspension and Steering Task: Balance tire-and-wheel assembly (static and/or dynamic).

Tools and Materials

On-car wheel balancer
Car
Wheel weights

Describe the Vehicle Being Worked On:

Year __________ Make ______________ Model ______________
VIN ____________________ Engine type and size ______________

Procedure

Task Completed

1. Wash mud and debris from the wheel and tire. ☐
2. Raise the wheel being balanced 5 in (12 cm) off the floor; be sure the chassis is securely supported on safety stands. ☐

CAUTION: Do not spin the front wheels on a front-wheel-drive vehicle with the floor jack under the chassis and the suspension dropped downward. Under this condition, severe angles exist in the front drive axle joints, and these joints may be damaged if the wheels are rotated with the balancer. Place the floor jack under the lower control arm to raise the wheel.

3. Remove stones and other objects from the tire tread.

   Are all objects removed from the tire tread? ☐ Yes ☐ No

   Instructor check ______________________________

4. Inspect the tire tread and sidewall condition.

   Tread and sidewall condition ______________________________

   ____

   Types of tire tread wear ______________________________

   ____

   Causes of tire tread wear ______________________________

   ____

   Based on your inspection of the tire tread and sidewall, state the necessary tire service.

____

____

5. Check the wheel bearing adjustment and adjust to specifications if necessary.

Wheel bearing adjustment: ☐ Satisfactory ☐ Unsatisfactory

6. Install the electronic vibration sensor between the lower control arm and the floor.

Is the vibration sensor properly installed? ☐ Yes ☐ No

Instructor check ______________________________

7. Chalk mark a reference mark on the outer sidewall of the tire.

> **CAUTION:** To obtain proper wheel balance, spin the wheel only to the speed where the vibration occurs. Do not spin the wheel at excessive speeds.

8. Spin the wheel just fast enough to produce vibration on the front bumper.

9. When vibration causes strobe light flashing, move the balancer drum away from the tire and allow the tire to spin freely.

10. Shine the strobe light around the tire sidewall and note the chalk-mark position.

Chalk-mark clock position ______________________________

11. Note the pointer position on the meter.

Meter pointer position ______________________________

12. Use the balancer's brake plate to slow and stop the wheel.

13. Rotate the wheel until the chalk mark is in the exact position where it appeared under the strobe light. The heavy spot is now at the bottom of the wheel and the balancing weight should be attached 180° from the heavy spot. Install the amount of weight indicated on the meter.

Amount of wheel weight installed ______________________________

14. Spin the wheel again. If the wheel balance is satisfactory, the meter pointer will read in the balanced position. If the pointer does not indicate a balanced wheel, shine the strobe light on the tire sidewall. If the installed wheel weight is at the 12 o'clock position, additional weight is required. A 6 o'clock weight position indicates excessive weight. A 3 o'clock or 9 o'clock weight position may be corrected by moving the weight 1 in (2.5 cm) toward the 12 o'clock position.

Tire and Wheel balance: ☐ Satisfactory ☐ Unsatisfactory

If the wheel balance is unsatisfactory, state the action required to balance tire and wheel.

____

____

Instructor's Response ______________________________

____

____

JOB SHEET 14

Name ____ Date ____________________

DIAGNOSE TIRE AND WHEEL VIBRATION, STEERING PULL, AND CHASSIS WADDLE

Upon completion of this job sheet, you should be able to diagnose tire and wheel vibration problems, steering pull, and chassis waddle.

ASE Correlation

This job sheet is related to the ASE Suspension and Steering Task: Diagnose wheel/tire vibration, shimmy, and noise problems; determine needed repairs. Diagnose tire pull (lead) problems; determine corrective actions.

Tools and Materials

Late model vehicle

Describe the Vehicle Being Worked On:

Year ____________ Make ______________________ Model ____________________
VIN ______________________ Engine type and size ______________________

Procedure

1. Drive the vehicle at 10 mph (16 kmh), 20 mph (32 kmh), 30 mph (48 kmh), 40 mph (64 kmh), 50 mph (80 kmh), 60 mph (96.5 kmh). Maintain each vehicle speed long enough to diagnose tire, steering, and chassis problems. Do not exceed the legal speed limit. Did the vehicle indicate any of the following problems at these various speeds?
2. Chassis waddle. Speed at which waddle occurred __________.

   Did the waddle occur at the front or the rear of the vehicle? __________

   List the possible causes of waddle and the neccessary diagnostic steps and service procedures to correct the problem.

   ____

   ____

   ____

3. Tire thump and vibration. Speed at which tire thump or vibration occurred __________. At which corner of the vehicle did the thump and vibration occur. __________

   List the possible causes of tire thump and vibration and the necessary diagnostic steps and service procedures to correct the problem.

   ____

   ____

   ____

4. Wheel shimmy. Speed at which wheel shimmy occurred. __________

List the possible cause of wheel shimmy, and the necessary diagnostic steps and service procedures to correct the problem.

____

____

____

5. Steering pull. Speed at which steering pull occurred. __________

Direction of steering pull. __________

List the possible causes of steering pull, and the necessary diagnostic steps and service procedures to correct the problem.

____

____

____

Instructor's Response ____

____

____

SHOCK ABSORBER AND STRUT DIAGNOSIS AND SERVICE

5

Upon completion and review of this chapter, you should be able to:

- Perform a visual shock absorber inspection.
- Perform a shock absorber bounce test, and determine shock absorber condition.
- Determine shock absorber condition from a manual shock absorber test.
- Remove and replace shock absorbers.
- Diagnose shock absorber and strut noise complaints.
- Remove and replace front and rear struts.
- Remove struts from coil springs.
- Install coil springs on struts.
- Follow the vehicle manufacturer's recommended strut disposal procedure.
- Perform off-car strut cartridge replacement procedures.
- Perform on-car strut cartridge replacement procedures.
- Diagnose electrically controlled shock absorbers.

Shock absorbers and struts must be in good condition to provide satisfactory ride quality and maintain vehicle safety. Worn-out shock absorbers and struts may cause excessive chassis oscillations and harsh ride quality with resulting passenger discomfort. On a severely rough road surface, the chassis oscillations caused by worn-out shock absorbers and struts may contribute to a loss of steering control, resulting in a vehicle collision. Therefore, technicians must be familiar with shock absorber and strut diagnosis and service procedures.

SHOCK ABSORBER VISUAL INSPECTION

Bolt Mounting

Shock absorbers should be inspected for loose mounting bolts and worn mounting bushings. If these components are loose, rattling noise is evident, and replacement of the bushings and bolts is necessary.

Bushing Condition

In some shock absorbers, the bushing is permanently mounted in the shock, and the complete unit must be replaced if the bushing is worn. When the mounting bushings are worn, the shock absorber will not provide proper spring control.

Oil Leakage

Shock absorbers and **struts** should be inspected for oil leakage. A slight oil film on the lower oil chamber is acceptable. Any indication of oil dripping is not acceptable, and unit replacement is necessary (Figure 5-1).

Shock absorbers and struts should be inspected visually for physical damage, such as a bent condition and severe dents or punctures. When any of these conditions are present, unit replacement is required (Figure 5-2).

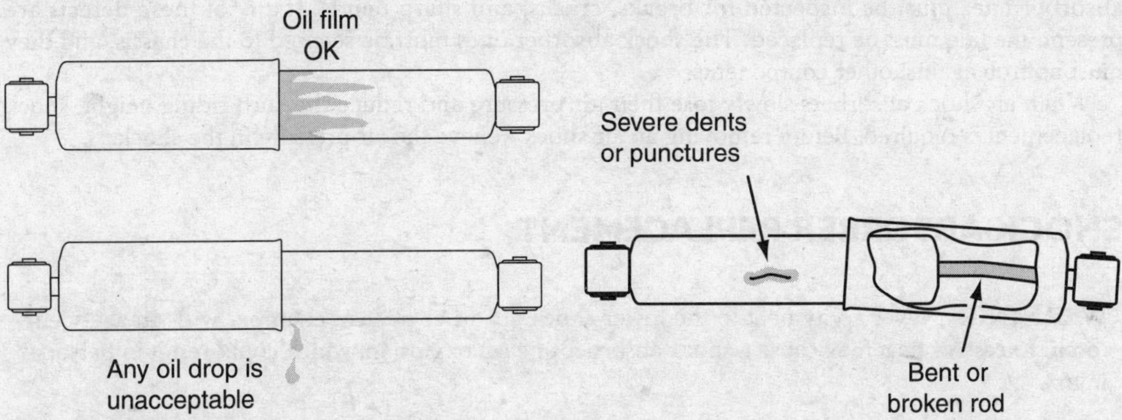

FIGURE 5-1 *Shock absorber and strut oil leak diagnosis.*

FIGURE 5-2 *Damaged shock absorber inspection.*

SHOCK ABSORBER OR STRUT BOUNCE TEST

When the **bounce test** is performed, the bumper is pushed downward with considerable weight applied on each corner of the vehicle. The bumper is released after this action, and one free upward bounce should stop the vertical chassis movement if the shock absorber or strut provides proper spring control. Shock absorber replacement is required if more than one free upward bounce occurs.

SHOCK ABSORBER MANUAL TEST

CAUTION: Gas-filled shock absorbers will extend when disconnected.

A **manual test** may be performed on shock absorbers. When this test is performed, disconnect the lower end of the shock, and move the shock up and down as rapidly as possible. A satisfactory shock absorber should offer a strong, steady resistance to movement on the entire compression and rebound strokes. The amount of resistance may be different on the compression stroke compared with the rebound stroke. If a loss of resistance is experienced during either stroke, shock replacement is essential.

Some defective shock absorbers or struts may have internal clunking, clicking, and squawking noises, or binding conditions. When these shock absorber noises or conditions are experienced, shock absorber or strut replacement is necessary.

AIR SHOCK ABSORBER DIAGNOSIS AND REPLACEMENT

Air shock absorbers are similar to conventional shocks except they have air pressure applied to them to control chassis curb height. Some air shock absorbers must be pressurized with the shop air hose. This type of unit contains a valve for inflation purposes. Other air shock absorbers are inflated by an onboard compressor with interconnecting plastic lines between the compressor and the shocks. Shock absorber lines must be inspected for breaks, cracks, and sharp bends. If any of these defects are present, the line must be replaced. The shock absorber lines must be secured to the chassis, and they must not rub against other components.

When air shock absorbers slowly lose their air pressure and reduce the curb riding height, shock replacement is required. Before removing an air shock, relieve the air pressure in the shock.

SHOCK ABSORBER REPLACEMENT

WARNING: Never apply heat to the lower shock absorber or strut chamber with an acetylene torch. Excessive heat may cause a shock absorber or strut explosion, which could result in personal injury.

When shock absorber replacement is necessary, follow this procedure:

1. Before replacing rear shock absorbers, lift the vehicle on a hoist and support the rear axle on safety stands so the shock absorbers are not fully extended.
2. When a front shock absorber must be changed, lift the front end on the vehicle with a floor jack, then place safety stands under the lower control arms. Lower the vehicle onto the safety stands and remove the floor jack.

3. Disconnect the upper shock mounting nut and grommet.
4. Remove the lower shock mounting nut or bolts, and remove the shock absorber.
5. Reverse steps 1 through 4 to install the new shock absorber and grommets.
6. With the full vehicle weight supported on the suspension, tighten the shock mounting nuts to the specified torque.

DIAGNOSIS OF FRONT SPRING AND STRUT NOISE

Strut chatter may be heard when the steering wheel is turned with the vehicle not moving or moving at low speed. To verify the location of this chattering noise, place one hand on a front coil spring while someone turns the steering wheel. If strut chatter is present, the spring binds and releases as it turns. This condition is caused by the upper spring seat binding against the strut bearing mount. A revised spring seat is available to correct this problem on some models.

A noise that occurs on sharp turns or during front suspension jounce may be caused by one of the following problems:

1. Interference between the upper strut rebound stop and the upper mount or **strut tower**
2. Interference between the coil spring and tower (Figure 5-3)
3. Interference between the coil spring and the upper mount (Figure 5-4)

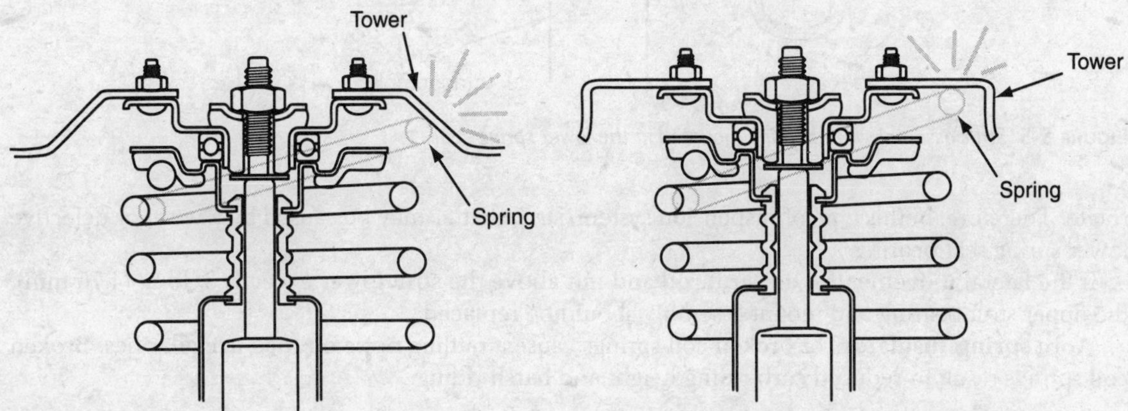

FIGURE 5-3 *Coil spring to upper strut tower interference.*

FIGURE 5-4 *Coil spring to upper mount interference.*

On some models, these coil spring interference problems may be corrected by installing upper coil spring spacers on top of the coil spring. Spring removal from the strut is required to install these spacers.

On many front suspension systems the strut is bolted to the upper end of the knuckle. When the front wheels are turned, the strut and coil spring rotate together and pivot on the upper strut mount bearing. In this type of suspension, a defective upper strut mount may cause strut chatter and noise.

On other front suspension systems, the strut extends downward and the lower ball joint retains the lower end of the strut to the lower control arm (Figure 5-5). The front hub is bolted to a flange on the knuckle. A bearing assembly is mounted in the lower spring seat. When the front wheels are turned, the strut rotates on the bearing in the lower spring seat, but the spring and upper strut mount do not

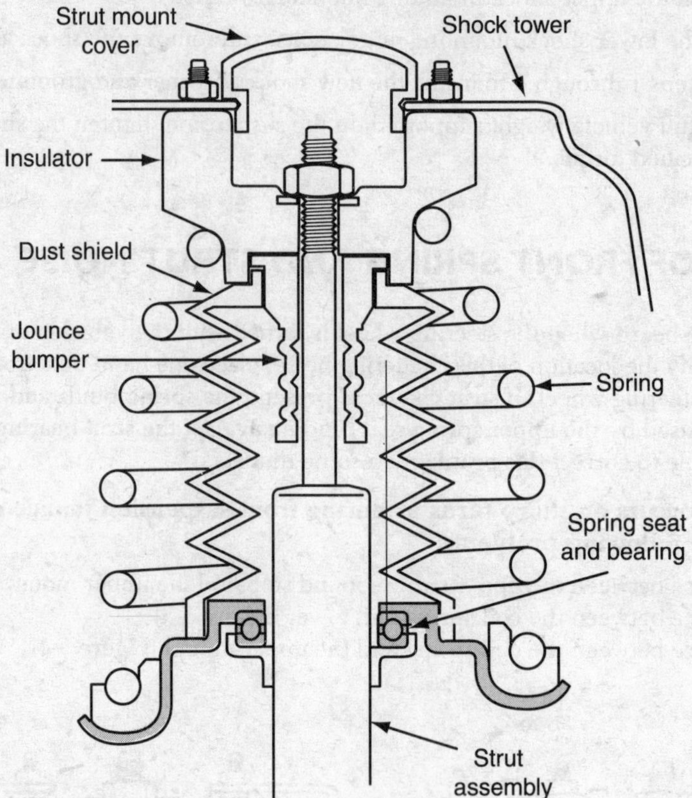

FIGURE 5-5 *Strut assembly with bearing mounted in the lower spring seat.*

rotate. Therefore, in this type of suspension system, strut chatter may be caused by a worn or defective lower spring seat bearing.

If the lateral movement of the strut rod and nut above the strut tower exceeds 3/16 in (4.76 mm), the upper strut bearing and mount assembly should be replaced.

Worn **spring insulators** or broken coil springs cause a rattling noise on road irregularities. Broken coil springs result in reduced curb riding height and harsh riding.

STRUT REMOVAL AND REPLACEMENT

Before a front strut-and-spring assembly is removed, the strut must be removed from the steering knuckle, and the top strut mount bolts must be removed from the strut tower. If an **eccentric camber bolt** is used to attach the strut to the knuckle, always mark the bolt head in relation to the strut and reinstall the bolt in the same position (Figure 5-6).

Always follow the vehicle manufacturer's recommended procedure in the service manual for removal of the strut-and-spring assembly.

A typical procedure for strut-and-spring assembly removal follows:

1. Raise the vehicle on a hoist or floor jack. If a floor jack is used to raise the vehicle, lower the vehicle onto safety stands placed under the chassis so the lower control arms and front wheels drop downward. Remove the floor jack from under the vehicle.

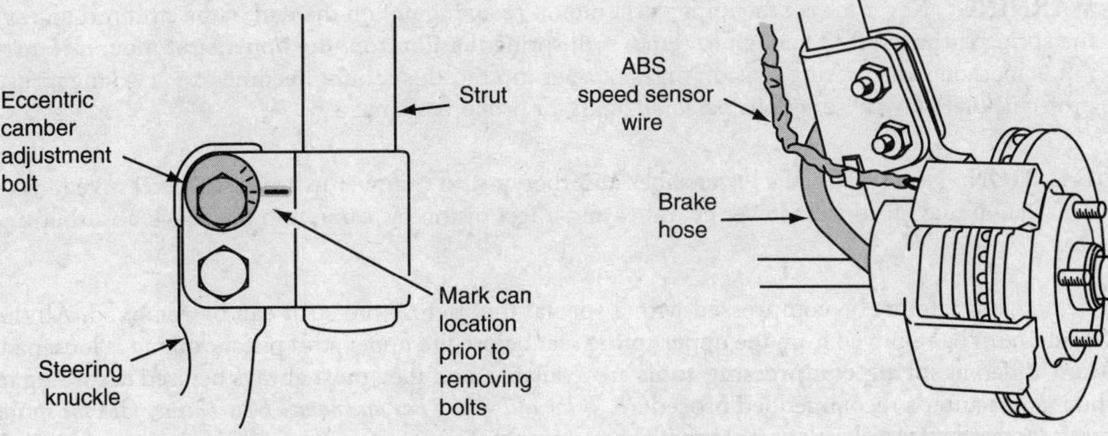

FIGURE 5-6 *Camber bolt marking for strut removal.*

FIGURE 5-7 *Brake line and ABS wheel-speed sensor wire removed from the strut.*

2. Remove the brake line and antilock brake system (ABS) wheel-speed sensor wire from clamps on the strut (Figure 5-7). In some cases, the clamps may also have to be removed from the strut.
3. Remove the strut-to-steering knuckle retaining bolts, and remove the strut from the knuckle (Figure 5-8).
4. Remove the upper strut mounting bolts on top of the strut tower, and remove the strut-and-spring assembly (Figure 5-9).

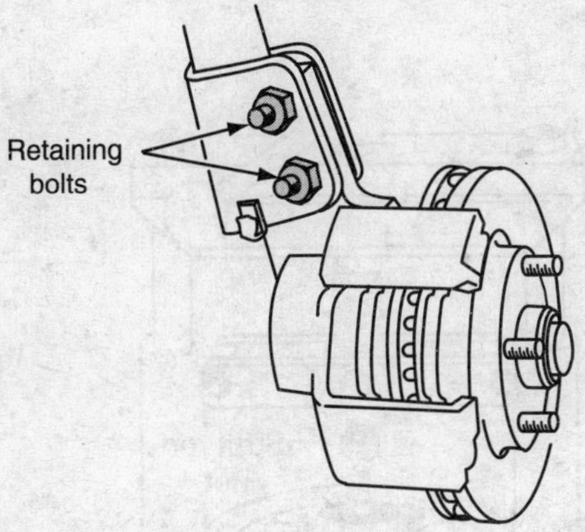

FIGURE 5-8 *Removing strut-to-steering knuckle retaining bolts.*

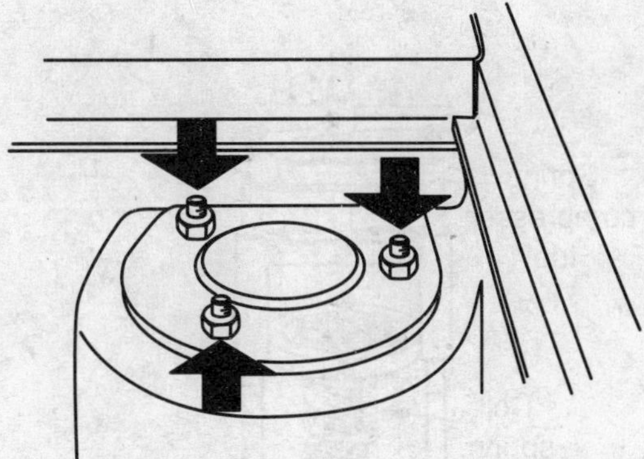

FIGURE 5-9 *Removing upper strut mounting bolts on top of strut tower.*

REMOVAL OF STRUT FROM COIL SPRING

WARNING: Always use a coil spring compressing tool according to the tool or vehicle manufacturer's recommended service procedure. Be sure the tool is properly installed on the spring. If a coil spring slips off the tool when the spring is compressed, severe personal injury or property damage may occur.

WARNING: Never loosen the upper strut mount retaining nut on the end of the strut rod unless the spring is compressed enough to remove all spring tension from the upper strut mount. If this nut is loosened with spring tension on the upper mount, this mount becomes a very dangerous projectile that may cause serious personal injury or property damage.

CAUTION: Never clamp the lower shock absorber or strut chamber in a vise with excessive force. This action may distort the lower chamber and affect piston movement in the shock absorber or strut.

The coil spring must be compressed with a special tool before the strut can be removed. All the tension must be removed from the upper spring seat before the upper strut piston rod nut is loosened. Many different **spring compressing tools** are available, and they must always be used according to the manufacturer's recommended procedure. *If the coil spring has an enamel-type coating, tape the spring where the compressing tool contacts the spring.* The spring may break prematurely if this coating is chipped.

A typical procedure for removing a strut from a coil spring follows:

1. Install the coil spring and strut assembly in the spring compressing tool according to the tool or vehicle manufacturer's recommended procedure.
2. Adjust the compressing arms on the spring compressing tool so the arms contact the coils farthest away from the center of the spring (Figure 5-10).
3. Turn the handle on top of the compressing tool until all the spring tension is removed from the upper strut mount (Figure 5-10).
4. Loosen and remove the nut on the upper strut rod (Figure 5-11). Be sure all the spring tension is removed from the upper strut mount before loosening this nut.
5. Remove the upper strut mount assembly and mount bearing, and then remove the upper spring seat and insulator (Figure 5-12).

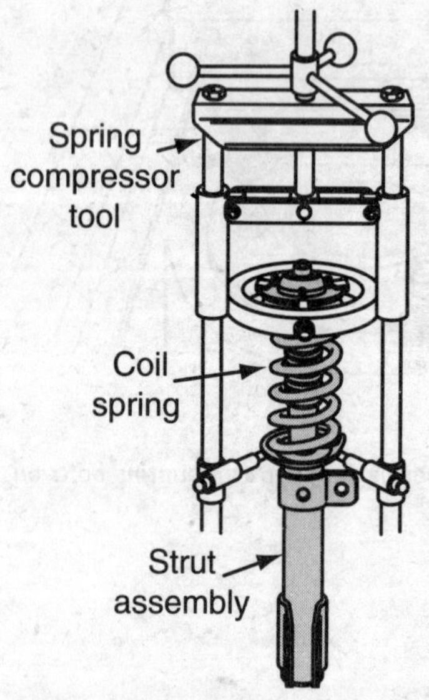

FIGURE 5-10 *Coil spring and strut assembly mounted in a spring compressing tool.*

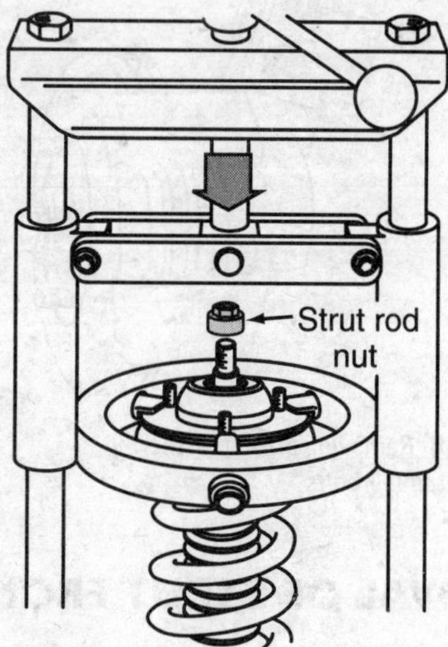

FIGURE 5-11 *After the compressing tool is operated to remove all the spring tension, remove the strut rod nut.*

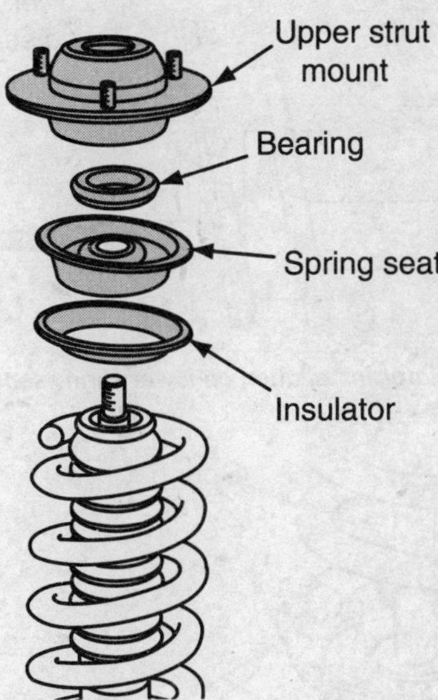

FIGURE 5-12 *Removal of the upper strut mount, bearing, upper spring seat, and insulator.*

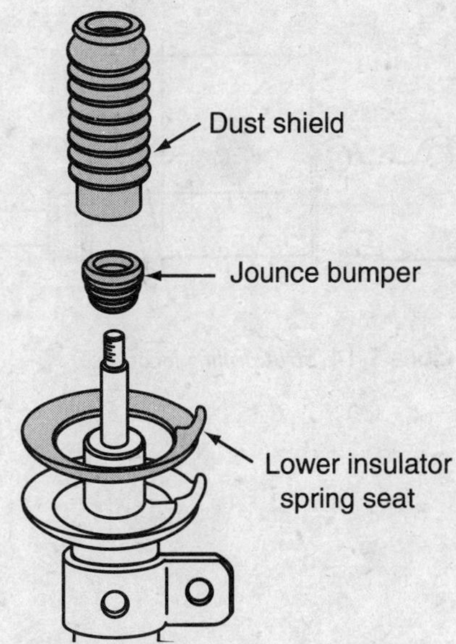

FIGURE 5-13 *Removal of the dust shield, jounce bumper, and lower spring insulator.*

6. Rotate the handle on the spring compressing tool to release all the tension on the coil spring, and then remove the spring.
7. Remove the dust shield and jounce bumper from the strut rod, and then remove the lower spring insulator (Figure 5-13).

STRUT DISPOSAL PROCEDURE

WARNING: Always follow the vehicle manufacturer's recommended procedure for strut disposal. Do not throw gas-filled shock absorbers or struts in a fire of any kind or in a dumpster. If the vehicle manufacturer recommends drilling the strut to release the gas charge, drill the strut at the manufacturer's recommended location.

The following is a typical strut drilling procedure that is performed prior to strut disposal:

1. Fully extend the strut rod.
2. Center punch the strut at the manufacturer's recommended drilling location (Figure 5-14).
3. Drill a small hole at the center-punched position.

INSTALLATION OF COIL SPRING ON STRUT

A typical procedure for installing a coil spring on a strut follows:

1. Install the lower insulator on the lower strut spring seat, and be sure the insulator is properly seated (Figure 5-15).
2. Install the spring bumper on the strut rod (Figure 5-16).

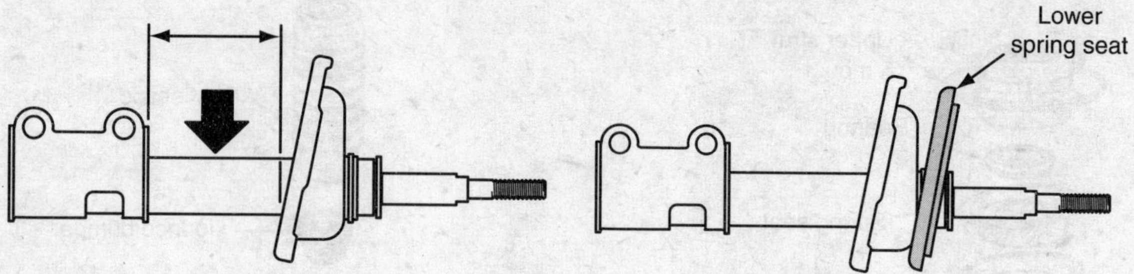

FIGURE 5-14 *Strut drilling location.*

FIGURE 5-15 *Insulator installation on lower spring seat.*

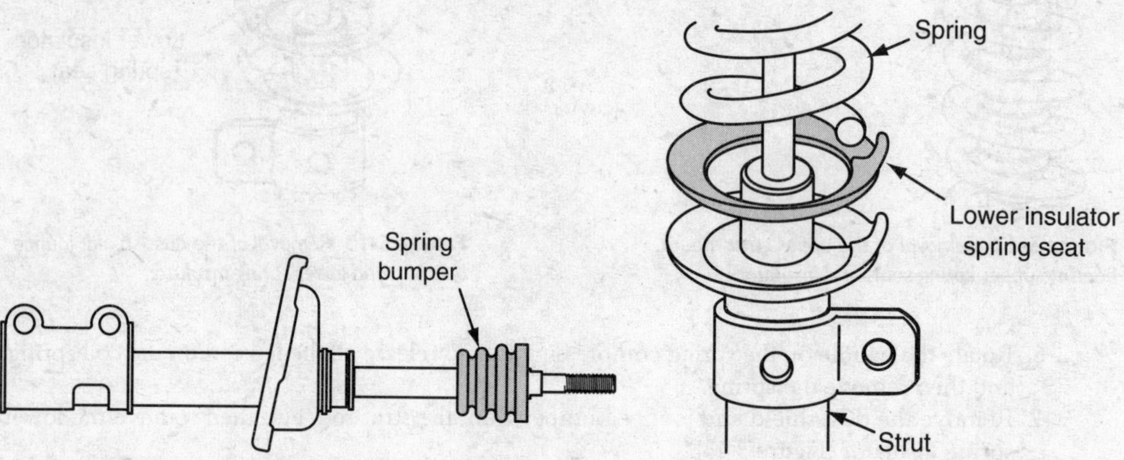

FIGURE 5-16 *Spring bumper installation on strut piston rod.*

FIGURE 5-17 *Installing strut in coil spring with proper lower spring seat alignment.*

3. With the coil spring compressed in the spring compressing tool, install the strut in the spring (Figure 5-17). Be sure the spring is properly seated on the lower insulator spring seat.
4. Be sure the strut piston rod is fully extended and install the upper insulator on top of the coil spring.
5. Install the upper strut mount on the upper insulator (Figure 5-18).
6. Be sure the spring, upper insulator, and upper strut mount are properly positioned and seated on the coil spring and strut piston rod (Figure 5-19).
7. Install the strut rod nut, and tighten this nut to the specified torque (Figure 5-20).
8. Rotate the upper strut mount until the lowest bolt in this mount is aligned with the tab on the lower spring seat (Figure 5-21).
9. Gradually loosen the handle on the compressing tool until all the spring tension is released from the tool, and remove the strut and spring assembly from the tool.

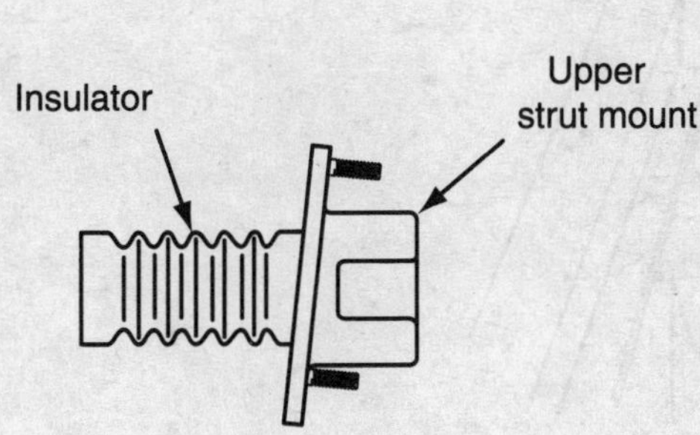

FIGURE 5-18 *Upper insulator and upper strut mount installed on coil spring.*

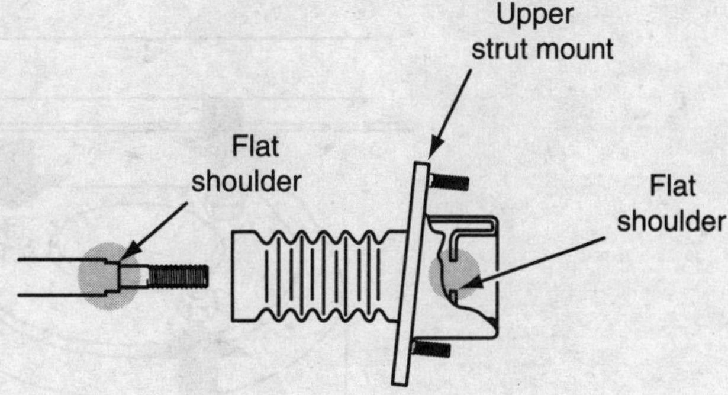

FIGURE 5-19 *Upper strut mount properly positioned on strut piston rod.*

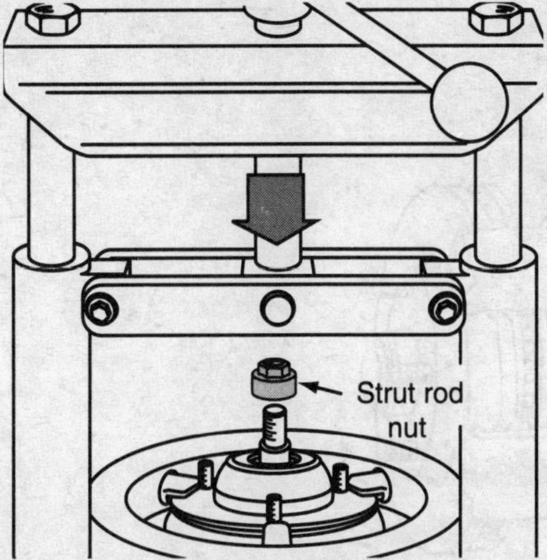

FIGURE 5-20 *Installing strut rod nut.*

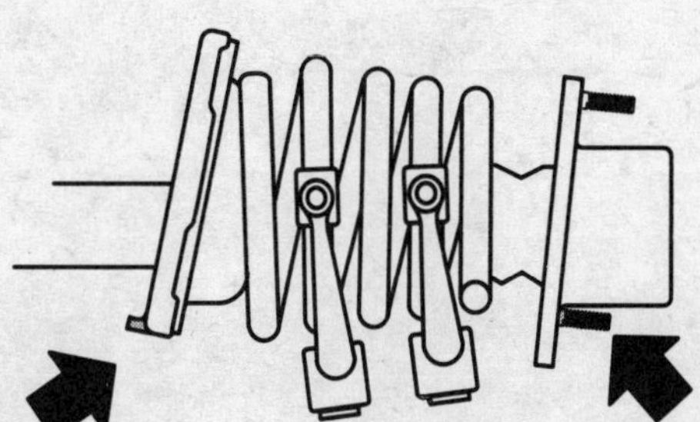

FIGURE 5-21 *Aligning lowest bolt on upper strut mount with tab on lower spring seat.*

INSTALLATION OF STRUT-AND-SPRING ASSEMBLY IN VEHICLE

A typical installation procedure for a strut-and-spring assembly follows:

1. Install the strut-and-spring assembly with the upper strut mounting bolts extending through the bolt holes in the strut tower. Tighten the nuts on the upper strut mounting bolts to the specified torque (Figure 5-22).
2. Install the lower end of the strut in the steering knuckle to the proper depth, and tighten the strut-to-knuckle retaining bolts to the specified torque (Figure 5-23). If one of the strut-to-knuckle bolts is an eccentric camber bolt, be sure the eccentric is aligned with the mark placed on the strut during the removal procedure.
3. Install the brake hose in the clamp on the strut. Place the ABS wheel-speed sensor wire in the strut clamp if the vehicle is equipped with ABS (Figure 5-24).

Photo Sequence 5 shows a typical procedure for removing and replacing a MacPherson strut.

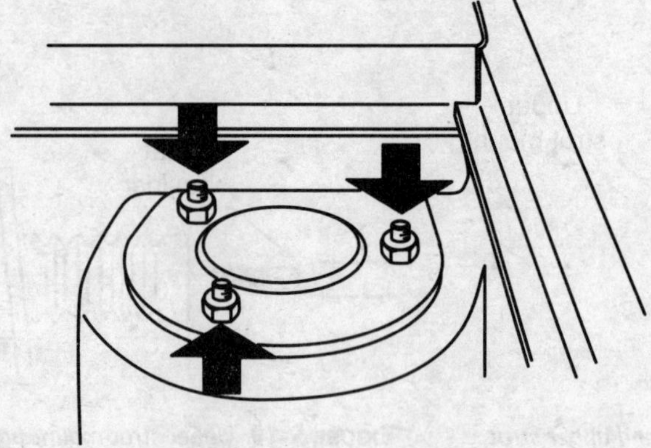

FIGURE 5-22 *Nuts installed on upper strut mount bolts.*

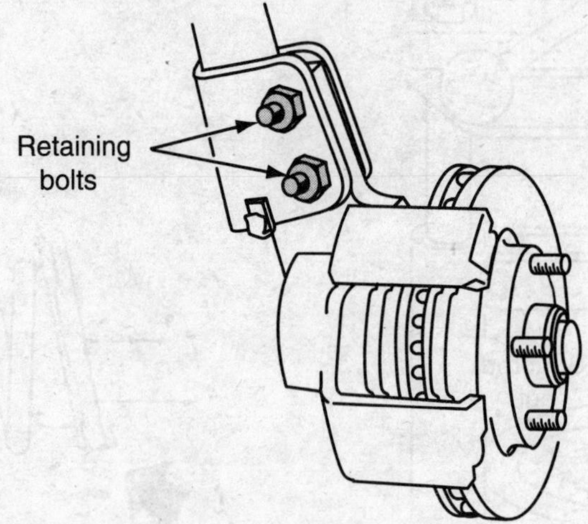

FIGURE 5-23 *Lower end of strut installed in steering knuckle.*

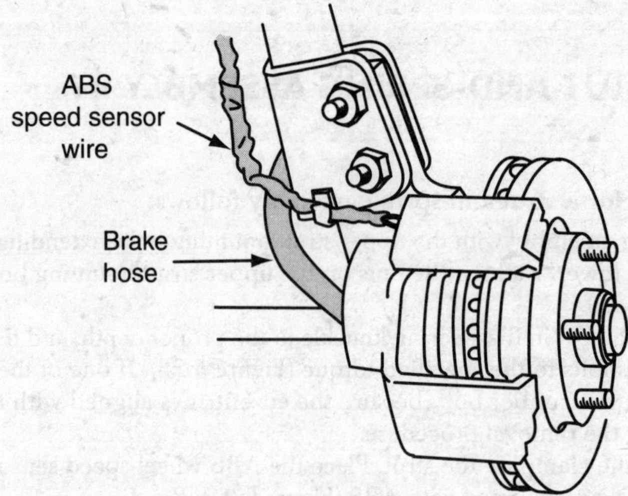

FIGURE 5-24 *Brake hose and ABS wire installed in strut clamps.*

PHOTO SEQUENCE 5
TYPICAL PROCEDURE FOR REMOVING AND REPLACING A MACPHERSON STRUT

P5-1 *The top of the strut assembly is mounted directly to the chassis of the car. Prior to loosening the strut-to-chassis bolts, scribe alignment marks on the strut bolts and the chassis.*

P5-2 *With the top strut bolts or nuts removed, raise the car to a working height. It is important that the car be supported on its frame and not on its suspension components.*

P5-3 *Remove the wheel assembly. The strut is accessible from the wheel well after the wheel is removed.*

P5-4 *Remove the bolt that fastens the brake line or hose to the strut assembly.*

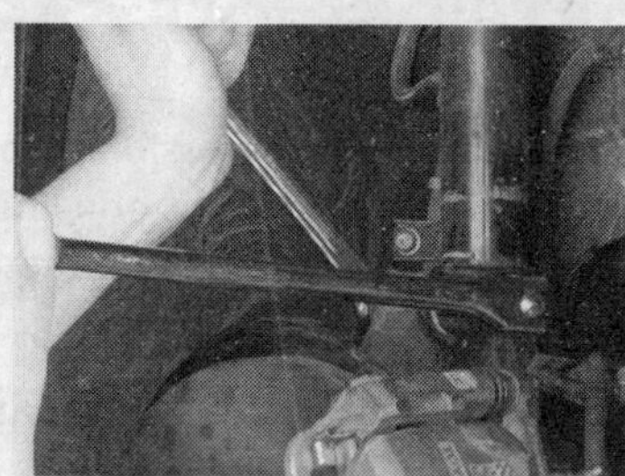

P5-5 *Remove the strut-to-steering knuckle bolts.*

P5-6 *Support the steering knuckle with wire and remove the strut assembly from the car.*

P5-7 *Install the strut assembly into the proper type spring compressor. Then compress the spring until it is possible to safely loosen the retaining bolts.*

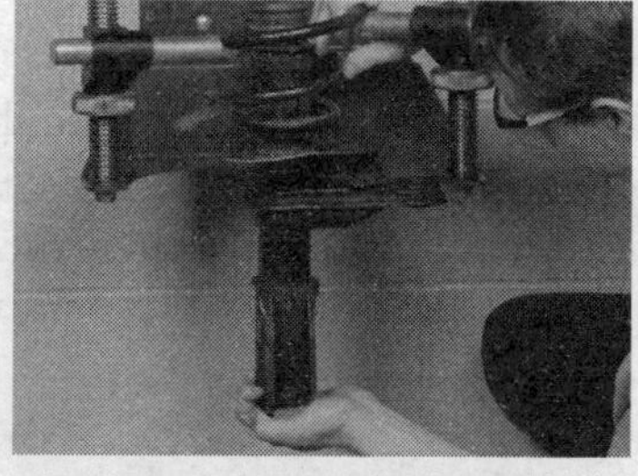

P5-8 *Remove the old strut assembly from the spring and install the new strut. Compress the spring to allow for reassembly and tighten the retaining bolts.*

P5-9 *Reinstall the strut assembly into the car. Make sure all bolts are properly tightened and in the correct locations.*

REAR STRUT REPLACEMENT

The rear strut replacement procedure varies depending on the type of rear suspension. Always follow the vehicle manufacturer's recommended procedure outlined in the appropriate service manual.

A typical rear strut replacement procedure follows:

1. Lift the vehicle with a floor jack and lower the vehicle onto safety stands placed under the chassis to support the vehicle weight.
2. Place the floor jack under the lower control arm and operate the jack to support some of the spring tension.
3. Remove the tire-and-wheel assembly.
4. Remove the strut-to-spindle bolts.
5. Pull upward on the strut to remove the strut from the spindle. If necessary, lower the floor jack slightly to remove the strut from the spindle.
6. Disconnect the upper strut mount from the chassis, and remove the strut.
7. When the new strut and/or mount is installed, reverse steps 1 through 6. Tighten all the bolts to the specified torque.
8. Check vehicle alignment.

The rear coil springs may be removed from the rear struts using the same basic procedure for spring removal from the front struts.

INSTALLING STRUT CARTRIDGE, OFF-CAR

Many struts are a sealed unit, and thus rebuilding is impossible. However, some manufacturers supply a replacement cartridge that may be installed in the strut housing after the strut has been removed from the vehicle. Always follow the **strut cartridge** manufacturer's recommended installation procedure.

The following is a typical off-car strut cartridge installation procedure:

1. Install a bolt and two nuts in the upper strut-to-knuckle mounting bolt hole. Place a nut on the inside and outside of the strut flange.
2. Clamp this bolt in a vise to hold the strut.
3. Locate the line groove near the top of the strut body, and use a pipe cutter installed in this groove to cut the top of the strut body.
4. After the cutting procedure, remove the strut piston assembly from the strut (Figure 5-25).
5. Remove the strut from the vise and dump the oil from the strut.
6. Place the special tool supplied by the vehicle manufacturer or cartridge manufacturer on top of the strut body. Strike the tool with a plastic hammer until the tool shoulder contacts the top of the strut body. This action removes burrs from the strut body and places a slight flare on the body.
7. Remove the tool from the strut body.
8. Install the required amount of oil in the strut, place the new cartridge in the strut body, and turn the cartridge until it settles into indentations in the bottom of the strut body.
9. Place the new nut over the cartridge.

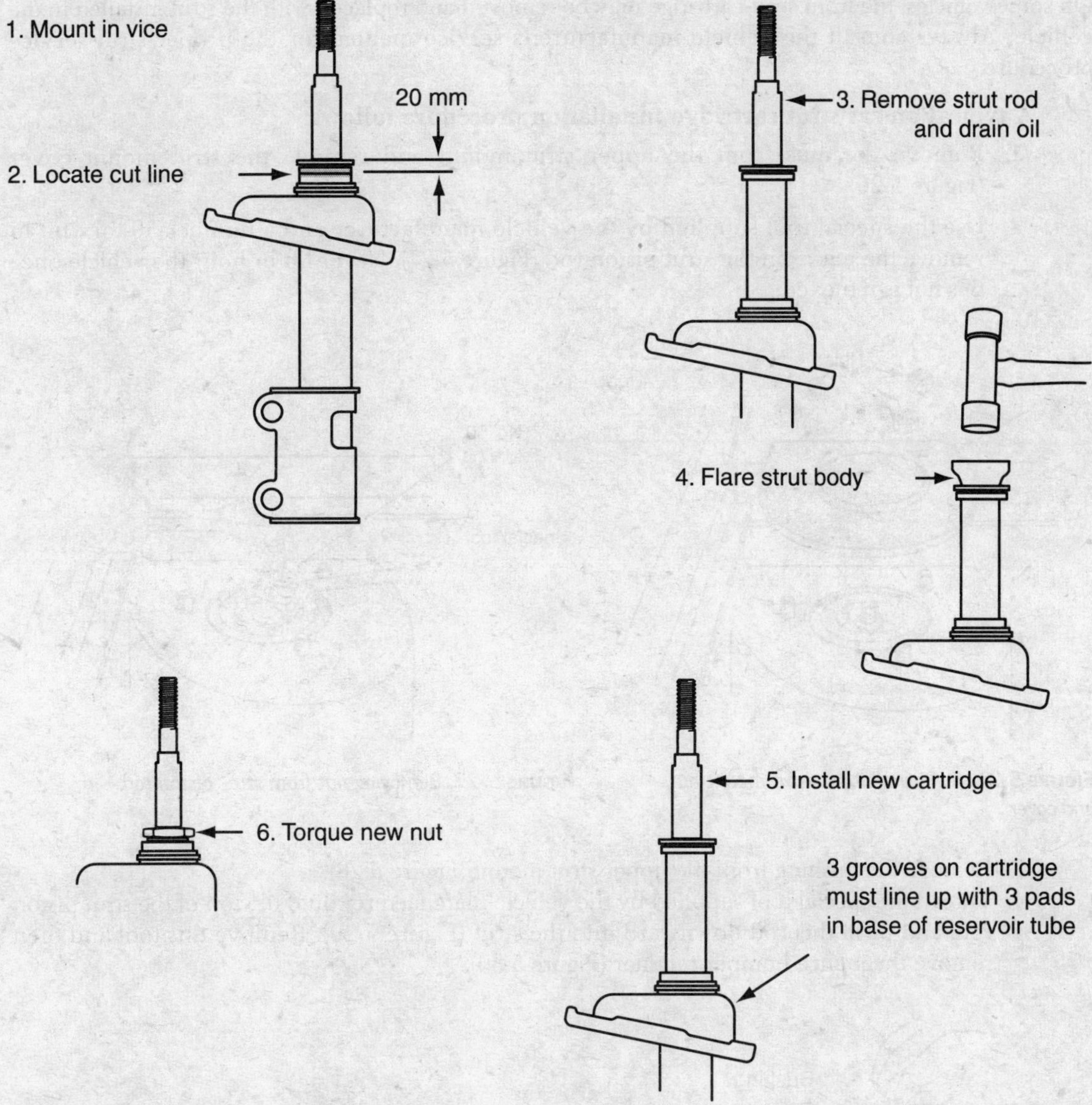

FIGURE 5-25 *Installation of strut cartridge.*

10. Using a special tool supplied by the vehicle or cartridge manufacturer, tighten the nut to the specified torque.
11. Move the strut piston rod in and out several times to check for proper strut operation.

INSTALLING STRUT CARTRIDGE, ON-CAR

WARNING: If a vehicle is hoisted or lifted in any way during an on-car strut car-tridge replacement, the coil spring may fly off the strut, causing vehicle damage and personal injury.

On some vehicles, the front strut cartridge may be removed and replaced with the strut installed in the vehicle. Always consult the vehicle manufacturer's service manual for the proper strut service procedure.

A typical on-car strut cartridge installation procedure follows:

1. Remove the nuts from the upper strut mount and remove the strut mount cover (Figure 5-26).
2. Use the special tool supplied by the vehicle manufacturer and a number 50 torx bit to remove the nut from the strut piston rod (Figure 5-27). Never lift or hoist the vehicle once this nut is removed.

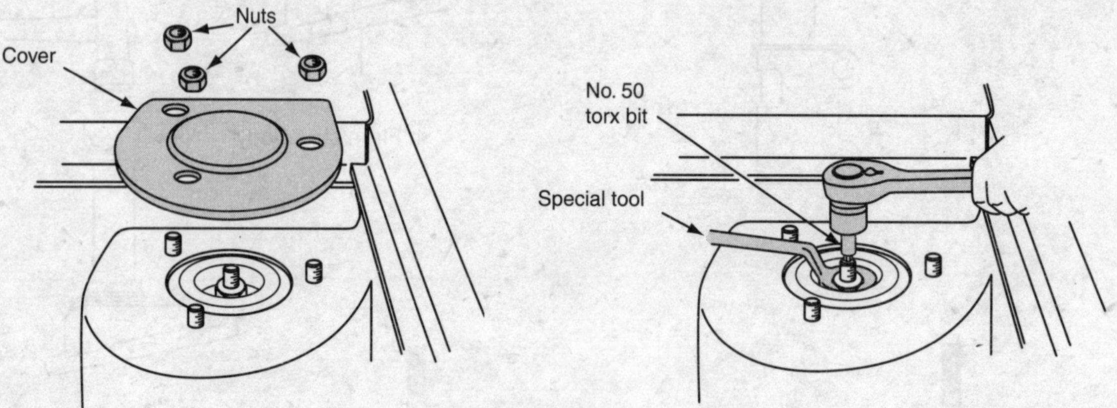

FIGURE 5-26 *Removing upper strut mount nuts and cover.*

FIGURE 5-27 *Removing nut from strut piston rod.*

3. Remove the bushing from the upper strut mount (Figure 5-28).
4. Thread the special tool supplied by the vehicle manufacturer onto the top of the strut piston rod, and push this rod downward into the strut (Figure 5-29). Remove this tool and then remove the jounce bumper retainer (Figure 5-30).

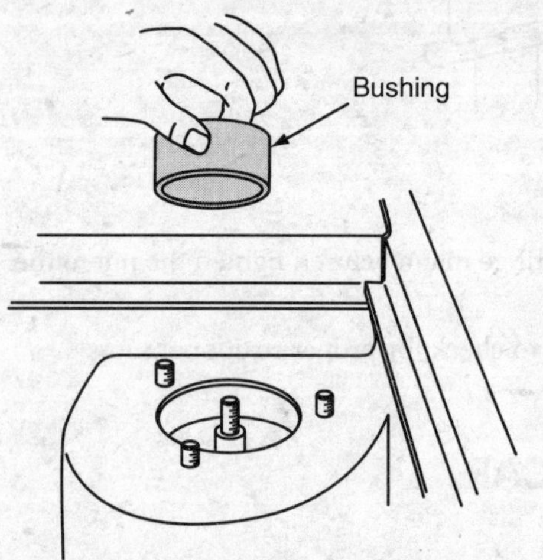

FIGURE 5-28 *Removing upper strut mount bushing.*

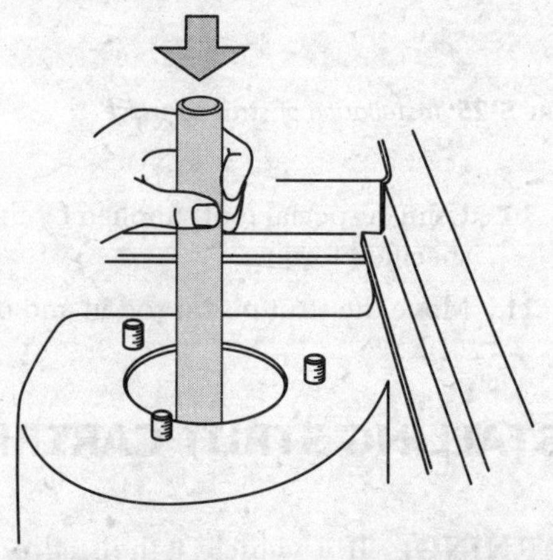

FIGURE 5-29 *Pushing strut piston rod downward.*

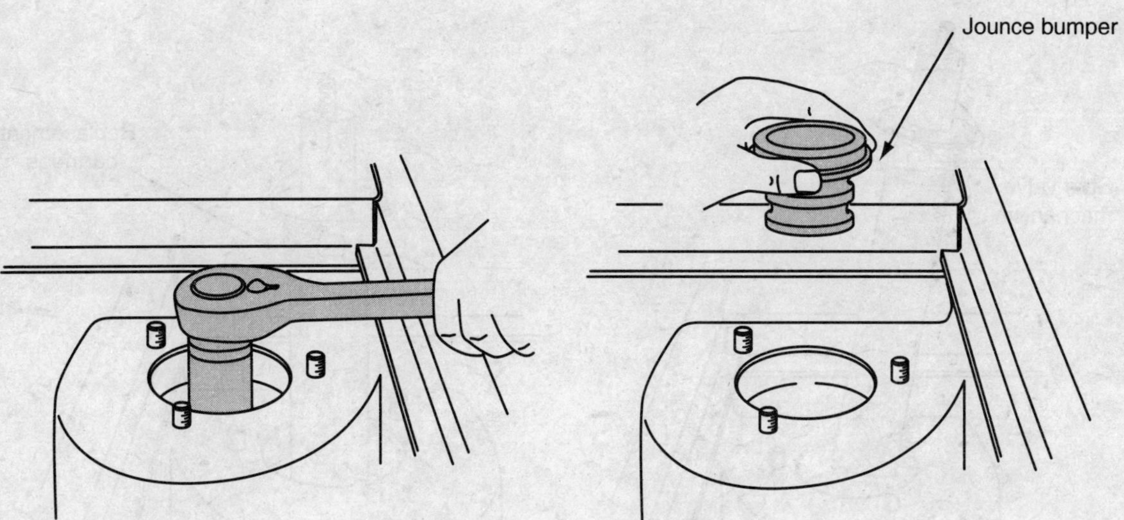

FIGURE 5-30 *Removing jounce bumper retainer.*

FIGURE 5-31 *Removing jounce bumper.*

5. Remove the jounce bumper (Figure 5-31).
6. Thread the special tool onto the strut piston rod, and re-extend this rod (Figure 5-32). Use the special tool supplied by the vehicle manufacturer to remove the closure nut on top of the strut (Figure 5-33).

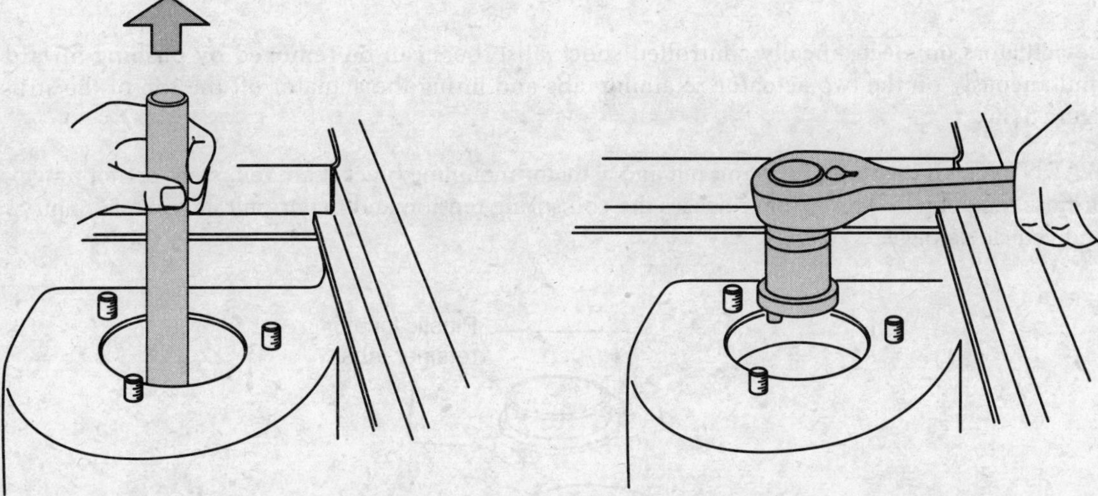

FIGURE 5-32 *Re-extending strut piston rod.*

FIGURE 5-33 *Removing strut closure nut.*

7. Grasp the top of the strut piston rod and remove the strut valve mechanism (Figure 5-34).
8. Remove the oil from the strut tube with a hand-operated suction pump.
9. Install the new strut cartridge in the strut, and tighten the closure nut to the specified torque (Figure 5-35). Reverse steps 1 through 6 to complete the strut cartridge replacement. Place a light coating of the vehicle manufacturer's recommended engine oil on the upper strut mount bushing prior to bushing installation.

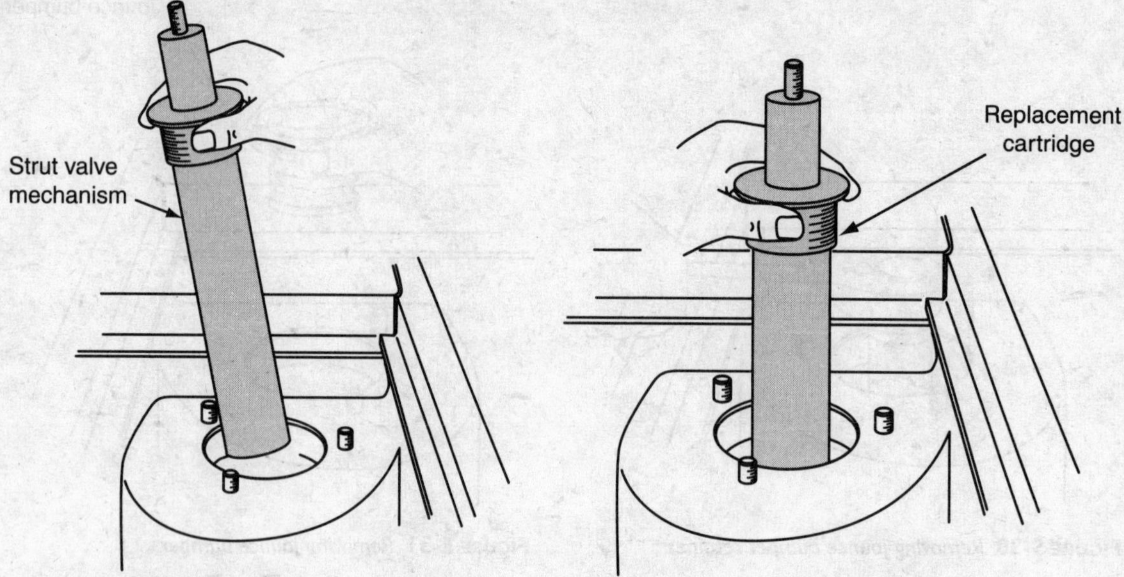

FIGURE 5-34 *Removing strut valve mechanism.*

FIGURE 5-35 *Installing new strut cartridge.*

DIAGNOSIS OF ELECTRONICALLY CONTROLLED SHOCK ABSORBERS

The actuators on electronically controlled shock absorbers can be removed by pushing inward simultaneously on the two actuator retaining tabs and lifting the actuator off the top of the strut (Figure 5-36).

WARNING: If the strut piston rod nut and actuator mounting bracket are removed, do not move or raise the vehicle. This action releases the coil spring tension and may result in personal injury and vehicle damage.

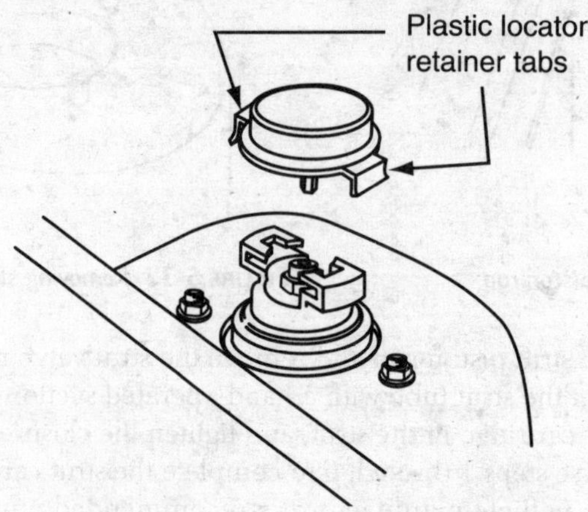

FIGURE 5-36 *Electronically controlled strut actuator.*

Follow these steps to diagnose the electronic actuator:

1. With the actuator removed from the strut and the actuator wiring harness connected, turn the ignition switch on. Move the ride control switch to the auto position and wait 5 seconds.
2. Move the ride control switch to the firm position, and wait 5 seconds. If the actuator control tube on the bottom of the actuator rotated, the actuator is operating. If the actuator control tube did not rotate, proceed with the actuator tests.
3. With the ride control switch in the firm position, place matching H's beside the control tube and the actuator.
4. With the ride control switch in the auto position, place matching S's beside the control tube and the actuator.
5. Turn the ignition switch off and disconnect the actuator electrical connector. The actuator control tube may be rotated with a small screwdriver.
6. Connect a pair of ohmmeter leads to the position sense wire and the signal return wire. The position sense wire is white or white with a colored tracer, and the signal return wire is yellow with a black tracer. With the actuator in the S position, the position sense should be closed and the ohmmeter should indicate less than 10 ohms.
7. Rotate the actuator to the H position. Under this condition, the position sense switch should be open and the ohmmeter should indicate over 1,000 ohms. If the ohmmeter readings are not within specifications, replace the actuator.
8. Connect the ohmmeter leads to the position sense wire and soft power terminal in the actuator electrical connector. The position sense wire is white or white with a colored tracer, and the soft power wire is tan with a red tracer. If the ohmmeter indicates over 1,000 ohms, the actuator is satisfactory. If the ohmmeter reading is below 10 ohms, replace the actuator.
9. Connect the ohmmeter leads from the signal return terminal in the wiring harness side of the actuator connector to a chassis ground. The ohmmeter should indicate less than 10 ohms. If the ohmmeter reading is higher than specified, check the signal return wire and the programmed ride control (PRC) module.

TABLE 1 *Shock Absorber and Strut Diagnosis*

PROBLEM	SYMPTOMS	POSSIBLE CAUSES
Harsh ride quality	Excessive chassis bouncing Excessive vertical wheel oscillations	Worn out shock absorbers or struts
Shock absorber or strut oil leaks	Oil dripping from shock absorber or strut	Worn out seal in shock absorber or strut, damaged lower shock absorber or strut housing
Rattling noise	Rattling noise in chassis when driving	Worn out shock absorber or strut mountings
Chattering noise	Chattering noise when turning the front wheels to the right or left	Worn out upper strut mount and bearing assembly
Worn, damaged rebound bumpers	Chassis bottoming out	Worn out shock absorbers or struts, low ride height

Case Study

A customer complained about a squeaking noise in the rear suspension of a 2002 Dodge Caravan. The customer said the noise occurred during normal driving at lower speeds. The technician lifted the car on a hoist and made a check of all rear suspension bushings in shock absorbers, track bar, and trailing arms. The spring insulators and all suspension bolts were checked visually. All of these items were in good condition, and there was no evidence of a squeaking noise as the chassis was bounced gently. Since the exact source of chassis noise can sometimes be difficult to locate, the technician performed a visual check of bushings, insulators, and fasteners in the front suspension. No problems were found in the front suspension.

One of the first requirements for successful automotive diagnosis is to obtain as much information as possible from the customer. The customer with the squeaking rear suspension in a Dodge Caravan lived in a part of the country where cold temperatures occur in the winter. This complaint occurred in January. The technician questioned the customer further about the conditions when the squeaking suspension noise was heard, and the customer revealed that the noise occurred when the temperature was severely cold. The customer also indicated that the noise disappeared at warmer temperatures.

The technician informed the customer that the only way to find the exact cause of this annoying squeak was to leave the car on the lot at the shop all night and check it first thing in the morning when it was colder. The customer complied with this suggestion, and the technician drove the car into the shop immediately the next morning. The squeaking noise occurred as the car was driven across the parking lot. The technician lifted the car on a hoist and listened with a stethoscope at each rear suspension bushing as a coworker gently bounced the rear suspension. No squeaking noise was heard at any of the rear suspension bushings. However, when the stethoscope pickup was placed on the left rear shock absorber, the squeaking noise was loud and clear. The shock absorber was quickly removed, and the squeaking noise was gone when the rear chassis was bounced gently. Replacement of the left rear shock absorber corrected this complaint and made the customer happy.

Service Tips

- During a visual shock absorber inspection, check the rebound, or strikeout, bumpers on the control arms or chassis. If the rebound bumpers are severely worn, the shock absorbers may be worn out.
- On twin I-beam front suspension systems, front wheel camber may be noticeably different after a bounce test.
- Because of high labor costs, it is often more economical for the customer if the technician replaces a strut and coil spring as a complete assembly rather than replacing these components individually. Many automotive parts suppliers market struts and coil spring as complete assemblies.
- Wiring harness colors vary depending on the vehicle make and model year. The wiring colors in the following steps are based on Ford vehicles. If you are working on a different make of vehicle, refer to the wire colors in the vehicle manufacturer's service information.

REVIEW QUESTIONS

1. A slight oil film appears on the lower shock absorber oil chamber, and the shock absorber performs satisfactorily in a bounce test:
Technician A says the shock absorber is satisfactory. *Technician B* says the shock absorber may contain excessive pressure.
Who is correct?
A. A only **C.** Both A and B
B. B only **D.** Neither A nor B

2. While discussing a shock absorber and strut bounce test:
Technician A says the shock absorber is satisfactory if the bumper makes two free upward bounces. *Technician B* says the bumper must be pushed downward with considerable force.
Who is correct?
A. A only **C.** Both A and B
B. B only **D.** Neither A nor B

3. While discussing a shock absorber manual test:
Technician A says the shock absorber's resistance to movement should be jerky and erratic. *Technician B* says the shock absorber's resistance to movement may be greater on the rebound stroke compared with the compression stroke.
Who is correct?
A. A only **C.** Both A and B
B. B only **D.** Neither A nor B

4. When the front wheels are turned on a vehicle equipped with front struts, the left front coil spring provides a chattering action and noise:
Technician A says the strut has internal defects, and strut replacement is necessary. *Technician B* says the upper strut bearing and mount is defective.
Who is correct?
A. A only **C.** Both A and B
B. B only **D.** Neither A nor B

5. While discussing enamel-coated coil springs:
Technician A says if the enamel-type coating on a coil spring is chipped, the spring may break prematurely. *Technician B* says coil springs should be taped in the compressing tool contact areas to prevent chipping of the enamel-type coating.
Who is correct?
A. A only **C.** Both A and B
B. B only **D.** Neither A nor B

6. During service procedures, gas-filled shock absorbers may:
A. Be heated with an acetylene torch.
B. Be thrown in an incinerator.
C. Extend when disconnected.
D. Retract when disconnected and extended.

7. During wheel jounce, a thumping noise is heard in the right front suspension, but the bounce test is satisfactory. All of these defects could cause the problem EXCEPT:
A. A worn upper strut mount.
B. Worn spring insulators.

C. A broken coil spring.
D. A fluid leak in the strut.

8. When removing and replacing a front strut on a MacPherson strut suspension:
A. The cam-type strut-to-knuckle bolt should be marked in relation to the strut.
B. The strut rod nut may be loosened with spring tension applied to the upper strut mount.
C. The lower strut chamber may be clamped in a vise to support the strut.
D. The spring compressor must be installed before the strut is removed from the vehicle.

9. When assembling and installing a strut and coil spring in a MacPherson strut front suspension:
A. The upper spring insulator should be installed between the upper strut mount and the strut tower.
B. The lower spring insulator should be installed between the coil spring and the spring bumper.
C. On some vehicles, the upper strut mount must be properly aligned in relation to the lower spring seat on the strut.
D. Final compressing of the coil spring may be done by tightening the nut on the strut rod.

10. During an on-car strut cartridge replacement:
A. Oil must be removed from the strut with a hand-operated suction pump.
B. The front suspension may be lifted with a floor jack.
C. The strut rod must be pulled upward before removing the jounce bumper.
D. The new strut cartridge must be filled with the manufacturer's specified fluid.

CHALLENGE QUESTIONS

1. A customer says his MacPherson strut front suspension is making a chattering noise when the steering wheel is turned hard to the left. He says he also feels a "kind of vibration" in the steering wheel when the chatter is heard. To correct this problem, you should:
A. Replace the front struts.
B. Check the lower strut spring seating.
C. Check the stabilizer links.
D. Check the upper bearing and strut mounting.

2. When performing a bounce test on a twin I-beam front suspension, the front tires noticeably flex as the front end of the vehicle is vigorously exercised. When the vehicle is released, the front end rebounds once then settles, but the front wheel now has a slight but obvious negative camber.
Technician A says the shock absorbers are worn and should be replaced. *Technician B* says the twin I-beam suspension can change camber during a bounce and rebound. Who is correct?
A. A only — **C.** Both A and B
B. B only — **D.** Neither A nor B

3. The front rebound bumpers on a coil spring suspension system are badly worn and damaged. *Technician A* says the shock absorbers may be worn out. *Technician B* says the coil springs may be weak.
Who is correct?
A. A only — **C.** Both A and B
B. B only — **D.** Neither A nor B

4. A manual test of a shock absorber shows a stronger resistance to rebound than compression. *Technician A* says the shock is defective. *Technician B* says the shock has a 50/50 ratio. Who is correct?
   A. A only
   B. B only
   C. Both A and B
   D. Neither A nor B

5. *Technician A* says any visible presence of oil on a strut or shock requires replacement. *Technician B* says a slight film of oil on a strut or shock is OK if it performs satisfactorily in a bounce test. Who is correct?
   A. A only
   B. B only
   C. Both A and B
   D. Neither A nor B

JOB SHEET 15

Name ______________________________ Date ______________

REMOVE STRUT-AND-SPRING ASSEMBLY AND DISASSEMBLE STRUT AND SPRING

Upon completion of this job sheet, you should be able to remove a strut-and-spring assembly from a car and disassemble the strut and spring.

ASE Correlation

This job sheet is related to the ASE Suspension and Steering Task: Inspect and replace front suspension system coil springs and spring insulators (silencers).

Tools and Materials

Front-wheel-drive car
Floor jack
Safety stands
Coil spring compressor

Describe the Vehicle Being Worked On:

Year __________ Make ______________ Model ______________
VIN ______________ Engine type and size ______________

Procedure

Task Completed

1. With the vehicle parked on the shop floor, perform a strut bounce test.

Based on the bounce test results, state the strut condition, and give the reason for your diagnosis.

____

____

2. Raise the vehicle on a hoist or with a floor jack. If a floor jack is used to raise the vehicle, lower the vehicle onto safety stands placed under the chassis so the lower control arms and front wheels drop downward. Remove the floor jack from under the vehicle.

Is the vehicle securely supported on safety stands? ☐ Yes ☐ No

Instructor check ______________________________

3. Remove the brake line and antilock brake system (ABS) wheel-speed sensor wire from clamps on the strut. In some cases, these clamps may have to be removed from the strut.

Is the brake line and ABS wheel-speed sensor wire disconnected? ☐ Yes ☐ No

Instructor check ______________________________

Task Completed

4. Punch mark the cam bolt in relation to the strut, remove the strut-to-steering knuckle retaining bolts, and remove the strut from the knuckle.

   Is the cam bolt marked in relation to the strut? ☐ Yes ☐ No

   Is the strut removed from the knuckle? ☐ Yes ☐ No

   Instructor check ______________________________

   State the reason for marking the cam bolt in relation to the strut.

   ____

   ____

☐ 5. Remove the upper strut mounting bolts on top of the strut tower; remove the strut-and-spring assembly.

WARNING: Always use a coil spring compressing tool according to the tool or vehicle manufacturer's recommended service procedure. Be sure the tool is properly installed on the spring. If a coil spring slips off the tool when the spring is compressed, severe personal injury or property damage may occur.

WARNING: Never loosen the upper strut mount retaining nut on the end of the strut rod unless the spring is compressed enough to remove all spring tension from the upper strut mount. If this nut is loosened with spring tension on the upper mount, this mount becomes a very dangerous projectile that may cause serious personal injury or property damage.

CAUTION: Never clamp the lower shock absorber or strut chamber in a vise with excessive force. This action may distort the lower chamber and affect piston movement in the shock absorber or strut.

6. Install the spring compressing tool on the coil spring according to the tool or vehicle manufacturer's recommended procedure.

   Is the compressing tool properly installed on the strut-and-spring assembly?
   ☐ Yes ☐ No

   Instructor check ______________________________

CAUTION: If the coil spring has an enamel-type coating and the compressing tool contacts the coil spring, tape the spring where the compressing tool contacts the spring.

☐ 7. Turn the nut on top of the compressing tool until all the spring tension is removed from the upper strut mount.

   Is all the spring tension removed from the upper strut mount? ☐ Yes ☐ No

   Instructor check ______________________________

Task Completed

8. Install a bolt and two nuts in the upper strut to knuckle mounting bolt holes. Install a nut on each side of the strut flange. Clamp this bolt securely in a vise to hold the strut-and-spring assembly and the compressing tool. ☐

9. Use the bar on the spring compressing tool to hold the strut-and-spring assembly from turning, and loosen the nut on the upper strut mount. Be sure all the spring tension is removed from the upper strut mount before loosening this nut.

   Is all the spring tension removed from the upper strut mount? ☐ Yes ☐ No

   Is the upper strut mount retaining nut loosened? ☐ Yes ☐ No

   Instructor check ______________________________

10. Remove the nut, upper strut mount, upper insulator, coil spring, spring bumper, and lower insulator. ☐

11. Inspect the strut, upper strut mount, coil spring, spring insulators, and spring bumper. On the basis of this inspection, list the necessary strut-and-spring service, and give the reasons for your diagnosis.

   ____

   ____

   ____

Instructor's Response ______________________________

____

____

JOB SHEET 16

Name ______________________________ Date ____________________

ASSEMBLE STRUT AND SPRING AND INSTALL STRUT-AND-SPRING ASSEMBLY

Upon completion of this job sheet, you should be able to assemble a strut and spring and install a strut-and-spring assembly in a car.

ASE Correlation

This job sheet is related to the ASE Suspension and Steering Task: Inspect and replace front suspension system coil springs and spring insulators (silencers).

Tools and Materials

Front-wheel-drive car
Floor jack
Safety stands
Coil spring compressor

Describe the Vehicle Being Worked On:

Year __________ Make ______________ Model ______________
VIN ______________ Engine type and size ______________

Procedure

Task Completed

1. Install a bolt in the upper strut-to-knuckle retaining bolt, and clamp this bolt in a vise to hold the strut, spring, and compressing tool as in the disassembly procedure. ☐
2. Install the lower insulator on the lower strut spring seat and be sure the insulator is properly seated.

   Is the lower insulator properly seated? ☐ Yes ☐ No

   Instructor check ______________________________
3. Install the spring bumper on the strut rod.

   Is the spring bumper properly installed? ☐ Yes ☐ No

   Instructor check ______________________________
4. With the coil spring compressed in the spring compressing tool, install the spring on the strut. Be sure the spring is properly seated on the lower insulator spring seat.

   Is the coil spring properly seated on the lower insulator? ☐ Yes ☐ No

   Instructor check ______________________________
5. Be sure the strut piston rod is fully extended and install the upper insulator on top of the coil spring.

   Is the strut rod fully extended? ☐ Yes ☐ No

   Is the upper insulator properly installed? ☐ Yes ☐ No

   Instructor check ______________________________

Task Completed

☐ **6.** Install the upper strut mount on the upper insulator.

7. Be sure the spring, upper insulator, and upper strut mount are properly positioned and seated on the coil spring and strut piston rod.

Are the spring, upper insulator, and upper strut mount properly positioned?
☐ Yes ☐ No

Instructor check ______________________

8. Use the compressing tool bar to hold the strut and spring from turning, then tighten the strut piston rod nut to the specified torque.

Specified strut piston rod nut torque ____________

Actual strut piston rod nut torque ____________

9. Rotate the upper strut mount until the lowest bolt in this mount is aligned with the tab on the lower spring seat.

Is the upper strut mount properly aligned? ☐ Yes ☐ No

Instructor check ______________________

☐ **10.** Gradually loosen the nut on the compressing tool until all the spring tension is released from the tool, and remove the tool from the spring.

11. Install the strut-and-spring assembly with the upper strut mounting bolts extending through the bolt holes in the strut tower. Tighten the nuts on the upper strut mounting bolts to the specified torque.

Specified upper strut mount nut torque ____________

Actual upper strut mount nut torque ____________

12. Install the lower end of the strut in the steering knuckle to the proper depth. Align the punch marks on the cam bolt and strut that were placed on these components during disassembly, and tighten the strut-to-knuckle retaining bolts to the specified torque.

Is the cam bolt properly positioned? ☐ Yes ☐ No

Specified strut-to-knuckle bolt torque ____________

Actual strut-to-knuckle bolt torque ____________

Instructor check ______________________

13. Install the brake hose in the clamp on the strut. Place the ABS wheel-speed sensor wire in the strut clamp if the vehicle is equipped with ABS.

Is the brake hose properly installed and tightened? ☐ Yes ☐ No

Is the ABS wheel-speed sensor properly installed and tightened? ☐ Yes ☐ No

Instructor check ______________________

☐ **14.** Raise the vehicle with a floor jack, remove the safety stands, and lower the vehicle onto the shop floor.

Instructor's Response ______________________

____

____

JOB SHEET 17

Name ______________________________ Date ______________

INSTALL STRUT CARTRIDGE OFF-CAR

Upon completion of this job sheet, you should be able to remove and replace a strut cartridge with the strut removed from the car.

ASE Correlation

This job sheet is related to the ASE Suspension and Steering Task: Inspect and replace MacPherson strut cartridge or assembly.

Tools and Materials

Front strut removed from car
Pipe cutter
Torque wrench

Describe the Vehicle Being Worked On:

Year __________ Make ______________ Model ______________
VIN ______________ Engine type and size ______________

Procedure

Task Completed

1. List the strut conditions and suspension operating conditions that indicate a strut should be serviced or replaced.

____

____

____

____

2. Install a bolt and two nuts in the upper strut to knuckle mounting bolt hole. Place a nut on the inside and outside of the strut flange. ☐
3. Clamp this bolt in a vise to hold the strut. ☐
4. Locate the line groove near the top of the strut body, and use a pipe cutter installed in this groove to cut the top of the strut body.
5. After the cutting procedure, remove the strut piston assembly from the strut.

   Is the strut piston assembly removed from the strut? ☐ Yes ☐ No

   Instructor check ______________________________
6. Remove the strut from the vise and dump the oil from the strut. ☐
7. Place the special tool supplied by the vehicle manufacturer or cartridge manufacturer on top of the strut body and strike the tool with a plastic hammer until the tool shoulder contacts the top of the strut body. This action removes burrs from the strut body and places a slight flare on the body.

Task Completed

Is the strut body properly flared? ☐ Yes ☐ No

Instructor check ____________________

☐ **8.** Remove the tool from the strut body.

9. Place the new cartridge in the strut body and turn the cartridge until it settles into indentations in the bottom of the strut body.

Is the new strut cartridge properly seated in strut body indentations? ☐ Yes ☐ No

Instructor check ____________________

☐ **10.** Place the new nut over the cartridge.

11. Using a special tool supplied by the vehicle or cartridge manufacturer, tighten the nut to the specified torque.

Specified strut nut torque __________

Actual strut nut torque __________

12. Move the strut piston rod in and out several times to check for proper strut operation.

Strut operation: ☐ Satisfactory ☐ Unsatisfactory

Instructor's Response ____________________

FRONT SUSPENSION SYSTEM SERVICE

6

Upon completion and review of this chapter, you should be able to:

- Measure curb riding height.
- Diagnose and correct curb riding height problems.
- Adjust torsion bars.
- Diagnose front suspension noise and body sway.
- Remove and replace ball joints, and check ball joint condition.
- Remove and replace steering knuckles, and check knuckle condition.
- Remove and replace lower control arms, and check control arm and bushing condition.
- Remove and replace coil springs, and check spring and insulator condition.
- Remove and replace upper control arms, and check control arm and bushing condition.
- Remove and replace control arm bushings.
- Inspect and replace rebound bumpers.
- Diagnose, remove, and replace stabilizer bars.
- Diagnose, remove, and replace strut rods.
- Diagnose, remove, and replace leaf springs.
- Replace torsion bars, and check torsion bar condition.

Proper front suspension system service is extremely important to provide adequate vehicle safety and to maintain ride comfort and normal tire life. If worn or loose front suspension system components are ignored, steering control may be adversely affected, which may result in loss of steering control and an expensive collision. Defective front suspension components, such as worn out shock absorbers or broken springs, may cause rough riding that results in driver and passenger discomfort. Other worn front suspension components, such as worn ball joints and control arm bushings, cause improper alignment angles that causes excessive front tire wear. Therefore, technicians must be familiar with front suspension service.

CURB RIDING HEIGHT MEASUREMENT

Regular inspection and proper maintenance of suspension systems is extremely important for maintaining vehicle safety. The **curb riding height** is determined mainly by spring condition. Other suspension components, such as control arm bushings, affect curb riding height if they are worn. Since incorrect curb riding height affects most of the other suspension angles, this measurement is critical.

Reduced curb riding height on the front suspension may cause decreased **directional stability.** If the curb riding height is reduced on one side of the front suspension, the steering may pull to one side. Reduced rear suspension height increases **steering effort** and causes rapid steering wheel return after turning a corner. Harsh riding occurs when the curb riding height is less than specified. The curb riding height must be measured at the vehicle manufacturer's specified location, which varies depending on the type of suspension system.

When the vehicle is on a level floor or on an alignment rack, measure the curb riding height from the floor to the center of the lower control arm mounting bolt on both sides of the front suspension (Figure 6-1). On the rear suspension system, measure the curb riding height from the floor to the center of the strut rod mounting bolt (Figure 6-2).

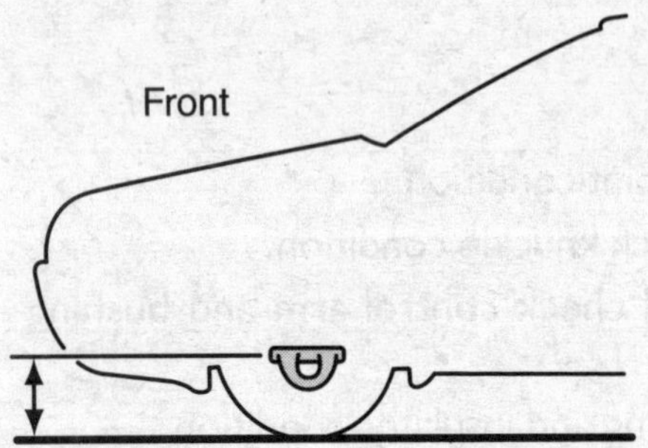

FIGURE 6-1 *Curb riding height measurement, front suspension.*

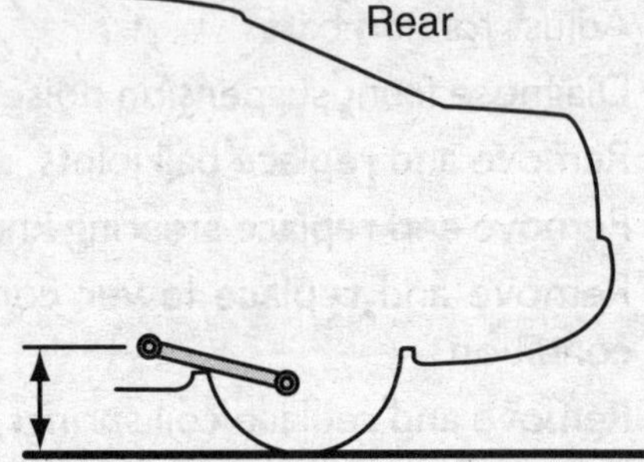

FIGURE 6-2 *Curb riding height measurement, rear suspension.*

If the curb riding height is less than specified, the control arms and bushings should be inspected and replaced as necessary. When the control arms and bushings are in normal condition, the reduced curb riding height may be caused by sagged springs that require replacement.

FRONT SUSPENSION DIAGNOSIS AND SERVICE

Torsion Bar Adjustment

On torsion bar front suspension systems, the torsion bars may be adjusted to correct the curb riding height. The curb riding height must be measured at the location specified by the vehicle manufacturer. On some torsion bar front suspension systems, the curb riding height is measured with the vehicle on a lift and the tires supported on the lift. Measure the distance from the center of the front lower control arm bushing to the lift. Then measure the distance from the lower end of the front spindle to the lift (Figure 6-3). The difference between these two readings is the curb riding height.

If the curb riding height is not correct on a torsion bar front suspension, the torsion bar anchor adjusting bolts must be rotated until the curb riding height equals the vehicle manufacturer's specifications (Figure 6-4).

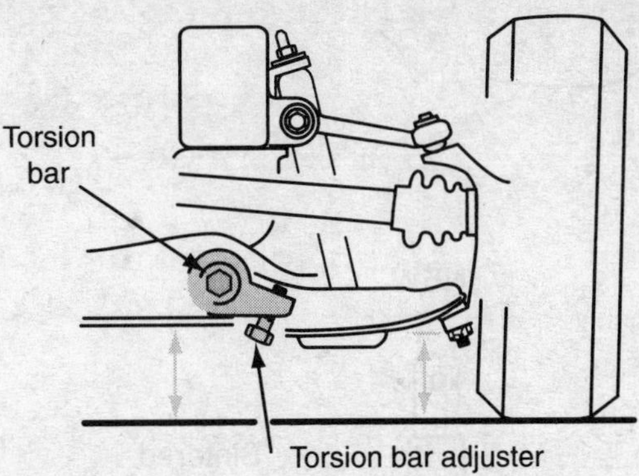

FIGURE 6-3 *Curb riding height measurement, torsion bar front suspension.*

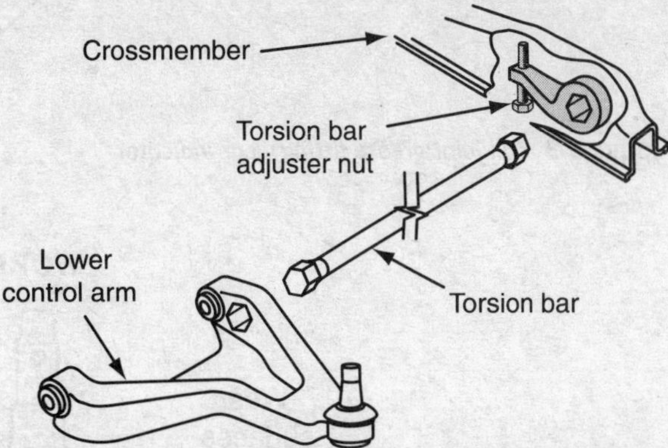

FIGURE 6-4 *Curb riding height adjustment, torsion bar front suspension.*

Inspecting Ball Joints

Wear Indicators. Some ball joints have a grease fitting installed in a floating retainer. The grease fitting and retainer may be used as a **ball joint wear indicator.** With the vehicle weight resting on the wheels, grasp the grease fitting and check for movement (Figure 6-5).

Some car manufacturers recommend ball joint replacement if any grease fitting movement is present. In some other ball joints, the grease fitting retainer extends a short distance through the ball joint surface (Figure 6-6). On this type of joint, replacement is necessary if the grease fitting shoulder is flush with or inside the ball joint cover.

Ball Joint Unloading

On many suspension systems, ball joint looseness is not apparent until the weight has been removed from the joint. When the coil spring is positioned between the lower control arm and the chassis, place a floor jack near the outer end of the lower control arm and raise the tire off the floor (Figure 6-7). Be sure the rebound bumper is not in contact with the control arm or frame.

When the coil springs are positioned between the upper control arm and the chassis, place a steel block between the upper control arm and the frame. With this block in place, raise the tire off the floor with a floor jack under the front crossmember (Figure 6-8).

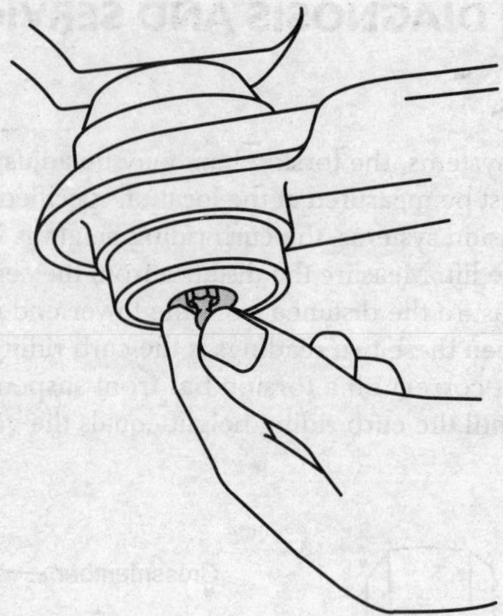

FIGURE 6-5 *Ball joint grease fitting wear indicator.*

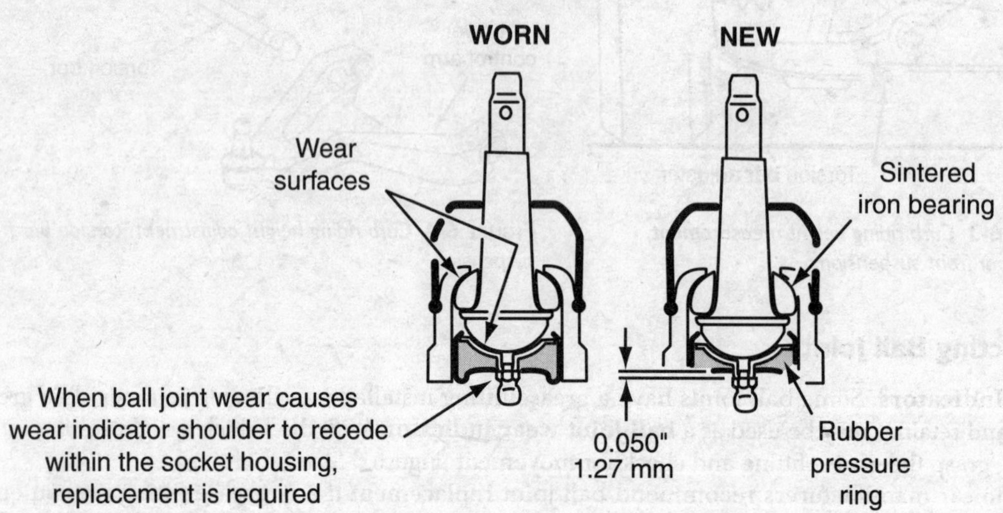

FIGURE 6-6 *Ball joint wear indicator with grease fitting extending from ball joint surface.*

Ball Joint Vertical Measurement

The vehicle manufacturer may provide ball joint vertical and horizontal tolerances. A dial indicator is one of the most accurate ball joint measuring devices (Figure 6-9). Always install the dial indicator at the vehicle manufacturer's recommended location for ball joint measurement. When measuring the **ball joint vertical movement** in a compression-loaded ball joint, attach the dial indicator to the lower control arm and position the dial indicator stem on the lower side of the steering knuckle beside the ball joint stud (Figure 6-10). Depress the dial indicator stem approximately 0.250 in (6.35 mm) and zero the dial indicator. Place a pry bar under the tire and pry straight upward while observing the

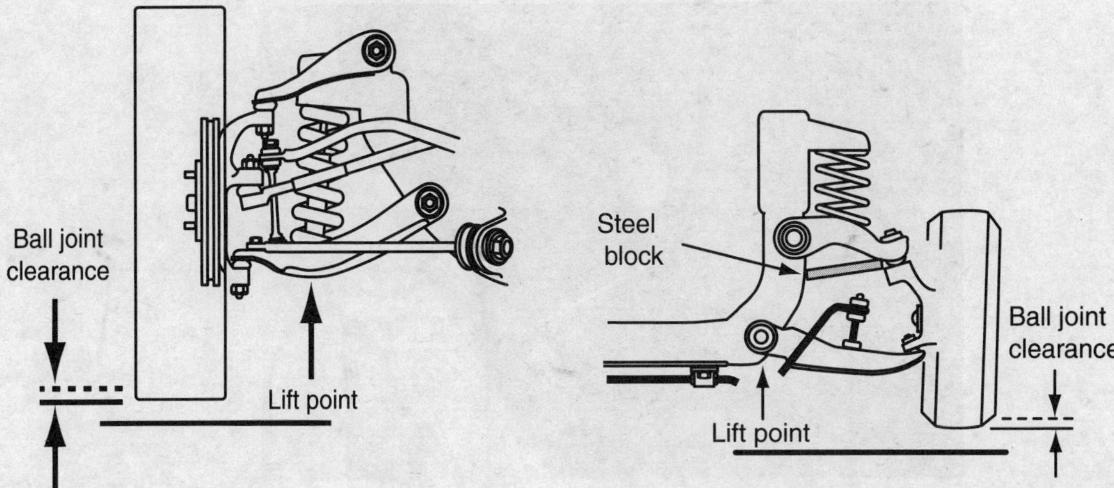

FIGURE 6-7 *Floor jack position to check ball joint wear with spring between the lower control arm and the chassis.*

FIGURE 6-8 *Floor jack position to check ball joint wear with spring between the upper control arm and the chassis.*

FIGURE 6-9 *Dial indicator designed for ball joint measurement.*

FIGURE 6-10 *Dial indicator installed to measure vertical ball joint movement on a compression-loaded ball joint.*

vertical ball joint movement on the dial indicator. If this movement is more than specified, ball joint replacement is necessary.

On a tension-loaded ball joint, clean the top end of the lower ball joint stud, and position the dial indicator stem against the top end of this stud. Depress the dial indicator plunger approximately 0.250 in (6.35 mm) and zero the dial indicator. Lift upward with a pry bar under the tire and observe the dial indicator reading. If the vertical ball joint movement exceeds the manufacturer's specifications, ball joint replacement is required.

Ball Joint Horizontal Measurement

Worn ball joints cause improper **camber angles** and **caster angles,** which result in reduced directional stability and tire tread wear. Connect the dial indicator to the lower control arm of the

FIGURE 6-11 *Dial indicator installed to measure radial ball joint movement.*

ball joint being checked and position the dial indicator stem against the edge of the wheel rim (Figure 6-11).

Be sure the front wheel bearings are adjusted properly prior to the ball joint horizontal measurement. While an assistant grasps the top and bottom of the raised tire and attempts to move the tire and wheel horizontally in and out, observe the reading on the dial indicator (Figure 6-12).

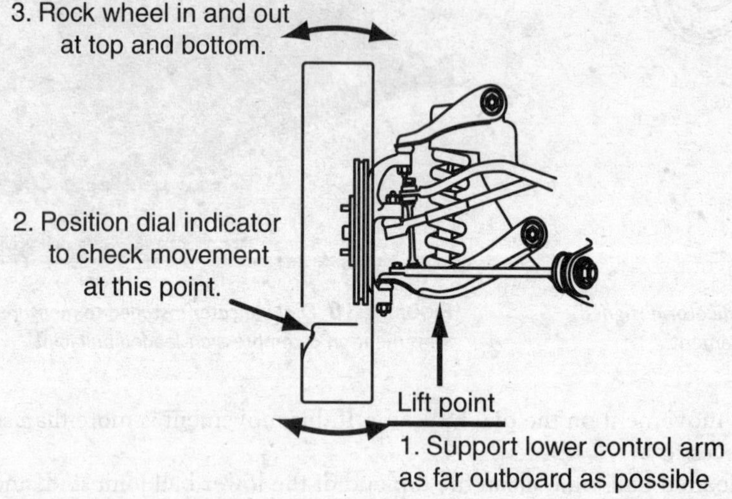

FIGURE 6-12 *Measuring radial ball joint movement.*

The lower ball joint on a MacPherson strut front suspension should be checked for radial movement with a dial indicator when the tire is lifted off the floor (Figure 6-13). Since the spring load is carried by the upper and lower spring seats when the tire is lifted off the floor, it is not necessary to unload this type of ball joint. Photo Sequence 6 shows a typical procedure for measuring the lower ball joint radial movement on a MacPherson strut front suspension.

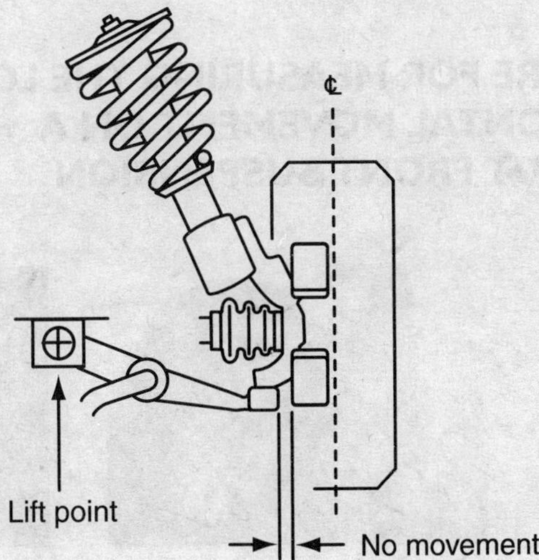

FIGURE 6-13 *Ball joint wear measurement on MacPherson strut front suspension.*

Checking Ball Joints, Twin I-Beam Axles

Follow these steps to check the ball joints on a twin I-beam axle:

1. Lift the front end of the vehicle with a floor jack and place safety stands near the outer end of the I-beams.
2. Lower the vehicle onto the safety stands.
3. While an assistant grasps the wheel at the bottom and moves the wheel in and out, watch for movement between the lower part of the axle jaw and the spindle lower arm. If this movement exceeds 1/32 in., replace the lower ball joint.
4. As an assistant grasps the top of the wheel and moves the wheel in and out, watch for movement between the upper axle jaw and the spindle upper arm. If this movement exceeds 1/32 in., replace the upper ball joint.

Front Steering Knuckle Diagnosis and Service, Front-Wheel-Drive Vehicle

Front Steering Knuckle Diagnosis. Steering looseness may be caused by a worn tie-rod end opening or ball joint opening in the steering knuckle. If these knuckle openings are worn, reduced directional stability may be experienced. Since a bent steering knuckle affects front suspension alignment angles, this problem may cause reduced directional stability and tire tread wear. Many steering arm and knuckle assemblies must be replaced as a unit. If the steering arms are bent, knuckle replacement is required.

Steering Knuckle Removal and Replacement. The steering knuckle replacement procedure varies depending on the type of front suspension. Always follow the vehicle manufacturer's steering knuckle replacement procedure in the service manual.

Follow these steps to replace the steering knuckle on a front-wheel-drive vehicle with a MacPherson strut front suspension system:

1. Remove the wheel cover and loosen the front wheel nuts and the drive axle nut.

PHOTO SEQUENCE 6
TYPICAL PROCEDURE FOR MEASURING THE LOWER BALL JOINT HORIZONTAL MOVEMENT ON A MACPHERSON STRUT FRONT SUSPENSION

P6-1 *Raise the front suspension with a floor jack and place safety stands under the chassis at the vehicle manufacturer's recommended lifting points.*

P6-2 *Grasp the front tire at the top and bottom and rock the tire inward and outward while a coworker visually checks for movement in the front wheel bearing. If there is movement in the front wheel bearing, adjust or replace the bearing.*

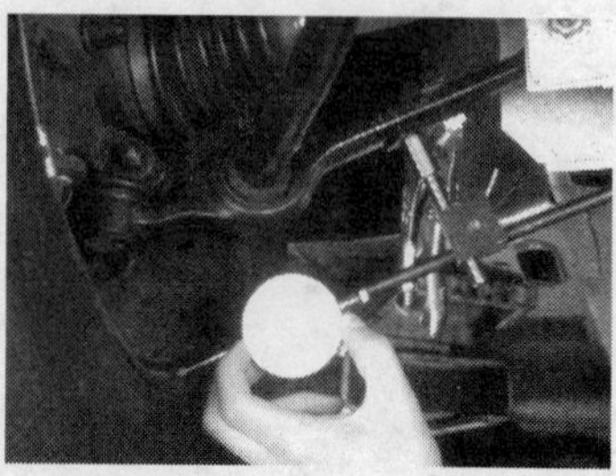

P6-3 *Position a dial indicator against the inner edge of the rim at the bottom. Preload and zero the dial indicator.*

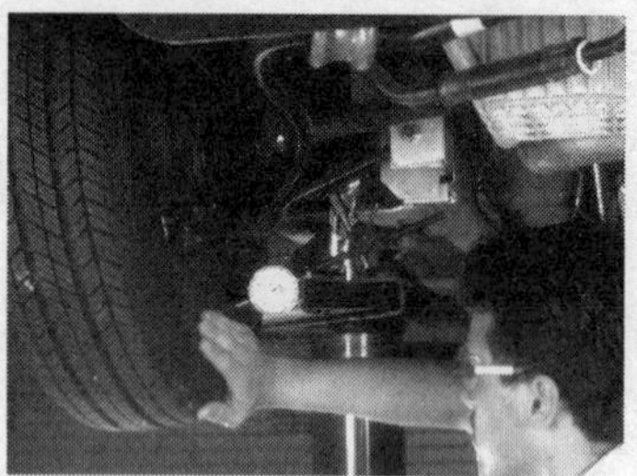

P6-4 *Grasp the bottom of the tire and pull outward.*

P6-5 *With the tire held outward, read the dial indicator.*

P6-6 *Push the bottom of the tire inward and be sure the dial indicator reading is zero. Adjust the dial indicator as required.*

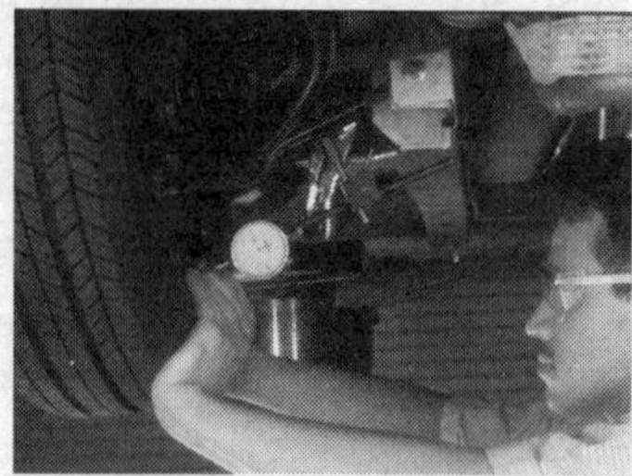

P6-7 *Grasp the bottom of the tire and pull outward.*

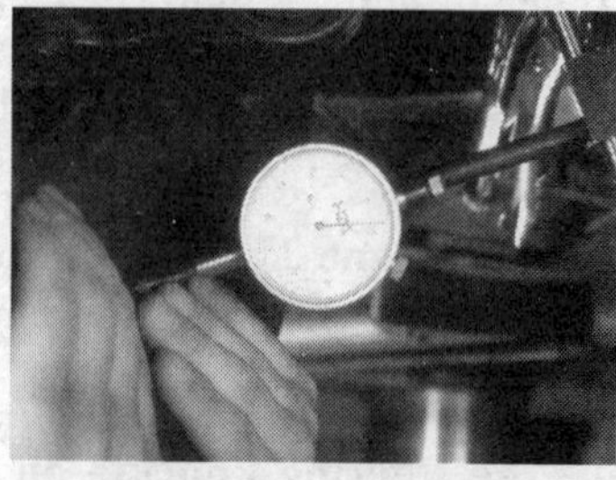

P6-8 *With the tire held in this position, read the dial indicator.*

P6-9 *If the dial indicator reading is more than specified, replace the lower ball joint.*

2. Lift the vehicle chassis on a hoist and allow the front suspension to drop downward. Remove the front wheel, brake caliper, brake rotor, and drive axle nut. Tie the brake caliper to a suspension component. Do not allow the caliper to hang on the end of the brake hose.
3. Remove the inner end of the drive axle from the transaxle with a pulling or prying action. On some Chrysler products, the differential cover must be removed and axle circlips compressed before the drive axle is removed from the transaxle.
4. Remove the outer end of the drive axle from the steering knuckle. On some early model Ford Escorts and Lynx, a puller is required for this operation.
5. Be sure the vehicle weight is supported on the hoist with the front suspension dropped downward. Disconnect the lower ball joint nuts from the mounting bolts in the lower control arm (Figure 6-14).

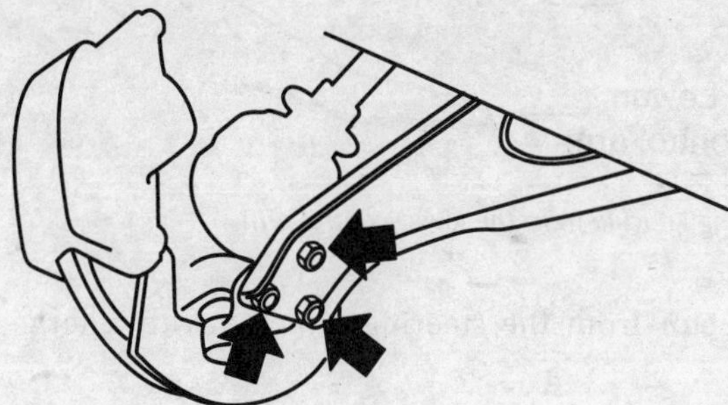

FIGURE 6-14 *Removing nuts from lower ball joint mounting bolts under the lower control arm.*

6. Remove the cotter pin from the outer tie-rod nut (Figure 6-15). Remove the outer tie-rod nut, and then use a puller to disconnect the tie-rod end from the steering knuckle (Figure 6-16).

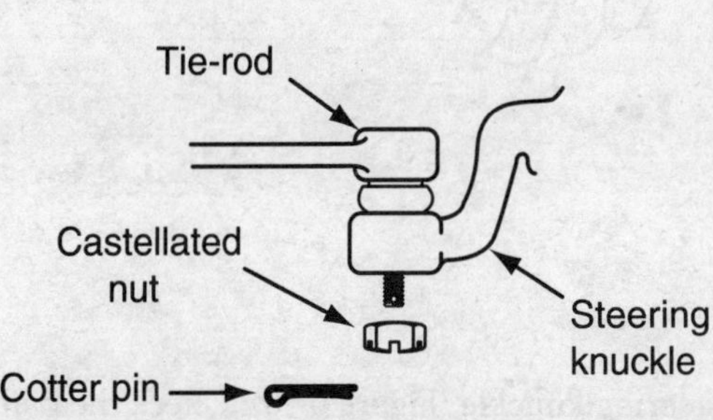

FIGURE 6-15 *Removing the cotter pin and nut from the outer tie-rod end.*

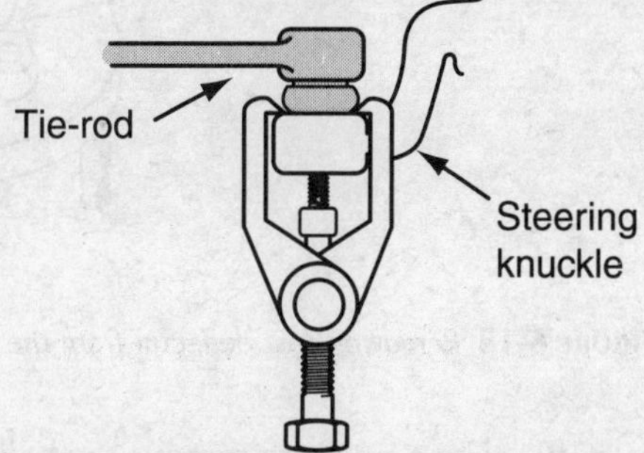

FIGURE 6-16 *Removing the outer tie-rod end from the steering knuckle.*

7. If an eccentric cam is used on one of the strut-to-knuckle bolts, mark the cam and bolt position in relation to the strut, and remove the strut-to-knuckle bolts.
8. Remove the knuckle from the strut, and lift the knuckle out of the chassis (Figure 6-17).

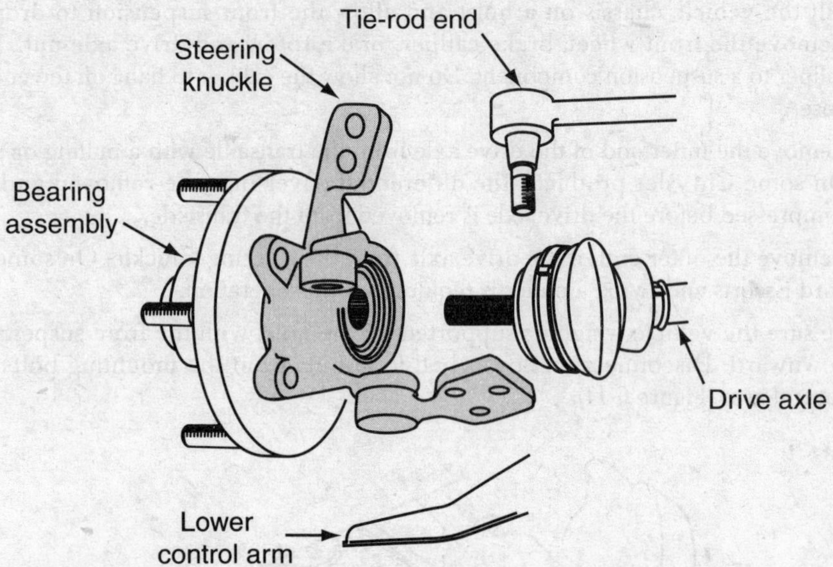

FIGURE 6-17 *Removing the steering knuckle from the lower control arm.*

9. Pry the dust deflector from the steering knuckle with a large flat-blade screwdriver (Figure 6-18).

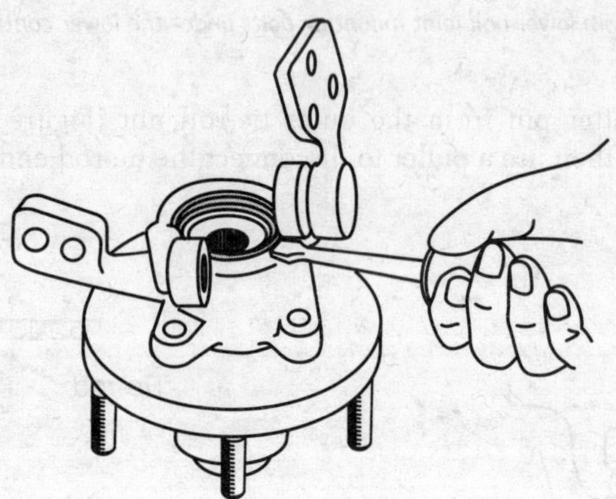

FIGURE 6-18 *Removing dust deflector from the steering knuckle.*

10. Use a puller to remove the ball joint from the steering knuckle (Figure 6-19). Check the ball joint and tie-rod end openings in the knuckle for wear and out-of-round. Replace the knuckle if these openings are worn or out-of-round.
11. Use the proper driving tool to reinstall the dust deflector in the steering knuckle (Figure 6-20).
12. Reverse steps 1 through 10 to reinstall the knuckle. Service or replace the wheel bearing as required. (Refer to Chapter 3 for wheel bearing service.) Torque all nuts to specifications and install cotter pins as required.

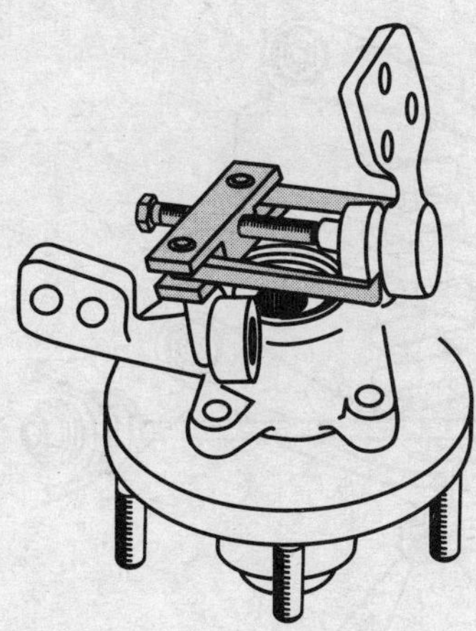

FIGURE 6-19 *Removing ball joint from the steering knuckle.*

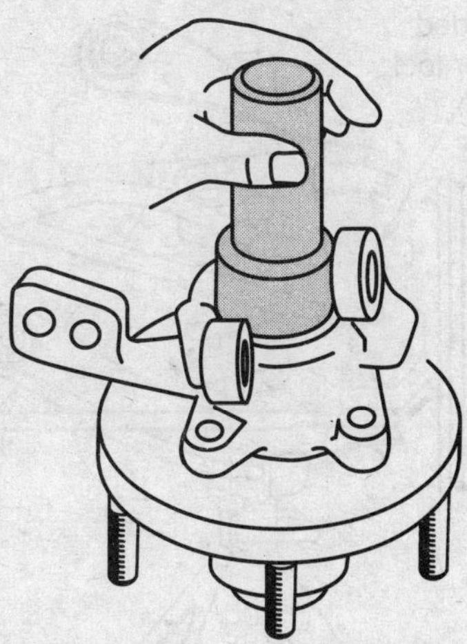

FIGURE 6-20 *Installing dust deflector in the steering knuckle.*

Front Steering Knuckle Replacement, Rear-Wheel-Drive Vehicle

Proceed as follows for steering knuckle replacement on short-and-long arm front suspension systems with the coil spring positioned between the lower control arm and the frame:

1. Remove the wheel cover and loosen the wheel nuts.
2. Lift the vehicle with a floor jack and place safety stands under the chassis so the front suspension drops downward. Lower the vehicle onto the safety stands and remove the floor jack.
3. Remove the front wheel, brake caliper, and the brake rotor and hub with the wheel bearings. Attach the brake caliper to a chassis component with a piece of wire. Do not allow the caliper to hang on the end of the brake hose.
4. Remove the outer tie-rod cotter pin and nut, and remove the outer tie-rod end from the steering arm.
5. Remove the cotter pins from the upper and lower ball joint nuts and loosen, but do not remove the nuts.

> **WARNING:** During the knuckle replacement procedure, the floor jack supports the spring tension when the ball joints are disconnected from the knuckle. Do not lower the floor jack. Chain the coil spring to the lower control arm as a safety precaution.

6. Support the lower control arm with a floor jack, and raise the floor jack until the spring tension is supported by the jack.
7. Remove both ball joint nuts, and remove the ball joint studs from the steering knuckle. A threaded spreader tool may be used to push the upper and lower ball joints from the knuckle (Figure 6-21 and Figure 6-22).
8. Pull upward on the upper control arm to remove the upper ball joint stud from the knuckle. Remove the knuckle from the lower ball joint stud. Check the ball joint and tie-rod end

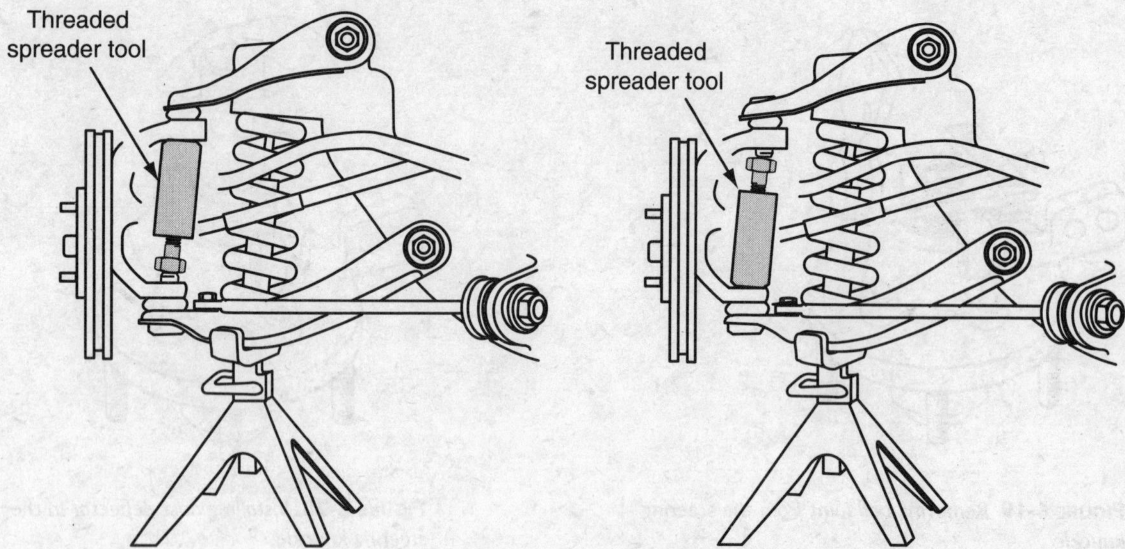

FIGURE 6-21 *Removing the lower ball joint from the steering knuckle.*

FIGURE 6-22 *Removing the upper ball joint from the steering knuckle.*

openings in the knuckle for wear and out-of-round. Replace the knuckle if these conditions are present.

9. Reverse steps 1 through 8 to install the steering knuckle. Tighten the ball joint nuts and the outer tie-rod nut to the specified torque, and install the cotter pins in these nuts. Adjust the front wheel bearings, and tighten the wheel nuts to the specified torque.

Ball Joint Replacement

Results of Ball Joint Wear. Worn ball joints affect steering angles and cause reduced directional stability and excessive tire tread wear.

Ball Joint Removal and Replacement. Ball joints may be pressed, bolted (or riveted), or threaded into the control arms (Figure 6-23). The ball joint replacement procedure varies depending on the type of suspension and the method of ball joint attachment. Always follow the vehicle manufacturer's recommended ball joint replacement procedure in the service manual.

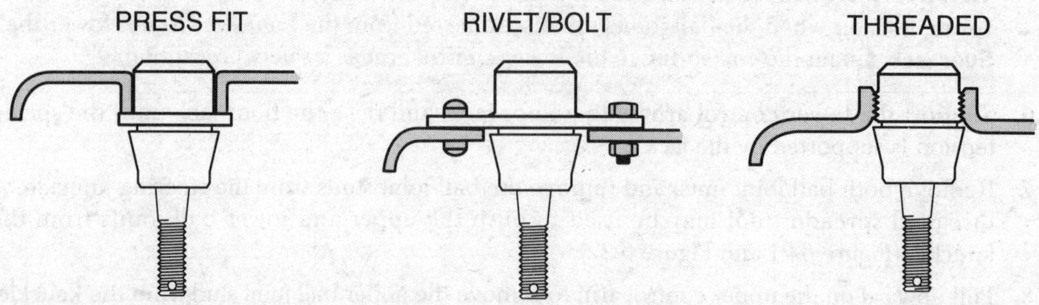

FIGURE 6-23 *Methods of ball joint attachment.*

The following are typical steps that apply to all three methods of ball joint attachment:

1. Remove the wheel cover and loosen the wheel nuts.
2. Lift the vehicle with a floor jack and place safety stands under the chassis so the front suspension is allowed to drop downward. Lower the vehicle onto the safety stands and remove the floor jack.
3. Remove the wheel and place a floor jack under the outer end of the lower control arm. Operate the floor jack and raise the lower control arm until the ball joints are unloaded. Remove other components, such as the brake caliper, rotor, and drive axle, as required to gain access to the ball joints.
4. Remove the cotter pin in the ball joint or joints that requires replacement, and loosen, but do not remove the ball joint stud nuts.
5. Loosen the ball joint stud tapers in the steering knuckle. A threaded expansion tool is available for this purpose.
6. Remove the ball joint nut and lift the knuckle off the ball joint stud. Block or tie up the knuckle and hub assembly to access the ball joint.
7. If the ball joint is riveted to the control arm, drill and punch out the rivets, and bolt the new ball joint to the control arm (Figure 6-24).

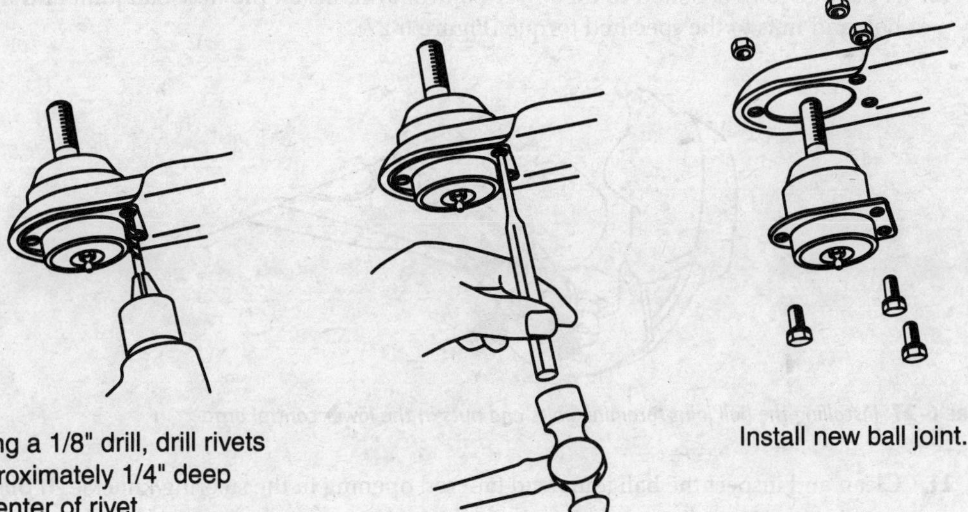

FIGURE 6-24 *Replacing the riveted ball joint.*

8. If the ball joint is pressed into the lower control arm, remove the ball joint dust boot, and use a pressing tool to remove and replace the ball joint (Figure 6-25 and Figure 6-26).
9. If the ball joint housing is threaded into the control arm, use the proper size socket to remove and install the ball joint. The replacement ball joint must be torqued to the

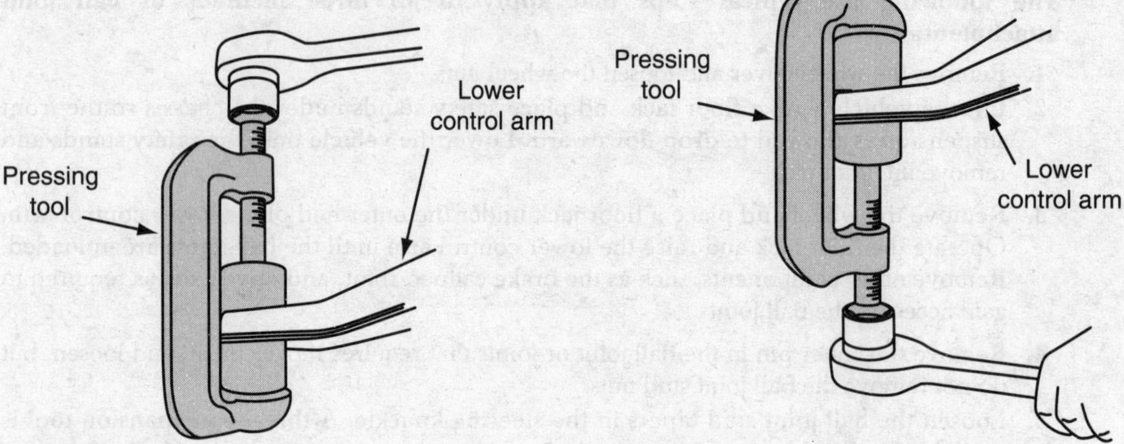

FIGURE 6-25 *Removing the pressed-in ball joint from the lower control arm.*

FIGURE 6-26 *Installing the pressed-in ball joint in the lower control arm.*

manufacturer's specifications. If a minimum of 125 ft.-lbs. of torque cannot be obtained, the control arm threads are damaged and control arm replacement is necessary.

10. If the ball joint is bolted to the lower control arm, install the new ball joint and tighten the bolt and nuts to the specified torque (Figure 6-27).

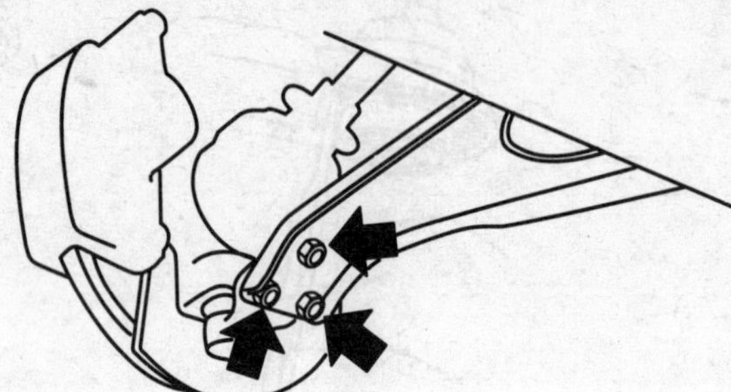

FIGURE 6-27 *Installing the ball joint retaining bolts and nuts in the lower control arm.*

11. Clean and inspect the ball joint stud tapered opening in the steering knuckle. If this opening is out-of-round or damaged, the knuckle must be replaced.
12. Check the fit of the ball joint stud in the steering knuckle opening. This stud should fit snugly in the opening and only the threads on the stud should extend through the knuckle. If the ball joint stud fits loosely in the knuckle tapered opening, either this opening is worn or the wrong ball joint has been supplied.

CAUTION: Never back off a ball joint stud nut to align the cotter pin openings in the nut and stud. This action may cause the ball joint stud to become loose in the opening where it is mounted. Always tighten the nut to the next hole to install the cotter pin.

13. Install the ball joint stud in the steering knuckle opening, making sure the stud is straight and centered. Install the stud nut and tighten this nut to the specified torque. Install a new

cotter pin through the stud and nut. Do not loosen the nut to align the nut and stud openings.

14. Reassemble the components that were removed in step 3. Make sure the wheel nuts are tightened to the specified torque.
15. After ball joint replacement, the front suspension alignment should be checked.

CONTROL ARM DIAGNOSIS AND SERVICE

Control Arm Diagnosis and Replacement

Upper and lower control arms should be inspected for cracks, bent conditions, and worn bushings. If the control arm bushings are worn, steering is erratic, especially on irregular road surfaces. Worn control arm bushings may cause a rattling noise while driving on irregular road surfaces. Dry or worn control arm bushings may cause a squeaking noise on irregular road surfaces. Caster and camber angles on the front suspension are altered by worn upper and lower control arm bushings. Incorrect caster or camber angles may cause the vehicle to pull to one side. Tire wear may be excessive when the camber angle is not within specifications.

Lower Control Arm Replacement, MacPherson Strut Suspension

The upper or lower control arm removal and replacement procedure varies depending on the type of suspension. Always follow the recommended procedure in the vehicle manufacturer's service manual.

The following is a lower control arm replacement procedure for a MacPherson strut front suspension:

1. Remove the wheel cover and loosen the wheel nuts and drive axle nut.
2. Lift the front of the vehicle with a floor jack and place jack stands under the chassis. Lower the vehicle onto the safety stands and allow the front suspension to drop downward.
3. Remove the front wheel and the front fender apron seal (Figure 6-28). Remove the drive axle nut (Figure 6-29).

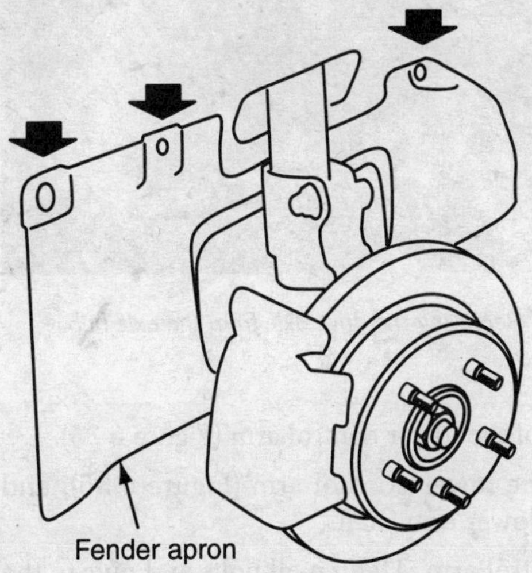

FIGURE 6-28 *Removing the front fender apron seal.*

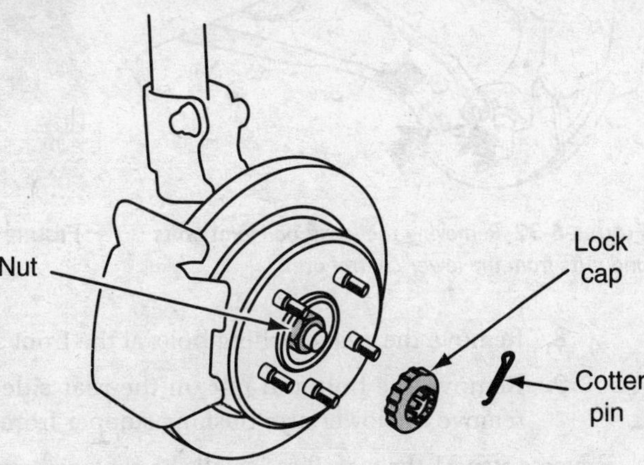

FIGURE 6-29 *Removing the drive axle cotter pin, lock, cap, and nut.*

4. Remove the cotter pin and nut from the outer tie-rod end, and use a puller to remove this tie-rod end from the steering arm (Figure 6-30).
5. Remove the stabilizer brackets from the lower control arm (Figure 6-31).

FIGURE 6-30 *Removing the outer tie-rod end.*

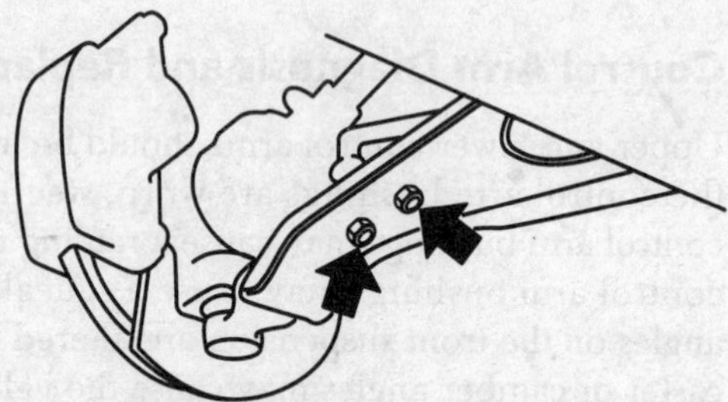

FIGURE 6-31 *Removing stabilizer brackets from the lower control arm.*

6. Remove the lower ball joint nuts and bolts from the lower control arm (Figure 6-32).
7. Remove the drive axle from the axle hub (Figure 6-33), and secure the drive axle to a suspension component with a piece of wire (Figure 6-34). Do not allow the drive axle to hang downward.

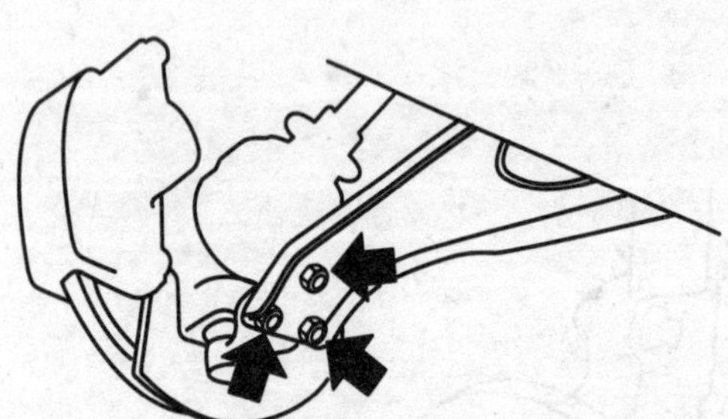

FIGURE 6-32 *Removing the lower ball joint bolts and nuts from the lower control arm.*

FIGURE 6-33 *Removing the drive axle from the axle hub.*

8. Remove the two attaching bolts at the front side of the lower control arm (Figure 6-35).
9. Remove the bolt and nut on the rear side of the lower control arm (Figure 6-36), and remove the lower arm bushing stopper from the lower arm shaft.

Reverse steps 1 through 9 to install the replacement control arm. Tighten all bolts and nuts to the specified torque, and install cotter pins as required.

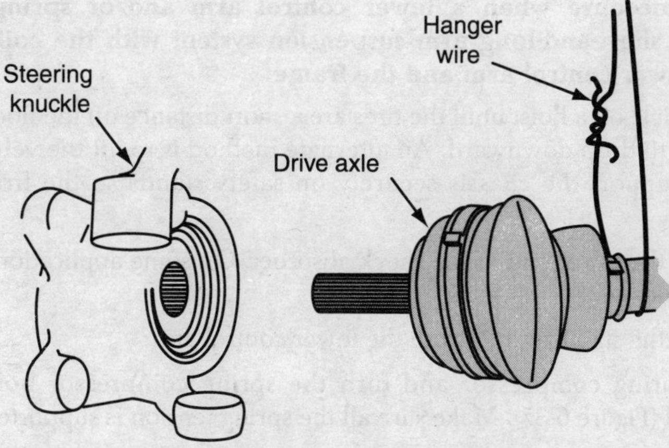

FIGURE 6-34 *Securing the drive axle with a piece of wire.*

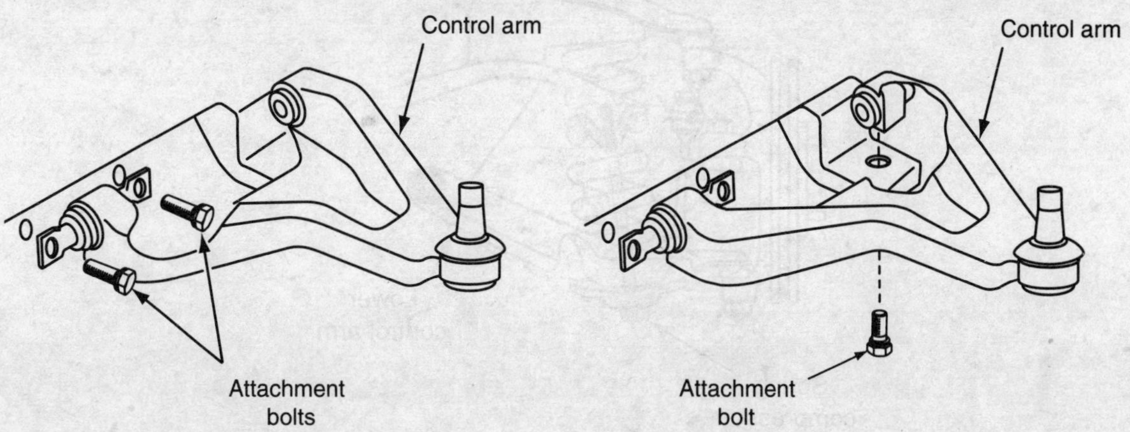

FIGURE 6-35 *Removing the bolts from the front side of the lower control arm.*

FIGURE 6-36 *Removing the bolt and nut from the rear side of the lower control arm.*

Lower Control Arm and Spring Replacement, Short-and-Long Arm Suspension

WARNING: During control arm and spring replacement, the coil spring tension is supported by a compressing tool or floor jack. Always follow the vehicle manufacturer's recommended control arm and spring replacement procedures very carefully. Serious personal injury or property damage may occur if the spring tension is released suddenly.

Broken coil springs may cause a rattling noise while driving on irregular road surfaces. Weak or broken coil springs also reduce curb riding height. A rattling noise while driving on road irregularities may also be caused by worn or broken spring insulators. Since weak or broken coil springs affect front suspension alignment angles, this problem may cause reduced directional stability, excessive tire wear, and harsh riding.

Follow this procedure when a lower control arm and/or spring is replaced on a vehicle with a short-and-long arm suspension system with the coil springs positioned between the lower control arm and the frame:

1. Lift the vehicle on a hoist until the tires are a short distance off the floor, and allow the front suspension to drop downward. An alternate method is to lift the vehicle with a floor jack, and then support the chassis securely on safety stands so the front suspension drops downward.
2. Disconnect the lower end of the shock absorber. On some applications, the shock absorber must be removed.
3. Disconnect the stabilizer bar from the lower control arm.
4. Install a spring compressor and turn the spring compressor bolt until the spring is compressed (Figure 6-37). Make sure all the spring tension is supported by the compressing tool.

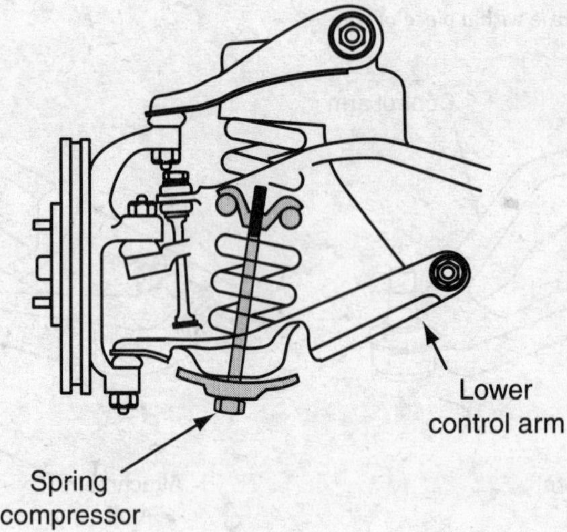

FIGURE 6-37 *Spring compressing tool installed on a spring in a short-and-long arm suspension system.*

5. Place a floor jack under the lower control arm, and raise the jack until the control arm is raised and the rebound bumper is not making contact.
6. Remove the lower ball joint cotter pin and nut, and use a threaded expansion tool to loosen the lower ball joint stud.
7. Lower the floor jack very slowly to lower the control arm and coil spring.
8. Disconnect the lower control arm inner mounting bolts, and remove the lower control arm.
9. Rotate the compressing tool bolt to release the spring tension, and remove the spring from the control arm.
10. Inspect the lower control arm for a bent condition or cracks. If either of these conditions is present, replace the control arm. Visually inspect all control arm bushings. Loose or worn bushings must be replaced. Visually inspect upper and lower spring insulators for cracks and wear, and inspect the spring seat areas in the chassis and lower control arm. Worn or cracked spring insulators must be replaced.

11. Reverse steps 1 through 9 to install the lower control arm. Be sure the coil spring and insulators are properly seated in the lower control arm and in the upper spring seat.

Note: See Chapter 5 for strut and spring service.

Upper Control Arm Removal and Replacement, Short-and-Long Arm Suspension System

Proceed as follows when replacing an upper control arm on a short-and-long arm suspension system with the front coil springs located between the lower control arm and the frame:

1. Remove the wheel cover and loosen the wheel nuts.
2. Lift the vehicle with a floor jack and install safety stands under the chassis. Lower the vehicle onto the safety stands so the front suspension drops downward.
3. Remove the front wheel and tire.
4. Place a floor jack under the lower control arm and raise this arm. Make sure the rebound bumper is not making contact.
5. Remove the cotter pin and loosen, but do not remove the upper ball joint nut.
6. Use a threaded expansion tool to loosen the ball joint stud in the control arm. Make sure the floor jack is supporting the spring tension.

CAUTION: Since the floor jack is supporting the spring tension, do not lower the floor jack until the ball joint is reconnected and the ball joint nut is tightened to the specified torque.

7. Remove the ball joint nut and the inner control arm mounting bolts. If shims are located on the inner control arm mounting bolts, note the shim position.
8. Remove the control arm from the chassis.
9. Visually inspect the upper control arm for a bent or cracked condition. Inspect the control arm bushing openings for wear, and replace the control arm if it is bent, cracked, or worn in the bushing areas. Inspect the control arm shaft and bushings for wear, and replace all worn parts (Figure 6-38).
10. Install the control arm and place the original number of shims on the inner mounting bolts. Tighten these bolts to the manufacturer's specifications.
11. Install the ball joint stud in the steering knuckle, and tighten the stud nut to the specified torque.
12. Install the upper ball joint cotter pin and the front wheel. Tighten the wheel nuts to the specified torque.

The front suspension alignment angles should be checked after upper control arm replacement.

Rebound Bumpers

Rebound bumpers are usually bolted to the lower control arm or to the chassis. Inspect the rebound bumpers for cracks, wear, and flattened conditions (Figure 6-39). Damaged rebound bumpers may be caused by sagged springs and insufficient curb riding height or worn-out shock absorbers and struts. If the rebound bumpers must be replaced, remove the mounting bolts and the bumper. Install the new bumper and tighten the mounting bolts to the specified torque.

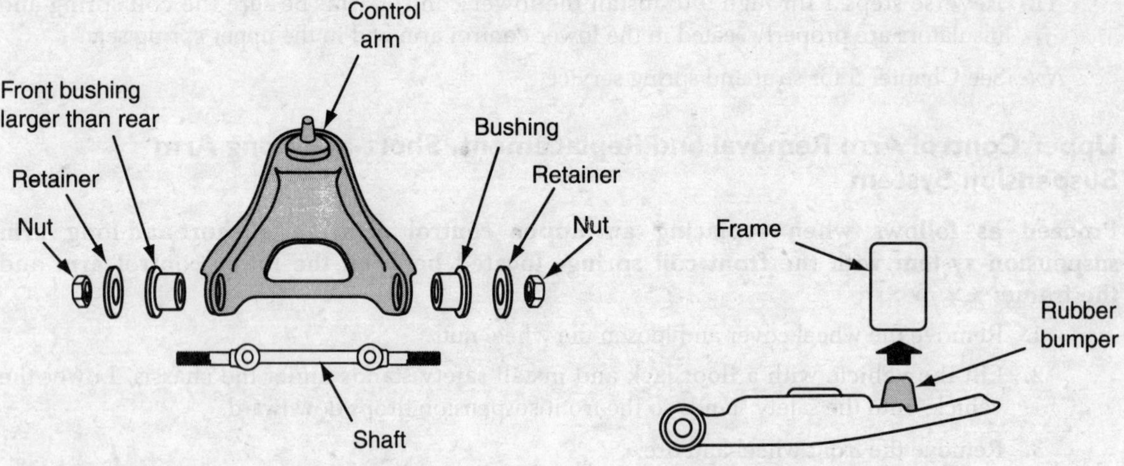

FIGURE 6-38 *Upper control arm components.*

FIGURE 6-39 *Rebound bumper.*

Front Lower Control Arm Bushing Removal and Replacement

All suspension bushings should be checked periodically for wear, looseness, and deterioration. These bushings are important for providing quiet suspension operation and preventing the transmission of suspension vibration to the chassis and passenger compartment. When a bushing is contained in a steel sleeve, press only on the outer sleeve during the removal and replacement procedure. The control arm bushing removal and replacement procedure varies depending on the type of suspension system. Always follow the vehicle manufacturer's recommended procedure in the service manual. Special bushing removal and replacement tools are required for control arm bushing replacement. A front control arm bushing removal tool and spacer is used to remove the control arm bushing (Figure 6-40). The spacer is installed between the bushing support lugs to prevent distorting these lugs during the bushing removal process.

A different tool is required to install the new front control arm bushing (Figure 6-41). The same spacer that is used during the bushing removal is installed between the bushing lugs during bushing installation.

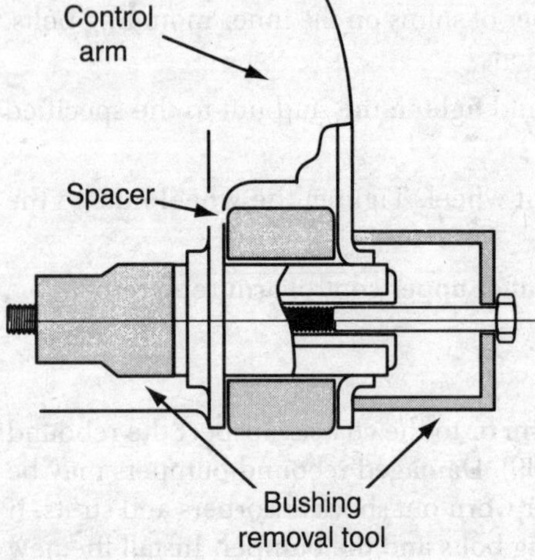

FIGURE 6-40 *Removing the front control arm bushing.*

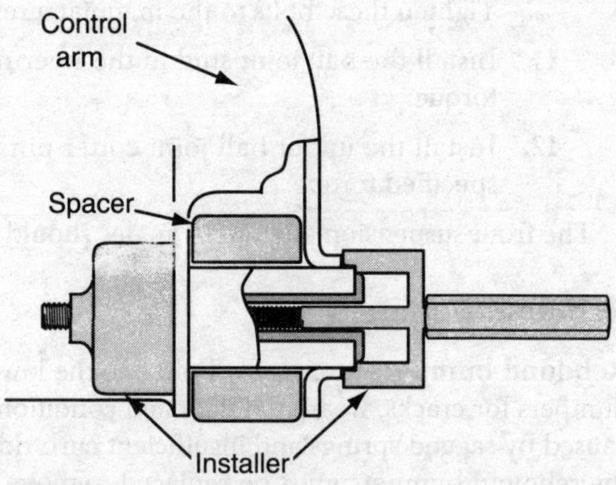

FIGURE 6-41 *Installing the front control arm bushing.*

After the front control arm bushing is installed, a bushing flaring tool is used to flare the bushing (Figure 6-42). Notice that a spacer is installed between the bushing lugs during the flaring process. Flaring retains the bushing securely (Figure 6-43).

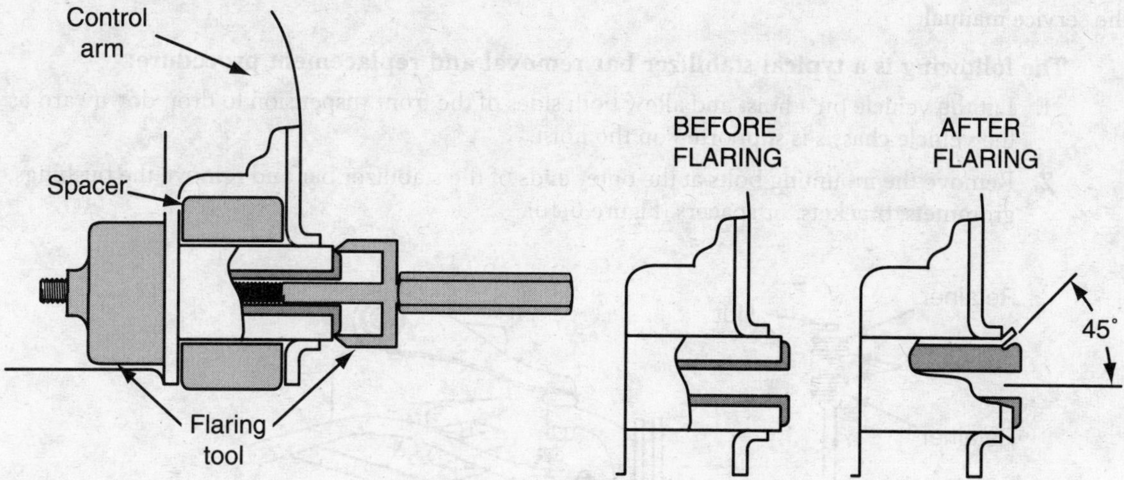

FIGURE 6-42 *Flaring the front control arm bushing.*

FIGURE 6-43 *Front control arm bushing after flaring.*

The rear control arm bushing is replaced with the same procedure as the front control arm bushing. Some of the same special tools are used for rear control arm bushing replacement (Figure 6-44 and Figure 6-45).

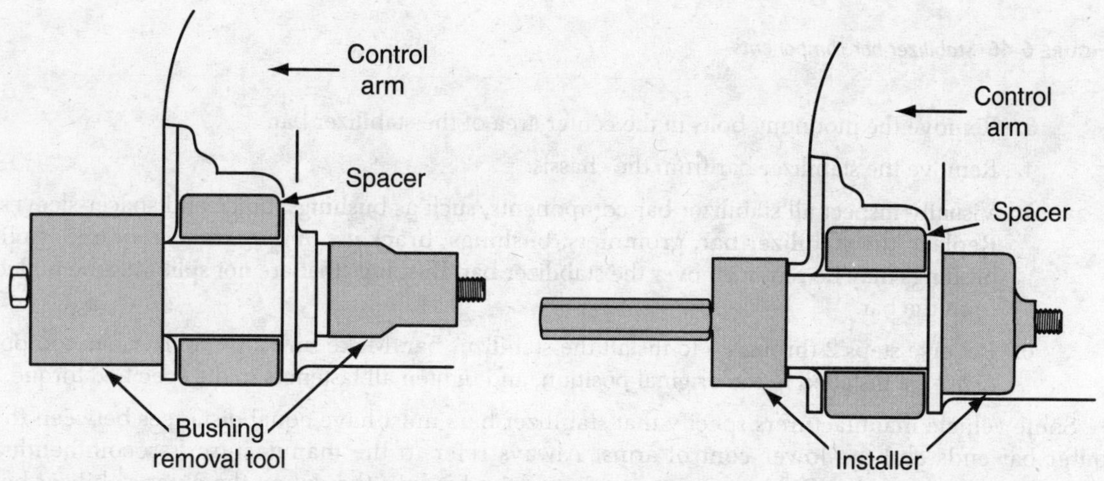

FIGURE 6-44 *Removing the rear control arm bushing.*

FIGURE 6-45 *Installing the rear control arm bushing.*

Stabilizer Bar Diagnosis and Replacement

Worn **stabilizer bar** mounting bushings, grommets, or mounting bolts cause a rattling noise as the vehicle is driven on irregular road surfaces. A weak stabilizer bar or worn bushings and grommets cause harsh riding and excessive body sway while driving on irregular road surfaces. Worn or very dry stabilizer bar bushings may cause a squeaking noise on irregular road surfaces. All stabilizer bar components should be visually inspected for wear. Stabilizer bar removal and replacement procedures vary depending on the vehicle. Always follow the vehicle manufacturer's recommended procedure in the service manual.

The following is a typical stabilizer bar removal and replacement procedure:

1. Lift the vehicle on a hoist and allow both sides of the front suspension to drop downward as the vehicle chassis is supported on the hoist.
2. Remove the mounting bolts at the outer ends of the stabilizer bar and remove the bushings, grommets, brackets, or spacers (Figure 6-46).

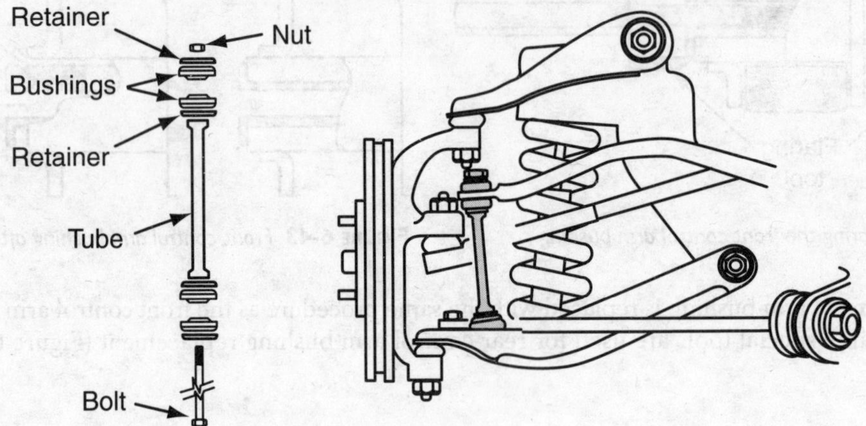

FIGURE 6-46 *Stabilizer bar components.*

3. Remove the mounting bolts in the center area of the stabilizer bar.
4. Remove the stabilizer bar from the chassis.
5. Visually inspect all stabilizer bar components, such as bushings, bolts, and spacer sleeves. Replace the stabilizer bar, grommets, bushings, brackets, or spacers as required. Split bushings may be removed over the stabilizer bar. Bushings that are not split must be pulled from the bar.
6. Reverse steps 2 through 4 to install the stabilizer bar. Make sure all stabilizer bar components are installed in the original position, and tighten all fasteners to the specified torque.

Some vehicle manufacturers specify that stabilizer bars must have equal distances between the outer bar ends and the lower control arms. Always refer to the manufacturer's recommended measurement procedure. If this measurement is required, adjust the nut on the outer stabilizer bar mounting bolt until equal distances are obtained between the outer bar ends and the lower control arms. Worn grommets cause these distances to be unequal.

Strut Rod Diagnosis and Replacement

Some front suspension systems have a **strut rod** connected from the lower control arm to the frame. Rubber grommets isolate the rod from the chassis components. Worn strut rod grommets may allow the lower control arm to move rearward or forward. This movement changes the caster angle, which may affect steering quality and cause the vehicle to pull to one side. A bent strut rod also causes steering pull. Worn strut rod grommets or loose mounting bolts cause a rattling noise while driving on irregular road surfaces. Inspect the strut rod grommets visually for wear and deterioration. With the vehicle lifted on a hoist, grasp the strut rod firmly and apply vertical and horizontal force to check the rod and grommets for movement. Worn grommets must be replaced. If a strut rod is bent, replace the rod.

Follow these steps for strut rod replacement:

1. Lift the vehicle on a hoist.
2. Remove the strut rod nut from the front end of the rod.
3. Remove the strut rod bolts from the lower control arm.
4. Pull the strut rod rearward to remove the rod (Figure 6-47).

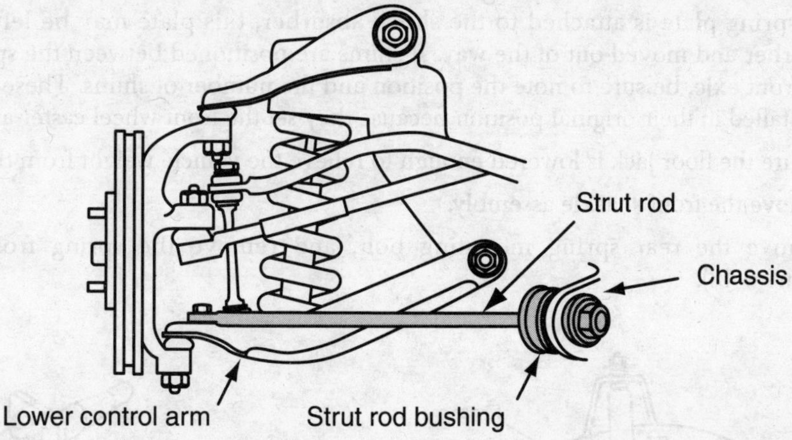

FIGURE 6-47 *Strut rod.*

5. Remove the bushings from the opening in the chassis.
6. Visually inspect the strut rod, bushings, washers, and retaining bolts. Replace all worn parts. Reverse steps 1 through 5 to reinstall the strut rod. Tighten the strut rod nut and bolts to the specified torque.

Since strut rod and bushing conditions affect front suspension alignment, check front suspension alignment after strut rod service.

Front Leaf Spring Inspection and Replacement

Front leaf springs are used in some truck suspension systems. These springs are mounted longitudinally with a spring on each side of the suspension. Many leaf springs have plastic silencers between the spring leafs. If these silencers are worn out, creaking and squawking noises will be heard when the vehicle is driven over road irregularities at low speeds.

When the silencers require checking or replacement, lift the vehicle with a floor jack and support the frame on safety stands so the suspension hangs downward. With the vehicle weight no longer applied to the springs, the spring leafs may be pried apart with a pry bar to remove and replace the silencers. On some leaf springs, the clamps must be removed to replace the silencers.

Leaf springs should be inspected for a sagged condition, which causes the curb riding height to be less than specified. Leaf springs should also be visually inspected for broken leafs, broken center bolts, and worn shackles or bushings. Weak or broken leaf springs affect front suspension alignment angles and cause excessive tire tread wear, reduced directional stability, and harsh riding. A rattling noise while driving on irregular road surfaces may be caused by worn shackles or bushings. A broken center bolt usually allows one side of the front suspension to move rearward in relation to the other side. This action may cause steering pull to one side. Worn shackles and bushings lower curb riding height and cause a rattling noise on road irregularities.

The following is a typical front leaf spring replacement procedure:

1. Lift the front end of the vehicle with a floor jack under the front axle and place safety stands under the frame. Lower the vehicle weight onto the safety stands, but leave the floor jack under the front axle to support some of the front suspension weight.
2. Remove the nuts from the spring U-bolts, and remove the U-bolts and lower spring plate. If the spring plate is attached to the shock absorber, this plate may be left on the shock absorber and moved out of the way. If shims are positioned between the spring plate and the front axle, be sure to note the position and the number of shims. These shims must be reinstalled in their original position because they set the front wheel caster angle.
3. Be sure the floor jack is lowered enough to relieve the vehicle weight from the springs.
4. Remove the front shackle assembly.
5. Remove the rear spring mounting bolt, and remove the spring from the chassis (Figure 6-48).

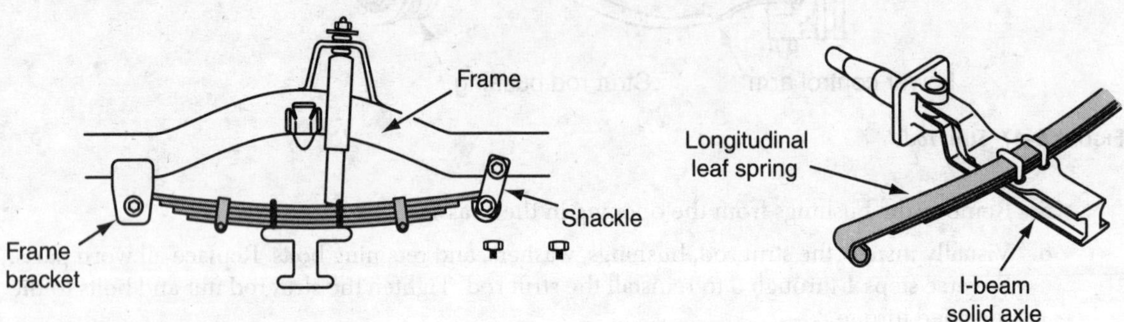

FIGURE 6-48 *Front leaf spring.*

6. Check all the spring hangers, bolts, bushings, and shackle plates for wear, and replace as required. Springs with broken or sagged leafs are usually sent to a spring rebuilding shop for repair.
7. Check the spring center bolt to be sure it is not broken.
8. Reverse steps 1 through 5 to install the front springs. Tighten all bolts to the manufacturer's specifications.

REMOVING AND REPLACING LONGITUDINALLY MOUNTED TORSION BARS

Worn torsion bar components, such as pivot cushion bushings and control arm bushings, result in harsh riding and suspension noise when driving on road irregularities. A worn torsion bar hex and anchor may cause a rattling noise while driving on irregular road surfaces. Weak torsion bars or those with worn bushings or anchors cause reduced curb riding height, which may result in reduced directional stability and excessive tire tread wear. Always follow the vehicle manufacturer's recommended procedure in the service manual for torsion bar removal and replacement.

The following is a typical torsion bar removal and replacement procedure:

> **WARNING:** Some torsion bar front suspension systems on sport utility vehicles (SUVs) are combined with an air suspension system. When servicing these systems, the air suspension switch in the rear jack storage area must be shut off before performing any suspension service or hoisting, jacking, or towing the vehicle. If this procedure is not followed, personal injury and vehicle damage may occur.

1. Raise the vehicle on a lift with the tires supported on the lift.
2. Remove the torsion bar cover plate bolts and the cover plate (Figure 6-49).
3. Measure and record the distance from the lip on the head of the torsion bar adjusting bolt to the casting surface this bolt is threaded into (Figure 6-50). When reinstalled, this bolt must be adjusted to this same measurement.

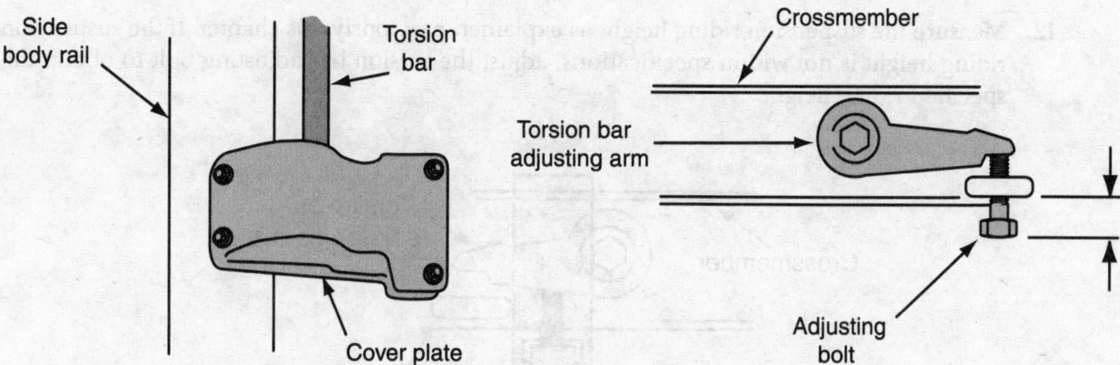

FIGURE 6-49 *Torsion bar cover plate.*

FIGURE 6-50 *Measuring the torsion bar adjusting bolt position.*

4. Install the torsion bar tool and adapters (Figure 6-51). Tighten this tool until the torsion bar adjuster lifts off the adjustment bolt.

> **CAUTION:** The torsion bar adjusting bolt is coated with a dry adhesive. This bolt must be replaced if it is backed off or removed. Failure to follow this procedure may cause the bolt to loosen during operation, resulting in improper wheel alignment, reduced steering control, increased tire wear, and reduced ride quality.

5. Remove the torsion bar adjustment bolt and nut.

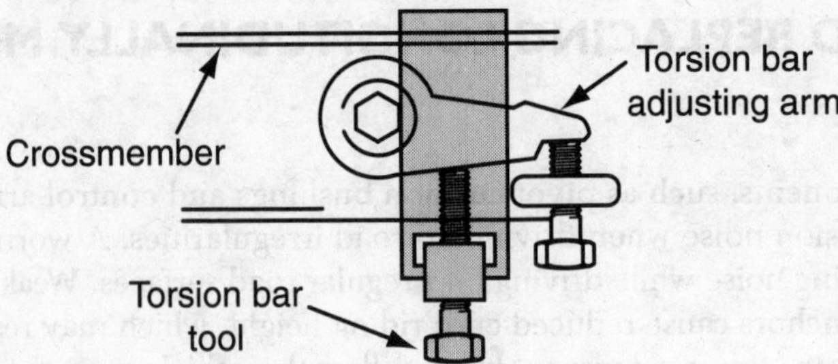

FIGURE 6-51 *Torsion bar tool and adapters.*

6. Loosen the torsion bar tool to remove all the tension from the torsion bar (Figure 6-52).
7. Use the end of a screwdriver to place matching alignment marks on the torsion bar and the adjuster so these components may be reassembled in the same position. Remove the torsion bar insulator. Pull the torsion bar to the rear to remove this bar from the lower control arm.
8. Position the torsion bar in the lower control arm.
9. Install the torsion bar adjuster on the torsion bar with the alignment marks properly aligned (Figure 6-53).
10. Install the torsion bar tool and adapters. Tighten the torsion bar tool until a new adjustment bolt can be installed. Tighten this bolt until the measurement obtained in step 3 is obtained between the head of the bolt and the casting the bolt is threaded into.
11. Install the torsion bar cover plate, and tighten the plate retaining bolts to the specified torque.
12. Measure the suspension riding height as explained previously this chapter. If the suspension riding height is not within specifications, adjust the torsion bar adjusting bolt to obtain the specified riding height.

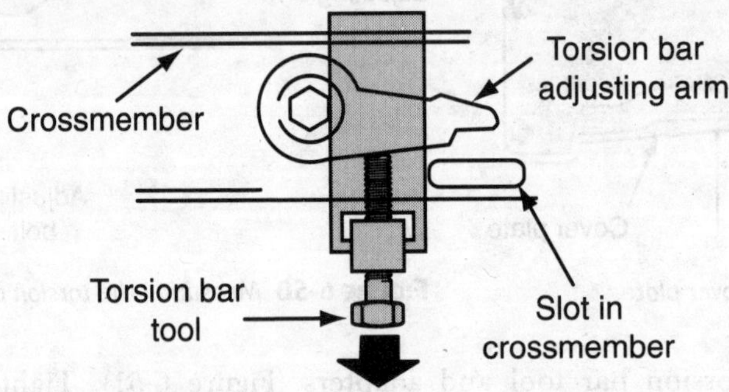

FIGURE 6-52 *Loosening the torsion bar tool.*

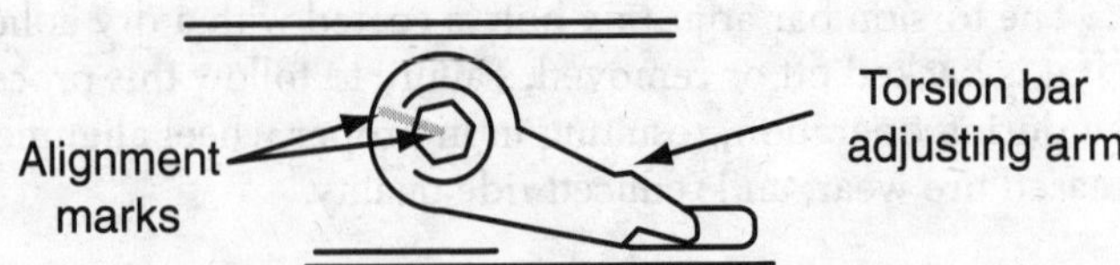

FIGURE 6-53 *Alignment marks placed on the torsion bar and adjuster.*

TABLE 6-1 *Front Suspension Diagnosis*

PROBLEM	SYMPTOMS	POSSIBLE CAUSES
Low riding height	Harsh ride quality, worn strikeout bumpers	Weak springs, worn control arm bushings, bent control arms, improper torsion bar adjustment
Steering wander, excessive edge wear on front tires	Erratic steering control when driving straight ahead	Worn ball joints, worn suspension or steering components, improper wheel alignment
Suspension noise	Rattling or squeaking noise when driving on road irregularities	Worn or dry stabilizer bar links and bushings, worn shock absorber or strut rod bushings
Improper steering control	Steering pull to the left or right when driving straight ahead	Improper wheel alignment, worn control arm bushings, bent control arms
Improper steering control while braking	Steering pull to the left or right only when braking	Worn strut rod bushings, loose strut rod mounting, worn lower control arm bushings
Leaf spring noise	Squeaking noise when driving on road irregularities	Worn silencers between the spring leafs

CASE STUDY

A customer complained about steering pull to the left while braking on a 2005 Chrysler 300. The technician questioned the customer about other symptoms, but the customer stated that the steering did not pull while driving, and the car had no other problems. Further questioning of the customer revealed that extensive brake work had been done in an attempt to correct the problem. The front brake pads had been replaced and the front brake rotors had been turned.

While performing a road test, the technician discovered the car had a definite pull to the left while braking, but the steering was normal while driving. During the road test, no other problems were evident. The technician removed the front wheels and brake rotors. A careful examination of the brake linings and rotor surfaces indicated these components were in excellent condition. The technician checked the rotor surfaces to be sure they were both in the same condition. The pistons in both front calipers moved freely. An inspection of the brake lines and hoses did not reveal any visible problems, and a pressure check at each front brake caliper indicated equal pressures at both front wheels during a brake application.

Next, the technician made a visual inspection of the steering and suspension components and discovered a worn, loose left front strut rod bushing. This bushing was replaced, and the strut rod nut tightened to the specified torque. The strut rod was in satisfactory condition. A road test of the car indicated no steering pull during brake application.

SERVICE TIPS

- Some ball joints have a tapered stud, and a nut is threaded onto the top of this stud to retain the ball joint in the steering knuckle. Other ball joints have a straight stud, and a pinch bolt extends through the steering knuckle and a notch in the side of the ball joint stud to hold the ball joint in the steering knuckle.
- Excessively worn rebound bumpers indicate worn-out shock absorbers, reduced curb riding height, or driving continually on irregular road surfaces.

REVIEW QUESTIONS

1. While discussing curb riding height:
   Technician A says worn control arm bushings reduce curb riding height. *Technician B* says incorrect curb riding height affects most other front suspension angles.
   Who is correct?
   A. Technician A **C.** Both A and B
   B. Technician B **D.** Neither A nor B
2. The shoulder on the ball joint grease fitting is inside the ball joint cover:
   Technician A says the ball joint should be replaced. *Technician B* says a longer grease fitting should be installed.
   Who is correct?
   A. Technician A **C.** Both A and B
   B. Technician B **D.** Neither A nor B
3. While discussing ball joint unloading on a short-and-long arm suspension system with the coil springs between the lower control arm and the chassis:
   Technician A says a steel spacer should be installed under the upper control arm. *Technician B* says a floor jack should be placed under the lower control arm to unload the ball joints.
   Who is correct?
   A. Technician A **C.** Both A and B
   B. Technician B **D.** Neither A nor B
4. While discussing ball joint radial measurement:
   Technician A says the dial indicator should be positioned against the top of the ball joint stud. *Technician B* says the front wheel bearing adjustment does not affect the ball joint radial measurement.
   Who is correct?
   A. Technician A **C.** Both A and B
   B. Technician B **D.** Neither A nor B
5. While discussing ball joint installation:
   Technician A says the ball joint nut may be backed off to install the cotter pin. *Technician B* says only the ball joint threads should extend above the opening in the steering knuckle.
   Who is correct?
   A. Technician A **C.** Both A and B
   B. Technician B **D.** Neither A nor B

6. When installing a new threaded ball joint in a lower control arm, the technician can only torque the ball joint to 90 ft.-lbs. The necessary repair for this problem is to:
   A. Weld the ball joint into the control arm.
   B. Place Loctite on the ball joint threads.
   C. Replace the lower control arm.
   D. Install a larger diameter ball joint.

7. All of these defects could result in worn-out rebound bumpers EXCEPT:
   A. Sagged springs.
   B. Worn-out shock absorbers.
   C. Continual driving on rough roads.
   D. Curb riding height more than specified.

8. When removing and replacing control arm bushings:
   A. If the bushing is contained in a steel sleeve, press on the rubber bushing.
   B. A spacer should be installed between the control arm support lugs during bushing removal and installation.
   C. The same tool is used for bushing removal and replacement.
   D. Bushing flaring is necessary to expand the bushing.

9. A car experiences excessive body sway when cornering, but there is no abnormal noise in the suspension. The most likely cause of this problem is:
   A. Stabilizer bar bushing is missing.
   B. A weak stabilizer bar.
   C. Stabilizer bar grommets are worn out.
   D. A broken stabilizer bar.

10. The steering on a vehicle pulls to the left while driving straight ahead. The most likely cause of this problem is:
   A. The left front strut rod is bent.
   B. The left lower ball joint is worn.
   C. Worn front stabilizer bushings on the left side.
   D. Reduced curb riding height on both sides of the front suspension.

CHALLENGE QUESTIONS

1. The customer says her 1987 Blazer pulls to the left. A cursory check of the vehicle shows that the right front tire height is too low. The next step to diagnose the condition would be:
   A. Check the ball joints.
   B. Check the torsion bar.
   C. Check the strut rod bushings.
   D. Check the stabilizer bar bushings.

2. A customer says her front-wheel-drive car has a steering wander problem on irregular road surfaces. All of the following could cause this problem EXCEPT:
   A. Worn stabilizer bar bushings.
   B. Worn ball joints.
   C. Worn strut rod bushings.
   D. Worn tie-rod ends.

3. While diagnosing a customer's complaint of steering instability on a MacPherson strut front suspension with wear indicator-type ball joints, an inspection of the ball joints shows the grease fittings to be solid.
Technician A says no movement of the fitting means the ball joint is good. *Technician B* says ball joint wear may not be apparent with the weight on the joint.
Who is correct?

A. A only | **C.** Both A and B
B. B only | **D.** Neither A nor B

4. A customer says her rear-wheel-drive car has excessive body sway while cornering. In diagnosing this problem, which of the following components should you check first?

A. Control arm bushings.
B. Strut rod bushings.
C. Stabilizer bar bushings.
D. Shock absorber bushings.

5. *Technician A* says a bent strut rod can cause a car to pull to one side. *Technician B* says a deteriorated strut rod bushing can cause steering and braking problems.
Who is correct?

A. A only | **C.** Both A and B
B. B only | **D.** Neither A nor B

JOB SHEET 18

Name ______________________________ Date ______________

MEASURE LOWER BALL JOINT VERTICAL AND RADIAL MOVEMENT, SHORT-AND-LONG ARM SUSPENSION SYSTEMS

Upon completion of this job sheet, you should be able to measure ball joint wear and determine the necessary ball joint service.

ASE Correlation

This job sheet is related to ASE Automotive Suspension and Steering Task: *Inspect and replace upper and lower ball joints.*

Tools and Materials

Ball joint dial indicator
Floor jack
Safety stands

Describe the Vehicle Being Worked On:

Year __________ Make ______________ Model ______________
VIN ____________________ Engine type and size ______________

Procedure

Task Completed

1. Raise the front of the vehicle with a floor jack lift pad positioned on the specified lifting point. ☐
2. Install safety stands near the outer ends of the lower control arms. Lower the floor jack so the control arms are supported on the safety stands. Remove the floor jack. ☐
3. Attach a dial indicator for ball joint measurement to the lower control arm, and position the dial indicator stem against the lower end of the steering knuckle next to the ball joint retaining nut if the suspension has a lower compression-loaded ball joint. When the suspension has a tension-loaded ball joint, place the indicator stem against the top of the ball joint stud.

   Type of ball joint

   Dial indicator stem position

4. Preload the dial indicator stem 0.250 in. (6.35 mm), and zero the dial indicator.

   Is the dial indicator preloaded and placed in the zero position? ☐ Yes ☐ No

   Instructor check ______________________________

5. Place a pry bar under the front tire and lift straight upward on the pry bar while a coworker observes the dial indicator. ☐

Task Completed

☐ **6.** Compare the reading on the dial indicator with the vehicle manufacturer's specifications. If the vertical ball joint movement exceeds specifications, replace the ball joint.

Specified ball joint vertical movement

Actual ball joint vertical movement

Necessary ball joint service

☐ **7.** Be sure the front wheel bearings are properly adjusted.

8. Attach the dial indicator to the lower control arm, and position the dial indicator against the inner edge of the wheel rim. Preload the dial indicator 0.250 in. (6.35 mm) and place the dial in the zero position.

Is the dial indicator preloaded and placed in the zero position? ☐ Yes ☐ No

Instructor check ______________________________

☐ **9.** Grasp the tire at the top and bottom, and try to rock the tire inward and outward while a coworker observes the dial indicator.

☐ **10.** Compare the reading on the dial indicator to the vehicle manufacturer's specifications. If the radial ball joint movement exceeds specifications, replace the ball joint.

Specified ball joint radial movement

Actual ball joint radial movement

☐ **11.** Repeat the measurements in steps 3 through 10 on the opposite side of the front suspension.

12. Based on your ball joint measurements, state all the necessary ball joint service and explain the reasons for your diagnosis.

____

____

____

Instructor's Response ______________________________

____

____

JOB SHEET 19

Name ______________________________ Date ______________

BALL JOINT REPLACEMENT

Upon completion of this job sheet, you should be able to remove and replace ball joints.

ASE Correlation

This job sheet is related to ASE Automotive Suspension and Steering Task: *Inspect and replace upper and lower ball joints.*

Tools and Materials

Floor jack
Safety stands
Ball joint loosening tool
Torque wrench

Describe the Vehicle Being Worked On:

Year __________ Make ______________ Model ______________
VIN ______________________ Engine type and size ______________________

Procedure

Task Completed

1. Remove the wheel cover and loosen the wheel nuts. ☐
2. Lift the vehicle with a floor jack and place safety stands under the chassis so the front suspension is allowed to drop downward. Lower the vehicle onto the safety stands and remove the floor jack. ☐
3. Remove the wheel and place a floor jack under the outer end of the lower control arm. Operate the floor jack and raise the lower control arm until the ball joints are unloaded.
   Are the ball joints properly unloaded? ☐ Yes ☐ No
   Instructor check ______________________
4. Remove other components, such as the brake caliper, rotor, and drive axle, as required to gain access to the ball joints. ☐
5. Remove the cotter pin in the ball joint or joints that require replacement, and loosen, but do not remove, the ball joint stud nuts.
   Is the ball joint stud nut loosened? ☐ Yes ☐ No
   Instructor check ______________________
6. Loosen the ball joint stud tapers in the steering knuckle. A threaded expansion tool is available for this purpose.
   Are the ball joint stud tapers loosened? ☐ Yes ☐ No
   Instructor check ______________________
7. Remove the ball joint nut and lift the knuckle off the ball joint stud. Block or tie up the knuckle and hub assembly to access the ball joint. ☐
8. If the ball joint is riveted to the control arm, drill and punch out the rivets and bolt the new ball joint to the control arm. ☐
9. If the ball joint is pressed into the lower control arm, remove the ball joint dust boot and use a pressing tool to remove and replace the ball joint. ☐

Task Completed

10. If the ball joint housing is threaded into the control arm, use the proper size socket to remove and install the ball joint. The replacement ball joint must be torqued to the manufacturer's specifications. If a minimum of 125 ft.-lbs. of torque cannot be obtained, the control arm threads are damaged and control arm replacement is necessary.

Ball joint torque, threaded ball joint ________________

Control arm condition, threaded ball joint: ☐ Satisfactory ☐ Unsatisfactory

11. If the ball joint is bolted to the lower control arm, install the new ball joint and tighten the bolt and nuts to the specified torque.

Ball joint bolt torque ________________

☐ **12.** Clean and inspect the ball joint stud tapered opening in the steering knuckle. If this opening is out-of-round or damaged, the knuckle must be replaced.

Condition of ball joint stud opening in the steering knuckle:

☐ Satisfactory ☐ Unsatisfactory

13. Check the fit of the ball joint stud in the steering knuckle opening. This stud should fit snugly in the opening and only the threads on the stud should extend through the knuckle. If the ball joint stud fits loosely in the knuckle tapered opening, either this opening is worn or the wrong ball joint has been supplied.

Ball joint stud smooth tapered area appearing above steering knuckle surface:

☐ Yes ☐ No

If the answer to this question is yes, state the necessary repairs and explain the reason for your diagnosis.

____

____

Ball joint stud fit in the steering knuckle opening:

☐ Satisfactory ☐ Unsatisfactory

If the ball joint stud fit in the steering knuckle opening is unsatisfactory, state the necessary repairs and explain the reason for your diagnosis.

____

____

CAUTION: Never back off a ball joint stud to align the cotter pin openings in the nut and stud. This may cause the ball joint stud to loosen, resulting in a suspension failure. Always tighten the nut to the next hole to install the cotter pin.

14. Install the ball joint stud in the steering knuckle opening, making sure the stud is straight and centered. Install the stud nut and tighten this nut to the specified torque. Install a new cotter pin through the stud and nut. Do not loosen the nut to align the nut and stud openings.

Specified ball joint nut torque ________________

Actual ball joint nut torque ________________

Is a new cotter pin properly installed? ☐ Yes ☐ No

Instructor check ________________________________

15. Reassemble the components that were removed in step 4. Make sure the wheel nuts are tightened to the specified torque.

Specified wheel nut torque ________________

Actual wheel nut torque ________________

Instructor's Response ________________________________

____

____

Job Sheet 20

Name ______________________________ Date ______________

STEERING KNUCKLE REMOVAL, MACPHERSON STRUT FRONT SUSPENSION

Upon completion of this job sheet, you should be able to remove the steering knuckle and determine knuckle condition on McPherson strut front suspension systems.

NATEF and ASE Correlation

This job sheet is related to ASE Automotive Suspension and Steering Task: *Inspect and replace steering knuckle/spindle assemblies and steering arms.*

Tools and Materials

Floor jack
Safety stands
Tire-rod end puller
Torque wrench
Driving tools

Procedure

Task Completed

1. Remove the wheel cover and loosen the front wheel nuts and the drive axle nut. ☐
2. Lift the vehicle chassis on a hoist and allow the front suspension to drop downward. Remove the front wheel, brake caliper, brake rotor, and drive axle nut. Tie the brake caliper to a suspension component; do not allow the caliper to hang on the end of the brake hose.

   Is the vehicle weight supported on hoist with front suspension dropped downward?
   ☐ Yes ☐ No

   Instructor check ______________________________
3. Remove the inner end of the drive axle from the transaxle with a pulling or prying action. On some Chrysler products, the differential cover must be removed and axle circlips compressed prior to drive axle removal from the transaxle.

   Is the inner end of drive axle removed from transaxle? ☐ Yes ☐ No

   Instructor check ______________________________
4. Remove the outer end of the drive axle from the steering knuckle and hub. On some early model Ford Escorts and Lynx, a puller is required for this operation.

   Is the outer end of drive axle removed from steering knuckle and hub?
   ☐ Yes ☐ No

   Instructor check ______________________________
5. Be sure the vehicle weight is supported on the hoist with the front suspension dropped downward. Remove the ball joint retaining nuts in the lower control arm.

   Are the lower ball joint retaining nuts removed? ☐ Yes ☐ No

   Instructor check ______________________________

Task Completed

6. Remove the cotter pin from the tie-rod nut. Remove the outer tie-rod nut and use a puller to disconnect the tie-rod end from the steering knuckle.

   Is the outer tie-rod end removed? ☐ Yes ☐ No

   Instructor check ______________________________

7. If an eccentric cam is used on one of the strut-to-knuckle bolts, mark the cam and bolt position in relation to the strut and remove the strut-to-knuckle bolts.

   Is the eccentric camber marked in relation to the strut? ☐ Yes ☐ No

   Instructor check ______________________________

☐ 8. Remove the knuckle from the strut and lift the knuckle out of the chassis.

☐ 9. Pry the dust deflector from the steering knuckle with a large flat-blade screwdriver.

10. Use a puller to remove the ball joint from the steering knuckle. Check the ball joint and tie-rod end openings in the knuckle for wear and out-of-round. Replace the knuckle if these openings are worn or out-of-round.

    Condition of ball joint opening in the knuckle:

    ☐ Satisfactory ☐ Unsatisfactory

    Condition of tie-rod end opening in the knuckle:

    ☐ Satisfactory ☐ Unsatisfactory

    State the necessary steering knuckle and related repairs, and explain the reason for your diagnosis.

    ____

    ____

☐ 11. Use the proper driving tool to reinstall the dust deflector in the steering knuckle.

Instructor's Response ______________________________

____

____

REAR SUSPENSION SERVICE

7

Upon completion and review of this chapter, you should be able to:

- Diagnose rear suspension vibration and noises.
- Diagnose rear suspension sway and lateral movement.
- Measure and correct rear suspension curb riding height.
- Remove and replace rear coil springs.
- Inspect rear springs, insulators, and seats.
- Inspect strut or shock absorber bushings and upper mount, and replace strut cartridge.
- Remove, inspect, and replace lower control arms.
- Inspect, remove, and replace rear ball joints.
- Inspect, remove, and replace suspension adjustment links.
- Diagnose, remove, and replace rear leaf springs.
- Diagnose, remove, and replace stabilizer bars.
- Diagnose, remove, and replace track bars.
- Inspect, remove, and replace tie-rods.

Rear suspension system diagnosis and service is extremely important to maintain vehicle safety, ride quality, and tire life. Many rear suspension components may create a safety hazard if they are not serviced properly. For example, if wheel nuts or spindle nuts are not tightened properly, a wheel assembly may come off the vehicle with disastrous results. Improper rear suspension curb riding height, worn struts or shock absorbers, and sagged or broken springs will result in harsh ride quality. Rear wheel toe and camber must be adjusted to specifications to provide normal tire tread life.

REAR SUSPENSION DIAGNOSIS AND SERVICE

Vibration Diagnosis

The technician must have a logical sequence for vibration diagnosis. This problem may be diagnosed using the same basic diagnostic procedure that is used for diagnosing defects in other parts of the vehicle.

A basic diagnostic procedure follows:

1. Question the customer regarding the vibration problem, and obtain as much information as possible from this source.
2. Be sure the complaint is identified. Road test the vehicle if necessary.
3. Think of the possible causes of the vibration.
4. Perform the necessary inspection and test procedures to locate the cause of the vibration.
5. Complete the necessary repairs to correct the problem(s) identified in the inspection and test procedures.
6. Be sure the original customer complaint is eliminated. If necessary, road test the vehicle.

When questioning the customer regarding the vibration problem, the technician should obtain the answers to these questions:

1. At what vehicle speed is the vibration most noticeable?
2. Is the vibration felt in the vehicle, and in what area of the vehicle is the vibration present? (For example, left front, right rear, under the vehicle floor.)
3. Can the customer hear the vibration?
4. Does engine load, such as hard acceleration, affect the vibration?
5. Does vehicle load, such as the number of passengers or weight in the trunk, affect the vibration?
6. Does the vibration occur in all transmission gear ranges?
7. When did the customer first notice the vibration? Did the vibration occur after some other service work was performed on the vehicle?

Basic Road Test

The purpose of a road test is to verify the vibration complaint and determine any operating conditions under which the vibration changes or is eliminated. A road test should also determine if the vibration is related to engine speed or vehicle road speed. During any road test for vibration diagnosis, if the vehicle does not have an in-dash tachometer, connect a tachometer to the ignition system, and install

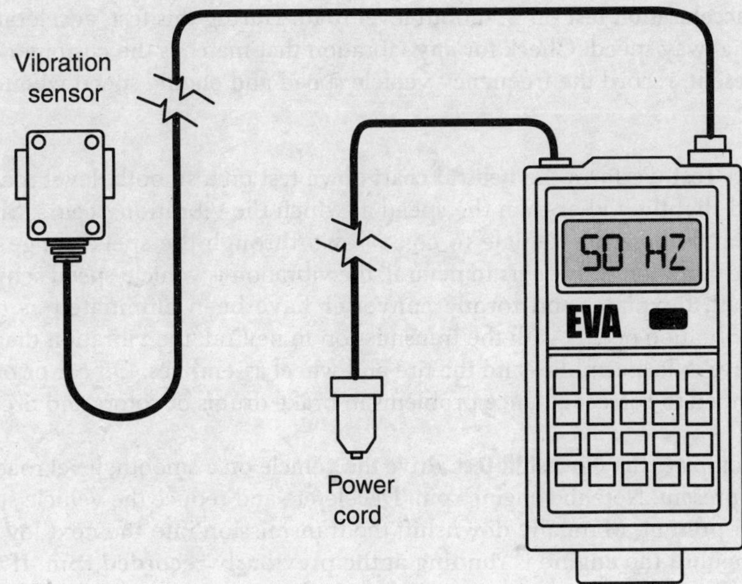

FIGURE 7-1 *Electronic vibration analyzer (EVA).*

the leads through one of the windows so the tachometer may be placed in view of the driver. Connect the power cord from an **electronic vibration analyzer (EVA)** to the cigarette lighter socket, and attach the EVA vibration sensor to the area where the suspected vibration is located (Figure 7-1).

When it is determined that the vibration is related to engine speed or vehicle road speed, the technician has to perform special test procedures to locate the cause of the vibration in one of these areas:

1. Engine, engine or transmission mount, clutch disc and pressure plate (manual transmission), flexplate and torque converter (automatic transmission)
2. Propeller shaft, transmission output shaft, differential pinion flange (rear-wheel-drive vehicles), front drive axles (front-wheel-drive vehicles)
3. Tires, wheels, hubs, and brake rotors

Special Road Tests

Slow Acceleration Test. All of the special road tests help the technician to locate the cause of the vibration. A tire and wheel inspection should be completed before any road test. Defects discovered during the tire inspection may explain the cause of the vibration that occurs during a road test.

Inspect the tires and wheel for these defects:

1. Check the inflation pressure in each tire.
2. Check for unusual tire wear such as cupping, excessive tread wear, and flat or bald spots. Inspect the tire sidewalls and tread area for bulges and ply separation. These tire defects may cause vibration, slapping noise, and tire growl or howl.
3. Inspect the rims for bends, damage, and excessive corrosion.

Perform the **slow acceleration test** on a smooth level road. During this test, accelerate the vehicle from a stop to legal highway speed. Check for any vibration that matches the customer's description. If any vibration is present, record the frequency vehicle speed and engine speed when the vibration occurred.

Neutral Coast-Down Test. Perform the **neutral coast-down** test on a smooth, level road. Accelerate the vehicle to a speed slightly higher than the speed at which the vibration occurs. Shift the transmission into neutral and allow the vehicle to coast down through the speed range at which the vibration occurs. If the vibration still occurs in neutral, the vibration is vehicle-speed sensitive, and the engine, propeller shaft, flexplate, and torque converter have been eliminated as causes of the vibration. When the vibration occurs with the transmission in neutral, the vibration diagnosis should concentrate on the drive axle assemblies and the tire-and-wheel assemblies. Off-car or on-car balance procedures are performed to correct balance problems in brake drums or rotors and tires and wheels.

Downshift Test. To complete the **downshift test**, drive the vehicle on a smooth, level road at the speed when the vibration is present. Note the engine rpm. Decelerate and reduce the vehicle speed until the vibration is no longer present. Manually downshift the transmission into the next lowest gear, and accelerate the vehicle until the engine is running at the previously recorded rpm. If the vibration returns at the same engine rpm, the engine, propeller shaft, flexplate and torque converter (automatic transmission) or clutch disc and pressure plate (manual transmission) are the most likely causes of the vibration.

Neutral Run-Up Test. Perform the **neutral run-up test** when the customer complains about vibration at idle speed or as a follow-up to the downshift test. To perform the neutral run-up test, slowly increase the engine rpm from idle. Note the engine rpm and frequency at which vibration occurs. If vibration occurs, the cause of the vibration is related to the engine, flexplate and torque converter (automatic transmission) or clutch disc and pressure plate (manual transmission).

Brake Torque Test. The **brake torque test** may be used to identify engine vibrations that were not present during the downshift and neutral run-up tests. This test may also be used when diagnosing vibrations that are sensitive to engine load.

To perform the brake torque test, follow this procedure:

1. Firmly apply the parking brake.
2. Block the front wheels.
3. Firmly apply the brake pedal.
4. Shift transmission into drive.
5. Slowly increase the engine speed to 1,200 rpm and check for vibrations.

CAUTION: Do not increase the engine rpm above 1,200, and limit this test to 10 seconds to protect the transmission from overheating.

6. Note the engine rpm when vibration occurred.

If engine vibrations occur during the brake torque test, but they did not occur during the downshift and neutral run-up tests, the engine and/or transmission mounts are a prime suspect for the cause of the vibration.

Steering Input Test. The **steering input test** may be performed to diagnose vibrations in suspension components. To perform this test, drive the vehicle through sweeping turns at the speed when the vibration occurs. Drive the vehicle when turning in one direction and then perform some turns in the opposite direction. If the vibration changes during these turns, the vibration is likely caused by defective wheel bearings, tire tread, or front drive axle shafts and joints.

Standing Acceleration Test. The **standing acceleration test** is used to diagnosis a vibration that may be called a launch shudder. To perform the standing acceleration test bring the vehicle to a complete stop. Place the transmission in drive and remove your foot from the brake pedal. Accelerate the vehicle to 30 to 40 mph (48 to 64 km/h), and check for vibrations that match the customer's complaint. If a shudder-type vibration occurs during the test, the cause of this vibration could be incorrect curb riding height, defective front drive axle joints, defective engine or transmission mounts, or faulty exhaust hangers or mounts.

Vibration Diagnosis with the Electronic Vibration Analyzer (EVA)

The EVA is helpful in locating the source of vibration problems.

Follow these steps to connect the EVA:

1. Be sure the correct software cartridge is securely installed in the bottom of the EVA.
2. Connect the vibration sensor cord to input A or B on the EVA. Position the release button facing downward on the lower side of this connector. Push the connector into the input port until the connector clicks and locks in place.

CAUTION: When installing the sensor connector in the EVA input terminal, do not twist the sensor connector. Do not remove this connector when the EVA is in use. This action may damage the EVA.

3. Follow these steps to perform the sensor calibration procedure:
   - **a.** Lay the sensor on a flat stationary surface, and be sure the side of the sensor marked UP is facing upward.
   - **b.** Plug the EVA power cord into a 12 V power supply, such as the cigarette lighter.
   - **c.** Press the "up" arrow key.
   - **d.** Press number 2 on the key pad three times until the word BURNING appears, followed by a request to turn the sensor over.
   - **e.** Turn the sensor over and press any key on the keypad to begin calibration. The calibration procedure takes approximately 20 seconds, and the display returns to the active mode when calibration is completed.
4. Two vibration sensors can be connected to ports A and B on the EVA at the same time, and the A/B button on the tester can be used to switch from one sensor to the other. Place the sensor(s) on any component that is suspected of being a vibration source. Each sensor has a 20-ft. cord, so it may be placed anywhere on the vehicle. Each sensor contains a magnet for attachment to metal surfaces. For attachment to nonmagnetic surfaces, use putty or a hook and loop fastener. Vibrations are usually felt in an up-and-down direction. Because the vibration sensor is directionally sensitive, this sensor must be mounted on the lower part of the suspected component with the marking on the sensor facing upward (Figure 7-2). When repeating a vibration test on the same component, always be sure the vibration sensor is mounted in the exact same location.

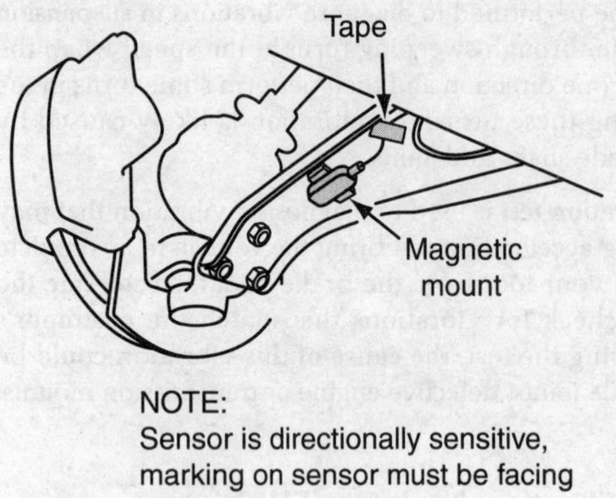

FIGURE 7-2 *Vibration sensor mounting.*

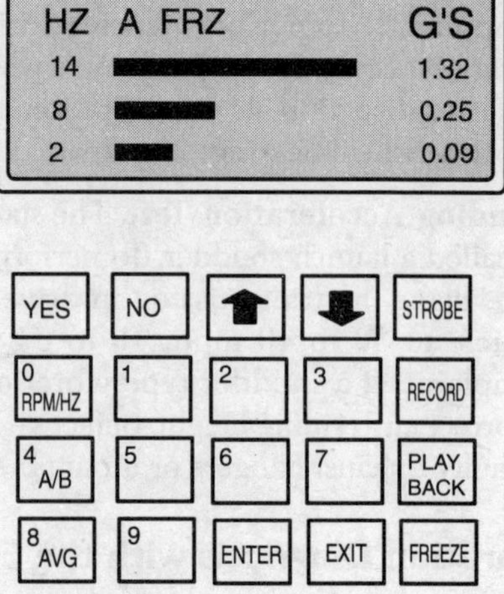

FIGURE 7-3 *Electronic vibration analyzer (EVA) display and keypad.*

Hertz or rpm are displayed on the left side of the EVA display. Either of these values may be selected by pressing the "RPM/Hertz" button on the tester. The selected value is displayed at the top of the left column on the display. A bar graph of the suspected source of the vibration is shown in the center of the display. When the AUTO mode is selected, the suspected vibration source is shown in the display. If the AUTO mode is not in use, the bar graph is indicated in the center of the display (Figure 7-3). The amplitude of each frequency indicated on the left of the screen is displayed on the right side of the screen. These amplitudes are displayed in Gs of acceleration force. Higher amplitudes indicate stronger vibration forces. The EVA displays up to three of the most dominant input frequencies in descending order of amplitude strength.

The technician may press the averaging (AVG) button to select this mode. In the AVG mode, the EVA displays the average of multiple vibration readings taken over a period of time. The EVA is usually operated in the AVG mode to minimize distractions caused by a sudden vibration that is not related to the main vibration source. These distractions could be caused by the vehicle wheels striking road irregularities. When the EVA is operating in the AVG mode and the AUTO Mode, "A" is displayed along the top of the screen. The AUTO mode is designed to be used with the vibration diagnosis tables in the appropriate service manual. If the EVA is operating in the AVG mode and the MANUAL mode, AVG is shown at the top of the screen. When the EVA is operating in the non-AVG mode and the AUTO mode, "I" is indicated at the top of the display. The top row on the display also indicates "A" or "B," representing the vibration sensor input port.

When the FREEZE button is pressed, the EVA displays FRZ on the top line of the display. In this mode the EVA will store data for a short time period when the RECORD button is pressed during various vibration tests. The technician may press the PLAY BACK button to display the recorded data. The technician presses the EXIT button to return the EVA to normal operation.

The EVA has a strobe light trigger wire that may be used with an inductive pickup timing light to balance rotating components such as propeller shafts.

Calculating Vibration Frequencies of Various Components

Calculating Tire/Wheel Frequency. The first step in calculating tire/wheel frequency is to divide the vehicle speed by five-mile-per-hour increments. There are 12 increments of 5 miles per hour, if the vehicle speed is 60 mph. The next step is to use the chart in Figure 7-4 to determine how many times

Tire Size	Tire Frequency at 5 mph	Tire Size	Tire Frequency at 5 mph
P145/80/13	1.31	215/70/15	1.08
155/80/13	1.27	215/75/15	1.05
175/65/14	1.26	215/75/16	1.01
185/65/14	1.23	215/85/16	0.95
185/70/14	1.20	220/75/15	1.03
185/75/14	1.16	225/45/17	1.16
195/60/15	1.20	225/55/17	1.08
195/65/15	1.16	225/60/16	1.09
195/70/14	1.17	225/70/15	1.06
195/75/14	1.13	225/70/16	1.02
195/75/15	1.09	225/75/15	1.02
205/55/15	1.21	225/75/16	0.99
205/55/16	1.16	235/70/15	1.04
205/60/14	1.22	235/75/15	1.00
205/60/15	1.17	235/75/16	0.97
205/65/15	1.14	245/70/15	1.02
205/70/14	1.14	245/70/16	0.98
205/70/15	1.10	245/75/16	0.95
205/75/14	1.11	275/40/17	1.13
205/75/15	1.07	295/40/20	0.99
215/50/17	1.14	335/35/17	1.10
215/55/16	1.14	30X9.5/15	0.98
215/65/15	1.11	31X10.5/15	0.95
215/65/16	1.07		

FIGURE 7-4 *Tire/wheel frequencies.*

a wheel and tire rotate per second at 5 mph. As indicated in this chart, if the tire size is 195/70/14, the tires revolve at 1.17 times per second for every 5 mph of vehicle speed. To calculate the tire/wheel frequency at 60 mph, multiply the number of five-mile-per-hour increments, 12, by the number of times the tire and wheel revolve in one second per 5 mph increment, 1.17. Therefore we have the calculation $12 \times 1.17 = 14.04$, and this size of tire and wheel on a vehicle traveling at 60 mph produces a vibration of approximately 14 hertz (Hz). With a vibration sensor attached to the lower control arm, if the EVA displays a vibration of 14 Hz, the tire and wheel mounted on the knuckle attached to the control arm has a vibration problem. This vibration problem could also be caused by a rotor or hub.

With a vibration of 14 Hz, a second-order vibration is 28 Hz, a third-order vibration is 42 Hz, and a fourth-order vibration is 56 Hz. On a front-wheel-drive vehicle, a worn constant velocity drive axle joint may cause a vibration in the fifth order of the tire/wheel vibration, and a defective tripod drive axle joint may result in a vibration of the third order of the tire/wheel vibration. On a rear-wheel-drive-vehicle if the tire/wheel frequency is 14 and the rear axle ratio is 3.42:1, the frequency of the drive shaft is $14 \times 3.42 = 47.88$.

Calculating Engine and Engine Firing Frequency. To calculate the engine frequency, divide the engine rpm by 60 seconds per minute. For example, if the engine rpm is 3,000, the engine frequency is $3{,}000 \div 60 = 50$ revolutions per second, or 50 Hz. To determine the engine firing frequency, divide the number of engine cylinders by two, and multiply the answer by the engine frequency. Let us assume we are working on a V6 engine running at 3,000 rpm. Divide the number of cylinders by two, and so $6 \div 2 = 3$. Then multiply this answer by the engine frequency of 50 to calculate the firing frequency. Therefore, $3 \times 50 = 150$ engine firing frequency. Because a cylinder in a four-cycle engine expels exhaust only once every two revolutions, a single cylinder frequency is one-half the engine frequency. Therefore, in our example if the engine frequency is 50, a single cylinder frequency is 25. This is the frequency of exhaust pulses in a single cylinder and also the frequency of the camshaft that turns at one-half the engine speed.

Calculating Accessory Drive Frequencies. To calculate the frequency of the belt-driven accessories, divide the diameter of the crankshaft pulley by the diameter of the pulley on the belt-driven accessory and multiply the answer by the engine frequency. Let us assume the we are still working on the engine in our previous example which is a V6 engine with a frequency of 50 running at 3,000 rpm. With a vibration sensor mounted on the engine the EVA displays a vibration of 160 Hz. The diameter of the crankshaft pulley is 8 inches, the diameter of the power steering pulley is 5 inches, the diameter of the A/C compressor pulley is 4.5 inches, and the diameter of the alternator pulley is 2.5 inches.

Therefore, we have the following calculations:

Power steering pump frequency: $8 \div 5 = 1.6 \times 50 = 80$

A/C compressor frequency: $8 \div 4.5 = 1.7 \times 50 = 85$

Alternator frequency: $8 \div 2.5 = 3.2 \times 50 = 160$

When we compare the vibration frequency displayed on the EVA to the belt-driven accessory frequencies, the alternator frequency matches the frequency on the EVA, indicating the alternator is the source of the vibration.

Diagnosis of Ride Harshness

When diagnosing a ride harshness condition, check these measurements and components:

1. Curb riding height–insufficient curb riding height causes ride harshness
2. Excessive vehicle load
3. Worn shock absorbers or struts
4. Broken or weak springs
5. Worn suspension bushings, such as strut mounts, control arm bushings, and shock absorber mounting bushings
6. Wheel alignment–excessive positive caster on front wheels causes ride harshness

Noise Diagnosis

A squeaking noise in the rear suspension may be caused by a suspension bushing or a defective strut or shock absorber.

If a rattling noise occurs in the rear suspension, check these components:

1. Worn or missing suspension bushings, such as control arm bushings, track bar bushings, stabilizer bar bushings, trailing arm bushings, and strut rod bushings
2. Worn strut or shock absorber bushings or mounts
3. Defective struts or shock absorbers
4. Broken springs or worn spring insulators
5. Broken exhaust system hangers or improperly positioned exhaust system components

Special tools can be used to locate noises at any location on the vehicle. A ChassisEar tool has six clamp-on sensors that are miniature microphones (Figure 7-5). These six sensors are connected to a switchbox that is also connected to a headset worn by the technician. The technician can rotate the switch on the switchbox to connect any sensor to the headset. The sensors can be mounted on various suspected noise sources. When the control on the switchbox is rotated, the technician can determine which sensor is connected to the noise source.

An electronic stethoscope can be used to locate the source of a noise. This tool has one pickup that is placed on or near a suspected noise source. The pickup is connected to an amplifier box, and the headset is also connected to this box (Figure 7-6). When the pickup is placed on the source of a noise, the noise is amplified in the headset.

FIGURE 7-5 *ChassisEar tool for locating noise sources.*

FIGURE 7-6 *Electronic stethoscope.*

Sway and Lateral Movement Diagnosis

Excessive **body sway,** or roll, on road irregularities may be caused by a weak stabilizer bar or loose stabilizer bar bushings. If lateral movement is experienced on the rear of the chassis, the track bar or track bar bushings may be defective. Lateral movement is sideways movement.

Curb Riding Height Measurement

Regular inspection and proper maintenance of suspension systems are extremely important to maintaining vehicle safety. The curb riding height is determined mainly by spring condition. Other suspension components, such as control arm bushings, affect curb riding height if they are worn. *Since incorrect curb riding height affects most of the other suspension angles, this measurement is critical.* Reduced rear suspension height increases steering effort and causes rapid steering wheel return after turning a corner. Harsh riding occurs when the curb riding height is less than specified. The curb riding height must be measured at the vehicle manufacturer's specified location, which varies depending on the type of vehicle and suspension system. On some vehicles, the curb riding height on the rear suspension is measured from the floor to the center of the strut rod mounting bolt when the vehicle is on a level floor or an alignment rack (Figure 7-7). Photo Sequence 7 shows a typical procedure for measuring front and rear curb riding height.

PHOTO SEQUENCE 7
TYPICAL PROCEDURE FOR MEASURING FRONT AND REAR CURB RIDING HEIGHT

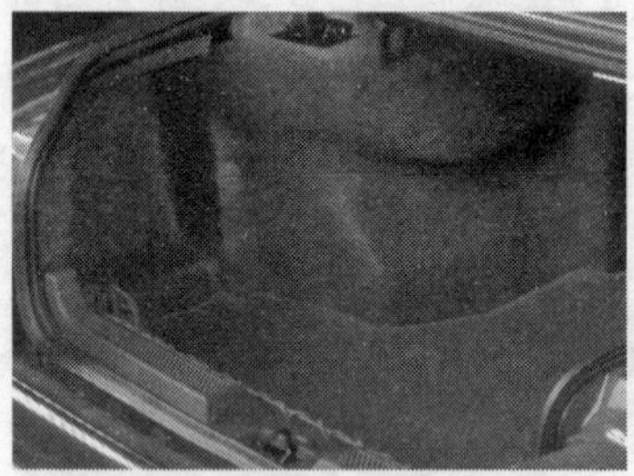

P7-1 *Check the trunk for extra weight.*

P7-2 *Check the tires for normal inflation pressure.*

P7-3 *Park the car on a level shop floor or alignment track.*

P7-4 *Find the vehicle manufacturer's specified curb riding height measurement locations in the service manual.*

P7-5 *Measure and record the right front curb riding height.*

P7-6 *Measure and record the left front curb riding height.*

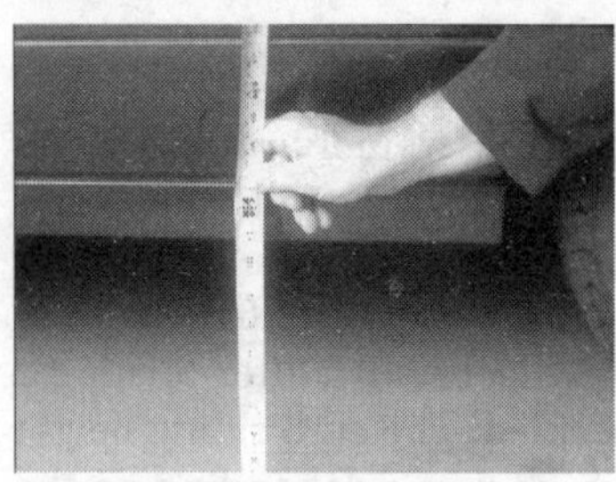

P7-7 *Measure and record the right rear curb riding height.*

P7-8 *Measure and record the left rear curb riding height.*

P7-9 *Compare the measurement results to the specified curb riding height in the service manual.*

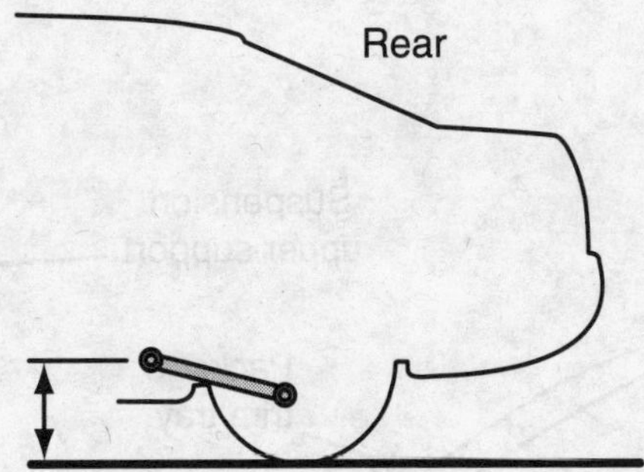

FIGURE 7-7 *Curb riding height measurement, rear suspension.*

Rear Strut, Coil Spring, and Upper Mount Diagnosis and Service

WARNING: When the rear coil springs are mounted on the struts, never loosen the upper strut nut until all the spring tension is removed from the upper support with a spring compressor. If this nut is removed with spring tension on the upper support, the spring tension turns the spring and the upper support into a dangerous projectile, which may cause serious personal injury and/or property damage.

Weak springs cause harsh riding and reduced curb riding height. Broken springs or spring insulators cause a rattling noise while driving on road irregularities. Worn-out struts or shock absorbers cause excessive chassis oscillations and harsh riding. (Refer to Chapter 5 for strut and shock absorber service.) Loose or worn strut or shock absorber bushings cause a rattling noise on road irregularities. The rear coil spring removal and replacement procedure varies depending on the type of rear suspension system. Always follow the vehicle manufacturer's recommended procedure in the service manual.

The following is a typical rear strut and spring removal and replacement procedure on a MacPherson strut independent rear suspension system with the coil springs mounted on the struts:

1. Remove the rear seat and the package trim tray (Figure 7-8).
2. Remove the wheel cover, and loosen the wheel nuts.
3. Lift the vehicle with a floor jack, and lower the chassis onto safety stands so the rear suspension is allowed to drop downward.
4. Place a floor jack lift pad under the rear spindle on the side where the strut and spring removal is taking place. Raise the floor jack to support some of the suspension system weight (Figure 7-9).
5. Remove the rear wheel, disconnect the nut from the small spring in the lower arm (Figure 7-10), and remove the brake hose and antilock brake system (ABS) wire from the strut (Figure 7-11).
6. Remove the stabilizer bar link from the strut (Figure 7-12), and loosen the strut-to-spindle mounting bolts (Figure 7-13).

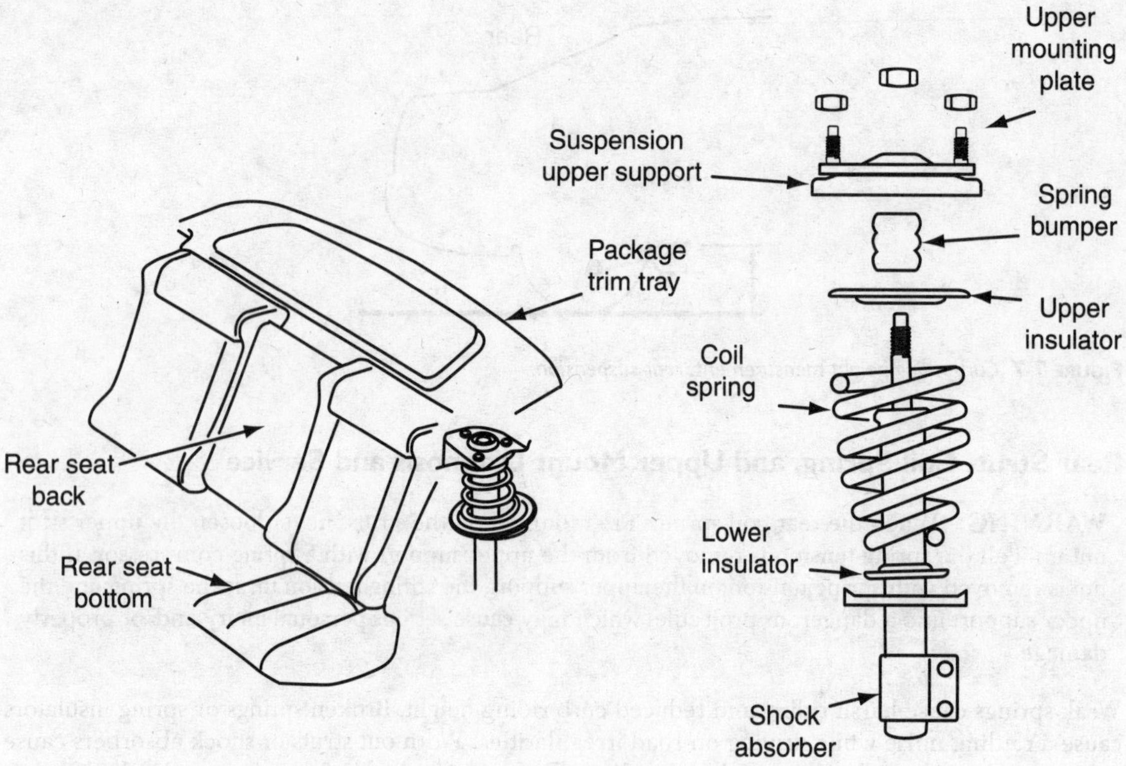

Upper mounting plate
Suspension upper support
Spring bumper
Upper insulator
Coil spring
Lower insulator
Shock absorber
Package trim tray
Rear seat back
Rear seat bottom

FIGURE 7-8 *Rear suspension with rear seat and package trim tray.*

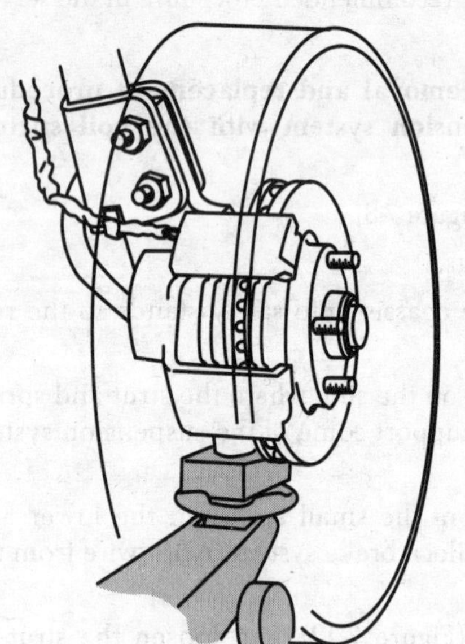

FIGURE 7-9 *Floor jack supporting some of the rear suspension weight.*

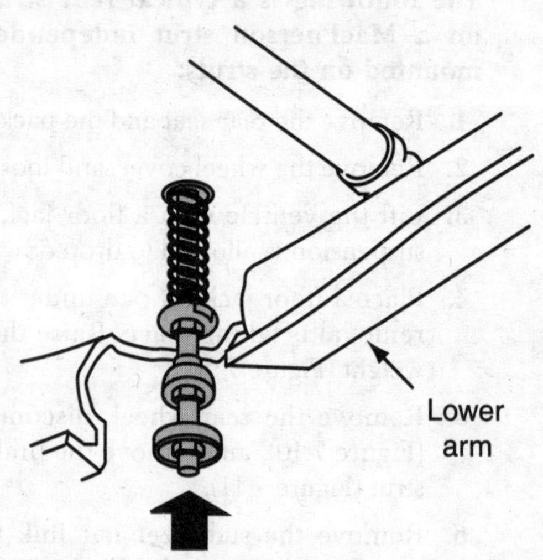

FIGURE 7-10 *Disconnecting nut from small spring in the lower arm.*

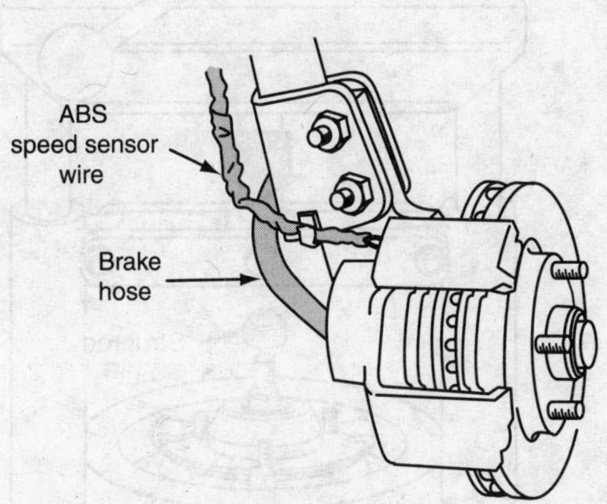

FIGURE 7-11 *Disconnecting brake hose and ABS wire from the rear strut.*

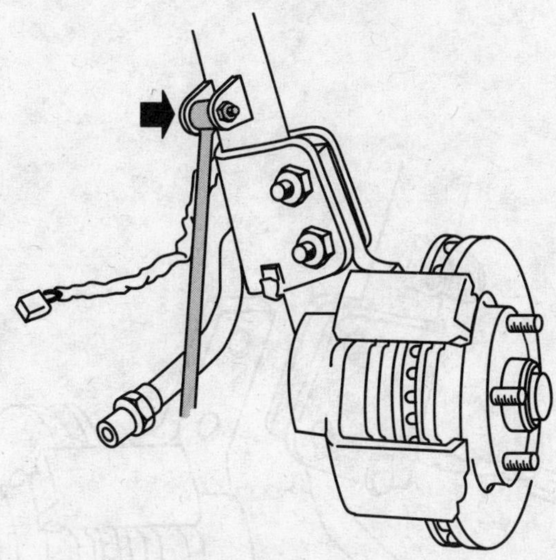

FIGURE 7-12 *Removing stabilizer bar from the rear strut.*

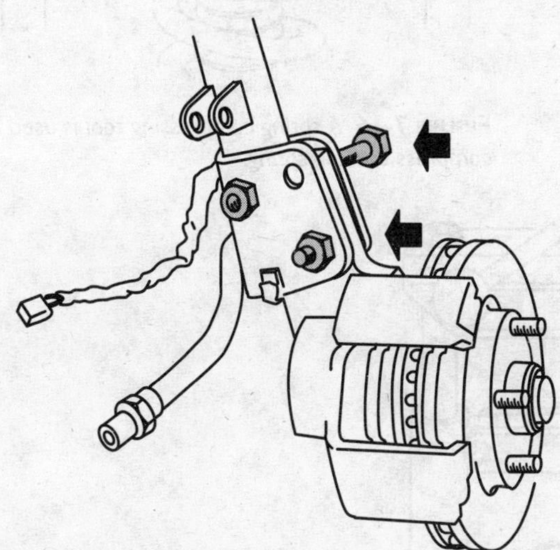

FIGURE 7-13 *Loosening strut-to-rear spindle bolts.*

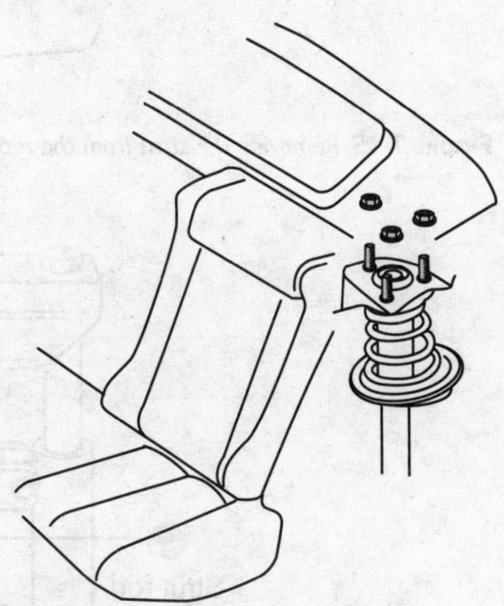

FIGURE 7-14 *Removing upper mount nuts.*

7. Remove the three upper support nuts under the package tray trim (Figure 7-14), and lower the floor jack to remove the strut from the knuckle (Figure 7-15). Remove the strut from the chassis.
8. Following the vehicle or equipment manufacturer's recommended procedure, install a spring compressing tool on the coil spring, and tighten the tool until all the spring tension is removed from the upper support (Figure 7-16).
9. Operate the compressing tool to remove all the spring tension from the upper strut mount and then remove the strut rod nut (Figure 7-17).
10. Remove the strut rod nut, upper support, and upper insulator.

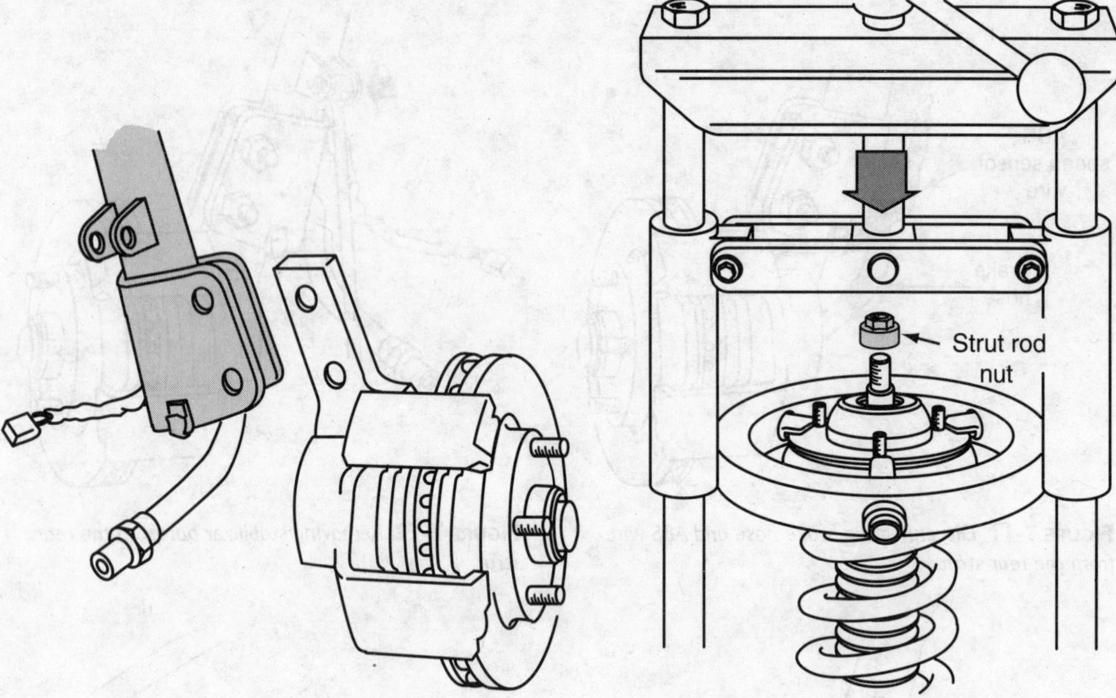

FIGURE 7-15 *Removing the strut from the rear spindle.*

FIGURE 7-16 *A spring compressing tool is used to compress the coil spring.*

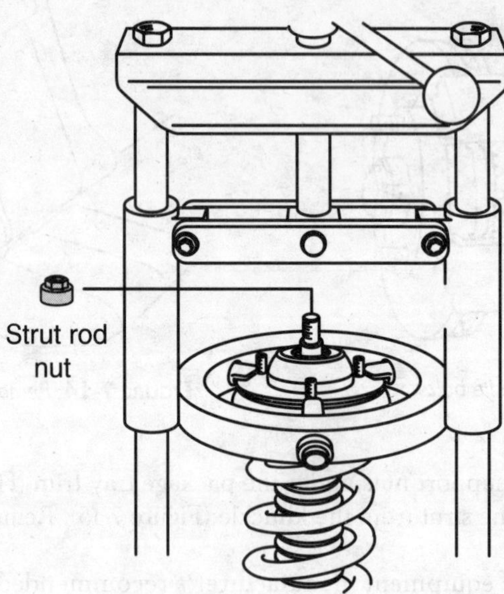

FIGURE 7-17 *After the compressing tool is operated to remove all the spring tension, remove the strut rod nut.*

11. Remove the strut from the lower end of the spring.
12. If the spring is to be replaced, rotate the compressing tool handle until all the spring tension is removed from the compressing tool, and then remove the spring from the tool.

13. Inspect the lower insulator and spring seat on the strut (Figure 7-18). If the spring seat is warped or damaged, replace the strut. A new cartridge may be installed in some rear struts. (The strut cartridge replacement procedure is explained in Chapter 5.)

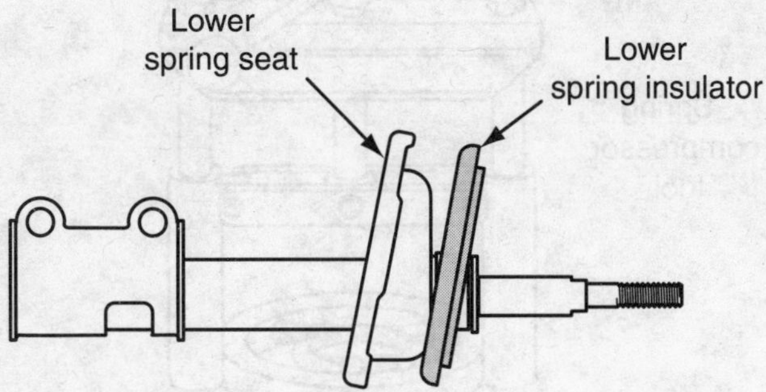

FIGURE 7-18 *Inspecting lower spring seat and insulator.*

14. Visually inspect the upper mount, insulator, and spring bumper. If any of these components are damaged, worn, or distorted, replacement is necessary. Worn upper mounts and insulators or damaged spring seats cause suspension noise while driving on road irregularities. Assemble the spring bumper, upper mount, and insulator (Figure 7-19), and then compress the coil spring in the compressing tool. Assemble the strut and related components into the spring (Figure 7-20). Tighten all fasteners to the specified torque.

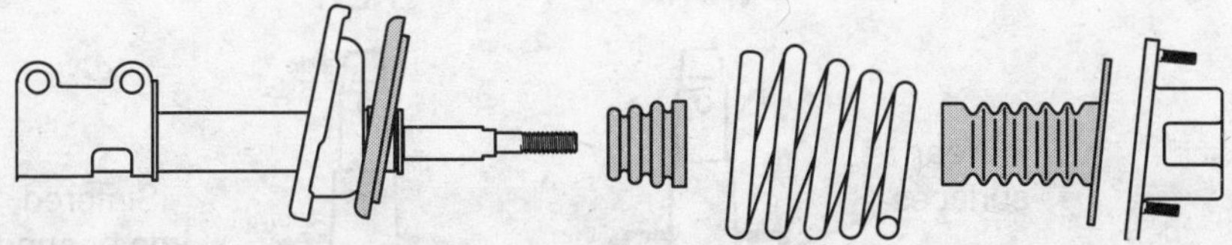

FIGURE 7-19 *Assembly of rear strut, spring bumper, spring, upper mount, and insulator.*

LOWER CONTROL ARM AND BALL JOINT DIAGNOSIS AND REPLACEMENT

Worn bushings on the lower control arms may cause incorrect rear wheel camber or toe, which results in rear tire wear and steering pull. Bent lower control arms must be replaced. When ball joints with **wear indicators** are in normal condition, there is 0.050 in. (1.27 mm) between the grease nipple shoulder and the cover. If the ball joint is worn, the grease nipple shoulder is flush with or inside the cover (Figure 7-21). A worn ball joint causes improper rear wheel toe and/or camber, which may result in tire tread wear or steering pull.

The lower control arm removal and replacement procedure varies depending on the vehicle and the type of suspension. Always follow the vehicle manufacturer's recommended procedure in the service manual.

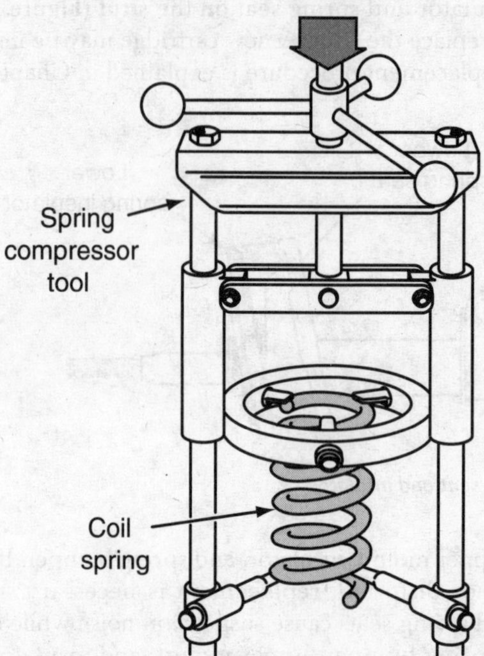

FIGURE 7-20 *Compressing the coil spring in the compressing tool prior to strut and spring assembly.*

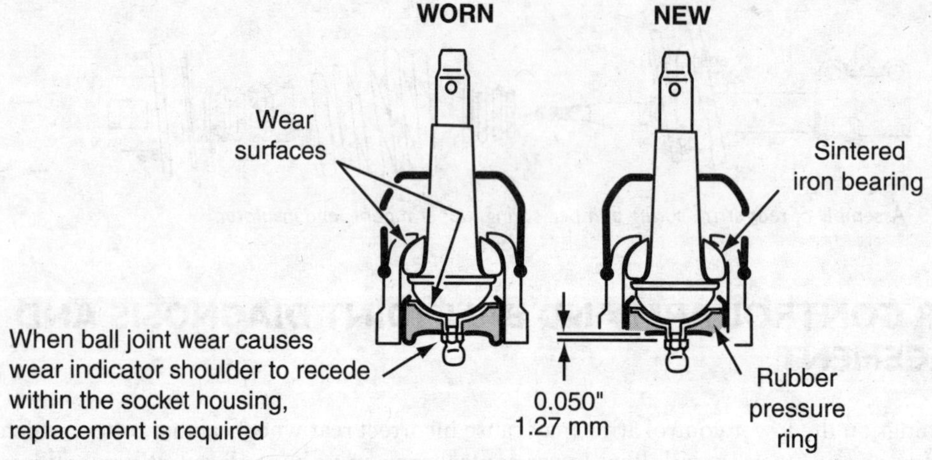

FIGURE 7-21 *Ball joint wear indicator.*

The following is a typical lower control arm removal procedure:

1. Lift the vehicle on a hoist with the chassis supported on the hoist and the control arms dropped downward. The vehicle may be lifted with a floor jack, and the chassis supported on safety stands.
2. Remove the tire-and-wheel assembly.
3. Remove the stabilizer bar from the knuckle bracket.
4. Remove the parking brake cable retaining clip from the lower control arm.

5. If the car has electronic level control (ELC), disconnect the height sensor link from the control arm.
6. Install a special tool to support the lower control arm in the bushing areas (Figure 7-22).

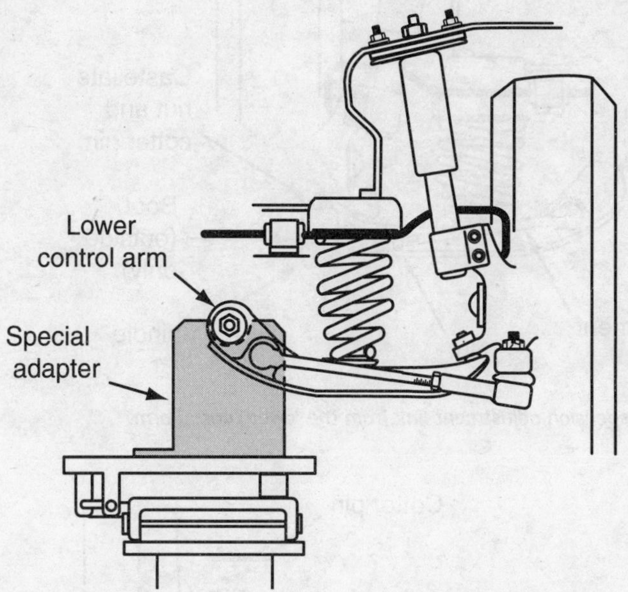

FIGURE 7-22 *Special tool installed to support the inner end of the lower control arm.*

7. Place a transmission jack under the special tool and raise the jack enough to remove the tension from the control arm bushing retaining bolts. If the car was lifted with a floor jack and supported on safety stands, place a floor jack under the special tool.
8. Place a safety chain through the coil spring and around the lower control arm.
9. Remove the bolt from the rear control arm bushing.
10. Be sure the jack is raised enough to relieve the tension on the front bolt in the lower control arm and remove this bolt.
11. Lower the jack slowly and allow the control arm to pivot downward. When all the tension is released from the coil spring, remove the safety chain, coil spring, and insulators.

Check the coil spring for distortion and proper free length. If the spring has a vinyl coating, check this coating for scratches and nicks. Check the spring insulators for cracks and wear.

After the coil spring is removed, follow these steps to remove the lower control arm:

1. Remove the nut on the inner end of the **suspension adjustment link,** and disconnect this link from the lower control arm (Figure 7-23).
2. Remove the cotter pin from the ball joint nut, and loosen, but do not remove, the nut from the ball joint stud.
3. Use a special ball joint removal tool to loosen the ball joint in the knuckle.
4. Remove the ball joint nut and the lower control arm (Figure 7-24).

Check the lower control arm for bends, distortion, and worn bushings. A special ball joint pressing tool is used to press the ball joint from the lower control arm (Figure 7-25), and the same pressing tool with different adapters is used to press the new ball joint into the control arm (Figure 7-26).

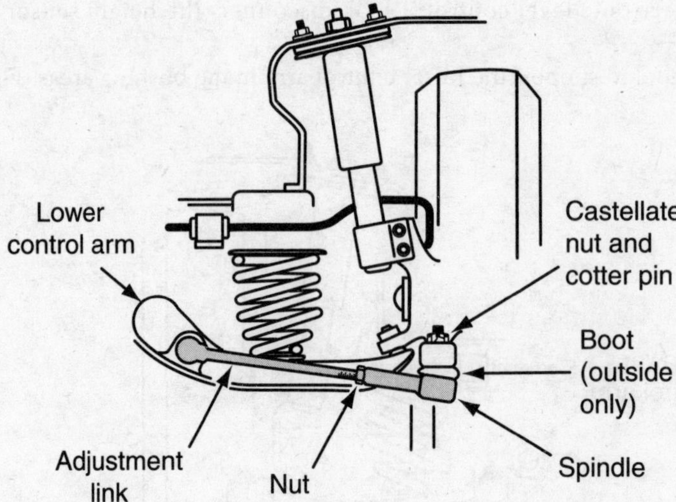

FIGURE 7-23 *Removing the suspension adjustment link from the lower control arm.*

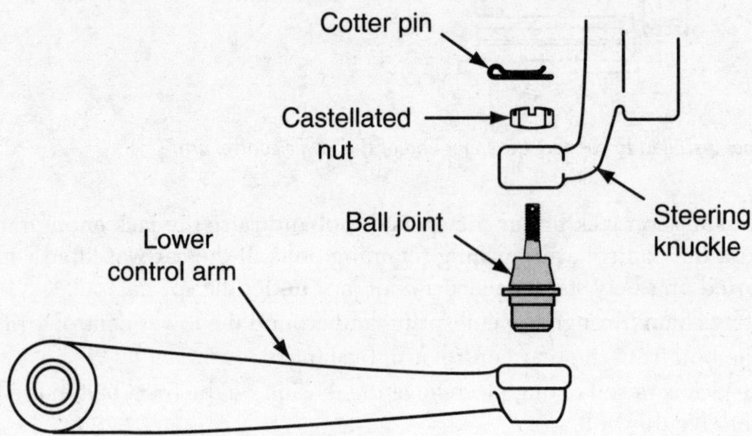

FIGURE 7-24 *Removing the lower control arm and ball joint.*

CAUTION: When disconnecting a linkage joint, such as the ends of the suspension adjustment link, do not use a wedge-type tool between the joint and the attached part. This method of joint removal may damage the joint seal.

Remove the nut and cotter pin on the outer end of the suspension adjustment link, and use a special puller to remove this link from the knuckle (Figure 7-27). Remove the suspension adjustment link and inspect the joints. If the joints are loose or the seals are damaged, joint replacement is necessary. The joint studs must fit snugly in the knuckle and lower control arm openings. When the joint studs are worn, joint replacement is necessary, and worn stud openings in the knuckle or lower control arm require component replacement.

FIGURE 7-25 *Removing the ball joint from the lower control arm.*

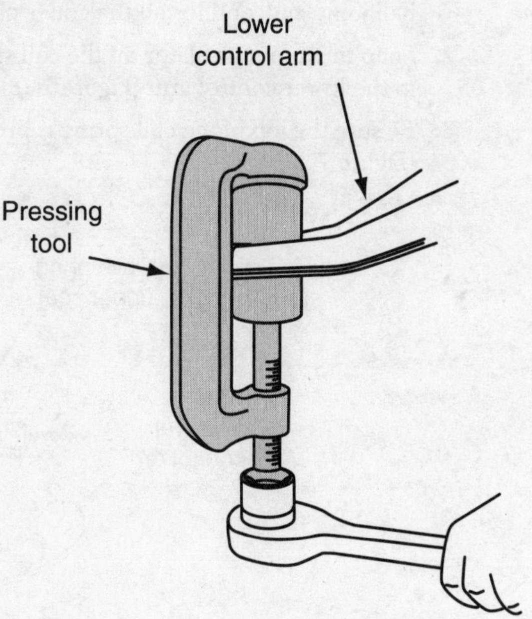

FIGURE 7-26 *Installing the ball joint in the lower control arm.*

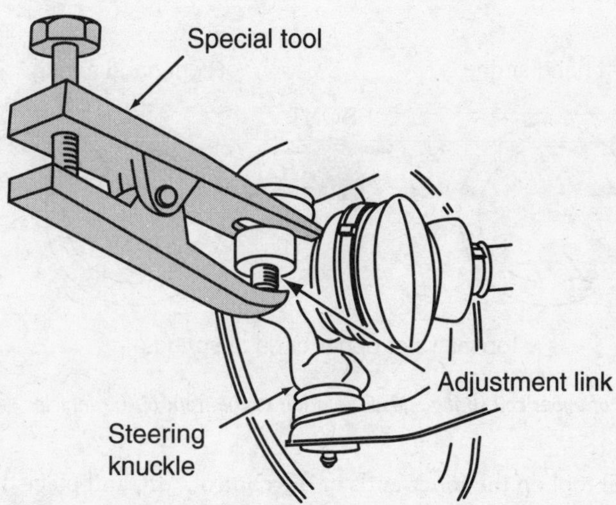

FIGURE 7-27 *Removing the suspension adjustment link from the knuckle.*

Follow this procedure to install the lower control arm and spring:

CAUTION: Never loosen a ball joint nut to install a cotter pin, because this action causes improper torquing of the nut.

1. Install the ball joint stud in the knuckle and install the nut on the ball joint stud. Tighten the ball joint nut to the specified torque, and then tighten the nut an additional 2/3 turn. If

necessary, tighten the nut slightly to align the nut castellations with the cotter pin hole in the ball joint stud, and install the cotter pin.

2. Snap the upper insulator on the coil spring. Install the lower spring insulator and the spring in the lower control arm (Figure 7-28).
3. Be sure the top of the coil spring is properly positioned in relation to the front of the vehicle (Figure 7-29).

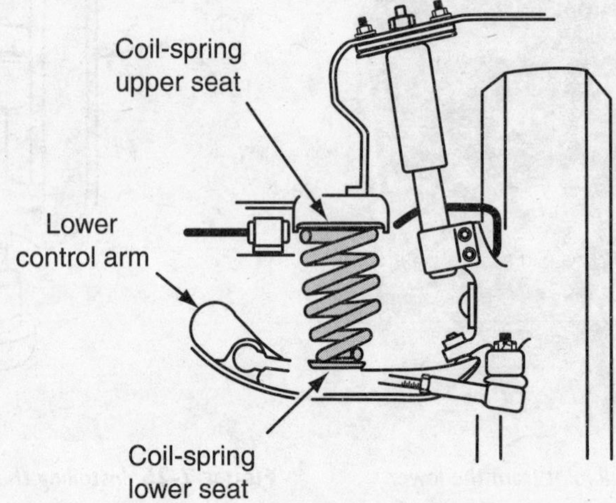

FIGURE 7-28 *Installing the spring and insulators.*

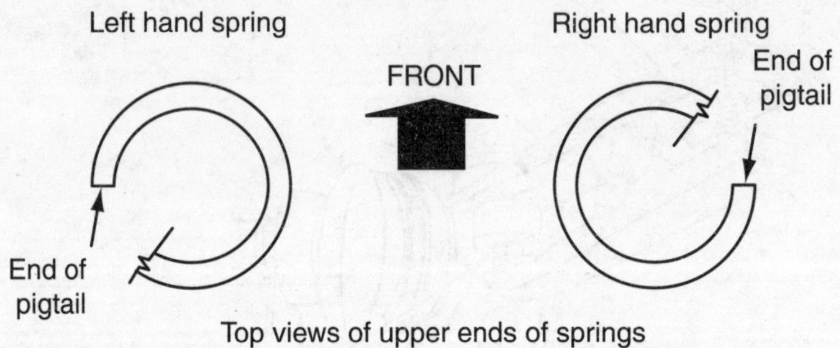

FIGURER 7-29 *Proper location of upper coil spring ends in relation to the front of the vehicle.*

4. Install the special tool on the inner ends of the control arm, and place the transmission jack under the special tool.
5. Slowly raise the transmission jack until the control arm bushing openings are aligned with the openings in the chassis.

CAUTION: The pivot bolts and nuts in the inner ends of the lower control arm must be tightened to the specified torque with the vehicle weight supported on the wheels and the suspension at normal curb height. Failure to follow this procedure may adversely affect ride quality and steering characteristics.

6. Install the bolts and nuts in the inner ends of the control arm. Do not torque these bolts and nuts at this time.
7. Install the stabilizer-bar-to-knuckle bracket and tighten the fasteners to the specified torque.
8. Install the parking brake retaining clip.
9. If the vehicle has ELC, install the height sensor link, and tighten the fastener to the specified torque.
10. Install the suspension adjustment link and tighten the retaining nuts to the specified torque. Install cotter pins as required.
11. Remove the transmission jack and install the tire-and-wheel assembly.
12. Lower the vehicle onto the floor and tighten the wheel hub nuts and lower control arm bolts and nuts to the specified torque.

REAR LEAF-SPRING DIAGNOSIS AND REPLACEMENT

This leaf-spring discussion applies to multiple-leaf springs on rear suspension systems that have two springs mounted longitudinally in relation to the chassis. Many leaf springs have plastic **spring silencers** between the spring leafs. If these silencers are worn out, creaking and squawking noises are heard when the vehicle is driven over road irregularities at low speeds.

When the silencers require checking or replacement, lift the vehicle with a floor jack and support the frame on safety stands so the rear suspension moves downward. With the vehicle weight no longer applied to the springs, the spring leafs may be pried apart with a pry bar to remove and replace the silencers.

Worn shackle bushings, brackets, and mounts cause excessive chassis lateral movement and rattling noises. With the normal vehicle weight resting on the springs, insert a pry bar between the rear outer end of the spring and the frame. Apply downward pressure on the bar and observe the rear shackle for movement. Shackle bushings, brackets, or mounts must be replaced if there is movement in the shackle. The same procedure may be followed to check the front bushing in the main leaf. A broken spring center bolt may allow the rear axle assembly to move rearward on one side. This movement changes rear wheel tracking, which results in handling problems, tire wear, and reduced directional stability. Sagged rear springs reduce the curb riding height. Spring replacement is necessary if the springs are sagged.

When rear leaf-spring replacement is necessary, proceed as follows:

1. Lift the vehicle with a floor jack and place safety stands under the frame. Lower the vehicle weight onto the safety stands, and leave the floor jack under the differential housing to support the rear suspension weight.
2. Remove the nuts from the spring U-bolts, and remove the U-bolts and lower spring plate (Figure 7-30). The spring plate may be left on the rear shock absorber and moved out of the way.
3. Be sure the floor jack is lowered sufficiently to relieve the vehicle weight from the rear springs.
4. Remove the rear shackle nuts, plate, shackle, and bushings.
5. Remove the front spring mounting bolt and remove the spring from the chassis. Check the spring center bolt to be sure it is not broken.

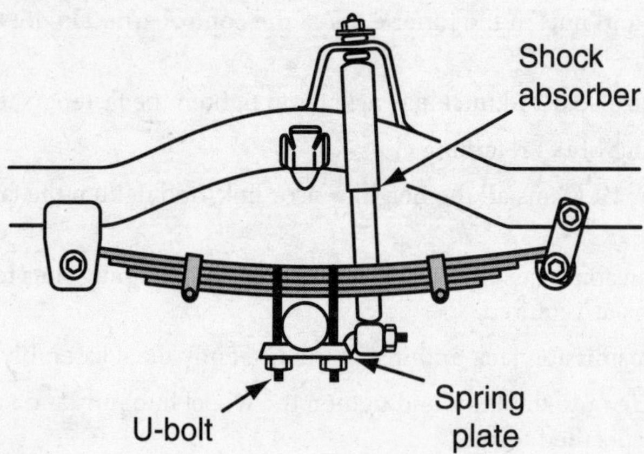

FIGURE 7-30 *Leaf-spring rear suspension.*

6. Check the front hanger, bushing, and bolt, and replace as necessary.
7. Check the rear shackle, bushings, plate, and mount; replace the worn components.
8. Reverse steps 1 through 5 to install the spring. Tighten all bolts and nuts to the specified torque.

TRACK BAR DIAGNOSIS AND REPLACEMENT

Some rear suspension systems have a track bar to control **lateral chassis movement**. Rubber mounting bushings insulate the track bar from the chassis components. Worn track bar mounts and bushings may cause rattling and excessive lateral chassis movement.

When the track bar is inspected, lift the vehicle on a hoist or floor jack with the rear suspension in the normal riding height position. If the vehicle is lifted with a floor jack, place safety stands under the rear axle to support the vehicle weight. Grasp the track bar firmly and apply vertical and horizontal force. If there is movement in the track bar mountings, track bar, or bushing, replacement is essential (Figure 7-31).

Another track bar checking method is to leave the vehicle on the shop floor and observe the track bar mounts as an assistant applies side force to the chassis or rear bumper. If there is lateral movement in the track bar bushings or brackets, replace the bushings and check the bracket bolts. Bent track bars must be replaced.

When the track bar is replaced, remove the mounting bolts, bushings, grommets, and track bar. Inspect the mounting bolt holes in the chassis for wear. After the track bar is installed with the proper grommets and bushings, tighten the mounting bolts to the specified torque.

STABILIZER BAR DIAGNOSIS AND SERVICE

Worn stabilizer bar mounting bushings, grommets, or mounting bolts cause a rattling noise as the vehicle is driven on irregular road surfaces. A weak stabilizer bar or worn bushings and grommets cause harsh riding and excessive body sway while driving on irregular road surfaces. Worn or very dry stabilizer bar bushings may cause a squeaking noise on irregular road surfaces. All stabilizer bar

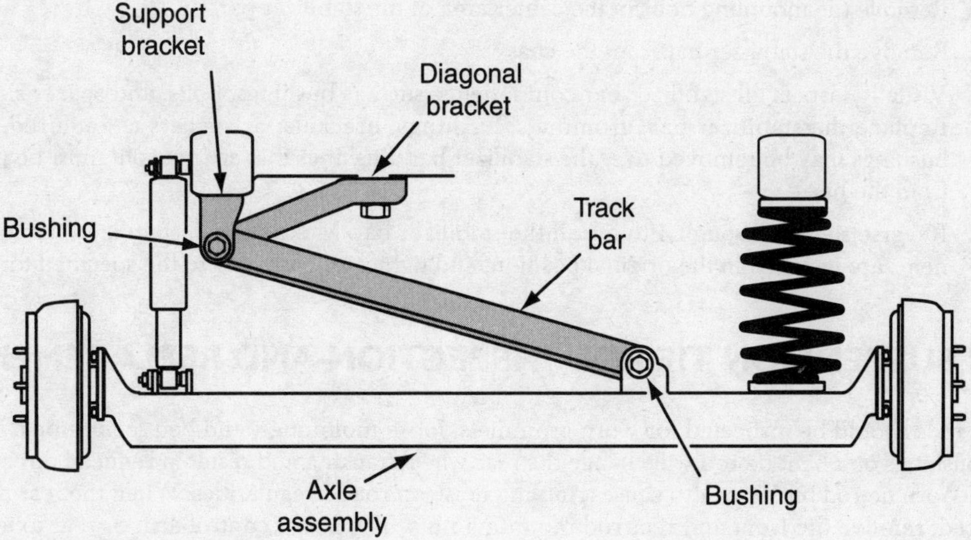

FIGURE 7-31 *Checking track bar bushings.*

components should be visually inspected for wear. Stabilizer bar removal and replacement procedures vary depending on the vehicle. Always follow the vehicle manufacturer's recommended procedure in the service manual.

Following is a typical rear stabilizer bar removal and replacement procedure:

1. Lift the vehicle on a hoist and allow both sides of the rear suspension to drop downward as the vehicle chassis is supported on the hoist.
2. Remove the mounting bolts at the outer ends of the stabilizer bar and remove the bushings, grommets, brackets, or spacers (Figure 7-32).

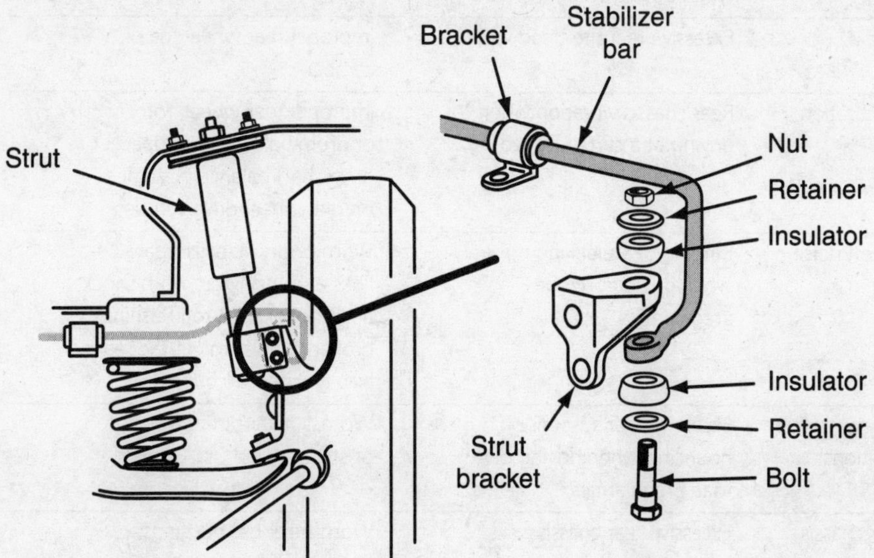

FIGURE 7-32 *Stabilizer bar, bushings, grommets, and brackets.*

3. Remove the mounting bolts in the center area of the stabilizer bar.
4. Remove the stabilizer bar from the chassis.
5. Visually inspect all stabilizer bar components, such as bushings, bolts, and spacer sleeves. Replace the stabilizer bar, grommets, bushings, brackets, or spacers as required. Split bushings may be removed over the stabilizer bar. Bushings that are not split must be pulled from the bar.
6. Reverse steps 2 through 4 to install the stabilizer bar. Make sure all stabilizer bar components are installed in the original position, and tighten all fasteners to the specified torque.

REAR SUSPENSION TIE ROD INSPECTION AND REPLACEMENT

Rear tie-rods should be inspected for worn grommets, loose mountings, and bent conditions. Loose tie-rod bushings or a bent tie-rod will change the rear wheel tracking and result in reduced directional stability. Worn tie-rod bushings also cause a rattling noise on road irregularities. When the rear tie-rod is replaced, remove the front and rear rod mounting nuts. The lower control arm or rear axle may have to be pried rearward to remove the tie-rod. Inspect the tie-rod grommets and mountings for wear, and replace parts as required. When the tie-rod is reinstalled, tighten the mounting bolts to specifications, and measure the rear wheel toe.

TABLE 7-1 *Rear Suspension Diagnosis*

PROBLEM	SYMPTOMS	POSSIBLE CAUSES
Low riding height	Harsh ride quality, worn strikeout bumpers	Weak springs, worn control arm bushings, bent trailing arms or control arms
Steering pull	Steering pulls to the right or left when driving straight ahead	Improper rear wheel toe
Rear tire wear	Excessive rear tire tread wear	Improper rear wheel toe or camber
Rear chassis vibration	Rear chassis vibration when driving at a certain speed	Improper rear wheel, rotor, or drum balance; improper drive shaft balance or angles on rear-wheel-drive vehicles
Rear suspension noise	Rattling or squeaking noise when driving on road irregularities	Worn or dry stabilizer bar links and bushings, worn shock absorber or strut rod bushings, broken tubular rod in the rear axle inverted U-channel
Excessive rear suspension vertical oscillations	Excessive rear suspension bouncing when driving or road irregularities	Worn out shock absorbers or struts
Excessive rear chassis waddle	Excessive rear chassis lateral oscillations	Worn track bar bushings, loose track bar or brace

Case Study

A customer complained about steering pull to the left on a Chevrolet Impala. The customer also said the problem had just occurred in the last few days. The technician road tested the car and found the customer's description of the complaint to be accurate. A careful inspection of the tires indicated there was no abnormal tire wear on the front or rear tires. The vehicle was inspected for recent collision damage, but there was no evidence of this type of damage. After lifting the vehicle on a hoist, the technician checked all the front suspension components, including ball joints, control arms, control arm bushings, and wheel bearings. However, none of these front suspension components indicated any sign of wear or looseness.

Realizing that improper rear wheel tracking causes steering pull, the technician inspected the rear suspension. A pry bar was used to apply downward and rearward force to the trailing arms on the rear suspension. When this action was taken on the right rear trailing arm, the technician discovered the trailing arm bushing was very loose. This defect had allowed the right side of the rear axle to move rearward a considerable amount, which explained why the steering pulled to the left.

After installing a new trailing arm bushing, the alignment was checked on all four wheels, and the wheel alignment was within specifications. A road test indicated no evidence of steering pull or other steering problems.

Service Tips

- Proper curb riding height must be maintained to provide normal steering quality and tire wear.
- If the plastic coating on a coil spring is chipped, the spring may break prematurely. The spring may be taped in the compressing tool contact areas to prevent chipping.
- On rear suspension systems with an inverted U-channel, the stabilizer bar inside the U-channel sometimes breaks away where it is welded to the end plate in the U-channel. This results in a rattling, scraping noise when the car is driven over road irregularities.

Review Questions

1. While discussing lateral movement of the rear chassis:
Technician A says this problem may be caused by loose stabilizer bar bushings. *Technician B* says this problem may be caused by loose track bar bushings.
Who is correct?

A. A only **C.** Both A and B
B. B only **D.** Neither A nor B

2. While discussing excessive rear body sway or roll when driving on road irregularities:
Technician A says this problem may be caused by worn spring insulators. *Technician B* says this problem may be the result of sagged rear springs.
Who is correct?

A. A only **C.** Both A and B
B. B only **D.** Neither A nor B

3. While discussing rear suspension curb riding height:
Technician A says reduced rear curb riding height causes harsh riding. *Technician B* says reduced rear curb riding height increases steering effort.
Who is correct?

A. A only	**C.** Both A and B
B. B only	**D.** Neither A nor B

4. While discussing curb riding height:
Technician A says the curb riding height is measured at the same location on each vehicle. *Technician B* says the curb riding height has no effect on other alignment angles.
Who is correct?

A. A only	**C.** Both A and B
B. B only	**D.** Neither A nor B

5. While discussing spring removal on a MacPherson strut rear suspension:
Technician A says all the spring tension must be removed from the upper mount before the upper strut nut is loosened. *Technician B* says a vinyl-coated spring should be taped in the compressing tool contact area.
Who is correct?

A. A only	**C.** Both A and B
B. B only	**D.** Neither A nor B

6. The most likely cause of excessive rear chassis lateral movement is (are):
A. A weak stabilizer bar.
B. Worn track bar bushings.
C. Worn-out struts.
D. Sagged rear coil springs.

7. All these statements about rear suspension systems with lower control arms and ball joints are true EXCEPT:
A. Worn lower control arm bushings do not affect tire tread wear.
B. Some rear suspension ball joints have wear indicators.
C. On some rear suspensions, the ball joint is pressed into the lower control arm.
D. On some vehicles, the vehicle weight must be resting on the tires when the inner, lower control arm bolts are tightened.

8. Rear suspension adjustment links:
A. May be lengthened or shortened to adjust rear wheel camber.
B. Are connected from the lower control arm to the knuckle.
C. May be loosened on each end with a wedge-type tool.
D. Prevent fore-and-aft control arm and wheel movement.

9. On a rear suspension system with longitudinally mounted leaf springs:
A. Improper vehicle tracking may be caused by a broken spring center bolt.
B. Worn spring silencers may cause reduced curb riding height.
C. A shackle is mounted between the front of the spring and the chassis.
D. Longitudinal rear leaf springs are usually installed on independent rear suspension systems.

10. While diagnosing improper rear wheel tracking:
A. Improper rear wheel tracking may be caused when both rear springs are sagged the same amount.
B. A bent rear suspension tie-rod does not affect rear wheel tracking.
C. Improper rear wheel tracking may result in steering pull when driving straight ahead.
D. Improper rear wheel tracking may cause front wheel shimmy.

CHALLENGE QUESTIONS

1. A squeak in the rear suspension could be caused by all of the following EXCEPT:
   A. The suspension bushing.
   B. Weak spring leaves.
   C. Worn spring antifriction pads.
   D. A defective shock absorber.

2. A vehicle with a live-axle coil spring rear suspension has become hard to steer with harsh ride quality. Which of the following could be the cause of this problem?
   A. Worn lateral link bushings.
   B. Weak rear coil springs.
   C. Bent rear shock rod.
   D. Worn stabilizer bar bushings.

3. A customer says his 1993 Isuzu Trooper has become "real antsy" on a curve. An initial check of the rear suspension by pushing sideways against the bumper with the truck on the floor indicates wear.
   Technician A says worn sway bar bushings could be the problem. *Technician B* says a worn shock mount could be the problem.
   Who is correct?
   A. A only **C.** Both A and B
   B. B only **D.** Neither A nor B

4. A car with independent rear suspension has excessive rear tire wear. An inspection of the rear tires shows they are worn on the inside edge and the tread is feathered.
   Technician A says the problem could be the tires are toeing out during acceleration. *Technician B* says worn control arm bushings could be the cause of the problem.
   Who is correct?
   A. A only **C.** Both A and B
   B. B only **D.** Neither A nor B

5. The steering on a front-wheel-drive car pulls to the right.
   Technician A says the strut on the right rear suspension assembly could be the problem. *Technician B* says worn bushings of the left rear lower arm assembly could be the problem.
   Who is correct?
   A. A only **C.** Both A and B
   B. B only **D.** Neither A nor B

JOB SHEET 21

Name ____ Date ______________

REMOVE AND SERVICE REAR SUSPENSION STRUT AND COIL SPRING ASSEMBLY

Upon completion of this job sheet, you should be able to remove and service rear suspension strut and coil spring assemblies.

ASE Correlation

This job sheet is related to ASE Automotive Suspension and Steering Tasks: *Inspect and replace rear suspension system coil springs and spring insulators. Inspect and replace rear MacPherson strut cartridge or assembly, and upper mount assembly.*

Tools and Materials

Floor jack
Safety stands
Hoist
Coil spring compressing tool

Describe the Vehicle Being Worked On:

Year ____________ Make ______________________ Model ______________
VIN ______________________ Engine type and size ______________

Procedure

Task Completed

1. Remove the rear seat and the package trim tray. ☐
2. Remove the wheel cover, and loosen the wheel nuts. ☐
3. Lift the vehicle with a floor jack, and lower the chassis onto safety stands so the rear suspension is allowed to drop downward.

   Is the rear suspension properly supported on the safety stands? ☐ Yes ☐ No

   Instructor check ____
4. Place the floor jack lift pad under the rear spindle on the side where the strut and spring removal is taking place. Raise the floor jack to support some of the suspension system weight.

   Is the floor jack placed under the rear spindle and supporting some of the vehicle weight? ☐ Yes ☐ No

   Instructor check ____
5. Remove the rear wheel, disconnect the nut from the small spring in the lower arm, and remove the brake hose and antilock brake system (ABS) wire from the strut. ☐
6. Remove the stabilizer bar link from the strut, and loosen the strut-to-spindle mounting bolts. ☐
7. Remove the three upper support nuts under the package tray trim, and lower the floor jack to remove the strut from the knuckle. Remove the strut from the chassis. ☐

Task Completed

SERVICE TIP: If the plastic coating on a coil spring is chipped, the spring may break prematurely. The spring may be taped in the compressing tool contact areas to prevent chipping.

8. Following the vehicle and equipment manufacturers' recommended procedures, install a spring compressor on the coil spring, and tighten the spring compressor until all the spring tension is removed from the upper support.

Is the spring compressor properly installed on the coil spring? ☐ Yes ☐ No

Is the spring compressor tightened so all tension is removed from the upper support?

Instructor check ______________________________

☐ **9.** Install a bolt in the upper strut-to-spindle bolt hole and tighten the two nuts on the end of this bolt. One nut must be on each side of the strut bracket.

Clamp this bolt in a vise to hold the strut, coil spring, and spring compressor.

10. Using the special tool to hold the spring and strut from turning, loosen the nut from the strut rod nut.

Is all the coil spring tension removed from the upper strut mount by the spring compressor? ☐ Yes ☐ No

Is the strut rod nut loosened? ☐ Yes ☐ No

Instructor check ______________________________

☐ **11.** Remove the strut rod nut, upper support, and upper insulator.

☐ **12.** Remove the strut from the lower end of the spring.

☐ **13.** If the spring is to be replaced, rotate the compressor bolt until all the spring tension is removed from the compressing tool, then remove the spring from the tool.

14. Inspect the lower insulator and spring seat on the strut. If the spring seat is warped or damaged, replace the strut. A new cartridge may be installed in some rear struts.

Lower insulator condition: ☐ Satisfactory ☐ Unsatisfactory

Spring seat condition: ☐ Satisfactory ☐ Unsatisfactory

Strut condition: ☐ Satisfactory ☐ Unsatisfactory

List all the components that require replacement and explain the reasons for your diagnosis.

____

____

15. Visually inspect the coil spring, upper mount, insulator, and spring bumper. If any of these components are damaged, worn, or distorted, replacement is necessary.

Coil spring condition: ☐ Satisfactory ☐ Unsatisfactory

Upper mount condition: ☐ Satisfactory ☐ Unsatisfactory

Insulator condition: ☐ Satisfactory ☐ Unsatisfactory

Spring bumper condition: ☐ Satisfactory ☐ Unsatisfactory

List all the components that require replacement and explain the reasons for your diagnosis.

____

Instructor's Response ______________________________

____

Job Sheet 22

Name ______________________________ Date ______________

REMOVE REAR SUSPENSION LOWER CONTROL ARM AND BALL JOINT ASSEMBLY

Upon completion of this job sheet, you should be able to remove rear suspension lower control arm and ball joint assemblies.

ASE Correlation

This job sheet is related to ASE Automotive Suspension and Steering Tasks: *Inspect and replace rear suspension system transverse links (track bars), control arms, stabilizer bars (sway bars), bushings, and mounts. Inspect and replace rear ball joints and tie-rod assemblies.*

Tools and Materials

Floor jack	Control arm removing tool
Safety stands	Transmission jack
Hoist	Ball joint removal and replacement tools

Describe the Vehicle Being Worked On:

Year __________ Make __________ Model __________

VIN ______________ Engine type and size ______________

Procedure

Task Completed

1. Lift the vehicle on a hoist with the chassis supported in the hoist and control arms dropped downward. The vehicle may be lifted with a floor jack and the chassis supported on safety stands. ☐
2. Remove the tire-and-wheel assembly. ☐
3. Remove the stabilizer bar from the knuckle bracket. ☐
4. Remove the parking brake cable retaining clip from the lower control arm. ☐
5. If the car has electronic level control (ELC), disconnect the height sensor link from the control arm. ☐
6. Install a special tool to support the lower control arm in the bushing areas. ☐
7. Place a transmission jack under the special tool and raise the jack enough to remove the tension from the control arm bushing retaining bolts. If the car was lifted with a floor jack and supported on safety stands, place a floor jack under the special tool.

   Is the special control arm support tool properly installed and supported?

   ☐ Yes ☐ No

   Instructor check ______________________________
8. Place a safety chain through the coil spring and around the lower control arm.

   Is the safety chain properly installed? ☐ Yes ☐ No

   Instructor check ______________________________

Task Completed

☐ **9.** Remove the bolt from the rear control arm bushing.

☐ **10.** Be sure the jack is raised enough to relieve the tension on the front bolt in the lower control arm and remove this bolt.

☐ **11.** Lower the jack slowly and allow the control arm to pivot downward. When all the tension is released from the coil spring, remove the safety chain, coil spring, and insulators.

12. Inspect the coil spring for distortion and proper free length. If the spring has a vinyl coating, check this coating for scratches or nicks. Check the spring insulators for cracks and wear.

Coil spring condition:: ☐ Satisfactory ☐ Unsatisfactory

List all the components that require replacement and explain the reasons for your diagnosis.

____

____

____

☐ **13.** Remove the nut on the inner end of the suspension adjustment link and disconnect this link from the lower control arm.

14. Remove the cotter pin from the ball joint nut, and loosen, but do not remove, the nut from the ball joint stud.

Is the ball joint nut loosened? ☐ Yes ☐ No

Instructor check ________________________________

☐ **15.** Use a special ball joint removal tool to loosen the ball joint in the knuckle.

☐ **16.** Remove the ball joint nut and the control arm.

17. Inspect the lower control arm for bends, distortion, and worn bushings.

Lower control arm condition: ☐ Satisfactory ☐ Unsatisfactory

List the control arm and related parts that require replacement and explain the reasons for your diagnosis.

____

____

Instructor check ________________________________

☐ **18.** Use a special ball joint pressing tool to press the ball joint from the lower control arm.

☐ **19.** Use the same pressing tool with different adapters to press the new ball joint into the control arm.

Instructor's Response ________________________________

____

____

JOB SHEET 23

Name ______________________________ Date ______________

INSTALL REAR SUSPENSION LOWER CONTROL ARM AND BALL JOINT ASSEMBLY

Upon completion of this job sheet, you should be able to install rear suspension lower control arm and ball joint assemblies.

NATEF and ASE Correlation

This job sheet is related to ASE Automotive Suspension and Steering Task: *Inspect and replace rear suspension system transverse links (track bars), control arms, stabilizer bars (sway bars), bushings, and mounts.*

Tools and Materials

Floor jack
Safety stands
Hoist
Control arm removing tool
Transmission jack

Describe the Vehicle Being Worked On:

Year ____________ Make ______________ Model ______________
VIN ________________ Engine type and size ______________

Procedure

Task Completed

1. Install the ball joint stud in the knuckle and install the nut on the ball joint stud. Tighten the ball joint nut to the specified torque, and then tighten the nut an additional 2/3 turn. If necessary, tighten the nut slightly to align the nut castellations with the cotter pin hole in the ball joint stud, and install the cotter pin.

Specified ball joint stud nut torque________

Actual ball joint stud nut torque________

2. Snap the upper insulator on the coil spring. Install the lower spring insulator and the spring in the lower control arm.

Is the coil spring and insulator properly installed in lower control arm?
☐ Yes ☐ No

Instructor check ______________________________

3. Be sure the top of the coil spring is properly positioned in relation to the front of the vehicle.

Is the top of the spring properly positioned? ☐ Yes ☐ No

Instructor check ______________________________

Task Completed

4. Install the special tool on the inner ends of the control arm, and place the transmission jack or floor jack under the special tool.

   Is the special tool properly supported on the control arm? ☐ Yes ☐ No

   Instructor check ______________________________

   Is the special tool properly supported on the transmission or floor jack?

   Instructor check ______________________________

☐ 5. Slowly raise the transmission jack until the control arm bushing openings are aligned with the openings in the chassis.

CAUTION: The pivot bolts and nuts in the inner ends of the lower control arm must be tightened to the specified torque with the vehicle supported on the wheels and the suspension at normal curb height. Failure to follow this procedure may adversely affect ride quality and steering characteristics.

☐ 6. Install the bolts and nuts in the inner ends of the control arm. Do not torque these bolts and nuts at this time.

7. Install the stabilizer-bar-to-knuckle bracket fasteners to the specified torque.

   Specified torque on stabilizer-bar-to-knuckle bracket fasteners________

   Actual torque on stabilizer-bar-to-knuckle bracket fasteners________

☐ 8. Install the parking brake retaining clip.

☐ 9. If the vehicle has ELC, install the height sensor link, and tighten the fastener to the specified torque.

10. Install the suspension adjustment link and tighten the fastener to the specified torque. Install cotter pins as required.

    Specified adjustment link retaining nut torque________

    Actual adjustment link retaining nut torque________

    Are the cotter pins properly installed in adjustment link retaining nuts?
    ☐ Yes ☐ No

    Instructor check ______________________________

☐ 11. Remove the transmission jack or floor jack, and install the tire-and-wheel assembly.

12. Lower the vehicle onto the floor. Tighten the wheel hub nuts and lower control arm bolts and nuts to the specified torque.

    Specified wheel nut torque________

    Actual wheel nut torque________

    Specified control arm retaining nut torque________

    Actual control arm retaining nut torque________

Instructor's Response ______________________________

____

____

COMPUTER-CONTROLLED SUSPENSION SYSTEM SERVICE

8

Upon completion and review of this chapter, you should be able to:

- Diagnose programmed ride control (PRC) systems.
- Diagnose electronic air suspension systems.
- Remove, replace, and inflate air springs.
- Adjust front and rear trim height on electronic air suspension systems.
- Service and repair nylon air lines.
- Diagnose vehicle dynamic suspension (VDS) systems.
- Remove and replace air springs on VDS systems.
- Perform an on-demand self-test on VDS systems.
- Diagnose electronic suspension control (ESC) systems.
- Display and interpret scan tool data on ESC systems.
- Use the output controls function to diagnose ESC systems.

Each year more vehicles are equipped with computer-controlled suspension systems, and these systems are becoming increasingly complex. Therefore, technicians must understand the correct procedures for diagnosing and servicing these systems. When a technician understands computer-controlled suspension systems and the proper diagnostic procedures for these systems, diagnosis becomes faster and more accurate.

PRELIMINARY INSPECTION OF COMPUTER-CONTROLLED SUSPENSION SYSTEMS

Prior to diagnosing a computer-controlled suspension system, a preliminary inspection should be performed. The preliminary inspection may locate a minor defect that is the cause of the problem. If the preliminary inspection is not performed, a lot of time may be wasted performing advanced diagnosis when the problem is a minor defect. When the preliminary diagnosis does not locate any minor problems, further diagnosis is required.

Follow these steps to complete the preliminary diagnosis:

1. Talk to the customer and find out the exact complaint regarding vehicle operation.
2. If necessary, road test the vehicle to determine the exact symptoms.
3. Inspect the vehicle for any work that was completed recently, including body work. Wires or air lines may have been damaged by a collision.
4. Check all electrical connections and wiring in the computer-controlled suspension system.
5. If the vehicle has a computer-controlled air suspension system, listen for air leaks in the system.
6. If the vehicle has a computer-controlled air suspension system, check all the air lines for cracks, breaks, damage, and kinks.
7. Measure the vehicle curb (trim) height.
8. Check the operation of the suspension warning light or observe the message center in the instrument panel for displayed suspension messages.

PROGRAMMED RIDE CONTROL SYSTEM DIAGNOSIS

General Diagnosis

The **programmed ride control** (PRC) module monitors the complete system while the vehicle is driven. If a defect occurs in the PRC system, the mode indicator light starts flashing. When the mode selector switch is moved to the opposite position and returned to the same position, erroneous codes are cleared from the control module memory. If the mode indicator light continues flashing, the self-test should be performed.

Self-Test

The self-test connector is located under the ash tray (Figure 8-1). This connector has two terminals that must be connected during the self-test. A jumper tool should be fabricated to connect these terminals, and this tool should be soldered to the end of a 7-inch slotted screwdriver blade to access the self-test terminals (Figure 8-2).

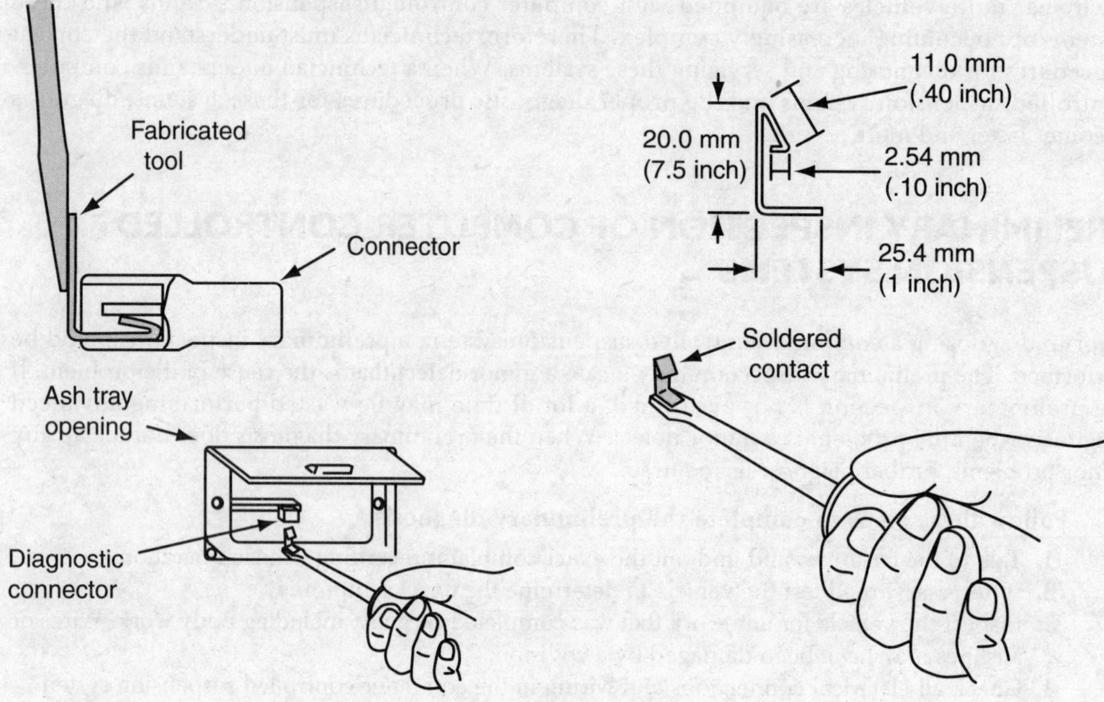

FIGURE 8-1 *Self-test terminals, programmed ride control system.*

FIGURE 8-2 *Fabricated tool to connect the self-test terminals.*

Follow this procedure to perform the self-test:

1. Turn the ignition switch off and be sure the headlights and parking lights are off. These lights must remain off during the self-test.
2. Position the mode select switch in the Auto position.
3. Remove the ash tray and insert the fabricated tool in the self-test connector terminals.
4. Start the engine and leave the mode select switch in the Auto position.
5. When the engine has been running for 20 seconds or more, remove the tool from the self-test connector.
6. Count the mode indicator light flashes to obtain the trouble codes. For example, if the light flashes six times, code 6 has been provided. The light flashes each code four times at nine-second intervals. The mode indicator light is in the tachometer (Figure 8-3).

Diagnostic Trouble Codes (DTCs)

Several DTCs are available on the PRC system (Figure 8-4). The DTCs vary depending on the vehicle make and year. Always use the DTC list in the manufacturer's service manual. A trouble code indicates a defect in a specific area. For example, if DTC 2 is received, the defect may be in the right rear actuator or in the connecting wires.

After a PRC system defect has been corrected, the DTCs should be cleared. The system should be checked for DTCs again to make sure there are no other faults in the system.

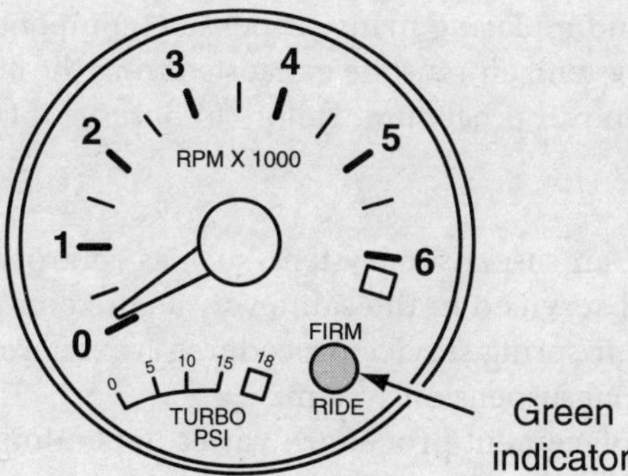

FIGURE 8-3 *Mode indicator in tachometer flashes trouble codes.*

PRC System Diagnostic Trouble Codes (DTCs)

Code	Defect
6	No problem
1	Left rear actuator circuit
2	Right rear actuator circuit
3	Right front actuator circuit
4	Left front actuator circuit
5	Soft relay control circuit shorted
7	PRC control module
13	Firm relay control circuit shorted
14	Relay control circuit

FIGURE 8-4 *PRC system diagnostic trouble codes (DTCs).*

ELECTRONIC AIR SUSPENSION DIAGNOSIS AND SERVICE

Air Spring Removal and Installation

WARNING: The system control switch must be in the Off position when system components are serviced to prevent personal injury and damage to system components.

WARNING: The system control switch must be turned off prior to hoisting, jacking, or towing the vehicle. If the front of the chassis is lifted with a bumper jack, the rear suspension moves downward. The electronic air suspension system will attempt to restore the rear trim height to normal, and this action may cause the front of the chassis to fall off the bumper jack, resulting in personal injury or vehicle damage.

WARNING: When air spring valves are being removed, always rotate the valve to the first stage until all the air escapes from the air spring. Never turn the valve to the second (release) stage until all the air is released from the spring. If this action is taken, the valve may be blown out of the air spring with considerable force, and this may cause personal injury.

WARNING: When removing and replacing many suspension components such as lower control arms in an air spring suspension system, air must be exhausted from the air spring to relieve tension on the components before the removal procedure. Failure to observe this precaution may result in personal injury.

Many components in an electronic air suspension system, such as control arms, shock absorbers, and stabilizer bars, are diagnosed and serviced in the same way as the components in a conventional suspension system. However, the air spring service procedures are different compared to coil-spring service procedures on a conventional suspension system.

The air spring removal and replacement procedure varies depending on the vehicle make and model year. For example, a different air spring removal and replacement procedure is required on vehicles with integral air springs and struts, and vehicles with the air springs mounted separately from the shock absorbers. Front and rear air spring removal and replacement procedures may vary. Always follow the exact air spring removal and replacement procedure in the vehicle manufacturer's service manual. The following is a typical air spring removal and replacement procedure for some vehicles with the air springs mounted separately from the shock absorbers:

Follow these steps for air spring removal:

1. Turn off the electronic air suspension switch in the trunk.
2. Hoist the vehicle and allow the suspension to drop downward, or lift the vehicle with a floor jack and place safety stands under the chassis. Lower the vehicle onto the safety stands and allow the suspension to drop downward.
3. Disconnect the nylon air line from the spring solenoid valve, and rotate the valve to the first stage to allow the air to escape from the spring. Never turn the valve to the second stage until all the air is exhausted from the spring.
4. Disconnect the lower spring retainer and remove the spring from the chassis.
5. Before an air spring is installed, it must be properly folded over the piston at the bottom of the membrane (Figure 8-5).
6. Install the spring in the chassis and connect the lower spring retainer. Be sure the top of the spring is properly seated in the spring seat. When an air spring is installed in the front or rear suspension, the spring must be properly positioned to eliminate folds and creases in the membrane (Figure 8-6)

Removal and Replacement of Air Springs with Integral Struts

Front or rear air springs with integral struts are sold only as an assembly. Do not attempt to service these components. The following is typical front air spring removal and replacement procedure on an automatic air suspension system with air springs containing integral struts:

1. Turn off the air suspension switch.
2. Raise the vehicle on a frame-contact lift and allow the suspension to drop downward.
3. Remove the wheel and tire assembly on the corner of the vehicle that requires air spring and strut removal.
4. Release the metal clip at the top height sensor mount, then remove the height sensor off the ball stud.
5. Remove the air spring solenoid retainer, loosen the air spring solenoid valve to the first position, and allow all the air pressure to be relieved from the air spring.

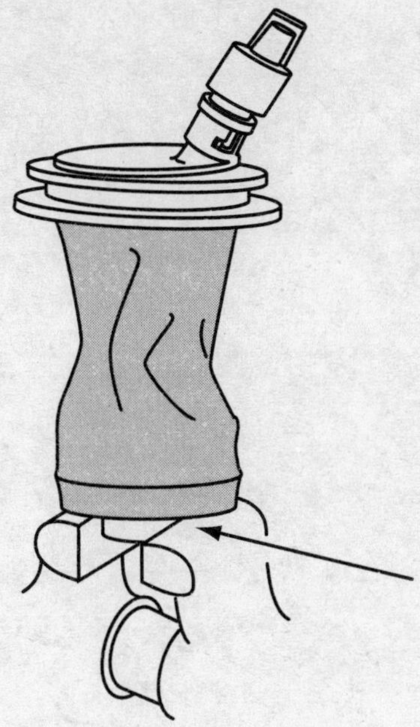

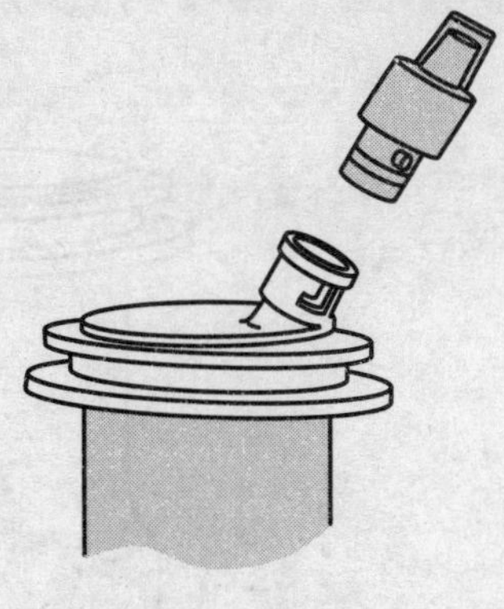

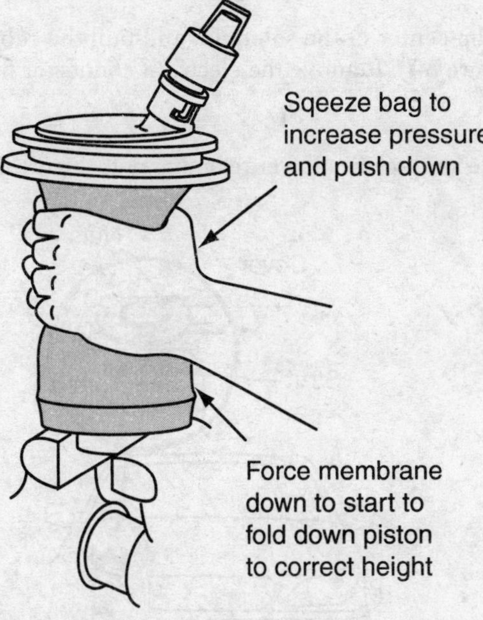

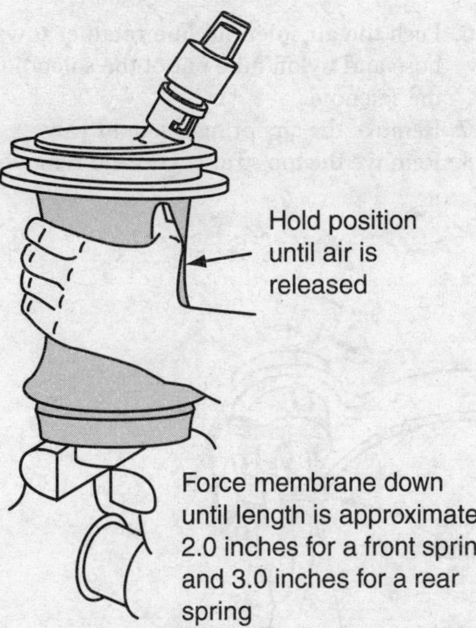

FIGURE 8-5 *Air spring folding.*

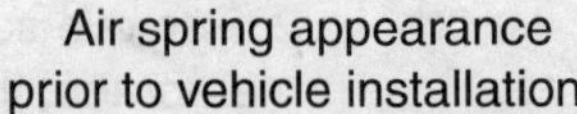

FIGURE 8-6 *When an air spring is installed in the front or rear suspension, the spring must be properly positioned to eliminate folds and creases in the membrane.*

6. Push the air solenoid line retainer toward the center of the solenoid, and pull the rubber hose and nylon tube out of the solenoid (Figure 8-7). Remove the electrical connector from the solenoid.
7. Remove the air spring solenoid valve.
8. Remove the top strut cover, and remove three strut-to-strut tower retaining nuts (Figure 8-8).

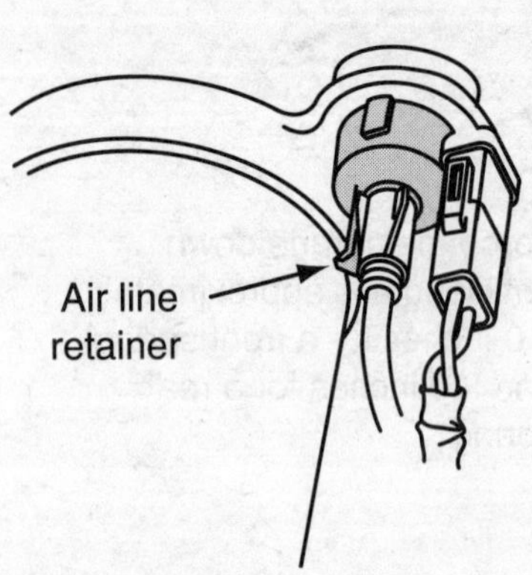

FIGURE 8-7 *Air line removal from the air spring solenoid valve.*

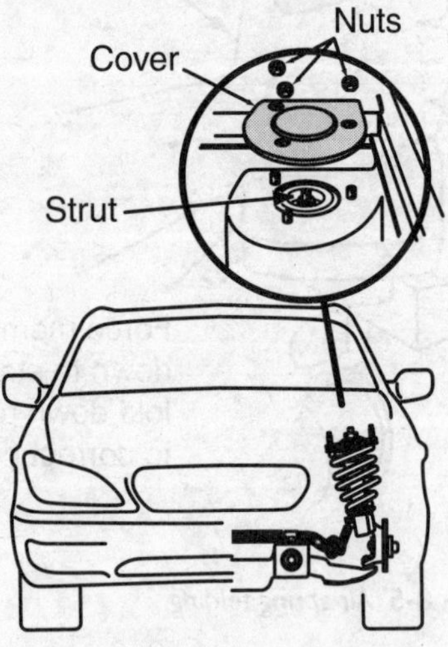

FIGURE 8-8 *Removing the upper strut mount retaining nuts.*

CAUTION: Loosening the large center nut on the top of the strut rod may cause a permanent leak through the top of the air spring.

9. Remove the strut-to-suspension arm retaining nut and bolt.
10. Remove the strut and spring assembly from the vehicle.

Follow these steps to install a replacement front air spring and integral strut:

1. Install the air spring and strut assembly into the front suspension until the upper strut mount retaining bolts extend through the bolt holes in the strut tower.
2. Install the upper strut mount retaining nuts and tighten these nuts to the specified torque.
3. Install the lower strut-to-suspension retaining bolt and nut, and tighten the nut until it is snug. The nut on this bolt must be tightened to the specified torque after the vehicle weight is applied to the suspension.
4. Install the air spring solenoid valve fully into the air spring, and install the valve retainer.
5. Install the air line and electrical connector into the solenoid valve.
6. Install the wheel and tire assembly and tighten the wheel nuts to the specified torque.
7. Perform an air spring fill procedure described in the next section.

Air Spring Inflation

If an air spring has been replaced, or the air has been completely exhausted from an air spring, a spring fill procedure is required to inflate the air spring. The air spring fill procedure varies depending on the vehicle make and model year. Always follow the air spring fill procedure in the vehicle manufacturer's service manual. The following air spring fill procedure is for a vehicle with the air springs separate from the shock absorbers.

CAUTION: Do not allow the suspension to compress an air spring until the air-spring is inflated. This action may damage the air spring.

The weight of the vehicle must not be allowed to compress an uninflated air spring.

When an air spring is being inflated, use this procedure:

1. With the vehicle chassis supported on a hoist, lower the hoist until a slight load is placed on the suspension. Do not lower the hoist until the suspension is heavily loaded.
2. Turn on the air suspension system switch.
3. Turn the ignition switch from Off to Run for 5 seconds with the driver's door open and the other doors shut. Turn the ignition switch off.
4. Ground the diagnostic lead.
5. Apply the brake pedal and turn the ignition to the Run position. The warning lamp will flash every 2 seconds to indicate the fill mode.
6. To fill a rear spring or springs, close and open the driver's door once. After a 6-second delay, the rear spring will fill for 60 seconds.
7. To fill a front spring or springs, close and open the driver's door twice. After a 6-second delay, the front spring will fill for 60 seconds.
8. When front and rear springs require filling, fill the rear springs first. Once the rear springs are filled, close and open the driver's door once to begin filling the front springs.
9. The spring fill mode is terminated if the diagnostic lead is disconnected from ground. Termination also occurs if the ignition switch is turned off or the brake pedal is applied.

Scan Tool Procedure for Air Spring Inflation

On some air suspension systems the **scan tool** is used to activate the air compressor and energize the appropriate air spring solenoid valve to inflate an air spring. The following is a typical spring fill procedure using a scan tool on an automatic air suspension system:

1. Turn off the air suspension switch.
2. Be sure the proper module is installed in the scan tool for suspension diagnosis and service on the vehicle being serviced.
3. Connect the scan tool to the **data link connector** (DLC) on the vehicle.
4. Be sure the vehicle is positioned on a frame-contact lift with the suspension dropped downward and no load on the suspension.
5. Connect a battery charger to the battery terminals with the correct polarity, and set the charger at a low charging rate.
6. Select Function Test on the scan tool, and select the desired function test number for the air spring being filled as follows: test number 212 – LH front air spring, test number 214 – RH front air spring, test number 216 – LH rear air spring, and test number 218 – RH rear air spring. When the proper function test number is selected, the scan tool commands the compressor and the appropriate air spring solenoid valve on, to allow air spring inflation.
7. When the compressor shuts off, the air spring inflation is complete, and any further air spring inflation or deflation is done during normal operation of the air suspension system.
8. Lower the vehicle onto the shop floor and completely lower the lift. Be sure the lift arms are not contacting the vehicle.
9. Inspect the air spring(s) that were completely deflated, and be sure there are no folds and creases in these springs.
10. Turn on the suspension switch.
11. If the lower front strut-to-control arm bolt and nut were removed and reinstalled during the suspension service procedure, use your knee to push downward and release the front bumper. Repeat this procedure three times.
12. Tighten the lower front strut-to-control arm nut and bolt to the specified torque.
13. Road test the vehicle and verify proper air suspension operation and trim height.

Trim Height Mechanical Adjustment

On some vehicles with air suspension, the trim height is adjusted by lengthening or shortening the front or rear height sensors. On other vehicles the manufacturer recommends using the scan tool to adjust the trim height. Always follow the trim height adjustment procedure in the vehicle manufacturer's service manual.

The **trim height** should be measured on the front and rear suspension at the locations specified by the vehicle manufacturer (Figure 8-10).

If the rear suspension trim height is not within specifications, it may be adjusted by loosening the attaching bolt on the top height sensor bracket (Figure 8-11). When the bracket is moved one index mark up or down, the ride height is lowered or raised 0.25 in. (6.35 mm).

The front suspension trim height may be adjusted by loosening the lower height sensor attaching bolt. Three adjustment positions are located in the lower front height sensor bracket (Figure 8-12). If the height sensor attaching bolt is moved one position up or down, the front suspension height is lowered or raised 0.5 in. (12.7 mm).

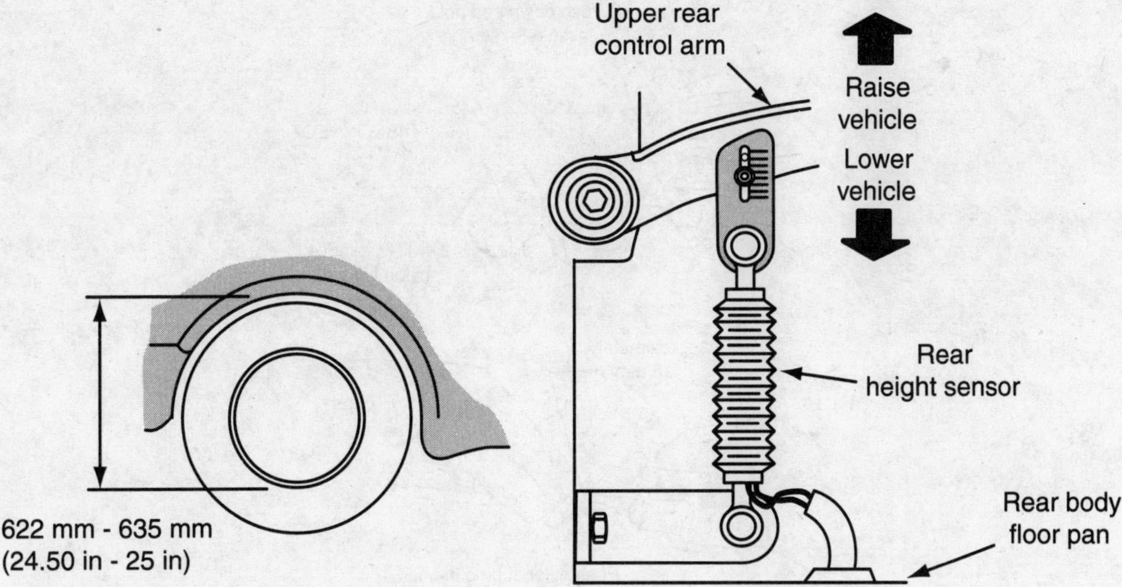

FIGURE 8-10 *Trim height measurement location.*

FIGURE 8-11 *Rear trim height adjustment.*

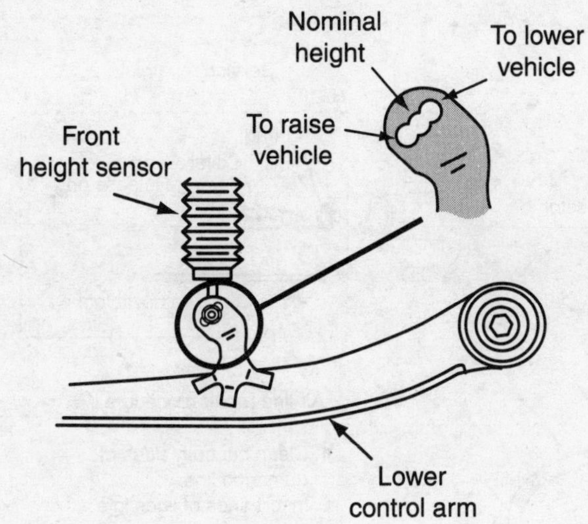

FIGURE 8-12 *Front trim height adjustment.*

Line Service

Nylon lines on the electronic air suspension system have quick disconnect fittings. These fittings should be released by pushing downward and holding the plastic release ring, and then pulling outward on the nylon line (Figure 8-13). Simply push the nylon line into the fitting until it seats to reconnect an air line.

If a line fitting is damaged, it may be removed by looping the line around your fingers and pulling on the line without pusning on the release ring (Figure 8-14). When a new collet and release ring are

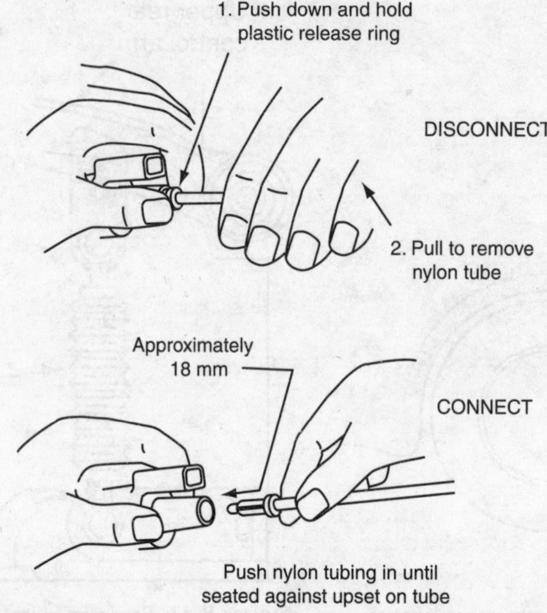

FIGURE 8-13 *Air line removed from the air spring valve or compressor outlets.*

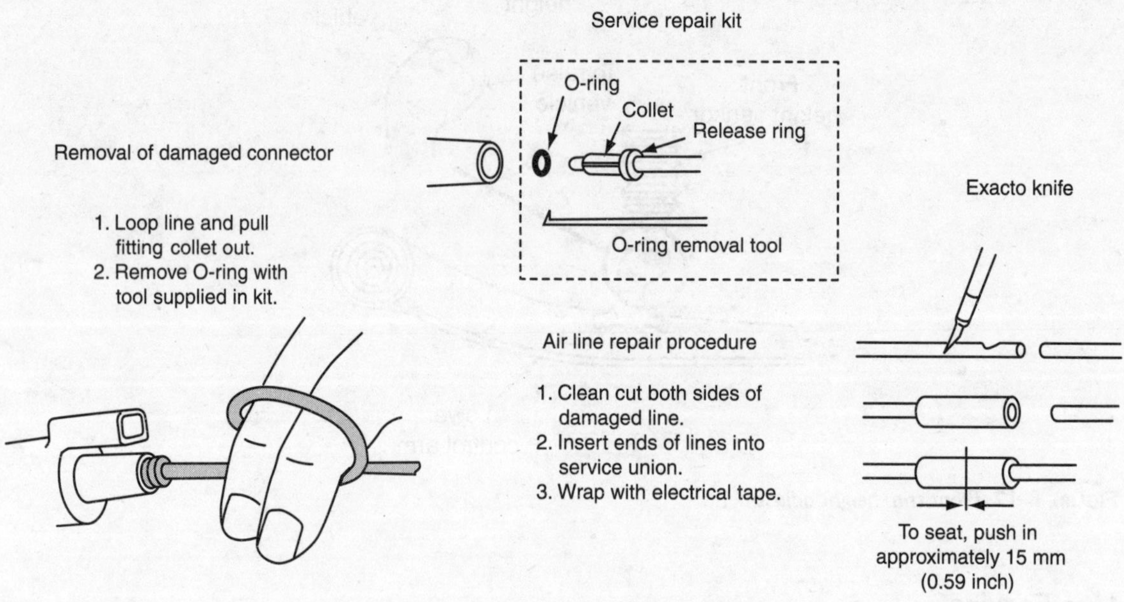

FIGURE 8-14 *Removing the quick disconnect fittings and air line repairs procedure.*

installed, the O-ring under the collet must be replaced. If a leak occurs in a nylon line, a sharp knife may be used to cut the defective area out of the line. A service fitting containing a collet fitting in each end is available for line repairs. After the defective area is cut out of the line, push the two ends of the line into the service fitting (Figure 8-14).

SERVICING AND DIAGNOSING VEHICLE DYNAMIC SUSPENSION SYSTEMS

On some vehicles the air suspension is referred to as a **vehicle dynamic suspension (VDS)**. Proper diagnosis of the VDS is extremely important to locate the exact root cause of the customer's complaint. Improper diagnosis may lead to wasted time and unnecessary replacement of expensive electronic components. The first step in VDS diagnosis is to visually inspect the system.

VDS Inspection and Verification

Follow these steps to inspect the VDS system and verify the symptoms:

1. Be sure the customer complaint is identified; road test the vehicle if necessary.
2. Be sure none of the DOOR AJAR indicators are illuminated.
3. Inspect the suspension system for anything that could result in restricted suspension movement.
4. Inspect the vehicle trunk for excessive loading.
5. Check the front and rear height sensors for loose or worn mountings.
6. Inspect the front and rear air springs for damage such as punctures and tears.
7. Check the suspension air lines for cuts, splits, or a crimped condition.
8. Check fuses 102, 30, 27, and 111 in the central junction box.
9. Inspect all VDS electrical connections for looseness and corrosion.
10. Be sure the air suspension switch is on.
11. Inspect the solenoid valves in the air springs for damage.

If the VDS inspection reveals an obvious problem, this defect must be corrected before proceeding with the electronic diagnosis. When the inspection and verification does not indicate any defects, proceed with the pneumatic test and the on-demand self test.

Ride Height Adjustment or Calibration

The ride height adjustment procedure with a scan tool may vary depending on the vehicle make and model year. The following is a typical ride height adjustment procedure with a scan tool for a 2005 Ford Expedition or Lincoln Navigator equipped with a vehicle dynamic suspension:

1. Be sure the air suspension switch is in the On position.
2. Be sure the battery is fully charged.
3. Turn off the ignition switch and exit the vehicle. Close all doors and wait 45 seconds for the air suspension system to vent down to the Kneel position.
4. Open the driver's door, and turn on the ignition switch.
5. Shift the transmission into drive and back into park.
6. Exit the vehicle, close all the doors, and wait 45 seconds for the suspension system to pump up to the trim height.
7. Use a tape measure to measure the ride height at the locations specified by the vehicle manufacturer (Figure 8-15 and Figure 8-16).
8. If the ride height does not equal the manufacturer's specifications, open the left-front door, and connect the scan tool to the DLC. Be sure the scan tool contains the proper module for the vehicle being tested.
9. Select the correct vehicle year, model, and engine type on the scan tool, and then select *Vehicle Dynamic Module* (VDM).

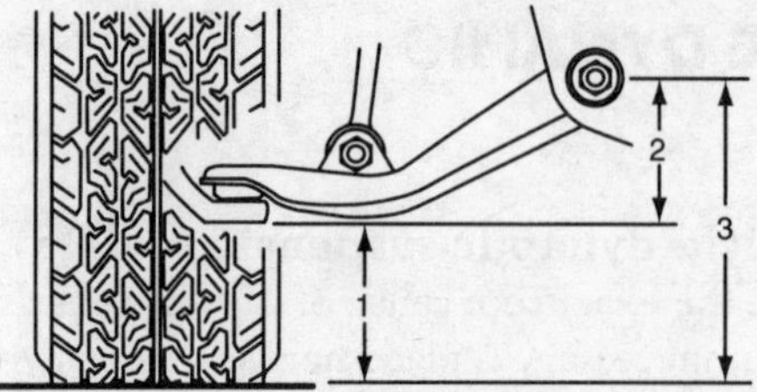

Item	Description
1	Distance between the ground and the lower knuckle surface near the ball joint
2	Ride height = 3 - 1
3	Distance between the ground and the center of the lower arm rearward mounting bolt

FIGURE 8-15 *Front ride height measurement.*

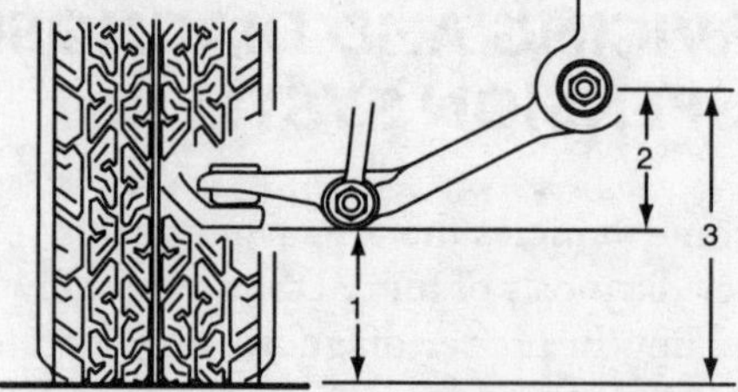

Item	Description
1	Distance between the ground and lower edge of arm below the shock absorber mounting bolt
2	Ride height = 3 - 1
3	Distance between the ground and the center of the lower arm mounting bolt

FIGURE 8-16 *Rear ride height measurement.*

10. Use the active command mode in the scan tool to vent or lift the vehicle to achieve the specified trim height.
11. When a tape measure indicates the specified front and rear ride height, select *Save Calibration Values* on the scan tool to calibrate the VDM to the specified trim height.
12. Road test the vehicle and verify the proper suspension height.

Pneumatic Test

The pneumatic test verifies the air lines are connected and the air compressor, air compressor vent solenoid, and air spring solenoid valves are functioning properly. Follow these steps to complete the pneumatic test:

1. Close all doors, liftgate, and liftgate glass.
2. Place the transmission selector in park.
3. Be sure the air suspension switch is on.
4. Connect the scan tool to the DLC. Be sure the correct module is installed in the scan tool.
5. Turn on the ignition switch and select *Vehicle Dynamic Module* followed by *Pneumatic Test* on the scan tool.
6. This scan tool selection causes the VDM to operate the VDS compressor, spring solenoid valves, and vent valve. While operating the system the VDM checks for proper response from the height sensors. If the VDM does not perform normal air spring fill and vent operations in the required time, the VDM sets diagnostic trouble codes (DTCs) in memory and displays appropriate messages in the message center or in the instrument panel if the vehicle does not have a message center. The results of the pneumatic test are also displayed on the scan tool.

On-Demand Self-Test

When the inspection, verification, and pneumatic tests do not indicate any defects, the on-demand self-test should be performed to locate the problem area in the VDS system.

Complete the following steps to perform the on-demand self-test:

1. Be sure the transmission is in park.
2. Be sure the battery is fully charged. A battery charger may be installed to maintain a fully charged battery.
3. Connect the scan tool to the DLC.
4. Lower the driver's window and close all doors, liftgate, and liftgate glass.
5. Be sure the 4L mode is not selected on four-wheel-drive models.
6. Turn on the ignition switch.
7. Select *Vehicle Dynamic Module* and *On-Demand Self-Test* on the scan tool.
8. Record all DTCs displayed on the scan tool.
9. Turn off the ignition switch.

When DTCs are displayed on the scan tool, interpret the meaning of the DTC and diagnose the root cause of the problem. Possible DTCs on the VDS system are these:

1. B1317 – high battery voltage
2. B1318 – low battery voltage
3. B1342 – VDM is defective
4. B2477 – variable assist power steering (VAPS) steering assist curve not complete
5. C1445 – vehicle speed sensor circuit defect
6. C1724 – air suspension height sensor power circuit failure
7. C1725 – air suspension front pneumatic failure
8. C1726 – air suspension rear pneumatic failure
9. C1760 – failure in rear height sensor signal circuit
10. C1770 – failure in vent solenoid output circuit
11. C1790 – L/R air spring solenoid valve output circuit failure
12. C1795 – R/R air spring solenoid valve output circuit failure
13. C1830 – failure in compressor relay circuit
14. C1840 – failure in air suspension On/Off switch
15. C1873 – R/F air spring solenoid valve output circuit failure
16. C1877 – L/F air spring solenoid valve output circuit failure
17. C1881 – failure in R/F height sensor circuit
18. C1889 – failure in L/F height sensor circuit
19. C1897 – failure in VAPS circuit loop
20. C1964 – compressor run time longer than specified
21. C1990 – VDM initialization required on replacement VDM
22. C1991 – factory trim height setting and/or tests not completed
23. U1900 – missing controller area network (CAN) messages
24. U2023 – improper CAN messages

If DTCs are displayed on the scan tool, detailed pinpoint tests are provided in the vehicle manufacturer's service manual to locate the exact cause of the problem. These pinpoint tests usually include voltmeter and ohmmeter tests. A DTC indicates the area in which a problem is pres-ent, but the pinpoint tests are used to locate the root cause of the defect. When DTC C1990 is displayed, perform the pneumatic test and ride height calibration procedure to initialize the VDM.

Removal and Disassembly of Combined Air Springs and Shock Absorbers on VDS Systems

The removal and disassembly procedures are similar for front and rear air springs. Follow these steps to remove and disassemble a combined air spring and shock absorber:

1. Position the vehicle on a lift and place the lift arms under the specified lift points on the vehicle.
2. Be sure the ignition switch and the VDS switch are turned off.
3. Connect the scan tool to the DLC, and use the scan tool to vent the air spring being removed.

> **WARNING:** Never remove an air spring or a component attached to the air spring without completely deflating the air spring. This action may cause personal injury.

4. Remove the upper strut mount retaining nuts on the air spring to be removed (Figure 8- 17). Discard the nuts.

> **CAUTION:** When removing and replacing components on the VDS, the vehicle manufacturer recommends replacing all the self-locking nuts. Failure to observe this service procedure may cause loose suspension components and component failure.

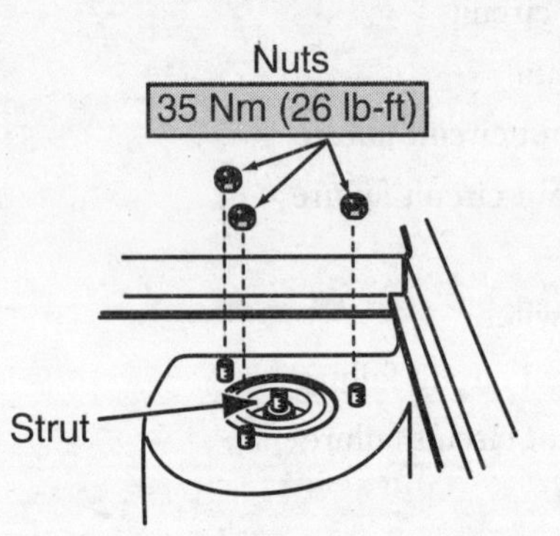

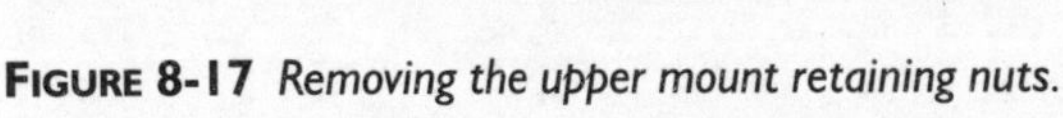

FIGURE 8-17 *Removing the upper mount retaining nuts.*

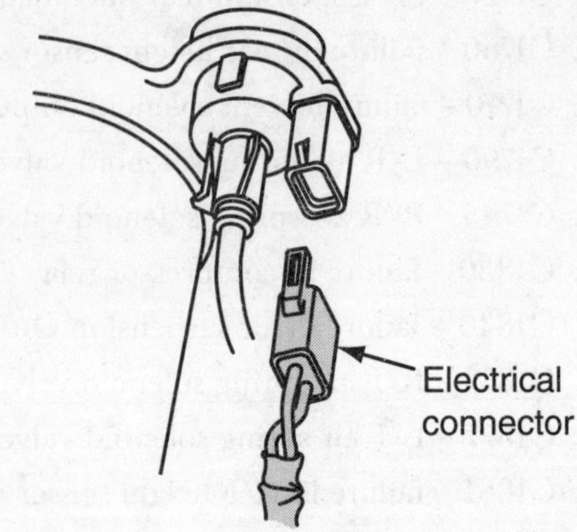

FIGURE 8-18 *Disconnecting the electrical connector from the air spring solenoid valve.*

5. Raise the vehicle to a comfortable working height. Disconnect the electrical connector from the air spring solenoid valve (Figure 8-18).
6. Compress the orange quick-disconnect connector on the air line connected to the air spring, and pull downward to disconnect the air line (Figure 8-19).
7. Use the appropriate socket and ratchet to remove the nut from the lower shock absorber mounting bolt, and remove this bolt (Figure 8-20).
8. Remove the air spring and shock absorber from the chassis.
9. Place a wrench on the hex on top of the shock absorber rod, and hold this rod from turning while loosening and removing the nut on the top of the shock absorber rod (Figure 8-21).

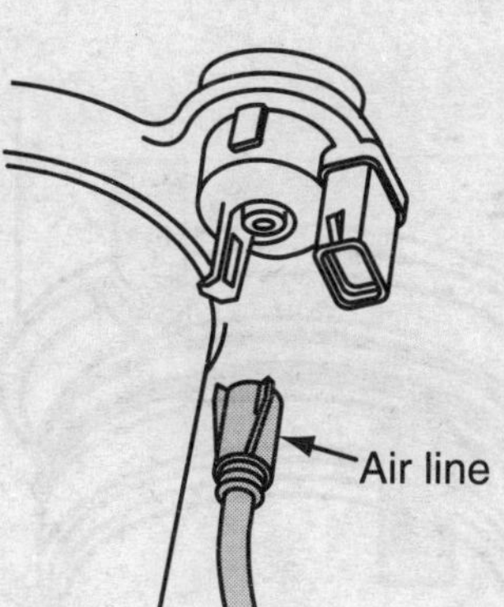

FIGURE 8-19 *Disconnecting the air line from the air spring solenoid valve.*

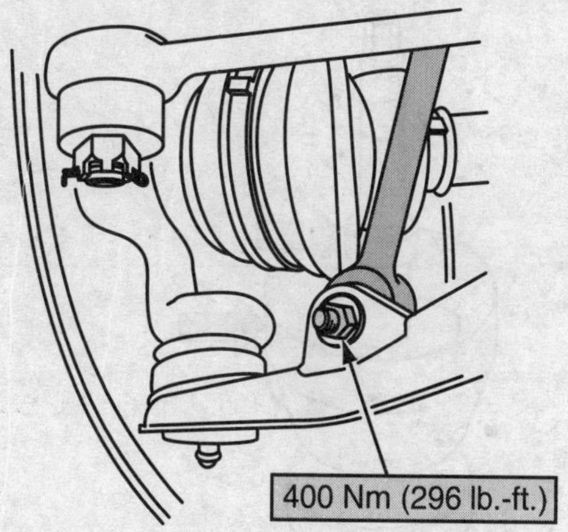

FIGURE 8-20 *Removing the lower shock absorber retaining bolt and nut.*

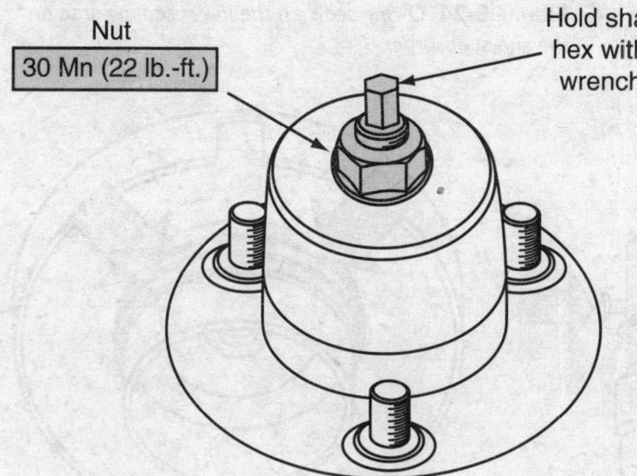

FIGURE 8-21 *Removing the nut from the upper end of the shock absorber rod.*

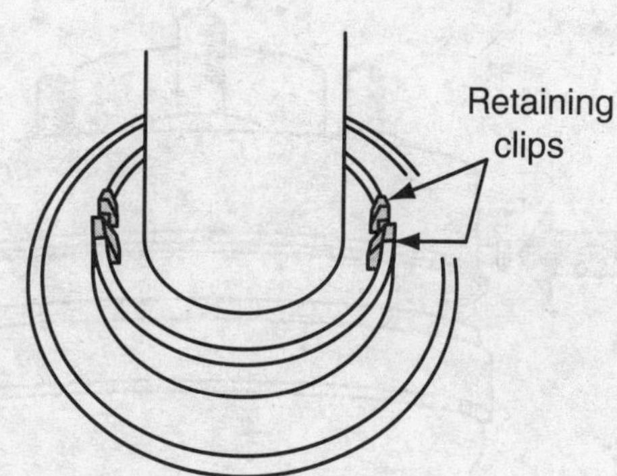

FIGURE 8-22 *Depressing the retaining tabs on the bottom end of the air spring.*

10. Place index marks on the lower end of the air spring and shock absorber so these components may be reassembled in the original position. Depress the retainer tabs on the bottom end of the air spring, and remove the air spring from the shock absorber (Figure 8-22).
11. Remove and discard the seal and washer on the upper end of the shock absorber rod (Figure 8-23).
12. Remove and discard the O-ring seals on the lower sealing area between the shock absorber and the air spring (Figure 8-24).
13. Remove and discard the retainer pins that hold the upper mount onto the air spring (Figure 8-25).
14. Remove and discard the O-ring seals on the upper mount area that provides a seal between the mount and the air spring (Figure 8-26).

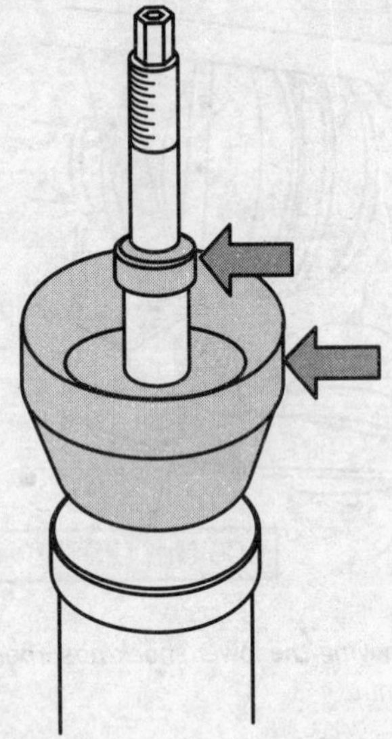

FIGURE 8-23 *Seal and washer on the upper end of the shock absorber rod.*

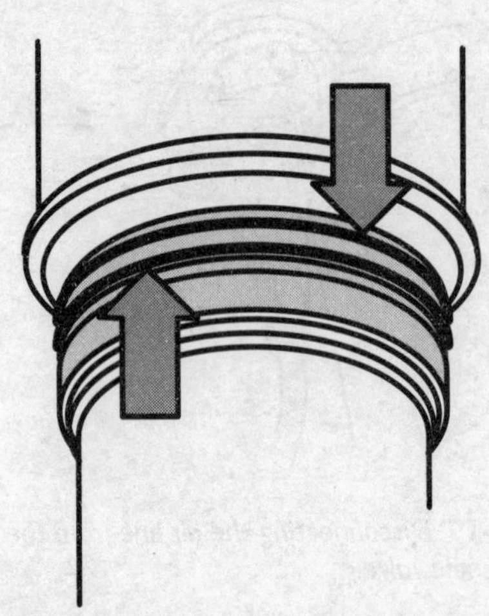

FIGURE 8-24 *O-ring seals on the lower sealing area on the shock absorber.*

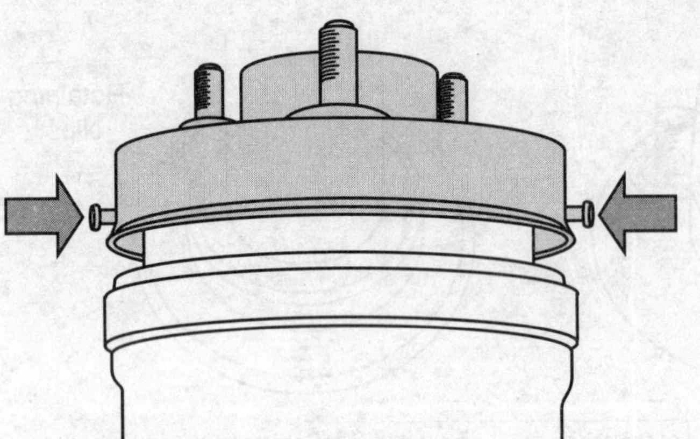

FIGURE 8-25 *Retaining pins on the upper air spring mount.*

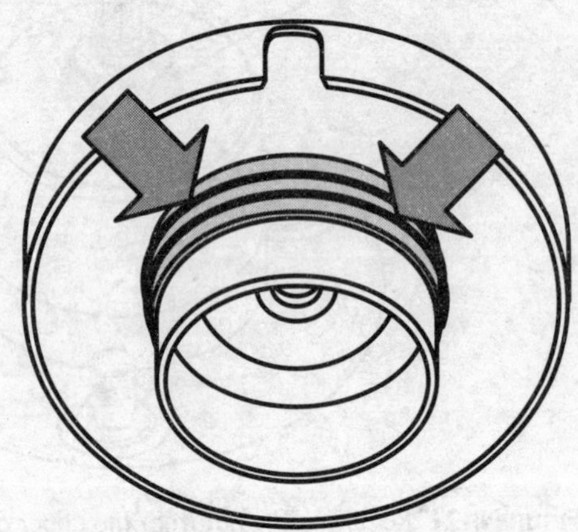

FIGURE 8-26 *O-ring seals on the upper spring mount.*

When reassembling the air spring and shock absorber, replace all the O-rings and self-locking nuts, and place a light coating of chassis lubricant on all the O-rings.

DIAGNOSIS OF ELECTRONIC SUSPENSION CONTROL SYSTEMS

Diagnostic Trouble Code (DTC) Display

CAUTION: Never remove or install the wiring connector on a computer or computer system component with the ignition switch on. This action may result in computer damage.

CAUTION: Do not supply voltage to or ground any circuit or component in a computer system unless instructed to do so in the vehicle manufacturer's service manual. This action may damage computer system components.

CAUTION: During computer system diagnosis, use only the test equipment recommended in the vehicle manufacturer's service manual to prevent damage to computer system components.

Vehicles equipped with the **electronic suspension control (ESC)** system may have a digital or an analog instrument panel cluster (IPC). If the vehicle has a digital IPC, the air-conditioning (A/C) control panel is contained in the IPC (Figure 8-27). A driver message center is located in the center of the IPC underneath the speedometer. This message center is a vacuum fluorescent (VF) display with twenty characters. The same message center is mounted in an analog IPC (Figure 8-28). If the car has an analog IPC, the A/C controls are mounted in a separate display (Figure 8-29).

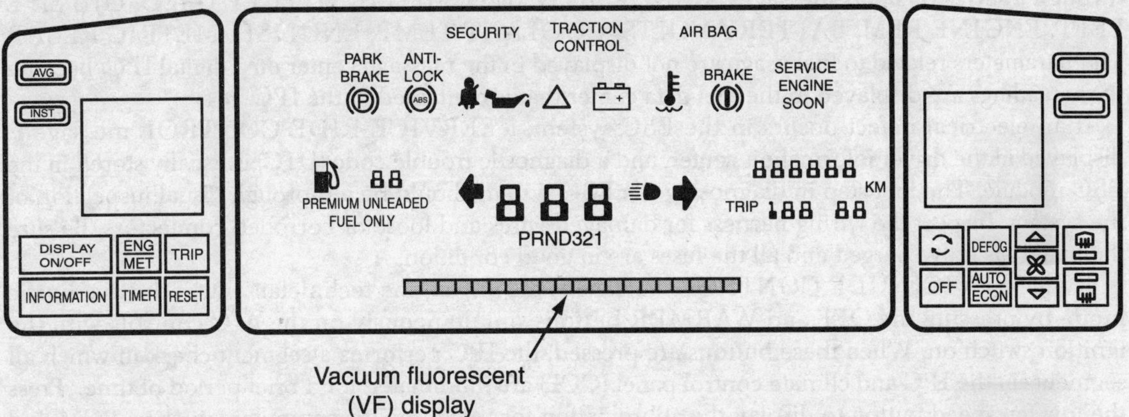

FIGURE 8-27 *Digital instrument panel cluster.*

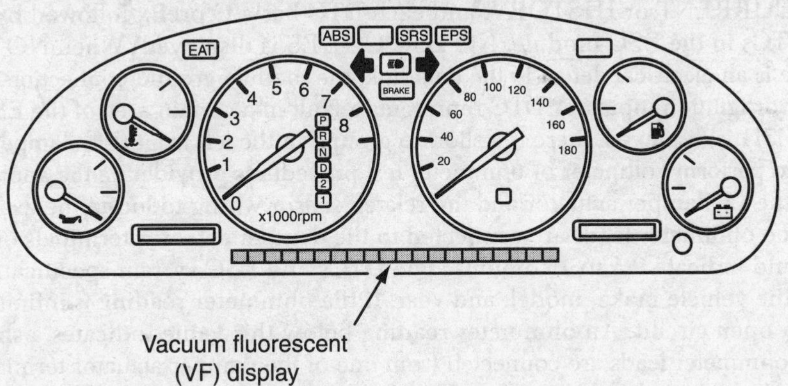

FIGURE 8-28 *Analog instrument panel cluster.*

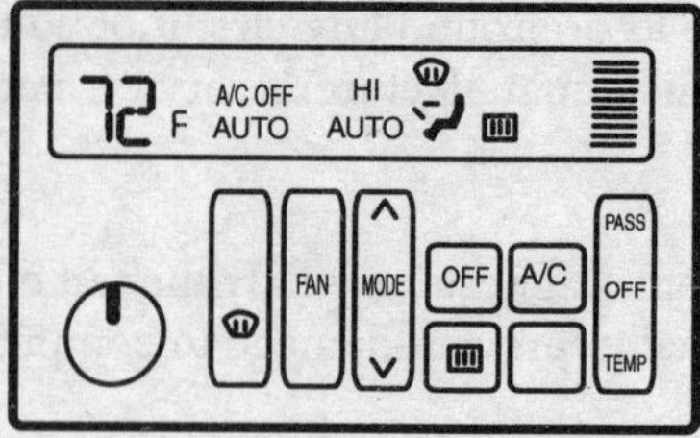

FIGURE 8-29 *A/C controls used with the analog instrument panel cluster.*

Early versions of the ESC system may be called **continuously variable road sensing suspension (CVRSS)** systems.

When the information (INFO) button is pressed in the IPC, the driver message center cycles through a series of status messages: RANGE, AVG MPG, MPG INST, FUEL USED, OIL LIFE LEFT, ENGINE RPM, BATTERY VOLTS, COOLANT TEMP, ENGLISH/METRIC RESET. The parameters related to fuel usage are not displayed in the message center on a digital IPC, because these readings are displayed in the fuel data center that is contained in the IPC.

If an electrical defect occurs in the ESC system, a SERVICE RIDE CONTROL message is displayed in the driver information center, and a diagnostic trouble code (DTC) is usually stored in the ESC module. The first step in diagnosing the ESC system should be a thorough visual inspection of the system. Inspect the wiring harness for damaged wires and loose or corroded connectors. Be sure the battery is fully charged and all the fuses are in good condition.

If the SERVICE RIDE CONTROL message is displayed, the technician enters the diagnostic mode by pressing the OFF and WARMER buttons simultaneously on the A/C controls with the ignition switch on. When these buttons are pressed, the IPC performs a segment check in which all segments in the IPC and climate control panel (CCP) are illuminated for a brief period of time. Press the low fan speed button to display the abbreviation for the on-board computers, such as PCM and IPC, one after the other. Continue pressing the low fan speed button until ESC appears in the driver message center. When ESC is displayed, press the increase fan speed button to select this parameter. When this action is taken, the ESC DTCs are displayed in the driver message center. Each DTC is designated as CURRENT or HISTORY, and each DTC has a C prefix followed by four digits. If there are no DTCs in the ESC module, NO ESC CODES is displayed. When NO ESC DATA is displayed, there is an electrical defect in the data link, the module ground connection, or in the ESC module battery or ignition inputs. A DTC represents a fault in a certain area of the ESC system. For example, if a C1711 is displayed, there is a short to ground in the left front (LF) damper actuator. The technician has to perform voltmeter or ohmmeter test procedures provided in the appropriate service manual to test the LF damper actuator and the related sensor wiring to locate the exact cause of the defect. When the ohmmeter leads are connected to the damper actuator terminals on the strut, the ohmmeter should indicate 9.5 to 15.5 ohms. The DTCs and ESC system specifications may vary depending on the vehicle make, model, and year. If the ohmmeter reading is infinite, the damper actuator has an open circuit. An ohmmeter reading below this value indicates a shorted damper actuator. If the ohmmeter leads are connected from one of the damper actuator terminals to ground, the ohmmeter should provide an infinite reading indicating this actuator is not grounded. When the ohmmeter indicates a low reading, the damper actuator is shorted to ground. Ohmmeter tests for shorts-to-ground and open circuits must also be performed on the wires from the damper actuator to the ESC module. The DTCs are displayed in the driver message center. The DTCs may be cleared from the ESC module by pressing the increase fan speed button when CLEAR DTCS is displayed in the driver message center. A scan tool may also be used to clear the DTCs. Disconnecting the battery or the ESC module connector will not clear the DTCs.

A scan tool also displays the DTCs and diagnoses the ESC system. The scan tool displays the voltage data from the wheel position sensors, steering sensor, vehicle speed sensor, and battery.

SCAN TOOL DIAGNOSIS OF ELECTRONIC SUSPENSION CONTROL

When diagnosing an ESC system, the first step is to identify the complaint. Listen to the customer's complaint, and road test the car if necessary to determine the exact problem. The next step in the diagnostic procedure is to visually inspect all ESC components. Check all the ESC wiring connections and wiring harnesses. Be sure all the ESC fuses are satisfactory. Check the shock absorbers, struts, and other suspension components for loose mountings and damage. Inspect the shock absorbers and struts for fluid leaks. Be sure the battery is fully charged.

Observe the message center for displayed messages related to the ESC system. ESC systems with computer-controlled solenoids in the shock absorbers or struts display SERVICE SUSPENSION SYSTEM or SPEED LIMITED TO XXX if a defect occurs in the ESC. If the vehicle has an ESC system with magneto-rheological fluid in the shock absorbers or struts, the ESC system displays SHOCKS INOPERATIVE, SERVICE RIDE CONTROL, OR MAXIMUM SPEED 129 km/h (80 mph) if a defect occurs in the system. The messages indicating a limited maximum vehicle speed are displayed only when the ESC module has detected a defect and shut down the electronic control of all shock absorbers or struts.

To locate a defect in an ESC system the next step is to perform a diagnostic system check. This check identifies the control modules in the system, and tests the ability of the control modules to communicate through the data link system. The diagnostic system check also displays all DTCs in the various modules related to ESC.

Follow these steps to complete a diagnostic system check:

1. Be sure the ignition switch is off, and connect a scan tool to the DLC.
2. Turn on the ignition switch.
3. Use the scan tool to select the various modules related to ESC control. These modules include the **powertrain control module (PCM)**, ESC module, and the electronic brake control module (EBCM).
4. Use the scan tool to display all the DTCs stored in each of the modules in step 3. Record all DTCs.
5. If a DTC is displayed that begins with a U, there is a problem with communications through the data links. When one or more of the displayed DTCs begins with a U, a lack of communication between the scan tool and one or more of the modules likely occurred in step 3.
6. The cause of the DTC beginning with a U must be corrected before proceeding with any further diagnosis. After the cause of the data link DTC is corrected, diagnose the cause of all other DTCs.

The following DTCs represent ESC defects:

1. C0550 – ESC module malfunction.
2. C0563 – ESC module calibration defect.
3. C0577, C0579, C0582, C0584, C0587, C0589, C0592, C0594 – the voltage is out of the normal range in one of the strut solenoids or electromagnets. Detailed DTC explanations and diagnostic procedures are provided in the vehicle manufacturer's service manual.

4. C0578, C0583, C0588, C0593 – ESC fault in one of the internal ESC module drivers that operate the strut solenoids or electromagnets.
5. C0615, C0620, C0625, C0630 – a fault exists in one of the position sensors that causes the sensor voltage to be below or above the normal range of 0.35 V to 4.75 V for more than 1 second.
6. C0635, C0638, C0640, C0643, C01252, C01253 – a defect in the two normal force signal circuits between the ESC module and the electronic brake control module (EBCM). The ESC module controls each shock absorber or strut actuator with a pulse width modulated (PWM) duty cycle or 10% to 90% depending on road surface conditions. The ESC module relays this PWM information through a normal force signal circuit to the EBCM, and the EBCM uses this information to provide improved braking on irregular road surfaces.
7. C0665 – the ESC module did not detect a low-to-high change in the lift/dive circuit within 31 seconds after it received the ignition switch on signal.
8. C0690, C0691, C0693 – a defect in the damper control relay circuit that is integral in the ESC module. If one or more of these DTCs is displayed, ESC module replacement is necessary.
9. C0696 – the 5 V reference voltage sent from the ESC module to each position sensor is out of the normal range of 3.75 V to 5.6 V.
10. C0710 – the ESC module does not detect a valid steering position signal from the EBCM for 5 seconds. The EBCM controls the ABS and the variable assist steering.
11. C0896 – the battery voltage is not within the normal range of 9 V to 15.5 V.
12. P1652 – the output driver module (ODM) in the PCM that controls suspension lift/dive has detected an improper circuit condition.

To set most DTCs in the ESC module, the module must sense a defect on three consecutive ignition cycles, or during the same ignition cycle after clearing the DTC with a scan tool.

Scan Tool Data Display

Select *Special Functions* on the scan tool to access the ESC system data. The ESC data is very helpful to pinpoint the exact cause of DTCs. The following ESC data may be displayed on the scan tool with the ignition switch on, the engine off, and the front wheels straight ahead:

1. Battery voltage signal – typical data 12.6 V.
2. DSP software version ID – numerical value.
3. EEPROM calibration ID – numerical value.
4. GM part number ESC module – numerical value.
5. ESC module software version – numerical value.
6. L/F damper actuator command – 0% to 100% – this percentage indicates the commanded on-time of the damper actuator. If the ESC module commands the damper actuator On, the percentage increases.
7. L/F position sensor – 0V to 5V – this voltage is the signal voltage sent from the position sensor to the ESC module. If downward force is supplied to the L/F of the chassis, the voltage reading should change. When the position sensor voltage does not change, the sensor and connecting wires must be tested to locate the exact cause of the problem. After repairs have been completed to correct a problem causing a DTC, the scan tool must be used to clear the DTC from the ESC module.
8. L/F normal force – 20% to 80% – this percentage indicates a measured level of the road surface condition sent from the ESC module to the EBCM, and the EBCM uses this information to improve antilock braking on irregular road surfaces.

9. The damper actuator command and position sensor data are displayed on the scan tool for the other three corners of the chassis. The normal force data is available only on the front wheels.
10. Lift/Dive status – active, inactive – if there is no change in chassis pitch, the scan tool displays Inactive. When a change is chassis pitch occurs, the scan tool displays Active.
11. Lift/Dive change – changed, unchanged – if there is no change in chassis pitch, Unchanged is displayed on the scan tool. A change in chassis pitch causes the scan tool to display Changed.
12. Steering position PWM – 0 ms to 10 ms – this PWM signal is sent from the EBCM to the ESC module when the steering wheel is turned while cornering. The ESC module commands a firmer shock absorber state when the vehicle is turning a corner.
13. Vehicle speed – 0 to 159 mph (0 to 255 km/h) – the vehicle speed sensor signal is relayed on the data links from the PCM to the ESC module.

Scan Tool Output Controls

The Output Controls are accessed on the scan tool under the Special Functions menu. When Output Controls are selected on the scan tool, followed by an individual damper solenoid selection, the solenoid is cycled on and off. When an individual damper solenoid actuator is cycled on and off, the technician may perform voltage tests to check the damper actuator and related circuit. The scan tool may also be used to cycle all the damper solenoids simultaneously.

In the Output Controls mode, the scan tool may be used to command the ESC module to send the L/F and R/F normal force percentage readings to be sent to the EBCM, and this percentage is displayed on the scan tool.

ESC Module Recalibration may also be selected on the scan tool in the Output Controls mode. This recalibration is necessary after a module replacement.

Photo Sequence 8 illustrates the procedure for reading scan tool data on an electronic suspension control system.

Diagnosis of Stability Control System

The stability control system module is combined with the **antilock brake system (ABS)** and traction control system (TCS) modules. Therefore, it is not possible to completely separate the diagnosis of these systems. However, our discussion is mostly concerned with the stability control system, and this diagnostic information pertains to the **Stabilitrak®** system. The Stabilitrak® system may be called a vehicle stability enhancement system (VSES).

The **electronic brake and traction control module (EBTCM)** performs an initialization test each time the vehicle is started and the EBTCM does not receive a brake switch input. During the initialization test, the EBTCM cycles each solenoid valve and the pump motor in the **brake pressure modulator valve (BPMV)** for 1.5 seconds. If the EBTCM detects an electrical fault during the initialization test, a DTC is set in the EBTCM, and the amber ABS light and the red brake light may be illuminated in the instrument panel, depending on the severity of the defect. During the initialization test, the customer may hear the solenoids clicking and the pump motor turning in the BPMV.

The first step in diagnosing the stability control system is a visual inspection of all system components, such as the module connectors, fuses, relays, wiring harness, and sensor mounting and wiring connector.

If the visual inspection did not reveal any problems, the next step is to perform a Stabilitrak® diagnostic test drive as follows:

1. Turn the ignition switch off.

PHOTO SEQUENCE 8
READING SCAN TOOL DATA ON AN ELECTRONIC SUSPENSION CONTROL SYSTEM

P8-1 Connect the scan tool to the DLC under the dash.

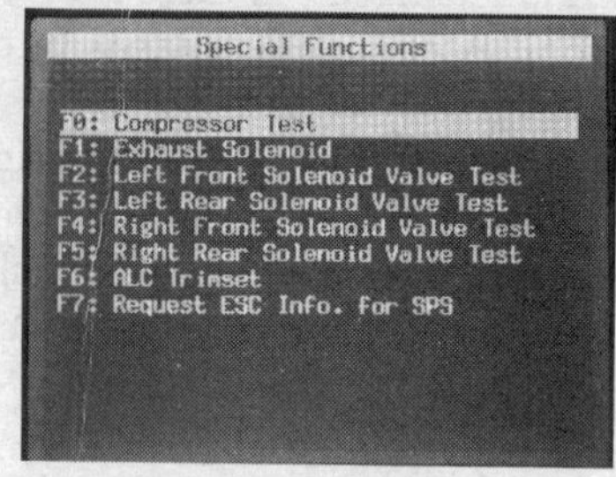

P8-2 Turn on the ignition switch, and select Special Functions in the ESC menu on the scan tool.

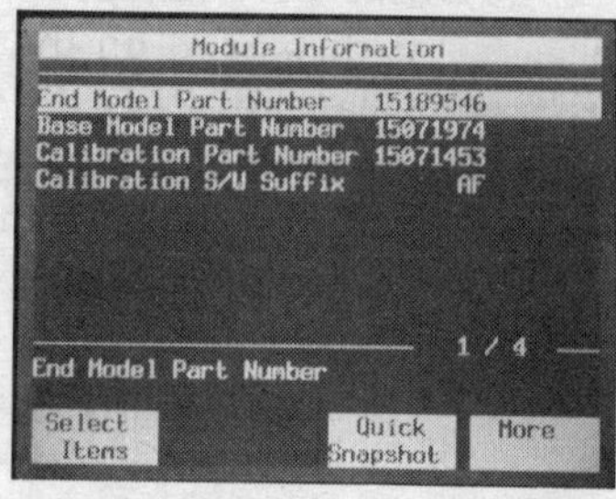

P8-3 Display and record the DSP software version ID, EEPROM Calibration ID, GM part number ESC module, and ESC module software version on the scan tool.

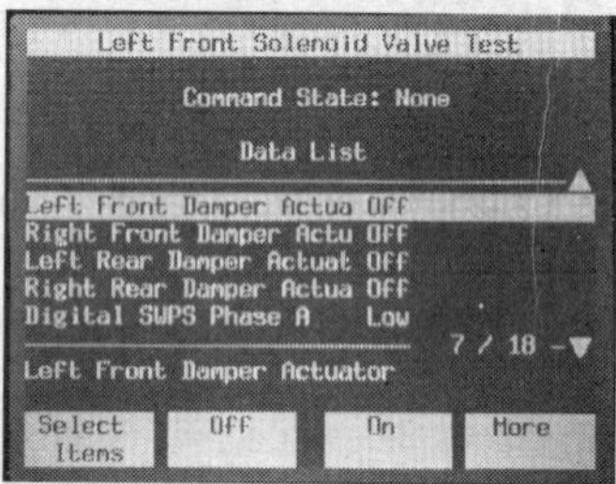

P8-4 Select the damper actuator command on each damper actuator. This percentage indicates the commanded on-time of the damper actuator.

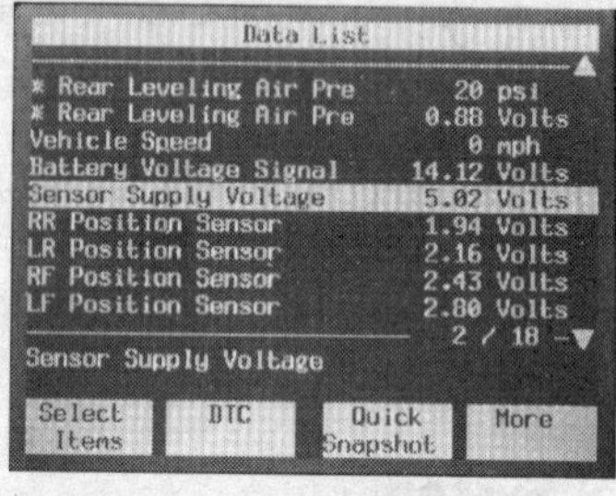

P8-5 Select the wheel position sensor voltage on each wheel position sensor. This voltage is the signal voltage sent from the position sensor to the ESC module.

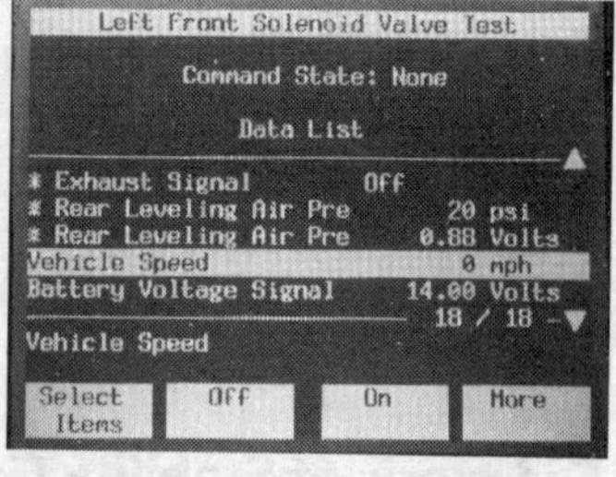

P8-6 Select the normal force display on the scan tool. This percentage indicates a measured level of the road surface condition sent from the ESC module to the EBCM, and the EBCM uses this information to improve antilock braking on irregular road surfaces.

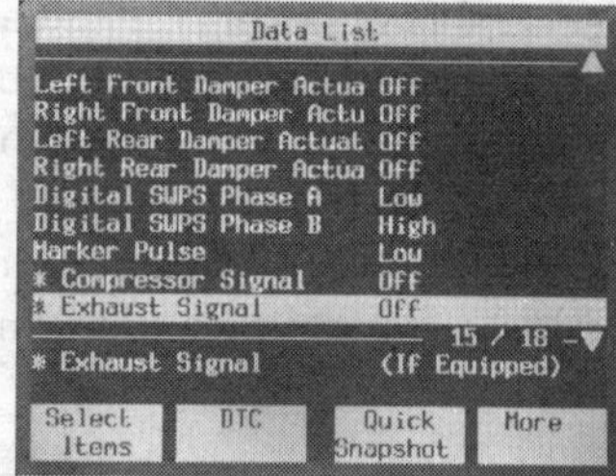

P8-7 Select the Lift/Dive status on the scan tool.

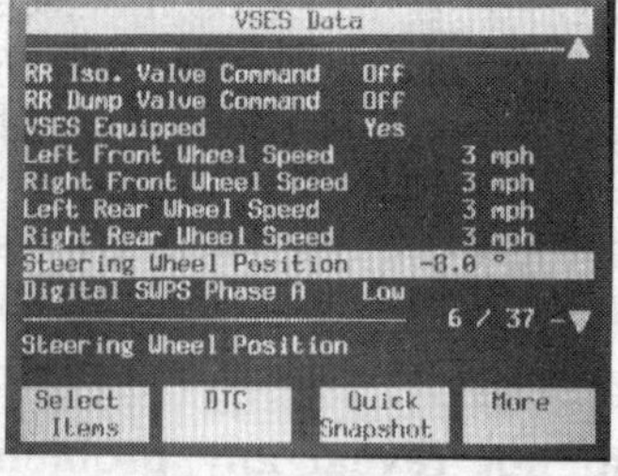

P8-8 Select Steering Position PWM on the scan tool.

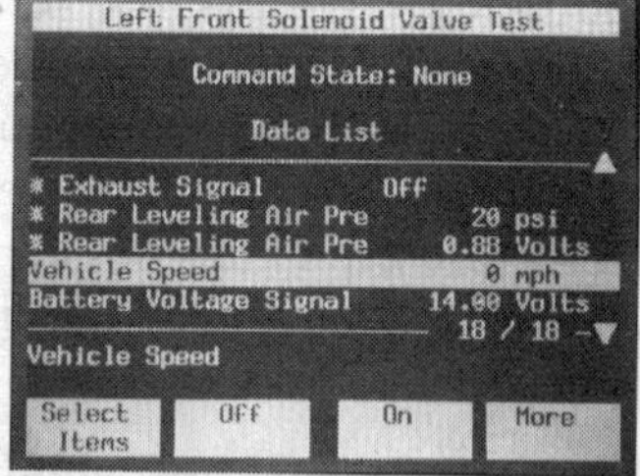

P8-9 Select Vehicle Speed on the scan tool.

2. Connect a scan tool to the data link connector (DLC) under the instrument panel. Be sure the correct module for the system being tested is securely installed in the bottom of the scan tool.
3. Start the engine.
4. Monitor the "steering wheel centered" parameter on the scan tool, and be sure the scan tool displays "Yes" while driving the vehicle straight ahead above 15 mph (24 km/h).
5. Drive the vehicle for at least 10 minutes under a variety of driving conditions: highway driving, rough road driving, and turning maneuvers, including freeway ramps and sharp turns on parking lots.
6. Perform any driving maneuvers under which the customer complaint(s) occurred.
7. With the engine still running, observe and record any DTCs displayed on the scan tool.

If there is a defect in the Stabilitrak® system, "Stability Reduced" may be displayed in the driver information center. When "Display ABS/TCM/ICCS DTCs" is selected on the scan tool, any of the following DTCs may be displayed as indicated in Figure 8-30 and Figure 8-31. The technician usually has to perform voltmeter or ohmmeter tests to locate the exact cause of a problem in the area indicated by the DTC.

DTC	DESCRIPTION
C1211	ABS Indicator Lamp Circuit Malfunction
C1214	Solenoid Valve Relay Contact or Coil Circuit Open
C1217	BPMV Pump Motor Relay Contact Circuit Open
C1221	LF Wheel Speed Sensor Input Signal - 0
C1222	RF Wheel Speed Sensor Input Signal - 0
C1223	LR Wheel Speed Sensor Input Signal - 0
C1224	RR Wheel Speed Sensor Input Signal - 0
C1225	LF - Excessive Wheel Speed Variation
C1226	RF - Excessive Wheel Speed Variation
C1227	LR - Excessive Wheel Speed Variation
C1228	RR - Excessive Wheel Speed Variation
C1232	LF Wheel Speed Sensor Circuit Open or Shorted
C1233	RF Wheel Speed Sensor Circuit Open or Shorted
C1234	LR Wheel Speed Sensor Circuit Open or Shorted
C1235	RR Wheel Speed Sensor Circuit Open or Shorted
C1236	Low System Voltage
C1237	High System Voltage
C1238	Brake Thermal Model Limit Exceeded
C1241	Magna Steer® Circuit Malfunction
C1242	BPMV Pump Motor Ground Circuit Open
C1243	BPMV Pump Motor Stalled
C1251	RSS Steering Sensor Data Malfunction
C1252	ICCS2 Data Link Left Malfunction
C1253	ICCS2 Data Link Right Malfunction
C1255 xx	EBTCM Internal Malfunction (ABS/TCS/ICCS Disabled)
C1256 xx	EBTCM Internal Malfunction
C1261	LF Hold Valve Solenoid Malfunction

FIGURE 8-30 *DTCs for ABS/TCS/ICCS systems.*

DTC	DESCRIPTION
C1262	LF Release Valve Solenoid Malfunction
C1263	RF Hold Valve Solenoid Malfunction
C1264	RF Release Valve Solenoid Malfunction
C1265	LR Hold Valve Solenoid Malfunction
C1266	LR Release Valve Solenoid Malfunction
C1267	RR Hold Valve Solenoid Malfunction
C1268	RR Release Valve Solenoid Malfunction
C1271	LF TCS Master Cylinder Isolation Valve Malfunction
C1272	LF TCS Prime Valve Malfunction
C1273	RF TCS Master Cylinder Isolation Valve Malfunction
C1274	RF TCS Prime Valve Malfunction
C1276	Delivered Torque Signal Circuit Malfunction
C1277	Requested Torque Signal Circuit Malfunction
C1278	TCS Temporarily Inhibited By PCM
C1281	Stabilitrak® Sensors Uncorrelated
C1282	Yaw Rate Sensor Bias Circuit Malfunction
C1283	Excessive Time to Center Steering
C1284	Lateral Accelerometer Sensor Self-Test Malfunction
C1285	Lateral Accelerometer Sensor Circuit Malfunction
C1286	Steering/Lateral Accelerometer Sensor Bias Malfunction
C1287	Steering Sensor Rate Malfunction
C1288	Steering Sensor Circuit Malfunction
C1291	Open Brake Lamp Switch During Deceleration
C1293	DTC C1291 Set In Current or Previous Ignition Cycle
C1294	Brake Lamp Switch Circuit Always Active
C1295	Brake Lamp Switch Circuit Open
C1297	PCM Indicated Brake Extended Travel Switch Failure
C1298	PCM Indicated Class 2 Serial Data Link Malfunction
U1016	Loss of PCM Communications
U1056	Loss of CVRSS Communications
U1255	Generic Loss of Communications
U1300	Class 2 Circuit Shorted to Ground
U1301	Class 2 Circuit Shorted to Battery +

FIGURE 8-31 *DTCs for ABS/TCS/ICCS systems (continued).*

Automated Test

An automated test may be selected on the scan tool. During this test, the EBTCM cycles all the solenoid valves and the pump motor in the BPMV, and DTCs are set in the EBTCM if there are defects in these components. This test is the same as the initialization test performed by the EBTCM when the engine is started. The scan tool also performs solenoid tests.

Valve Solenoid/Pressure Hold Test

To perform the valve solenoid/pressure hold test, follow this procedure:

1. Be sure the scan tool is properly connected to the DLC.
2. Turn on the ignition switch.
3. Raise the vehicle on a lift so all four wheels are at least 6 in. (15 cm) off the floor.
4. Select Valve Solenoid Test on the scan tool followed by Hold Pressure on a specific wheel.
5. Hold the brake pedal in the applied position.
6. Have a co-worker try to turn the wheel being tested. If the hold pressure solenoid is operating properly, the co-worker should be able to turn the wheel.
7. Repeat steps 4 through 6 on the other wheels.

Valve Solenoid/Pressure Release Test

To perform a valve solenoid/pressure release test, follow this procedure:

1. Be sure the scan tool is properly connected to the DLC.
2. Turn on the ignition switch.
3. Raise the vehicle on a lift so all four wheels are at least 6 in. (15 cm) off the floor.
4. Hold the brake pedal in the applied position.
5. Select Valve Solenoid Test on the scan tool followed by Release Pressure on a specific wheel.
6. Have a co-worker try to turn the wheel being tested. If the release pressure solenoid is operating properly, the co-worker should be able to turn the wheel.
7. Repeat steps 4 through 6 on the other wheels.

If any of the hold or release solenoids do not operate properly, the BPMV requires replacement. The solenoids in the BPMV are not serviceable.

Case Study

A customer complained about the SERVICE RIDE CONTROL light being illuminated on his 2005 Cadillac XLR. When the technician visually inspected the ESC system, no defects were evident. During a diagnostic system check, the scan tool displayed DTC C0577. The detailed DTC explanation in the vehicle manufacturer's service manual indicated this DTC represented a short to ground in the L/F shock absorber damper solenoid circuit.

When the technician disconnected the wiring connector from the L/F damper solenoid and measured the solenoid resistance with an ohmmeter, he discovered the solenoid had the specified resistance of 2.0 ohms.

The technician disconnected the wiring connectors from the ESC module and identified the L/F damper solenoid wires connected to the module. When the technician connected a pair of ohmmeter leads across the wires from the ESC module terminals to the L/F damper solenoid terminals, each wire had very low resistance. Next the technician connected the ohmmeter leads from each terminal in the L/F damper solenoid connector to the ground. When connected to one of the damper solenoid terminals, the ohmmeter displayed an infinite reading indicating the wire was not grounded. However, when the ohmmeter leads were connected from the other damper solenoid terminal to the ground, the ohmmeter indicated a very low reading indicating contact between this wire and the chassis.

A closer examination of the L/F damper solenoid wires indicated these wires were jammed against the chassis about 2 ft. from the damper solenoid. The insulation was worn on the wires, and one wire was contacting the chassis. The technician repaired the wiring insulation and re-positioned the harness so the wires were not jammed against the chassis. The technician used the scan tool to clear the DTC from the ESC module, and road tested the car to be sure the DTC did not reset and illuminate the SERVICE RIDE CONTROL light.

SERVICE TIPS

- **Diagnostic trouble codes (DTCs)** together with the vehicle manufacturer's service manual diagnostic procedures will usually locate the problem in a PRC system.
- Some on-board diagnostic I (OBD I) vehicles have a separate suspension DLC positioned on the right-front strut tower. Other OBD I vehicles have the suspension DLC in the trunk. **OBD II computer systems** have a universal 16-terminal DLC mounted under the left side of the dash near the steering column (Figure 8-9). Data links are connected from various on-board computers including the suspension computer to the DLC to allow the on-board computers to communicate with the scan tool and vice versa.

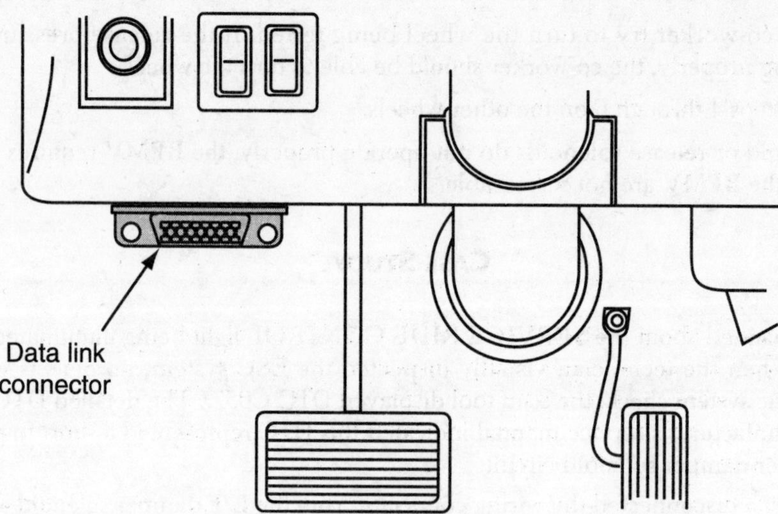

FIGURE 8-9 *Data link connector (DLC), on-board diagnostic II (OBD-II) system.*

- If a door ajar indicator is illuminated even when all the doors, liftgate, and liftgate glass are closed, the VDS will not operate properly. The problem with the door ajar indicator must be repaired before proceeding with the VDS diagnosis.
- The ride height adjustment procedure must be completed before a wheel alignment is performed.
- The ride height adjustment must be performed after a VDM is replaced.

- If the retainer tabs on the lower end of the air spring are broken, air spring replacement is necessary.
- When removing, replacing, or servicing an electronic component on a vehicle, always disconnect the negative battery cable before starting the service procedure. If the vehicle is equipped with an air bag or bags, wait one minute after the battery negative cable is removed to prevent accidental air bag deployment. Many air bag computers have a backup power supply capable of deploying the air bag for a specific length of time after the battery is disconnected.

REVIEW QUESTIONS

1. When performing a self-test on a programmed ride control system:
A. The mode select switch must be in the Auto position.
B. One of the wires in the self-test connector must be grounded.
C. The engine must be off and the ignition switch turned on.
D. The headlights must be on during the self-test.

2. When servicing a vehicle with an air suspension system, the air suspension switch must be turned off:
A. When changing the engine oil and filter.
B. When changing the spark plugs.
C. When jacking the vehicle to change a tire.
D. During any of the above service procedures.

3. To deflate an air spring prior to removal of the spring:
A. Disconnect the air line from the air spring.
B. Turn the air spring solenoid valve to the first stage.
C. Turn the air spring solenoid valve to the second stage.
D. Energize the vent solenoid in the air compressor.

4. When using the scan tool to inflate an air spring:
A. The vehicle must be raised on a tire-contact lift.
B. The scan tool commands the air compressor on.
C. The air suspension switch must be on.
D. The scan tool commands the vent solenoid on.

5. When using a scan tool to perform a ride height adjustment on a vehicle dynamic suspension (VDS), *Technician A* says the VDS switch must be in the Off position. *Technician B* says if the ride height does not equal the manufacturer's specifications, the scan tool is used to command the VDS to lower or lift the vehicle to obtain the specified ride height. Who is correct?
A. A only
B. B only
C. Both A and B
D. Neither A nor B

6. All of these statements about performing an on-demand self-test on a VDS system are true EXCEPT:
A. The battery must be fully charged.

B. The ignition switch must be on.
C. The vehicle must be raised on a lift.
D. The 4L mode must not be selected on four-wheel-drive vehicles.

7. When diagnosing a VDS system, a U1900 DTC is obtained. This DTC indicates a defect in the:
A. Controller area network (CAN).
B. L/R air spring solenoid.
C. Vent solenoid.
D. R/F height sensor.

8. When diagnosing an electronic suspension control (ESC) system, *Technician A* says defects represented by a DTC with a U prefix must be repaired before proceeding with further diagnosis or service. *Technician B* says ESC system operation may be affected by low battery voltage. Who is correct?
A. A only
B. B only
C. Both A and B
D. Neither A nor B

9. On an ESC system a normal voltage signal from a wheel position sensor is:
A. 2.5 V.
B. 5.5 V.
C. 6.1 V.
D. 6.8 V.

10. While discussing ESC system diagnosis, *Technician A* says the normal force signal on a scan tool indicates a measured level of road surface condition sent from the ESC module to the EBCM. *Technician B* says the normal force data is sent from the front and rear wheels. Who is correct?
A. A only
B. B only
C. Both A and B
D. Neither A nor B

CHALLENGE QUESTIONS

1. *Technician A* says during air spring inflation the vehicle weight must be applied to the suspension system. *Technician B* says during air spring inflation the vehicle should be positioned on a lift so the wheels are dropped downward. Who is correct?
A. A only
B. B only
C. Both A and B
D. Neither A nor B

2. All of these statements about a programmed ride control system are true EXCEPT:
A. An air spring is mounted at each corner of the vehicle.
B. An electric actuator is located in each strut.

C. A mode indicator light is positioned in the tachometer.
D. The PRC module provides a firm ride during severe braking.

3. *Technician A* says the suspension switch must be turned off before raising any corner of a car with an electronic air suspension. *Technician B* says the ignition switch must not be turned on while any corner of a car with electronic air suspension is raised.
Who is correct?
A. A only
B. B only
C. Both A and B
D. Neither A nor B

4. A vehicle with an electronic air suspension system with mechanical trim height adjustment requires front and rear trim height adjustment. *Technician A* says to adjust the front trim height, rotate the threaded mounting bolt in the upper end of the height sensor. *Technician B* says to adjust the rear trim height, loosen the attaching bolt(s) on the upper height sensor bracket and move the bracket upward or downward. Who is correct?
A. A only
B. B only
C. Both A and B
D. Neither A nor B

5. When removing and replacing an air spring and shock absorber assembly on a VDS:
A. The self-locking nuts on the upper strut mount can be reused.
B. Retainer tabs on the lower end of the spring must be depressed to separate the spring and the shock absorber.
C. The spring must be vented by loosening the spring solenoid valve to the first stage.
D. The VDS switch and the ignition switch must be in the On position.

JOB SHEET 24

Name ______________________ Date __________

INSPECTION AND PRELIMINARY DIAGNOSIS OF COMPUTER-CONTROLLED SUSPENSION SYSTEM

Upon completion of this job sheet, you should be able to inspect computer-controlled suspension systems.

ASE Correlation

This job sheet is correlated with ASE Automotive Suspension and Steering Task: *Diagnose, inspect, adjust, repair, or replace components of electronically controlled suspension systems including primary and supplemental air suspension systems.*

Tools and Materials

Modern vehicle with electronically controlled suspension system.

Describe the Vehicle Being Worked On

Year __________ Make __________ Model __________

VIN ______________________ Engine Type and Size __________

Procedure

Task Completed

1. Discuss the vehicle complaint with the customer.

Describe the customer complaint(s). ______________________

____

____

2. Road test the vehicle and verify the vehicle complaint. ☐

Describe the vehicle complaint experienced during the road test.

____

____

____

3. Inspect the vehicle for collision damage or other damage that could affect the computer-controlled suspension system. ☐

Describe any collision or other vehicle damage that could affect the computer-controlled suspension system ______________________

____

____

4. Inspect all electrical connections and wiring harness in the suspension system. ☐

Wiring connection and harness condition, Satisfactory ☐ Unsatisfactory ☐

Task Completed

If the wiring connection and harness condition are unsatisfactory, explain the wiring connection and/or harness defects.

____

____

5. If the vehicle has an air suspension system, listen for air leaks near the air-operated components and air lines, and inspect all the air lines for cracks, breaks, damage, and kinks.

Air line condition, Satisfactory ☐ Unsatisfactory ☐

If the air line condition is unsatisfactory, explain the air line defects.

____

____

6. Measure the vehicle ride (trim) height.

Ride height, L/F __________, R/F __________, L/R __________, R/R __________

Specified ride height, Front __________ Rear __________

7. Observe the operation of the suspension warning light or message display in the instrument panel.

8. Suspension warning light or message display operation,
Normal ☐ Abnormal ☐

9. Based on your inspection and preliminary diagnosis of the computer-controlled suspension system, list the problems in the system and explain the required further diagnostic and service procedures.

____

____

____

____

Instructor's Response ____

____

____

JOB SHEET 25

Name ______________________________________ Date ______________

ADJUST VEHICLE RIDE (TRIM) HEIGHT WITH A SCAN TOOL

Upon completion of this job sheet, you should be able to adjust the vehicle ride height with a scan tool on computer-controlled suspension systems.

ASE Correlation

This job sheet is correlated with ASE Automotive Suspension and Steering Task: *Diagnose, inspect, adjust, repair, or replace components of electronically controlled suspension systems including primary and supplemental air suspension systems.*

Tools and Materials

Modern vehicle with a vehicle dynamic suspension (VDS) system.
Scan Tool
Tape Measure

Describe the Vehicle Being Worked On

Year __________ Make ____________________ Model ______________
VIN ______________________________ Engine Type and Size ______________

Procedure

Task Completed

1. Be sure the air suspension switch is in the On position.

   Air suspension switch On, ☐ Yes ☐ No

2. Be sure the battery is fully charged.

   Battery fully charged, ☐ Yes ☐ No

3. Turn off the ignition switch and exit the vehicle. Close all doors and wait 45 seconds for the air suspension system to vent down to the kneel position.

   VDS suspension in the kneel position, ☐ Yes ☐ No

4. Open the driver's door, and turn on the ignition switch.

   Ignition switch on, ☐ Yes ☐ No

5. Shift the transmission into Drive and back into Park.

   Transmission shifted into Drive and back into Park, ☐ Yes ☐ No

6. Exit the vehicle, close all the doors, and wait 45 seconds for the suspension system to pump up to the trim height.

   VDS system in the trim height position, ☐ Yes ☐ No

7. Use a tape measure to measure the ride height at the locations specified by the vehicle manufacturer.

   Specified ride height, Front __________ Rear ____________

   Actual ride height, L/F _______, R/F ________, L/R _____ R/R _____

Task Completed

8. If the ride height does not equal the manufacturer's specifications, open the left-front door, and connect the scan tool to the DLC.

Scan tool properly connected to the DLC, ☐ Yes ☐ No

9. Select the correct vehicle year, model, and engine type on the scan tool, and then select *Vehicle Dynamic Module* (VDM).

Scan tool selections, Vehicle year ________ Model ________

Engine Size ________

Vehicle Dynamic Module (VDM) selected on scan tool,

☐ Yes ☐ No

10. Use the active command mode in the scan tool to vent or lift the vehicle to achieve the specified trim height.

Active command mode on scan tool used to lift or vent VDS system to specified trim height, ☐ Yes ☐ No

11. When a tape measure indicates the specified front and rear ride height, select *Save Calibration Values* on the scan tool to calibrate the VDM to the specified trim height.

Actual ride height, L/F ______, R/F ________, L/R ______ R/R ______

Instructor's Response ____

____

____

JOB SHEET 26

Name ______________________________ Date ____________

PERFORM AN ON-DEMAND SELF-TEST ON A VEHICLE DYNAMIC SUSPENSION (VDS) SYSTEM

Upon completion of this job sheet, you should be able to perform an On-Demand Self-Test on a vehicle dynamic suspension (VDS) system.

ASE Correlation

This job sheet is correlated with ASE Automotive Suspension and Steering Task: *Diagnose, inspect, adjust, repair, or replace components of electronically controlled suspension systems including primary and supplemental air suspension systems.*

Tools and Materials

Modern vehicle with a vehicle dynamic suspension (VDS) system.
Scan tool

Describe the Vehicle Being Worked On

Year __________ Make ________________ Model ______________
VIN ________________________ Engine Type and Size ____________

Procedure

Task Completed

1. Be sure the transmission is in Park.

   Transmission in Park, ☐ Yes ☐ No

2. Be sure the battery is fully charged.

   Battery fully charged, ☐ Yes ☐ No

3. Connect the scan tool to the DLC.

   Scan tool properly connected to the DLC, ☐ Yes ☐ No

4. Lower the driver's window and close all doors, liftgate, and liftgate glass.

   Driver's window down, ☐ Yes ☐ No

   All doors, liftgate, and liftglass closed, ☐ Yes ☐ No

5. Be sure the 4L mode is not selected on four-wheel-drive models.

   4L switch off, ☐ Yes ☐ No

6. Turn on the ignition switch.

   Ignition switch on, ☐ Yes ☐ No

7. Select *Vehicle Dynamic Module* and *On-Demand Self-Test* on the scan tool.

   Vehicle Dynamic Module selected on scan tool, ☐ Yes ☐ No

   On-Demand Self-Test selected on scan tool, ☐ Yes ☐ No

Task Completed ______________

8. Record all the DTCs displayed on the scan tool.

____

____

____

9. Use the vehicle manufacturer's service information to interpret the meaning of each DTC, and list the meaning of each DTC in the spaces below.

____

____

____

10. Turn off the ignition switch, and disconnect the scan tool.

Ignition switch OFF, ☐ Yes ☐ No

Scan tool disconnected, ☐ Yes ☐ No

Instructor's Response ____

____

____

STEERING COLUMN AND LINKAGE DIAGNOSIS AND SERVICE

9

Upon completion and review of this chapter, you should be able to:

- Diagnose steering columns.
- Remove and replace steering wheels on air-bag-equipped vehicles and non-air-bag-equipped vehicles.
- Remove and replace air bag deployment modules and clock spring electrical connectors.
- Remove and replace steering columns.
- Inspect collapsible steering columns for damage.
- Disassemble steering columns.
- Inspect steering column components and replace necessary parts.
- Assemble steering columns.
- Diagnose and service flexible couplings and universal joints.
- Diagnose steering linkage mechanisms.
- Diagnose, remove, and replace tie-rod ends.
- Diagnose, remove, and replace pitman arms.

- Diagnose, remove, and replace center links.
- Diagnose, remove, and replace idler arms.
- Diagnose, remove, and replace steering dampers.
- Diagnose steering arms.

When servicing or replacing steering wheels, columns, and linkages, technicians actually have the customer's life in their hands. If steering components are not serviced properly and not tightened to the specified torque, the steering may become disconnected, resulting in a complete loss of steering control. This condition may cause a collision, resulting in vehicle damage, personal injury, and an expensive lawsuit for the technician and the shop where he or she is employed. Therefore, when performing any automotive service, always be sure the vehicle manufacturer's recommended service procedures and torque specifications are followed.

AIR BAG DEPLOYMENT MODULE, STEERING WHEEL, AND CLOCK SPRING ELECTRICAL CONNECTOR REMOVAL AND REPLACEMENT

CAUTION: Always disconnect the negative battery terminal and wait one minute before diagnosing or servicing any air bag system component. Failure to observe this precaution may result in accidental air bag deployment. Air bag service precautions vary depending on the vehicle. Always follow the vehicle manufacturer's air bag service precautions in the service manual.

CAUTION: On an air-bag-equipped vehicle, the wait time prior to servicing electrical components after the negative battery terminal is disconnected varies depending on the vehicle make and model year. Always follow the wait time and all other service precautions recommended in the vehicle manufacturer's service manual.

CAUTION: Always use the vehicle manufacturer's recommended tools when diagnosing or servicing an air bag system or the electrical system on an air-bag-equipped vehicle. Do not use a 12-V test light or a self-powered test light to diagnose air bag systems or electrical systems on air-bag-equipped vehicles. **Accidental air bag deployment** may result from improper use of tools.

Prior to working on an air bag system, always disconnect the negative battery cable and wait one minute before proceeding with the diagnostic or service work. Many air bag systems have a **backup power supply** circuit designed into the air bag computer or located in a separate module. This backup power supply provides power to deploy the air bag for a specific length of time after the battery power is disconnected in a collision. One minute after the negative battery terminal is disconnected, this backup power supply is powered down, and no power is available to deploy the air bag while the battery remains disconnected.

An air bag warning light in the instrument panel indicates the status of the air bag system. On some vehicles, this warning light should be illuminated for a few seconds when the ignition switch is turned on. The warning light should remain off while cranking the engine, and it should be on for a few seconds after the engine starts. After the engine has been running for a few seconds, the air bag warning light should remain off. On other vehicles, the air bag warning light flashes 7 to 9 times when the ignition switch is turned on and after the engine is started. The air bag warning light operation varies depending on the make and model year of the vehicle. Always check the vehicle manufacturer's service manual for the exact air bag warning light operation. When the air bag warning light does not operate as specified by the vehicle manufacturer, the air bag system is defective, and the air bag or bags will probably not deploy if the vehicle is involved in a collision.

Air bag module and steering wheel removal and replacement procedures vary depending on the vehicle. Always follow the vehicle manufacturer's recommended procedure in the service manual.

The following is a typical air bag module and steering wheel removal and replacement procedure:

1. Turn the ignition switch to the Lock position and place the front wheels facing straight ahead.
2. Remove the negative battery terminal and wait for the specified time period.
3. Loosen the three air-bag-retaining Torx screws under the steering wheel (Figure 9-1).
4. Loosen the other two air-bag-retaining Torx screws under the steering wheel (Figure 9-2). Loosen all five Torx screws until the groove along the screw circumference catches on the screw case.

WARNING: When an air bag deployment module is temporarily stored on the workbench, always place this module face upward. If the air bag deployment module accidentally deployed when facing downward, the module would become a projectile, and personal injury might result.

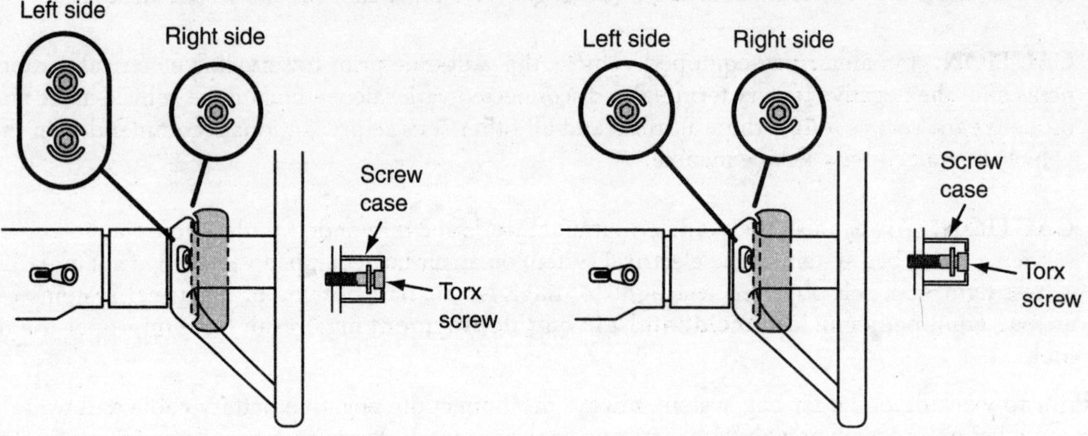

FIGURE 9-1 *Three air-bag–retaining Torx screws.* **FIGURE 9-2** *Two air-bag–retaining Torx screws.*

5. Pull the **air bag deployment module** from the steering wheel and disconnect the air bag module electrical connector (Figure 9-3). Do not pull on the air bag wires in the steering column. Place the air bag deployment module face upward on the workbench.
6. Disconnect the air bag wiring retainer in the steering wheel (Figure 9-4).
7. Use the proper size socket and a ratchet to remove the steering wheel retaining nut.

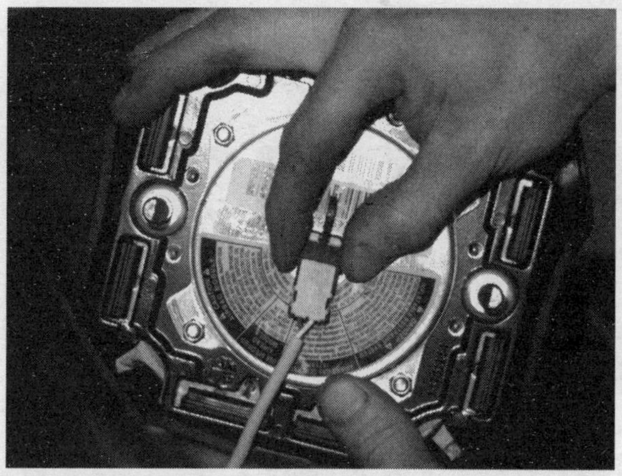

FIGURE 9-3 *Disconnecting the air bag module electrical connector.*

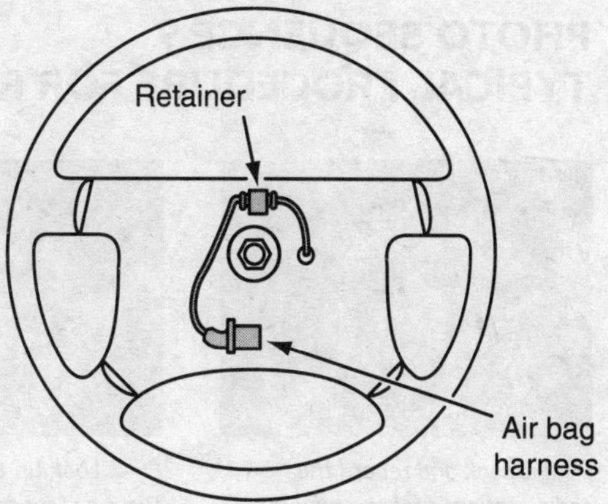

FIGURE 9-4 *Disconnecting the air bag wiring retainer.*

8. Observe the matching alignment marks on the steering wheel and the steering shaft. If these alignment marks are not present, place alignment marks on the steering wheel and steering shaft with a center punch and a hammer.

CAUTION: Do not hammer on the top of the steering shaft to remove the steering wheel. This action may damage the shaft.

CAUTION: If the steering wheel puller bolts are too long, they will extend through the steering wheel and damage the clock spring.

WARNING: Photo Sequence 9 shows a typical procedure for removing a steering wheel. Do not pull on the steering wheel in an attempt to remove it from the steering shaft. The steering wheel may suddenly come off, resulting in personal injury, or the steering wheel may be damaged by the pulling force.

9. Install a steering wheel puller with the puller bolts threaded into the bolt holes in the steering wheel. Tighten the puller nut to remove the steering wheel (Figure 9-5). Visually check the steering wheel condition. If the steering wheel is bent or cracked, replace the wheel.
10. Disconnect the four retaining screws and remove the **clock spring electrical connector** (Figure 9-6).
11. Be sure the front wheels are facing straight ahead. Turn the clock spring electrical connector counterclockwise by hand until it becomes harder to turn as it becomes fully wound in that direction.

CAUTION: Failure to center a clock spring prior to installation may cause a broken conductive tape in the clock spring.

12. Turn the clock spring electrical connector clockwise three turns and align the red mark on the center part of the spring face with the notch in the cable circumference (Figure 9-7). This action centers the clock spring electrical connector.

PHOTO SEQUENCE 9
TYPICAL PROCEDURE FOR REMOVING A STEERING WHEEL

P9-1 Check and record the radio stations programmed in the stereo system.

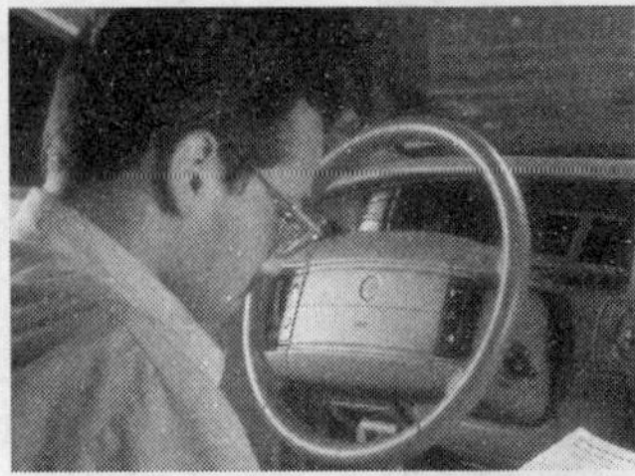

P9-2 Look up the car manufacturer's steering wheel removal procedure in the service manual.

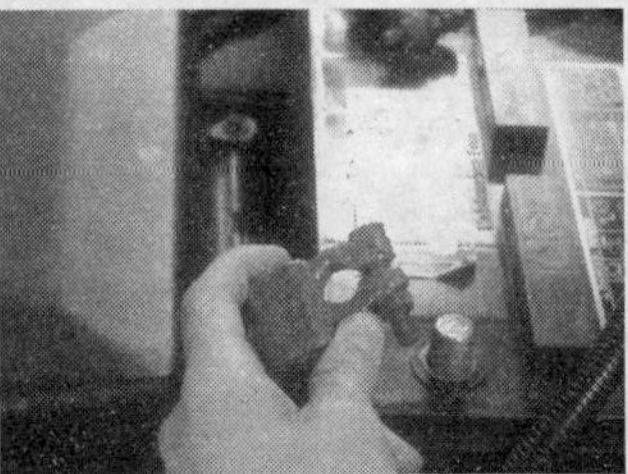

P9-3 Disconnect the negative battery cable, and wait for the car manufacturer's specified length of time.

P9-4 Remove the air bag deployment module retaining screws under the steering wheel.

P9-5 Lift the air bag deployment module upward from the steering wheel, and disconnect the module wiring connector.

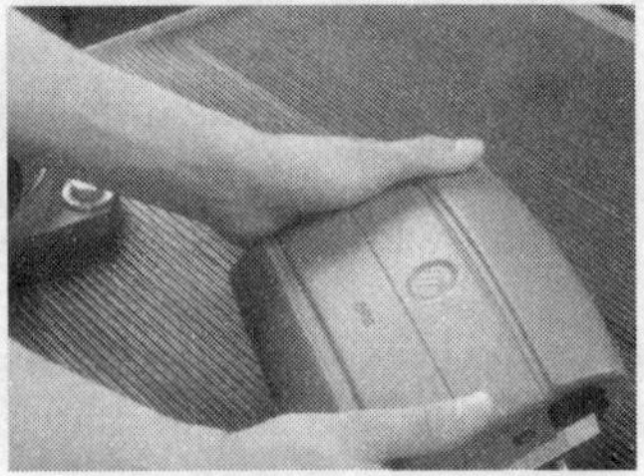

P9-6 Set the air bag deployment module face upward on the workbench.

P9-7 Loosen and remove the steering wheel retaining nut.

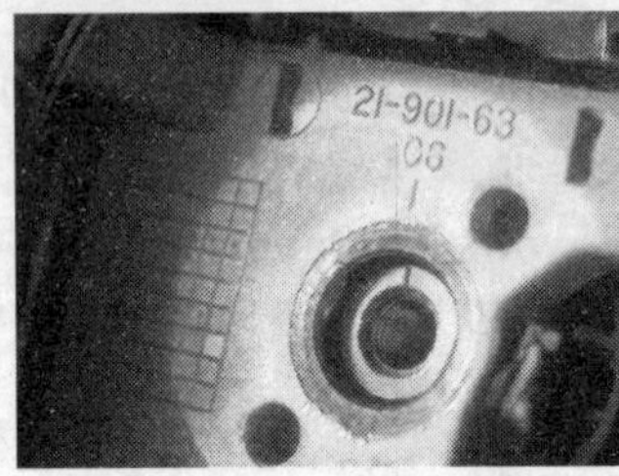

P9-8 Observe the alignment marks on the steering wheel and shaft.

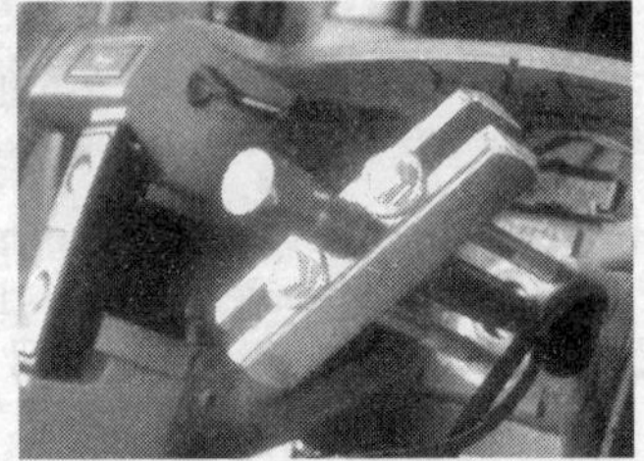

P9-9 Connect the proper steering wheel puller to the steering wheel.

P9-10 Turn the puller screw to loosen the steering wheel on the shaft.

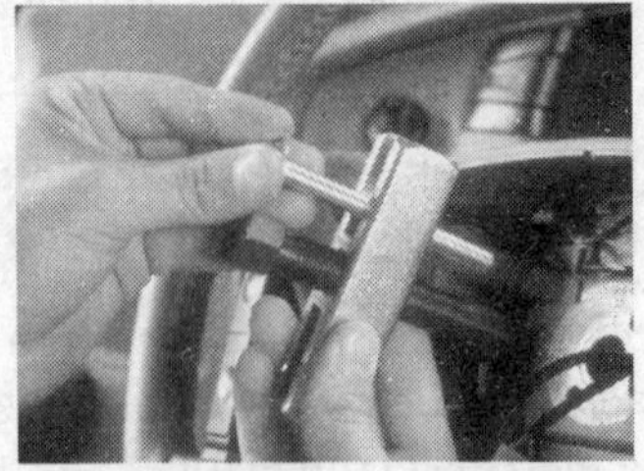

P9-11 Remove the puller from the steering wheel.

P9-12 Lift the steering wheel off the shaft.

FIGURE 9-5 *Removing steering wheel with the proper steering wheel puller.*

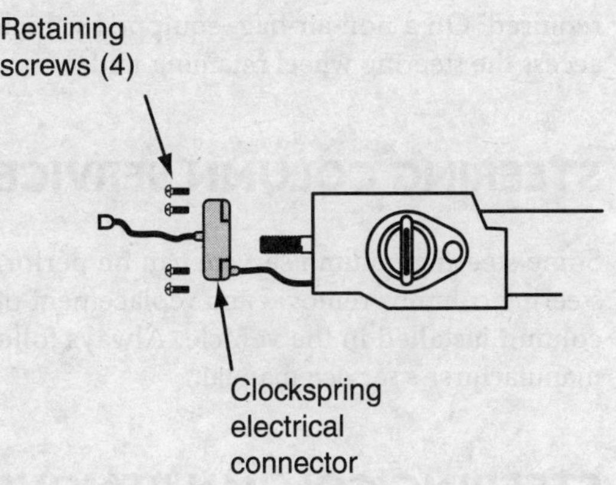

FIGURE 9-6 *Removing clock spring electrical connecter.*

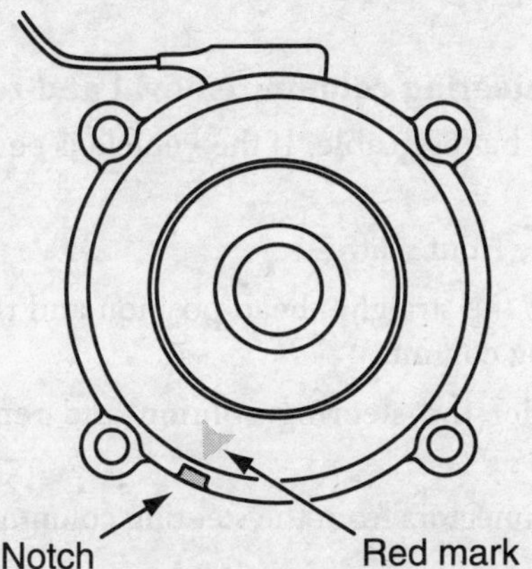

FIGURE 9-7 *Centering clock spring electrical connecter.*

13. Install the clock spring electrical connector and tighten the four retaining screws to the specified torque.
14. Align the marks on the steering wheel and the steering shaft, and install the steering wheel on the shaft.
15. Install the steering wheel retaining nut and tighten this nut to the specified torque.
16. Install the air bag wiring retainer in the steering wheel.
17. Hold the air bag deployment module near the top of the steering wheel and connect the air bag module connector.
18. Install the air bag deployment module in the top of the steering wheel and tighten the five retaining Torx screws.
19. Reconnect the negative battery cable.
20. Reset the clock and radio.

If the vehicle is not equipped with an air bag, the steering wheel removal and replacement procedure is basically the same, but all steps pertaining to the air bag module and clock spring are not required. On a non-air-bag–equipped vehicle, the center steering wheel cover must be removed to access the steering wheel retaining nut.

STEERING COLUMN SERVICE

Some steering column service can be performed with the column installed in the vehicle. In some steering columns removal and replacement of the various switches in the column is possible with the column installed in the vehicle. Always follow the recommended service procedure in the vehicle manufacturer's service manual.

STEERING COLUMN REMOVAL AND REPLACEMENT

Steering column removal and replacement procedures vary depending on the vehicle make, type of steering column, and gearshift lever position. Always follow the vehicle manufacturer's recommended procedure in the service manual.

The following is a typical steering column removal and replacement procedure:

1. Disconnect the negative battery cable. If the vehicle is equipped with an air bag, wait one minute.
2. Install a seat cover on the front seat.
3. Place the front wheels in the straight-ahead position and remove the ignition key from the switch to lock the steering column.
4. Remove the cover under the steering column and remove the lower finish panel if necessary.
5. Disconnect all wiring connectors from the steering column.
6. If the vehicle has a column-mounted gearshift lever, disconnect the gearshift linkage at the lower end of the steering column. If the vehicle has a floor-mount gearshift, disconnect the shift interlock.
7. Remove the retaining bolt or bolts in the lower universal joint or flexible coupling.
8. Remove the steering-column-to-instrument-panel mounting bolts.
9. Carefully remove the steering column from the vehicle. Be careful not to damage the upholstery or paint.
10. Install the steering column under the instrument panel and insert the steering shaft into the lower universal joint.
11. Install the steering-column-to-instrument-panel mounting bolts. Be sure the steering column is properly positioned, and tighten these bolts to the specified torque.
12. Install the retaining bolt or bolts in the lower universal joint or flexible coupling, and tighten the bolts to the specified torque.
13. Connect the gearshift linkage if the vehicle has a column-mounted gearshift.
14. Connect all the wiring harness connectors to the steering column connectors.
15. Install the steering column cover and the lower finish panel.

16. Reconnect the negative battery cable.
17. Road test the vehicle and check for proper steering column operation.

COLLAPSIBLE STEERING COLUMN INSPECTION

Since steering column design varies depending on the vehicle, the **collapsible steering column** inspection procedure should be followed in the vehicle manufacturer's service manual.

The following is a typical collapsible steering column inspection procedure:

1. Measure the clearance between the capsules and the slots in the steering column bracket (Figure 9-8). If this measurement is not within specifications, replace the bracket.
2. Inspect the contact between the bolt head and the bracket (Figure 9-9). If the bolt head contacts the bracket, the shear load is too high, and the bracket must be replaced.

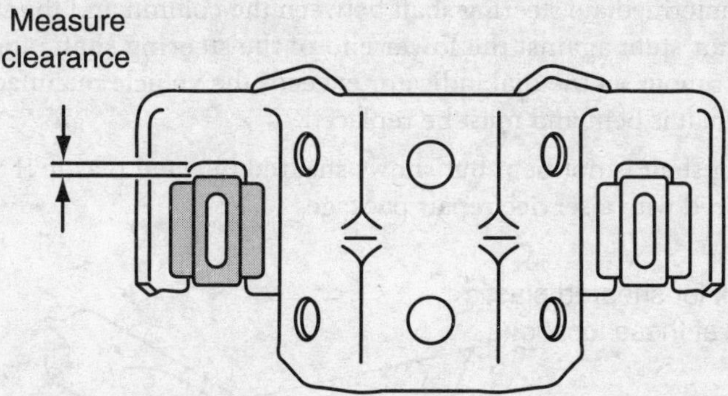

FIGURE 9-8 *Capsules in steering column bracket.*

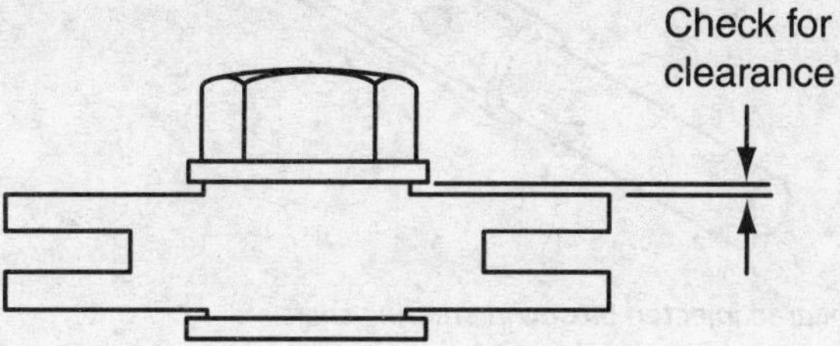

FIGURE 9-9 *Bolt head to bracket clearance.*

3. Inspect the steering column jacket for **sheared injected plastic** in the openings on the side of the jacket (Figure 9-10). If sheared plastic is present, the column is collapsed. Measure the distance from the end of the bearing assembly to the lower edge of the upper steering column jacket (Figure 9-11). If this distance is not within the vehicle manufacturer's specification, a new jacket must be installed.
4. Visually inspect the gearshift tube for sheared injected plastic. If the gearshift tube indicates sheared plastic, replace the tube.

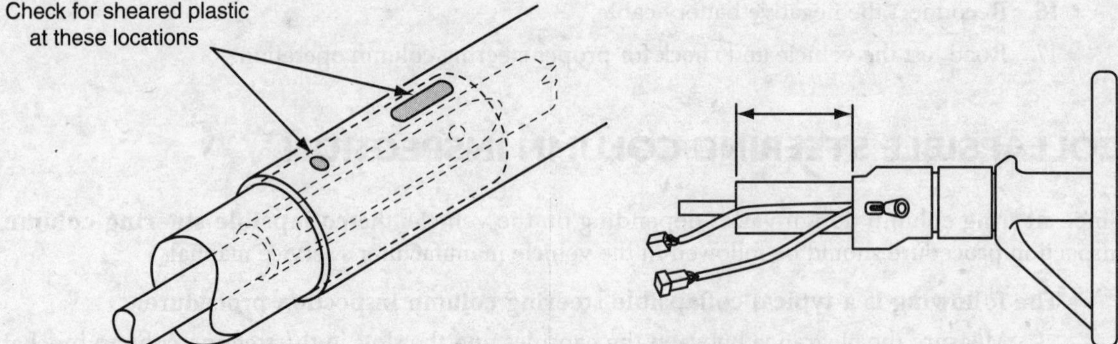

FIGURE 9-10 *Inspecting for sheared plastic in jacket openings.*

FIGURE 9-11 *Measuring distance from the end of the bearing assembly to the upper steering column jacket.*

5. Remove the intermediate steering shaft between the column and the steering gear. Position a dial indicator stem against the lower end of the steering shaft, and rotate the steering wheel. If the runout on the dial indicator exceeds the vehicle manufacturer's specification, the steering shaft is bent and must be replaced.
6. If the steering shaft is not bent but shows sheared injected plastic (Figure 9-12), this shaft may be repaired with a service repair package.

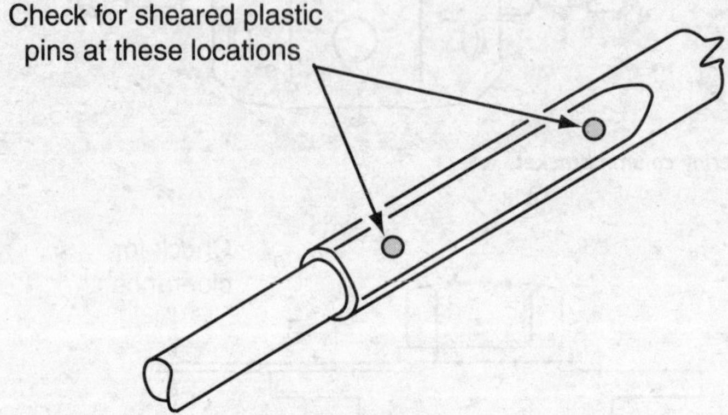

FIGURE 9-12 *Inspecting for sheared injected plastic in steering shaft.*

TILT STEERING COLUMN DISASSEMBLY

Since there are many variations in steering column design, always follow the vehicle manufacturer's recommended steering column disassembly procedure in the service manual.

The following is a typical tilt steering column disassembly procedure:

1. Remove the air bag deployment module, steering wheel, and spiral cable, as mentioned previously in this chapter.

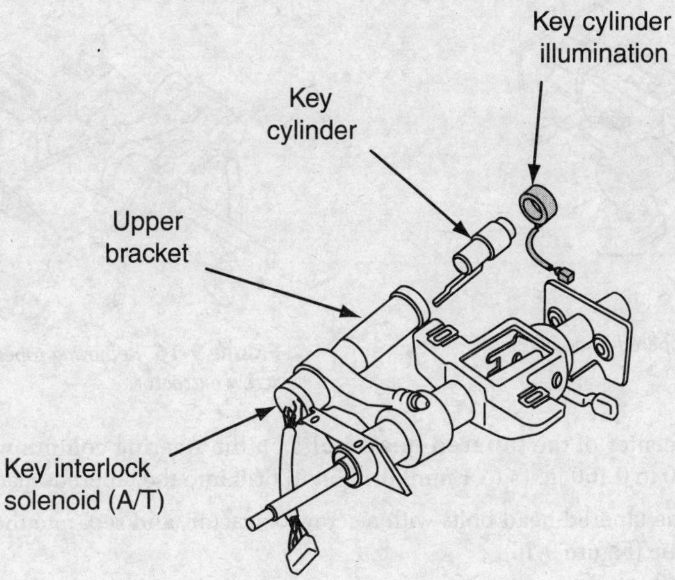

FIGURE 9-13 *Ignition key cylinder illumination mounted above ignition switch cylinder.*

2. Remove the ignition key cylinder illumination mounted on top of the ignition switch cylinder (Figure 9-13).
3. Remove the universal joint from the lower end of the steering shaft.
4. Remove the steering column protector and the wiring harness clamp mounted under the steering column.
5. Remove the steering damper mounted near the top of the column.
6. Remove the retaining screw and the combination switch with the wiring harness (Figure 9-14).

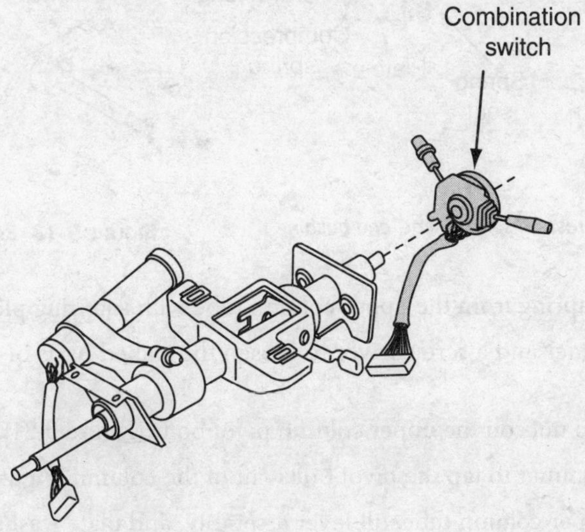

FIGURE 9-14 *Removing combination switch and wiring harness.*

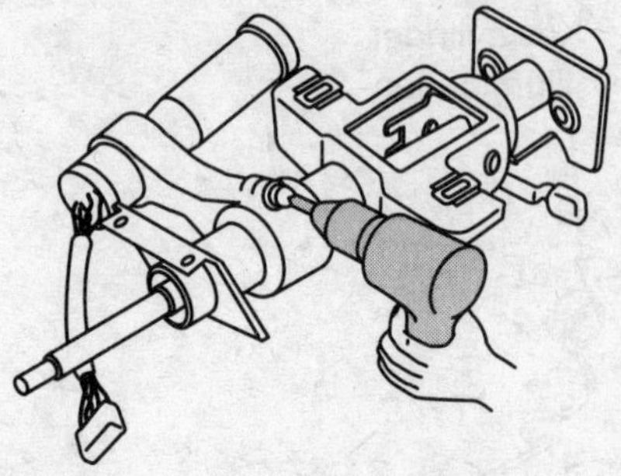

FIGURE 9-15 *Drilling tapered-head bolts.*

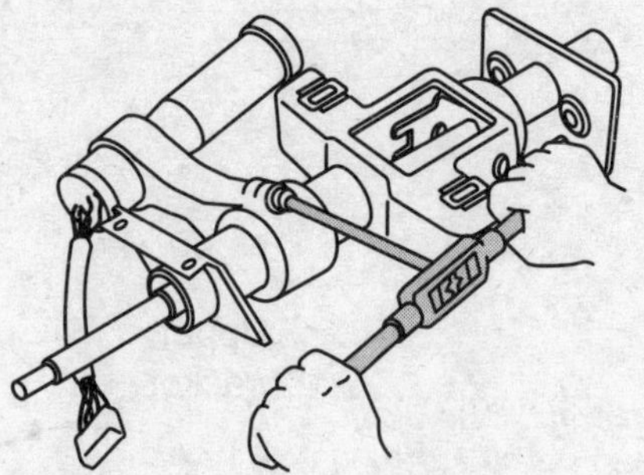

FIGURE 9-16 *Removing tapered-head bolts with a screw extractor.*

7. Mark the center of the **tapered-head bolts** on the steering column with a center punch. Use a 0.120 to 0.160 in. (3 to 4 mm) drill bit to drill into the tapered-head bolts (Figure 9-15).
8. Remove the tapered-head bolts with a screw extractor, and separate the upper bracket and column tube (Figure 9-16).
9. Grasp the compression spring seat with a pair of pliers and turn the seat to release the seat, compression spring, and bushing (Figure 9-17).
10. Grasp the tension spring with a pair of pliers and extend this spring to remove it from the column (Figure 9-18).

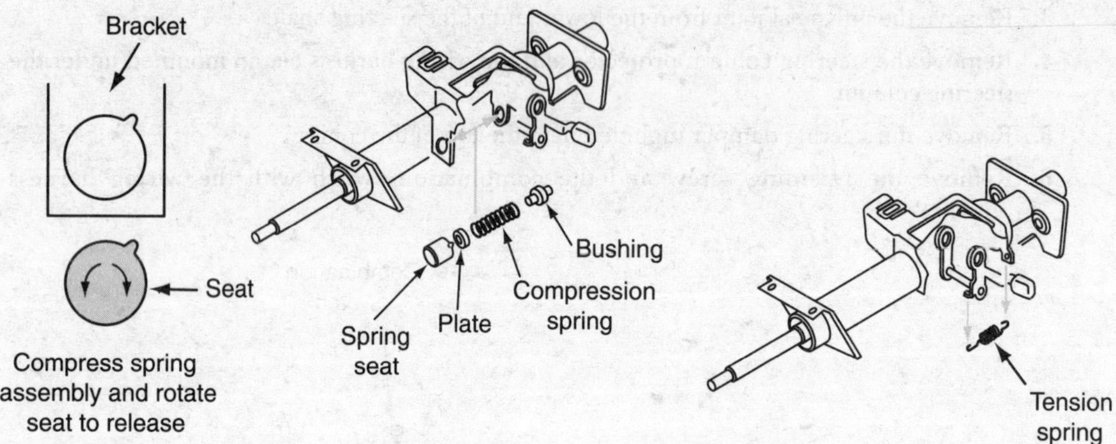

FIGURE 9-17 *Removing compression spring, seat, and bushing.*

FIGURE 9-18 *Removing tension spring.*

11. Remove the snapring from the upper column tube with snapring pliers (Figure 9-19).
12. Use a soft hammer and a screwdriver to loosen the staked parts of the upper column tube (Figure 9-20).
13. Remove the two nuts on the upper column pivot bolts (Figure 9-21).
14. Use a plastic hammer to tap the pivot bolts out of the column (Figure 9-22).
15. Remove the upper column tube, tilt lever assembly, and plate washers (Figure 9-23).
16. Remove the steering shaft from the column (Figure 9-24).

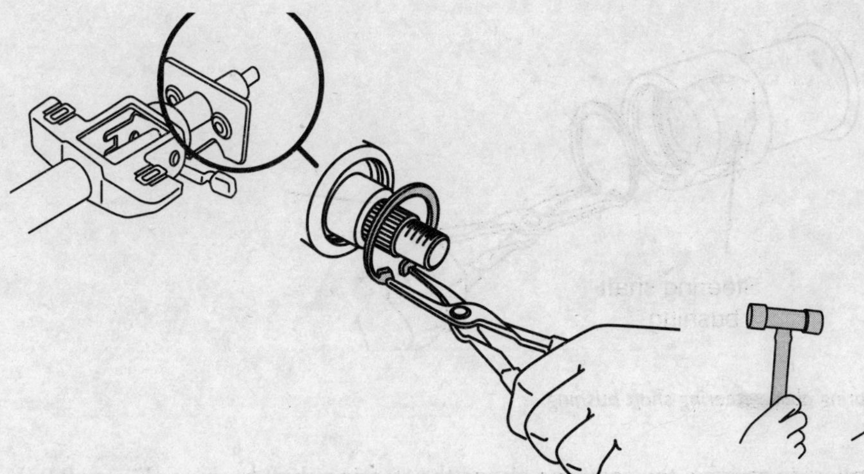

FIGURE 9-19 *Removing snapring from upper column tube.*

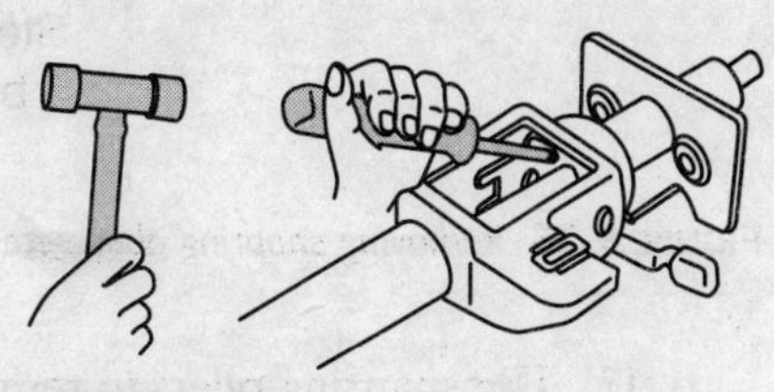

FIGURE 9-20 *Loosening staked parts in upper column tube.*

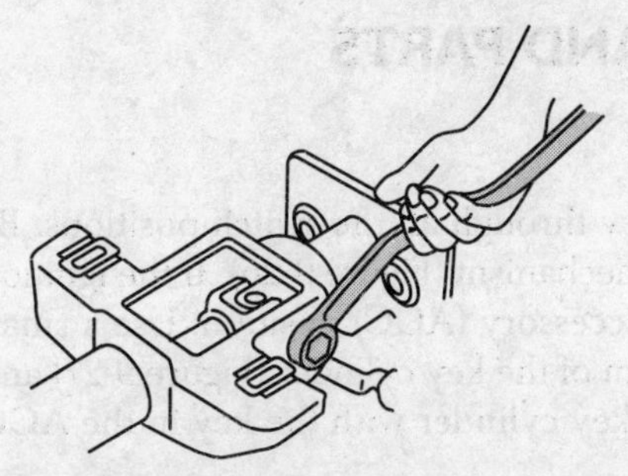

FIGURE 9-21 *Removing nuts on upper column pivot bolts.*

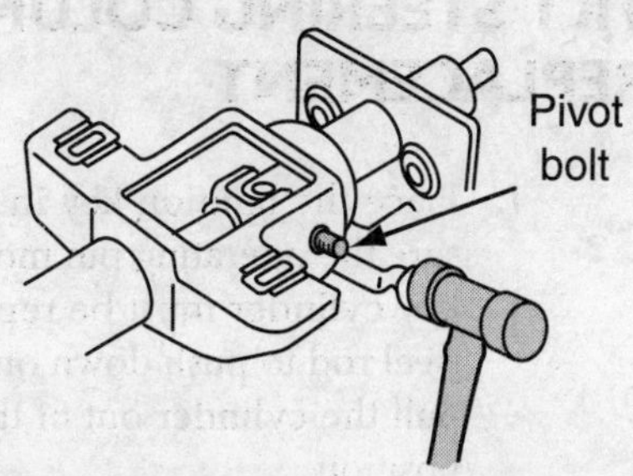

FIGURE 9-22 *Removing pivot bolts from steering column.*

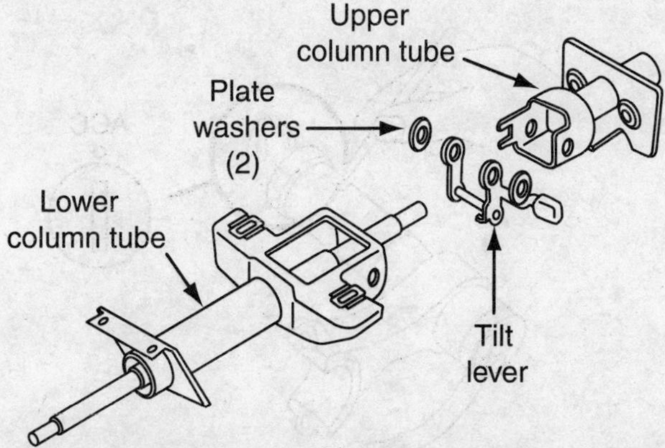

FIGURE 9-23 *Removing upper column tube, tilt lever assembly, and plate washers.*

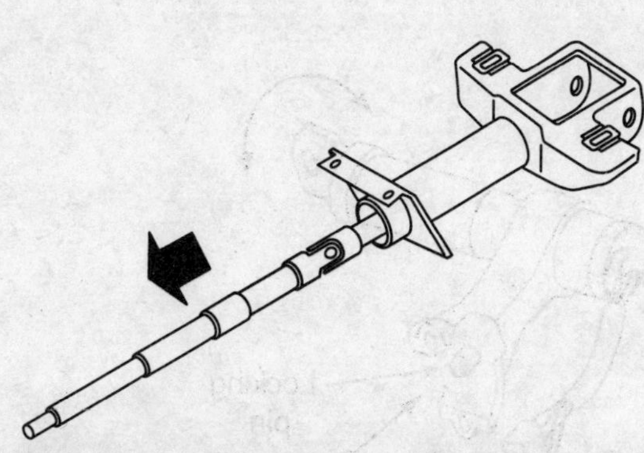

FIGURE 9-24 *Removing steering shaft from the steering column.*

FIGURE 9-25 *Removing snapring above steering shaft bushing.*

17. Use snapring pliers to remove the snapring above the steering shaft bushing (Figure 9-25). Remove the steering shaft bushing.

TILT STEERING COLUMN INSPECTION AND PARTS REPLACEMENT

1. Place the ignition key in the switch and move the key through all the switch positions. Be sure the operating pin moves properly in the switch mechanism (Figure 9-26). If the ignition key cylinder must be replaced, turn the key to the accessory (ACC) position. Use a small steel rod to push down on the stop pin near the bottom of the key cylinder (Figure 9-27) and pull the cylinder out of the housing. Install the new key cylinder with the key in the ACC position.
2. Rotate the upper steering shaft bearing and inspect for noise, looseness, and wear (Figure 9-28). If any of these conditions are present, replace the upper tube.
3. Inspect the lower steering shaft bearing for noise, looseness, and wear (Figure 9-29). Replace this bearing if necessary.

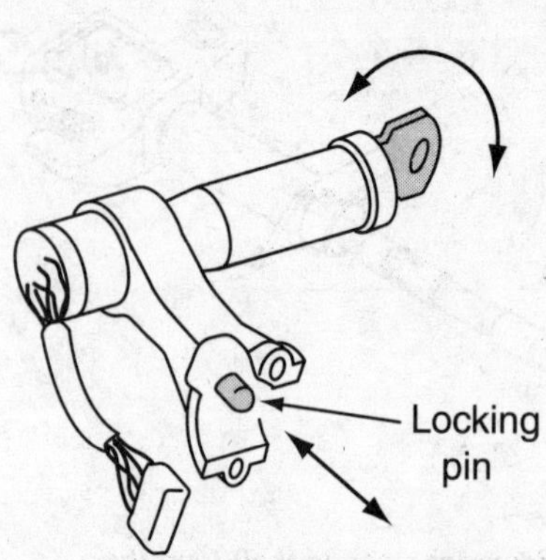

FIGURE 9-26 *Inspecting ignition switch operation.*

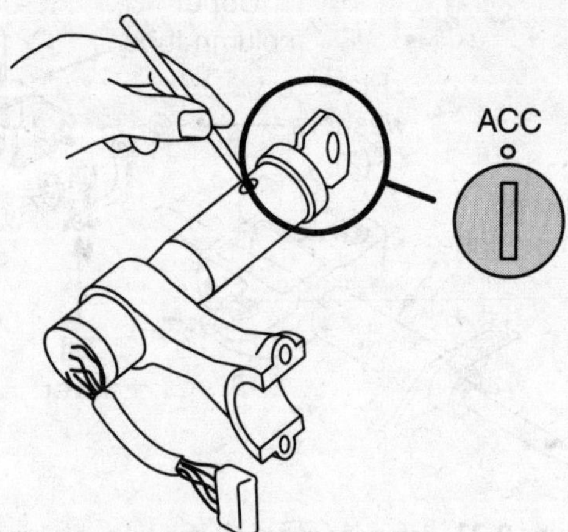

FIGURE 9-27 *Depressing stop pin in release ignition switch cylinder.*

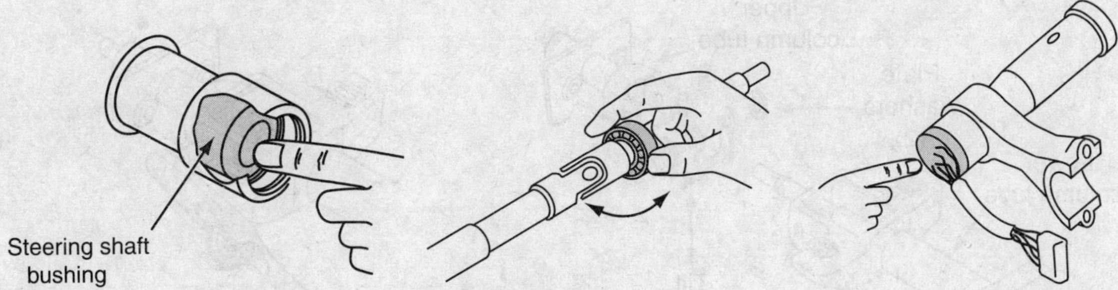

FIGURE 9-28 *Inspecting upper steering shaft bearing.*

FIGURE 9-29 *Inspecting lower steering shaft bearing.*

FIGURE 9-30 *Inspecting ignition key interlock solenoid.*

4. Inspect the ignition key interlock solenoid for damaged wires and loose mounting screws (Figure 9-30). Repair or replace this solenoid as required.

TILT STEERING COLUMN ASSEMBLY

1. Coat all rubbing parts with **molybdenum disulphide lithium-based grease.** Install the steering shaft bushing and the bushing snapring (Figure 9-31).
2. Install the steering shaft in the lower tube (Figure 9-32).

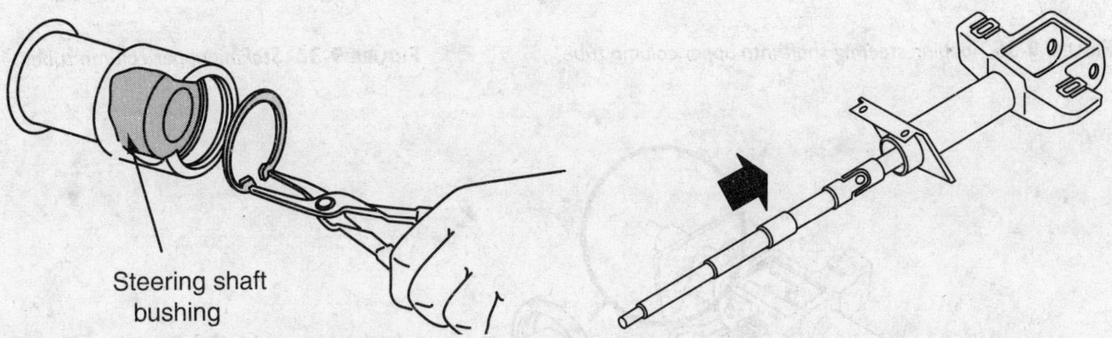

FIGURE 9-31 *Installing steering shaft bushing and snapring.*

FIGURE 9-32 *Installing the steering shaft in the lower tube.*

3. Install the upper column tube, tilt lever mechanism, and two plate washers (Figure 9-33). Install the two pivot bolts.
4. Install the pivot bolt nuts and tighten these nuts to the specified torque (Figure 9-34).
5. Use a brass bar and a hammer to tap the steering shaft into the upper column tube (Figure 9-35).
6. Stake the upper column tube with a pin punch and a hammer (Figure 9-36).
7. Install the snapring in the top of the upper column tube (Figure 9-37).
8. Install the tension spring (Figure 9-38). Assemble the compression spring, bushing, plate, and seat. Use a vise to install the compression spring and related components (Figure 9-39).

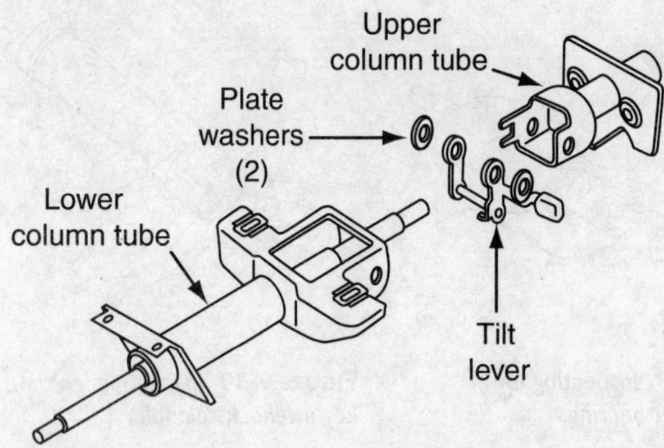

FIGURE 9-33 *Installing upper column tube, tilt lever mechanism, and two plate washers.*

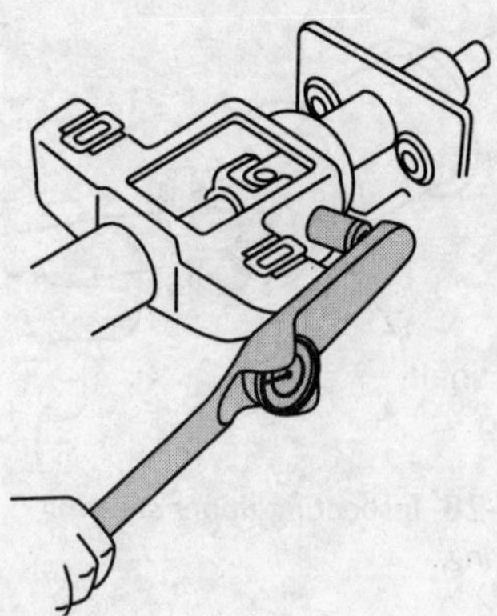

FIGURE 9-34 *Tightening pivot bolt nuts.*

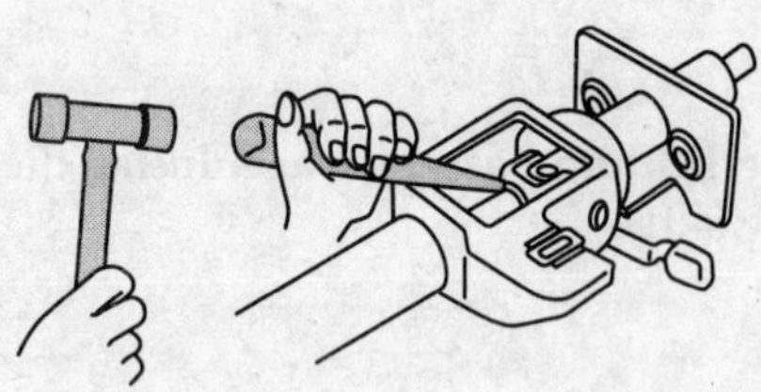

FIGURE 9-35 *Tapping steering shaft into upper column tube.*

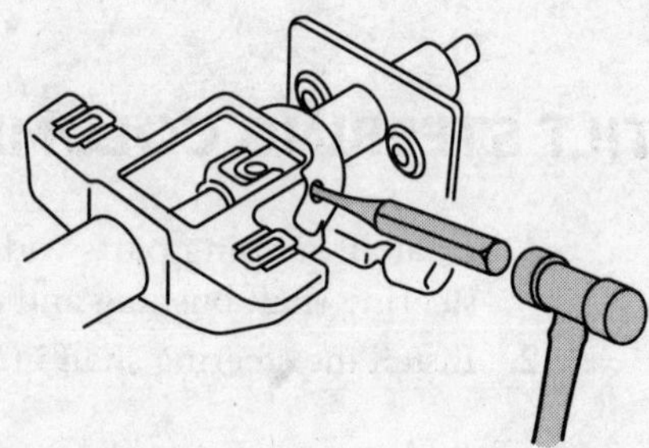

FIGURE 9-36 *Staking upper column tube.*

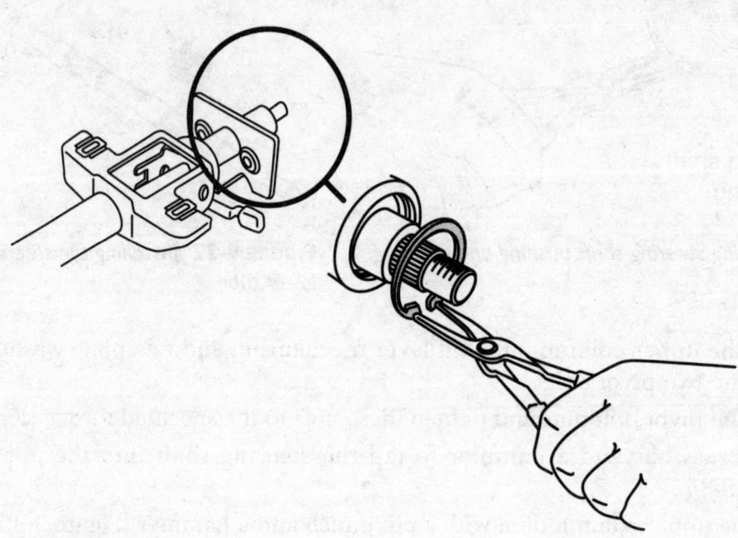

FIGURE 9-37 *Installing snapring in upper column tube.*

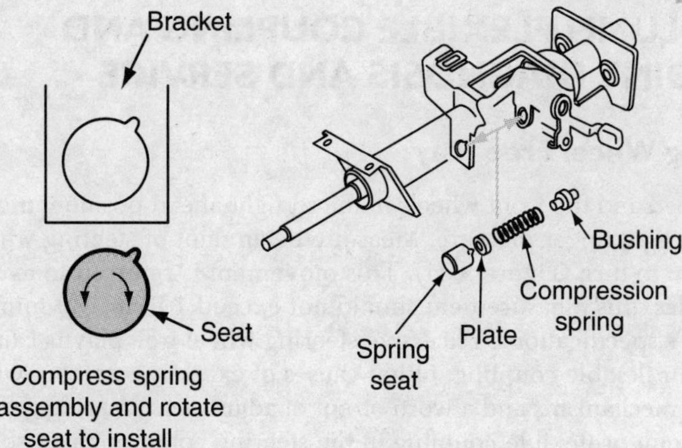

FIGURE 9-38 *Installing tension spring.*

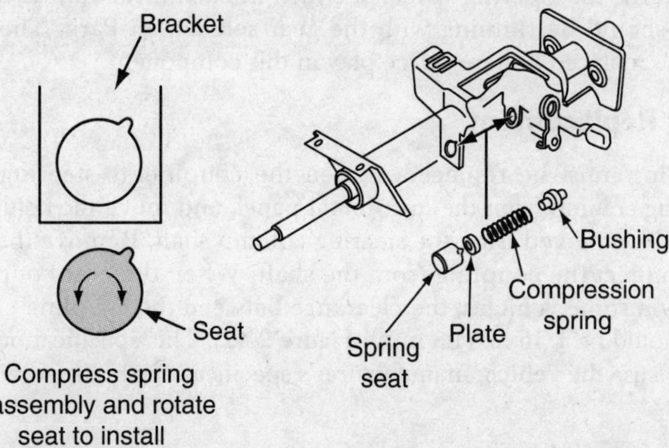

FIGURE 9-39 *Installing compression spring.*

9. Install the upper bracket with two new tapered-head bolts. Tighten the tapered-head bolts until the tapered head breaks off (Figure 9-40).
10. Install the protector and wiring harness clamp.
11. Install the steering damper and ignition key illumination.
12. Install the universal joint on the bottom of the steering shaft and tighten the retaining bolt to the specified torque.
13. Install the combination switch and wiring harness and tighten the retaining screw to the specified torque.

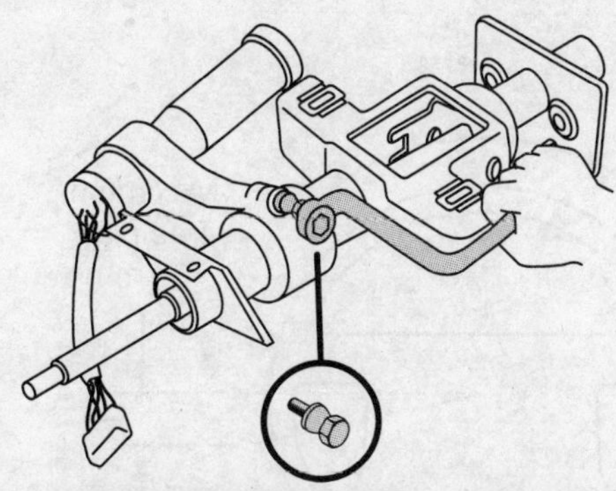

FIGURE 9-40 *Tightening tapered-head bolts in upper bracket.*

14. Install the spiral cable, steering wheel, and air bag deployment module as mentioned earlier in this chapter.

STEERING COLUMN FLEXIBLE COUPLING AND UNIVERSAL JOINT DIAGNOSIS AND SERVICE

Checking Steering Wheel Free Play

With the engine stopped and the front wheels in the straight-ahead position, move the steering wheel in each direction with light finger pressure. Measure the amount of steering wheel movement before the front wheels begin to turn (Figure 9-41). This movement is referred to as **steering wheel free play.** On some vehicles, this measurement should not exceed 1.18 in. (30 mm). Always refer to the vehicle manufacturer's specifications. Excessive steering wheel free play is caused by worn steering shaft universal joints or flexible coupling. Other causes of excessive steering wheel free play include worn steering linkage mechanisms and a worn or out of adjustment steering gear.

A worn universal joint or flexible coupling in the steering column may also cause rattling noises. The rattling noises may occur while driving the vehicle straight ahead on irregular road surfaces. With the normal vehicle weight resting on the front suspension, observe the flexible coupling or universal joint as an assistant turns the steering wheel 1/2 turn in each direction. If the vehicle has power steering, the engine should be running with the gear selector in Park. The flexible coupling or universal joint must be replaced if there is free play in this component.

Flexible Coupling Replacement

If the flexible coupling must be replaced, loosen the coupling-to-steering-gear-stub-shaft bolt. Disconnect the steering column from the instrument panel, and move the column rearward until the flexible coupling can be removed from the steering column shaft. Remove the coupling-to-steering-shaft bolts, and disconnect the coupling from the shaft. When the new coupling and the steering column are installed on some vehicles, the clearance between the coupling clamp and the steering gear adjusting plug should be 1/16 in. (1.5 mm) (Figure 9-42). This specification may vary depending on the vehicle. Always use the vehicle manufacturer's specifications in the service manual.

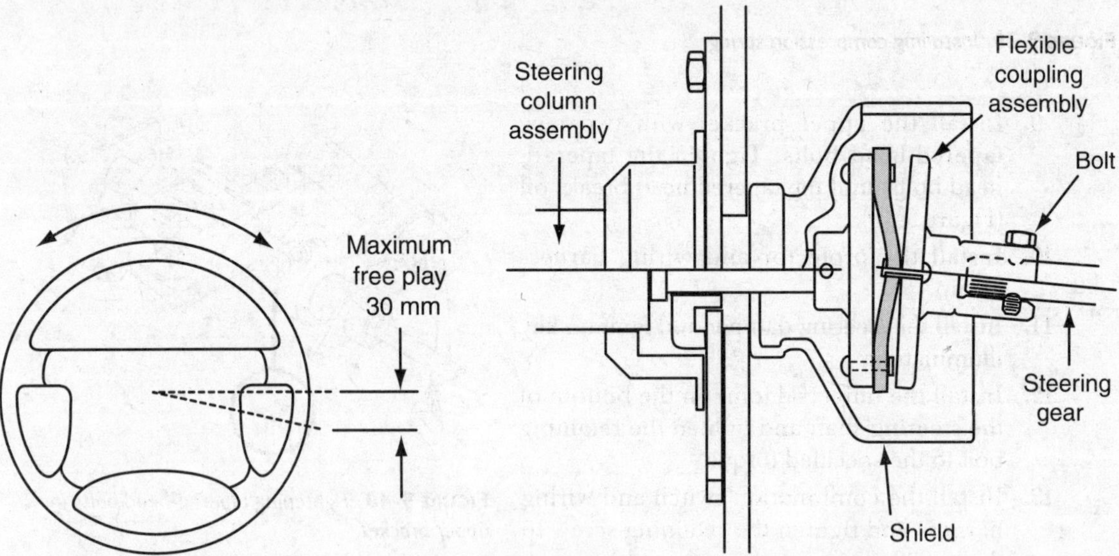

FIGURE 9-41 *Measuring steering wheel free play.*

FIGURE 9-42 *Flexible coupling installation.*

STEERING COLUMN DIAGNOSIS

There are variations in steering columns depending on the vehicle, type of transmission, and the transmission gear selector position. Thus different column diagnostic procedures may be required. See Table 9-1, Table 9-2, and Table 9-3 for a typical steering column diagnosis.

TABLE 9-1 *Automatic Transmission—Steering Column Diagnosis*

CONDITION	POSSIBLE CAUSE	CORRECTION
Lock system—will not unlock	1. Lock bolt damaged	1. Replace lock bolt.
	2. Defective lock cylinder	2. Replace or repair lock cylinder.
	3. Damaged housing	3. Replace housing.
	4. Damaged or collapsed sector	4. Replace sector.
	5. Damaged rack	5. Replace rack.
	6. Shear flange on sector shaft collapsed	6. Replace.
Lock system—will not lock	1. Lock bolt spring broken or defective	1. Replace spring.
	2. Damaged sector tooth, or sector installed incorrectly	2. Replace, or install correctly.
	3. Defective lock cylinder	3. Replace lock cylinder.
	4. Burr on lock bolt or housing	4. Remove burr.
	5. Damaged housing	5. Replace housing.
	6. Transmission linkage adjustment incorrect	6. Readjust.
	7. Damaged rack	7. Replace rack.
	8. Interference between bowl and coupling (tilt)	8. Adjust or replace as necessary.
	9. Ignition switch stuck	9. Readjust or replace.
	10. Actuator rod restricted or bent	10. Readjust or replace.
Lock system—high effort	1. Lock cylinder defective	1. Replace lock cylinder.
	2. Ignition switch defective	2. Replace switch.
	3. Rack preload spring broken or deformed	3. Replace spring.
	4. Burr on sector, rack, housing, support, tang of shift gate, or actuator rod coupling	4. Remove burr.
	5. Bent sector shaft	5. Replace shaft.
	6. Distorted rack	6. Replace rack.
	7. Misalignment of housing to cover (tilt)	7. Replace either or both.
	8. Distorted coupling slot in rack (tilt)	8. Replace rack.
	9. Bent or restricted actuator rod	9. Straighten, remove restriction, or replace.
	10. Ignition switch mounting bracket bent	10. Straighten or replace.
Lock cylinder—high effort between Off and Off-lock positions	1. Burr on tang of shift gate	1. Remove burr.
	2. Distorted rack	2. Replace rack.

TABLE 9-1 *Automatic Transmission—Steering Column Diagnosis (continued)*

CONDITION	POSSIBLE CAUSE	CORRECTION
Sticks in Start position	1. Actuator rod deformed	1. Straighten or replace.
	2. Any high effort condition	2. Check items under high effort section.
Key cannot be removed in Off-lock position	1. Ignition switch not set correctly	1. Readjust ignition switch.
	2. Defective lock cylinder	2. Replace lock cylinder.
Lock cylinder can be removed without depressing retainer	1. Lock cylinder with defective retainer	1. Replace lock cylinder.
	2. Lock cylinder without retainer	2. Replace lock cylinder.
	3. Burr over retainer slot in housing cover	3. Remove burr.
Lock bolt hits shaft lock in Off and Park positions	Ignition switch not set correctly	Readjust ignition switch.
Ignition system—electrical system does not function	1. Defective fuse in "accessory" circuit	1. Replace fuse.
	2. Connector body loose or defective	2. Tighten or replace.
	3. Defective wiring	3. Repair or replace.
	4. Defective ignition switch	4. Replace ignition switch.
	5. Ignition switch not adjusted properly	5. Readjust ignition switch.
Switch does not actuate mechanically	Defective ignition switch	Replace ignition switch.
Switch cannot be set correctly	1. Switch actuator rod deformed	1. Repair or replace switch actuator rod.
	2. Sector to rack engaged in wrong tooth (tilt)	2. Engage sector to rack correctly.
Noise in column	1. Coupling bolts loose	1. Tighten pinch bolts to specified torque.
	2. Column not correctly aligned	2. Realign column.
	3. Coupling pulled apart	3. Replace coupling and realign column.
	4. Sheared intermediate shaft plastic joint	4. Replace or repair steering shaft and realign column.
	5. Horn contact ring not lubricated	5. Lubricate with Lubriplate.
	6. Lack of grease on bearings or bearing surfaces	6. Lubricate bearings.
	7. Lower shaft bearing tight or frozen	7. Replace bearing. Check shaft and replace if scored.
	8. Upper shaft tight or frozen	8. Replace housing assembly.

TABLE 9-1 *Automatic Transmission—Steering Column Diagnosis (continued)*

CONDITION	POSSIBLE CAUSE	CORRECTION
	9. Shaft lock plate cover loose	9. Tighten three screws or, if missing, replace. CAUTION: Use specified screws (15 inch-pounds).
	10. Lock plate snapring not seated	10. Replace snapring. Check for proper seating in groove.
	11. Defective buzzer dog cam on lock cylinder	11. Replace lock cylinder.
	12. One click when in Off-lock position and the steering wheel is moved	12. Normal condition: lock bolt is seating.
Steering shaft—high effort	1. Column assembly misaligned in vehicle	1. Realign.
	2. Improperly installed or deformed dust seal	2. Remove and replace.
	3. Tight or frozen, upper or lower bearing	3. Replace affected bearing or bearings.
	4. Flash on ID of shift tube from plastic joint	4. Replace shift tube.
High shift effort	1. Column not aligned correctly in car	1. Realign.
	2. Improperly installed dust seal	2. Remove and replace.
	3. Lack of grease on seal or bearing areas	3. Lubricate bearings and seals.
	4. Burr on upper or lower end of shift tube	4. Remove burr.
	5. Lower bowl bearing not assembled properly (tilt)	5. Reassemble properly.
	6. Wave washer with burrs (tilt)	6. Replace wave washer.
Improper transmission shifting	1. Sheared shift tube joint	1. Replace shift tube assembly.
	2. Improper transmission linkage adjustment	2. Readjust linkage.
	3. Loose lower shift lever	3. Replace shift tube assembly.
	4. Improper gate plate	4. Replace with correct part.
	5. Sheared lower shift lever weld	5. Replace tube assembly.
Lash in mounted column assembly	1. Instrument panel mounting bolts loose	1. Tighten to specifications (20 foot-pounds).
	2. Broken weld nuts on jacket	2. Replace jacket assembly.
	3. Instrument panel bracket capsule sheared	3. Replace bracket assembly.
	4. Instrument panel to jacket mounting bolts loose	4. Tighten to specifications (15 foot-pounds).

TABLE 9-1 *Automatic Transmission—Steering Column Diagnosis (continued)*

CONDITION	POSSIBLE CAUSE	CORRECTION
	5. Loose shoes in housing (tilt)	5. Replace.
	6. Loose tilt head pivot pins (tilt)	6. Replace.
	7. Loose shoe lock pin in support (tilt)	7. Replace.
Miscellaneous	1. Housing loose on jacket noticed with ignition in Off-lock position and a torque applied to the steering wheel	1. Tighten four mounting screws (60 inch-pounds).
	2. Shroud loose on shift bowl	2. Bend tabs on shroud over lugs on bowl.

TABLE 9-2 *Manual Transmission—Steering Column Diagnosis*

CONDITION	POSSIBLE CAUSE	CORRECTION
Shift lever sticking	1. Defective upper shift lever	1. Replace shift lever.
	2. Defective shift lever gate	2. Replace shift lever gate.
	3. Loose relay lever on shift tube	3. Replace shift tube assembly.
	4. Wrong shift lever	4. Replace with current lever.
High shift effort	1. Column not aligned correctly	1. Realign column.
	2. Lower bowl bearing not assembled correctly	2. Reassemble correctly.
	3. Improperly installed seal	3. Remove and replace.
	4. Wave washer in lower bowl bearing defective	4. Replace wave washer.
	5. Improper adjustment of lower shift levers	5. Readjust.
	6. Lack of grease on seal, bearing areas, or levers	6. Lubricate seal, levers, and bearings.
	7. Damaged shift tube in bearing areas	7. Replace shift tube assembly.
Improper transmission shifting	Loose relay lever on shift tube	Replace shift tube assembly.

TABLE 9-3 *Manual Transmission—Tilt Column Diagnosis*

CONDITION	POSSIBLE CAUSE	CORRECTION
Housing scraping on bowl	Bowl bent or not concentric with hub	Replace bowl.
Steering wheel loose	1. Excessive clearance between holes in support or housing and pivot pin diameters	1. Replace either or both.
	2. Defective or missing antilash spring in spheres	2. Add spring or replace both.
	3. Upper bearing seat not seating in bearing	3. Replace both.

TABLE 9-3 *Manual Transmission—Tilt Column Diagnosis (continued)*

CONDITION	POSSIBLE CAUSE	CORRECTION
	4. Upper bearing inner race seat missing	4. Install seat.
	5. Loose support screws	5. Tighten to 60 inch-pounds.
	6. Bearing preload spring missing or broken	6. Replace preload spring.
Steering wheel loose every other tilt position	Loose fit between shoe and shoe pivot pin	Replace both.
Noise when tilting column	1. Upper tilt bumper worn	1. Replace tilt bumper.
	2. Tilt spring rubbing in housing or dirt	2. Lubricate.
Steering column not locking in any tilt position	1. Shoe seized on its pivot pin	1. Replace shoe and pivot pin.
	2. Shoe grooves might have burrs	2. Replace shoe.
	3. Shoe lock spring weak or broken	3. Replace lock spring.
Steering wheel fails to return to top tilt position	1. Pivot pins bound up	1. Replace pivot pins.
	2. Wheel tilt spring defective	2. Replace tilt spring.
	3. Turn signal switch wires too tight	3. Reposition wires.

STEERING LINKAGE DIAGNOSIS AND SERVICE

Diagnosis of Center Link, Pitman Arm, and Tie-Rod Ends

The vehicle should be raised and safety stands positioned under the lower control arms to support the vehicle weight. Use vertical hand force to check for looseness in all the pivots on the tie-rod ends and the center link. Inspect the seals on each tie-rod end and pivot on the center link or pitman arm for damage and cracks. Cracked seals allow dirt to enter the pivoted joints, which results in rapid wear. If looseness or damaged seals are found on any pivoted joint on the tie- rods and center link, these components must be replaced.

The second part of this diagnosis is done with the front wheels resting on the shop floor. If the vehicle is equipped with power steering, start the engine and allow the engine to idle with the transmission in Park and the parking brake applied. While someone turns the steering wheel one-quarter turn in each direction from the straight-ahead position, observe all the pivoted joints on the tie-rod ends and center link. This test allows the technician to check the steering linkage pivots under load. If any of the pivoted joints show a slight amount of play, they must be replaced.

Tie-Rod End Replacement

Worn tie-rod ends result in these problems:

1. Excessive steering wheel free play
2. Incorrect front wheel toe setting
3. Tire squeal on turns

4. Tread wear on front tires
5. Front wheel shimmy
6. Rattling noise on road irregularities

The cotter pin and nut must be removed prior to tie-rod end replacement. A puller is used to remove the tie-rod end from the steering arm (Figure 9-43). Tie-rod ends with rubber-encapsulated ball studs require special inspection and diagnostic procedures (Figure 9-44). On this type of tie-rod end, inspect for looseness of the ball stud in the rubber capsule and looseness of the stud and rubber capsule in the outer housing. If any looseness is present, replace the tie-rod end. Tie-rod end replacement is also necessary if there is any indication of the rubber capsule starting to come out of the outer housing.

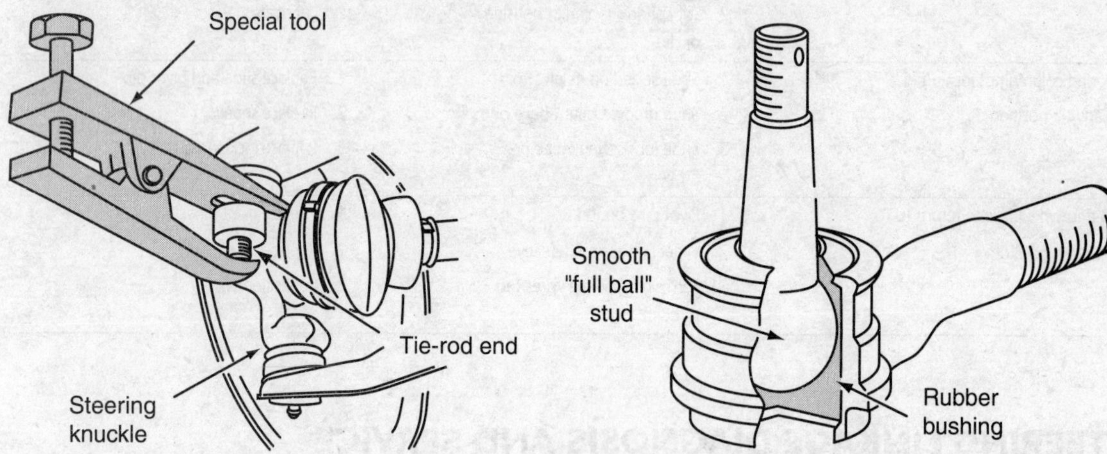

FIGURE 9-43 *Removing tie-rod end.*

FIGURE 9-44 *Tie-rod end with rubber encapsulated ball stud.*

After the tie-rod end is removed from the steering arm, install two nuts on the stud threads and tighten these nuts against each other. Use the proper size of socket and a torque wrench to rotate the ball stud through a 40° arc (Figure 9-45). If the ball stud turning torque is less that 20 ft.-lb. (27 Nm), replace the tie-rod end.

The tie-rod clamp must be loosened before the tie-rod end is removed from the sleeve. Count the number of turns required to remove the tie-rod end from the sleeve, and install the new tie-rod with the same number of turns. Even when this procedure is followed, the toe must be checked after the steering linkage components are replaced. Before the new tie-rod end is installed, center the stud in the tie-rod end. When the tie-rod end stud is installed in the steering arm opening, only the threads should be visible above the steering arm surface. If the machined surface of the tie-rod end stud is visible above the steering arm surface, or if the stud fits loosely in the steering arm opening, this opening is worn or the tie-rod end is not correct for that application. The tie-rod end nut must be torqued to the manufacturer's specifications, and the cotter pin must be installed through the tie-rod end and nut openings (Figure 9-46).

The tie-rod end nut must never be loosened from the specified torque to install the cotter pin. Another method of positioning replacement tie-rod ends is to measure the distance from the center of the tie-rod stud to the end of the sleeve prior to removal. When the new tie-rod end is installed, be sure this measurement is the same. The slots in the tie-rod sleeve must be positioned away from the opening in the sleeve clamps (Figure 9-47). Leave the sleeve clamps loose until the front wheel toe is

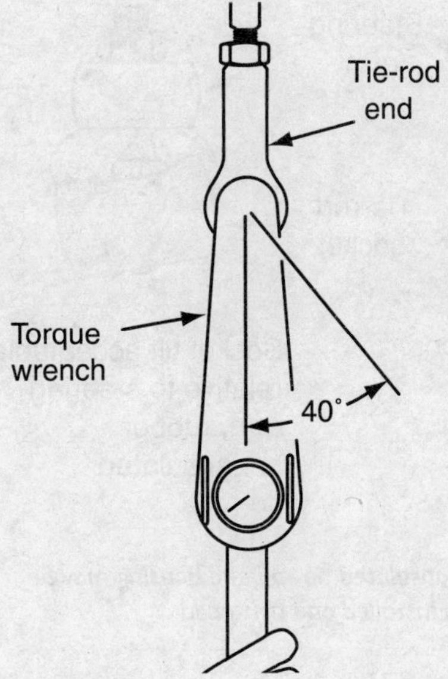

FIGURE 9-45 *Measuring turning torque on a rubber-encapsulated tie-rod end.*

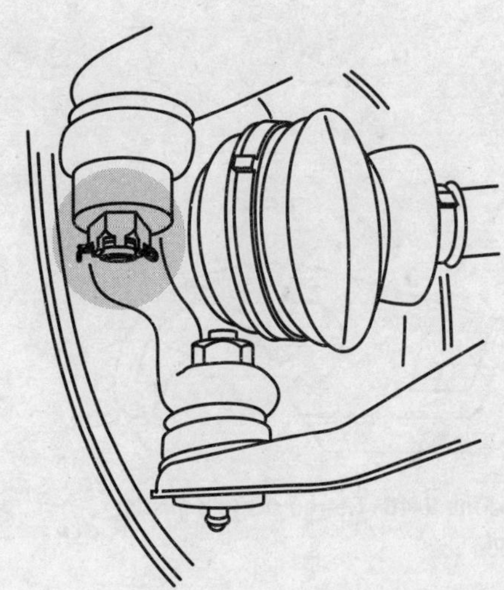

FIGURE 9-46 *Tie-rod nut and cotter pin installation.*

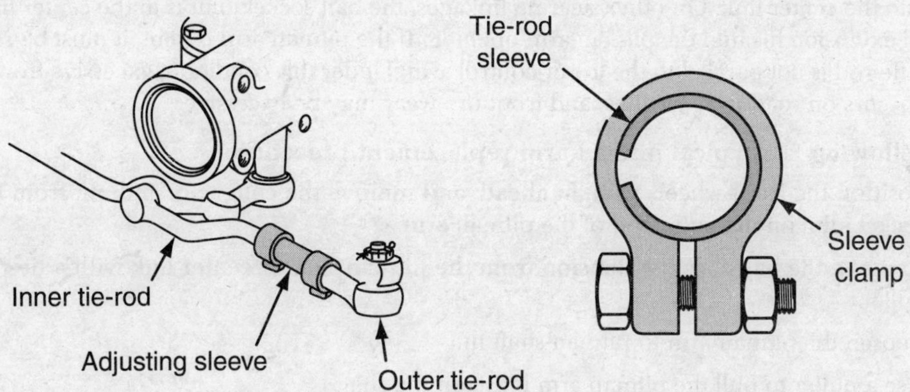

FIGURE 9-47 *Proper slot and clamp position on tie-rod sleeves.*

checked, and then tighten the sleeve clamp bolts to the specified torque. A special tool is available to rotate the tie-rod sleeves and set the front wheel toe (Figure 9-48).

CAUTION: If rubber-encapsulated tie-rod ends are tightened with the front wheels in any position but straight ahead, steering pull and wander may occur.

When rubber-encapsulated tie-rod ends are installed and tightened to the specified torque, the front wheels must be straight ahead. Tightening this type of tie-rod end with the front wheels in any other position but straight ahead may cause steering pull or wander. After rubber-encapsulated tie-rod ends are tightened to the specified torque, it is acceptable for the tie-rod end housing to be tilted to one side (Figure 9-49).

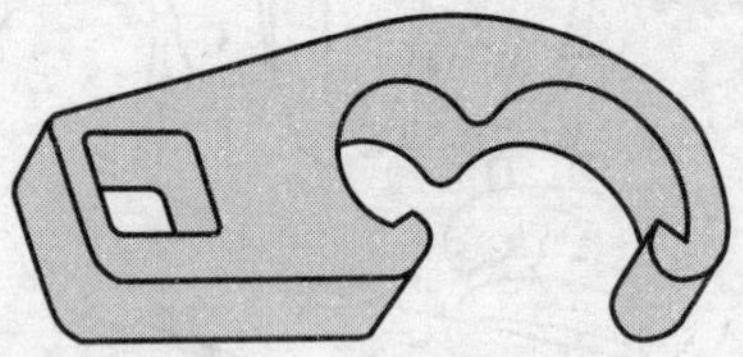

FIGURE 9-48 *Tie-rod sleeve adjusting tool.*

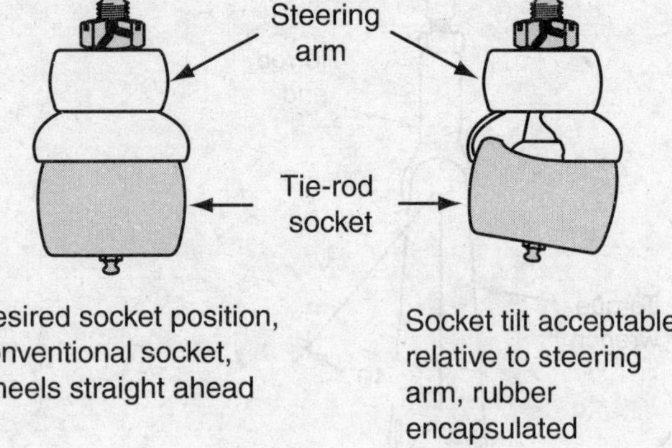

FIGURE 9-49 *Rubber-encapsulated tie-rod end housing may be tilted to one side after it is installed and tightened.*

Pitman Arm Diagnosis and Replacement

Some pitman arms contain a ball socket joint on the outer end. The threaded extension on this ball socket fits into the center link. On other steering linkages, the ball socket joint is in the center link, and the threaded extension fits into the pitman arm opening. If the pitman arm is bent, it must be replaced because the tie-rod is not parallel to the lower control arm. Under this condition, excessive front wheel toe change occurs on road irregularities, and front tire wear may be excessive.

The following is a typical pitman arm replacement procedure:

1. Position the front wheels straight ahead, and remove the cotter pin and nut from the ball socket joint on the outer end of the pitman arm.
2. Remove the ball socket extension from the pitman arm or center link with a tie-rod end puller.
3. Loosen the pitman-arm-to-pitman-shaft nut.
4. Use a puller to pull the pitman arm loose on the shaft.
5. Remove the nut, lock washer, and pitman arm.
6. Check the pitman shaft splines. If the splines are damaged or twisted, the shaft must be replaced.
7. Reverse steps 1 through 5 to install the pitman arm. The pitman arm-to-shaft nut and the ball socket extension nut must be tightened to the manufacturer's specified torque. Be sure the pitman arm is installed in the correct position on the shaft splines. Install the cotter pin in the ball socket extension.

Center Link Diagnosis and Replacement

A bent center link must be replaced. Do not attempt to straighten this rod. If the ball socket joints are loose on either end of the rod, center link assembly replacement is necessary. If the ball stud openings in the center link are worn, replace the center link.

Follow these steps for a typical center link replacement:

1. Remove the cotter pins from the tie-rod-to-center-link nuts, and the idler arm and pitman-arm-to-center-link nuts.
2. Remove the nuts on the tie-rod inner ends, idler-arm-to-center-link ball socket extension, and the pitman-arm-to-center-link ball socket extension.
3. Use a tie-rod end puller to pull the inner tie-rods from the center link. Follow the same procedure to remove the center-link-to-pitman-arm ball socket extension.
4. Remove the idler arm from the center link; then remove the center link.
5. Reverse steps 1 through 4 to install the center link. Tighten all the ball socket nuts to the manufacturer's specified torque, and install cotter pins in all the nuts. If the ball sockets have grease fittings, lubricate the ball sockets with a grease gun and chassis lubricant.

Idler Arm Diagnosis

To measure idler arm vertical movement, attach the magnetic base of a dial indicator to the frame near the idler arm. Position the dial indicator stem against the upper side on the outer end of the idler arm. Preload the dial indicator stem and zero the dial. Use a pull scale to apply 25 lbs. (11.34 kg) of force downward and upward on the idler arm (Figure 9-50). Observe the total vertical idler arm movement on the dial indicator. If this vertical movement exceeds the vehicle manufacturer's specifications, replace the idler arm. Typical maximum vertical idler arm movement from the downward to the upward position is 0.250 in. (63.5 mm). If idler arm vertical movement is excessive, the tie-rod is not parallel to the lower control arm.

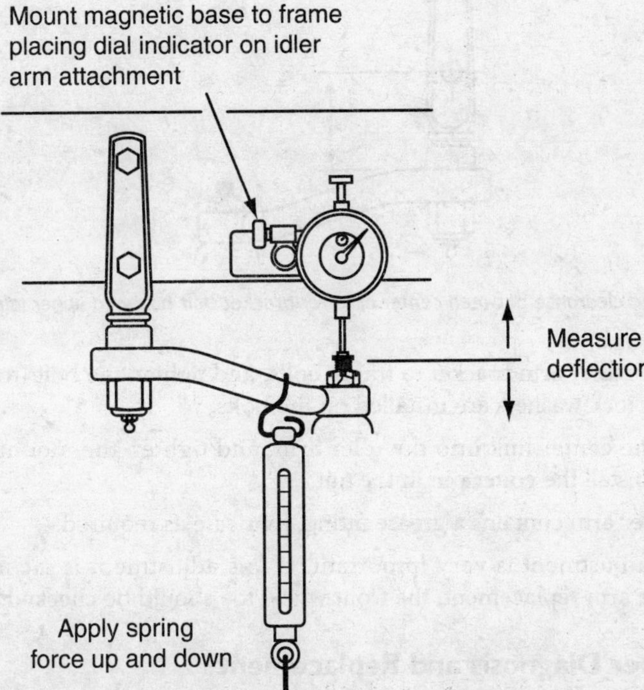

FIGURE 9-50 *Measuring idler arm vertical movement.*

Excessive idler arm vertical movement causes these steering problems:

1. Excessive toe change and front tire tread wear
2. Excessive steering wheel free play and reduced steering control
3. Front end shimmy

Binding idler arm bushings result in these complaints:

1. Hard steering
2. Squawking noise when the front wheels are turned
3. Poor steering wheel returnability

Some idler arms contain steel bushings, whereas others are equipped with rubber bushings.

The following is a typical idler arm removal and replacement procedure:

1. Remove the idler-arm-to-center-link cotter pin and nut.
2. Remove the center link from the idler arm.
3. Remove the idler arm bracket mounting bolts, and remove the idler arm.
4. If the idler arm has a steel bushing, thread the bracket into the idler arm bushing until the specified clearance is obtained between the center of the lower bracket bolt hole and the upper idler arm surface (Figure 9-51).

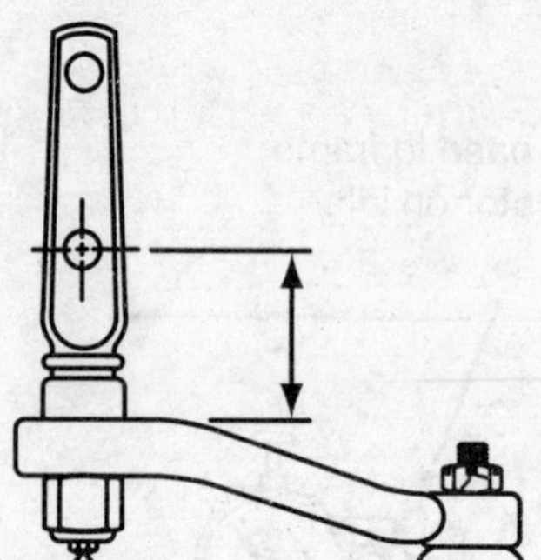

FIGURE 9-51 *Specified clearance between center of lower bracket bolt hole and upper idler arm surface.*

5. Install the idler arm bracket to frame bolts, and tighten the bolts to the specified torque. Be sure that lock washers are installed on the bolts.
6. Install the center link into the idler arm, and tighten the mounting nut to the specified torque. Install the cotter pin in the nut.
7. If the idler arm contains a grease fitting, lubricate as required.

The idler arm adjustment is very important. If this adjustment is incorrect, front wheel toe is affected. After idler arm replacement, the front wheel toe should be checked.

Steering Damper Diagnosis and Replacement

Some steering systems have a damper connected between the center link and the chassis. A damper is similar to a small shock absorber. The purpose of the damper is to prevent the transfer of steering shock and vibrations to the steering wheel. A worn-out steering damper may cause excessive steering shock and vibration on the steering wheel, especially on irregular road surfaces. A rattling noise occurs if the damper mounting bolts or brackets are loose.

The following is a typical steering damper checking and replacement procedure:

1. Lift the vehicle on a hoist, and grasp the damper firmly. Apply vertical and horizontal pressure to the damper, and check for movement in the damper mounts. If movement exists, tighten or replace the damper mounting bushings or brackets.
2. Visually inspect the damper for oil leaks. A slight film of oil on the damper body near the shaft seal is acceptable. If there is any indication of oil dripping from the damper, the unit must be replaced.
3. Disconnect one end of the damper, and pull the damper back and forth horizontally. The damper should offer a slight equal resistance to movement in either direction. When this resistance is not felt in one or both directions, replace the damper.
4. To replace the damper, remove the mounting bolts from the chassis and the center link.
5. When the new damper is installed, tighten the mounting bolts to the specified torque. Turn the steering wheel fully in each direction, and be sure the damper does not restrict linkage movement.

Steering Arm Diagnosis

If the front rims have been damaged, the steering arms should be checked for a bent condition. Measure the distance from the center of the tie-rod end stud to the edge of the rim on each side. Unequal readings may indicate a bent steering arm. Bent steering arms must be replaced. Steering linkage diagnosis is summarized in Table 9-4.

TABLE 9-4 *Steering Linkage Diagnosis*

CONDITION	POSSIBLE CAUSE	CORRECTION
Excessive play or looseness in steering system	1. Front wheel bearings loosely adjusted	1. Adjust bearings to obtain proper endplay.
	2. Worn steering shaft couplings	2. Replace part.
	3. Worn upper ball joints	3. Check and replace if necessary.
	4. Steering wheel loose on shaft or loose pitman arm, tie-rods, steering arms, or steering linkage ball studs	4. Tighten to specified torque, or replace if necessary.
	5. Steering gear thrust bearings loosely adjusted	5. Adjust preload to specifications.
	6. Excessive over-center lash in steering gear	6. Adjust preload to specifications per shop manual.
	7. Worn intermediate rod or tie-rod sockets	7. Replace worn part.

TABLE 9-4 *Steering Linkage Diagnosis (continued)*

CONDITION	POSSIBLE CAUSE	CORRECTION
Excessive looseness in tie-rod or intermediate rod pivots, or excessive vertical lash in idler support	Seal damage and leakage resulting in loss of lubricant, corrosion, and excessive wear	Replace damaged parts as necessary. Properly position upon reassembly.
Hard steering—excessive effort required at steering wheel	1. Low or uneven tire pressure	1. Inflate to specified pressures.
	2. Steering linkage or bolt joints need lubrication	2. Lube with specified lubricant.
	3. Tight or frozen intermediate rod, tie-rod, or idler socket	3. Lube, replace, or reposition as necessary.
	4. Steering gear-to-column misalignment	4. Align column.
	5. Steering gear adjusted too tightly	5. Adjust over-center and thrust bearing preload to specification.
	6. Front wheel alignment incorrect (manual gear)	6. Check alignment and correct as necessary.
Poor returnability	1. Steering linkage or ball joints need lubrication	1. Lube with specified lubricant.
	2. Steering gear adjusted too tightly	2. Adjust over-center and thrust bearing preload to specifications.
	3. Steering gear-to-column misalignment	3. Align columns.
	4. Front wheel alignment incorrect (caster)	4. Check alignment and correct as necessary.

CASE STUDY

A customer complained about excessive steering effort and poor steering wheel returnability after a turn on a 2005 General Motors Sierra truck with power steering. The technician road tested the car and found the customer's description of the problems to be accurate except for one point. The steering continually required excessive steering effort, and the steering wheel did not return properly after a turn. However, the customer did not mention, or possibly did not notice, that a squawking and creaking noise was sometimes heard during a turn.

The technician checked the power steering fluid level and condition, and found this fluid to be in good condition and at the proper level. Next, the technician checked the power steering belt condition and the power steering pump pressure. The belt tension and condition were satisfactory, and the power steering pump pressure was normal. A check of the power steering pump mounting bolts and brackets indicated they were in good condition. The technician disconnected the center link from the pitman arm and rotated the steering wheel with the engine running. Under this condition, the steering wheel turned very easily. Therefore, the technician concluded the excessive steering effort and poor returnability problems were not in the steering column or steering gear. Next, the technician disconnected the idler arm from the center link. When the technician attempted to move the idler arm back and forth, the idler arm had a severe binding problem. After an idler arm replacement, a road test revealed the excessive steering effort and poor returnability problems had disappeared.

SERVICE TIPS

- When servicing air bag components on some recent model vehicles, the vehicle manufacturer recommends disconnecting the air bag components only in the zone or area on the vehicle where service work is required rather than disconnecting the negative battery cable.
- Never attempt to straighten steering linkage components. This action may weaken the metal and cause sudden component failure, vehicle damage, and personal injury.
- A binding idler arm may suddenly break off and cause complete loss of steering control, vehicle damage, and personal injury.

REVIEW QUESTIONS

1. While discussing steering column service on an air-bag-equipped vehicle:
Technician A says service personnel should disconnect the negative battery cable and wait one minute prior to servicing an air bag system component. *Technician B* says a 12-V test lamp may be used to diagnose an air bag system.
Who is correct?
A. A only **C.** Both A and B
B. B only **D.** Neither A nor B

2. While discussing steering column service on an air-bag-equipped vehicle:
Technician A says an air bag deployment module should be placed face downward on the workbench. *Technician B* says the backup power supply provides power to deploy the air bag if the battery is disconnected during a frontal collision.
Who is correct?
A. A only **C.** Both A and B
B. B only **D.** Neither A nor B

3. While discussing steering wheel and clock spring electrical connector removal and replacement on an air-bag–equipped vehicle:
Technician A says the steering may bind if the clock spring is improperly installed. *Technician B* says when the clock spring electrical connector is installed, the front wheels should be straight ahead, and the clock spring should be turned fully clockwise.
Who is correct?
A. A only **C.** Both A and B
B. B only **D.** Neither A nor B

4. While discussing steering wheel removal:
Technician A says a steering wheel should be marked in relation to the steering shaft. *Technician B* says the steering wheel should be grasped firmly with both hands and pulled from the shaft.
Who is correct?
A. A only **C.** Both A and B
B. B only **D.** Neither A nor B

5. While discussing collapsible steering column damage:
   Technician A says if the vehicle has been in a frontal collision, the injected plastic in the column jacket, gearshift tube, and steering shaft may be sheared.
   Technician B says after a collision, some steering columns may be shifted on the bracket.
   Who is correct?
   A. A only **C.** Both A and B
   B. B only **D.** Neither A nor B
6. All of these statements about steering column service are true EXCEPT:
   A. Many ignition switches must be in the ACC position before removing the switch cylinder.
   B. An improperly installed dust seal may cause excessive steering wheel free play.
   C. High steering effort may be caused by an improperly aligned steering column.
   D. A worn steering shaft universal joint may cause excessive steering wheel free play.
7. A rattling noise in the steering column and linkage may be caused by:
   A. A bent center link.
   B. A binding idler arm.
   C. A worn steering shaft U-joint.
   D. Loose tie-rod sleeve clamps.
8. When diagnosing and servicing tie-rod ends:
   A. Rubber-encapsulated tie-rod ends should be tightened with the wheels turned fully to the right or left.
   B. The machined part of the tie-rod stud should be visible above the surface of the steering arm.
   C. The nut on the tie-rod stud may be loosened to install the cotter pin.
   D. If the turning torque on a rubber-encapsulated tie-rod end is less than specified, the tie-rod end must be replaced.
9. When diagnosing and servicing steering linkages:
   A. A worn tie-rod end causes excessive front wheel toe change.
   B. Bent steering linkages may be straightened in a hydraulic press.
   C. The slot in a tie-rod sleeve clamp must be positioned above the slot in the tie-rod sleeve.
   D. Front wheel shimmy may be caused by a binding idler arm.
10. An idler arm has 5/8 in. (15.8 mm) vertical movement. To correct this problem it is necessary to:
    A. Install thicker shims between the idler arm and the bracket.
    B. Install an oversize bushing in the idler arm.
    C. Replace the idler arm assembly.
    D. Replace the Belleville washer and spacer under the bushing.

CHALLENGE QUESTIONS

1. A preliminary steering inspection reveals that the steering wheel has nearly 1/2 inch of movement in either direction before the pitman arm begins to move. All of the following could cause this problem EXCEPT:
   A. Coupling joints.
   B. U joints.

C. Tight or seized shaft bearing.
D. Worn or out-of-adjustment steering gear.

2. A customer complains that sometimes the ignition switch won't unlock and the key won't turn. A preliminary inspection reveals that turning the steering wheel does not help but repositioning the key, after several attempts, unlocks the ignition.
   Technician A says the problem could be the column assembly is misaligned. *Technician B* says the problem could be the ignition key is worn.
   Who is correct?
   A. A only **C.** Both A and B
   B. B only **D.** Neither A nor B

3. If the clock spring electrical connector is not properly centered before it is installed:
   A. The steering may pull to one side.
   B. The clock spring electrical connector may be broken.
   C. The air bag may deploy without the vehicle being in an accident.
   D. The steering may have a binding condition.

4. A customer says the steering on his vehicle is very hard to turn in both directions. A preliminary inspection reveals no problems with the manual rack and pinion steering gear.
   Technician A says the problem could be a misaligned steering column. *Technician B* says the problem could be tight or frozen tie-rod ends.
   Who is correct?
   A. A only **C.** Both A and B
   B. B only **D.** Neither A nor B

5. A customer says his steering has a shimmy problem above 50 mph (80 km/h). Preliminary inspection indicates excessive wear on the right front tire.
   Technician A says the problem could be a worn tie-rod end. *Technician B* says the problem could be a worn idler arm ball joint.
   Who is correct?
   A. A only **C.** Both A and B
   B. B only **D.** Neither A nor B

JOB SHEET 27

Name ______________________ Date ______________________

REMOVE AND REPLACE AIR BAG INFLATOR MODULE AND STEERING WHEEL

Upon completion of this job sheet, you should be able to remove and replace an air bag inflator module and steering wheel.

ASE Correlation

This job sheet is related to ASE Automotive Suspension and Steering Task: *Inspect and replace steering shaft U-joint(s), flexible coupling(s), collapsible columns, and steering wheels (includes steering wheels with air bags and/or other steering wheel-mounted controls and components).*

Tools and Materials

Steering wheel puller
Torque wrench

Describe the Vehicle Being Worked On:

Year ____________ Make ____________ Model ____________
VIN ____________ Engine type and size ____________

Procedure

Task Completed

1. Turn the ignition switch to the Lock position and place the front wheels facing straight ahead. ☐
2. Remove the negative battery terminal and wait the time period specified by the vehicle manufacturer before servicing air bag components.

   Specified waiting period ____________

   After the negative battery cable is disconnected, explain why a waiting period is necessary before working on the air bag system.

   ____

   ____

   ____

   ____

3. Loosen the air bag retaining screws under the steering wheel. ☐
4. Loosen the other two air bag retaining screws under the steering wheel. ☐

   Loosen all the screws until the groove along the screw circumference catches on the screw case.

WARNING: When an air bag deployment module is temporarily stored on the workbench, always place this module face upward. If the air bag deployment module accidentally deployed when facing downward, the module would become a projectile and personal injury may result.

Task Completed

☐ **5.** Pull the air bag deployment module from the steering wheel, and disconnect the air bag module electrical connector. Do not pull on the air bag wires in the steering column. Place the air bag deployment module face upward on the workbench.

☐ **6.** Disconnect the air bag wiring retainer in the steering wheel.

☐ **7.** Use the proper size socket and a ratchet to remove the steering wheel retaining nut.

☐ **8.** Observe the matching alignment marks on the steering wheel and the steering shaft. If these alignment marks are not present, place alignment marks on the steering wheel and steering shaft with a center punch and a hammer.

Alignment marks on steering wheel and steering shaft:
☐ Satisfactory ☐ Unsatisfactory

CAUTION: Do not hammer on the top of the steering shaft to remove the steering wheel. This action may damage the shaft.

WARNING: Do not pull on the steering wheel in an attempt to remove it from the steering shaft. The steering wheel may suddenly come off, resulting in personal injury, or the steering wheel may be damaged by the pulling force.

☐ **9.** Install a steering wheel puller with the puller bolts threaded into the bolt holes in the steering wheel. Tighten the puller nut to remove the steering wheel. Visually check the steering wheel condition. If the steering wheel is bent or cracked, replace the wheel.

Steering wheel condition: ☐ Satisfactory ☐ Unsatisfactory

☐ **10.** Disconnect the four retaining screws, and remove the clock spring electrical connector.

☐ **11.** Be sure the front wheels are facing straight ahead. Turn the clock spring electrical connector counterclockwise by hand until it becomes harder to turn as it becomes fully wound in that direction.

CAUTION: Failure to center a clock spring prior to installation may cause a broken conductive tape in the clock spring.

12. Turn the clock spring electrical connector clockwise three turns, and align the red mark on the center part of the spring face with the notch in the cable circumference. This action centers the clock spring electrical connector.

Is the clock spring centered? ☐ Yes ☐ No

Instructor check ______________________________

Explain why the clock spring electrical connector must be centered before it is installed.

____

____

____

☐ **13.** Install the clock spring electrical connector, and tighten the four retaining screws to the specified torque.

Task Completed

14. Align the marks on the steering wheel and the steering shaft, and install the steering wheel on the shaft.

Are the marks on the steering wheel and steering shaft aligned? ☐ Yes ☐ No

Instructor check ______________________________

15. Install the steering wheel retaining nut, and tighten this nut to the specified torque.

Specified steering wheel retaining nut torque __________

Actual steering wheel retaining nut torque __________

16. Install the air bag wiring retainer in the steering wheel. ☐

17. Hold the air bag deployment module near the top of the steering wheel, and connect the air bag module connector. ☐

18. Install the air bag deployment module in the top of the steering wheel, and tighten the retaining screws. ☐

19. Reconnect the negative battery cable. ☐

20. Reset the clock and radio. ☐

21. Turn on the ignition switch and start the vehicle. Check the operation of the air bag system warning light.

Explain the air bag system warning light operation that indicates normal air bag system operation.

____

____

____

Instructor's Response ______________________________

____

____

JOB SHEET 28

Name ______________________________ Date ______________

REMOVE AND REPLACE STEERING COLUMN

Upon completion of this job sheet, you should be able to remove and replace a steering column.

ASE Correlation

This job sheet is related to ASE Automotive Suspension and Steering Task: *Inspect and replace steering shaft U-joint(s), flexible coupling(s), collapsible columns, and steering wheels (includes steering wheels with air bags and/or other steering wheel-mounted controls and components).*

Tools and Materials

Seat cover
Torque wrench

Describe the Vehicle Being Worked On:

Year __________ Make ____________________ Model ______________
VIN ____________________ Engine type and size ______________

Procedure

Task Completed

1. Disconnect the negative battery cable. If the vehicle is equipped with an air bag, wait for the time period specified by the vehicle manufacturer.

   Specified waiting period prior to servicing air bag components __________

   Explain why it is necessary to disconnect the battery before removing the steering column.

   ____

   ____

   ____

2. Install a seat cover on the front seat. ☐
3. Place the front wheels in the straight-ahead position and remove the ignition key from the switch to lock the steering column.

   Are the front wheels straight? ☐ Yes ☐ No

   Is the ignition key removed?

   Instructor check ______________________________

4. Remove the cover under the steering column and remove the lower finish panel if necessary. ☐
5. Disconnect all wiring connectors from the steering column. ☐
6. If the vehicle has a column-mounted gearshift lever, disconnect the gearshift linkage at the lower end of the steering column. ☐
7. Remove the retaining bolt or bolts in the lower universal joint or flexible coupling. ☐

Task Completed

☐ **8.** Remove the steering-column-to-instrument-panel mounting bolts.

☐ **9.** Carefully remove the steering column from the vehicle. Be careful not to damage the upholstery or paint.

☐ **10.** Install the steering column under the instrument panel and insert the steering shaft into the lower universal joint.

11. Install the steering column to instrument panel mounting bolts. Be sure the steering column is properly positioned, and tighten these bolts to the specified torque.

Specified torque, steering column mounting bolts ___________

Actual torque, steering column mounting bolts ___________

12. Install the retaining bolt or bolts in the lower universal joint or flexible coupling, and tighten the bolt(s) to the specified torque.

Specified torque, lower U-joint retaining bolt(s)___________

Actual torque, lower U-joint retaining bolt(s) ___________

☐ **13.** Connect the gearshift linkage if the vehicle has a column-mounted gearshift.

☐ **14.** Connect all the wiring harness connectors to the steering column connectors.

☐ **15.** Install the steering column cover and the lower finish panel.

☐ **16.** Reconnect the negative battery cable.

☐ **17.** Road test the vehicle, and check for proper steering column operation.

Steering column operation: ☐ Satisfactory ☐ Unsatisfactory

Instructor's Response ____

____

____

JOB SHEET 29

Name ______________________________ Date ______________

DIAGNOSE, REMOVE, AND REPLACE IDLER ARM

Upon completion of this job sheet, you should be able to diagnose, remove, and replace an idler arm.

ASE Correlation

This job sheet is related to ASE Automotive Suspension and Steering Task: *Inspect, adjust (where applicable), and replace idler arm and mountings.*

Tools and Materials

Pull scale
Dial indicator
Torque wrench
Grease gun

Describe the Vehicle Being Worked On:

Year __________ Make ______________ Model ____________
VIN ________________ Engine type and size ______________

Procedure

Task Completed

1. Attach the magnetic base of a dial indicator to the frame near the idler arm. ☐
2. Position the dial indicator stem against the upper side on the outer end of the idler arm. Preload the dial indicator stem, and zero the dial. ☐
3. Use a pull scale to apply 25 lbs. (11.34 kg) of force downward and then upward on the idler arm. Observe the total vertical idler arm movement on the dial indicator. If this vertical movement exceeds the vehicle manufacturer's specifications, replace the idler arm.

   Specified vertical idler arm movement __________

   Actual vertical idler arm movement __________

   Recommended idler arm service __________

   Explain the effect of idler arm wear on steering quality.

   ____

   ____

   ____

4. Remove the idler arm to center link cotter pin and nut. ☐
5. Remove the center link from the idler arm. ☐
6. Remove the idler arm bracket mounting bolts and remove the idler arm. ☐

Task Completed

7. If the idler arm has a steel bushing, thread the bracket into the idler arm bushing until the specified clearance is obtained between the center of the lower bracket bolt hole and the upper idler arm surface.

   Specified distance from center of lower bracket hole to upper idler arm surface

   ____

   Actual distance from center of lower bracket hole to upper idler arm surface

   ____

8. Install the idler arm bracket to frame bolts and tighten the bolts to the specified torque. Be sure that lock washers are installed on the bolts.

   Specified idler arm retaining bolt torque ____________

   Actual idler arm retaining bolt torque ____________

9. Install the center link into the idler arm and tighten the mounting nut to the specified torque. Install the cotter pin in the nut.

   Specified center link to idler arm retaining nut torque ____________

   Actual center link to idler arm retaining nut torque ____________

☐ 10. If the idler arm has a grease fitting, lubricate as required.

Instructor's Response ____

____

____

JOB SHEET 30

Name ______________________________ Date ______________

REMOVE AND REPLACE OUTER TIE-ROD END, PARALLELOGRAM STEERING LINKAGE

Upon completion of this job sheet, you should be able to remove and replace outer tie-rod ends in a parallelogram steering linkage.

ASE Correlation

This job sheet is related to ASE Automotive Suspension and Steering Task: *Inspect, replace, and adjust tie-rods, tie-rod sleeves, clamps, and tie-rod ends (sockets).*

Tools and Materials

Tie-rod puller

Describe the Vehicle Being Worked On:

Year ____________ Make ______________ Model ______________
VIN ______________________ Engine type and size ______________

Procedure

1. Raise the vehicle on a lift with the tires supported on the lift. If the vehicle has rubber-encapsulated tie-rod ends, be sure the front wheels are straight ahead.
2. Loosen the nut on the tie-rod sleeve bolt that retains the sleeve to the tie-rod ends.
3. Measure from the top center of the tie-rod end ball stud to the outer end of the tie-rod sleeve, and record the measurement.

   Distance from the center of the tie-rod end ball stud to the outer end of the tie-rod sleeve __________
4. Remove the cotter pin from the tie-rod end retaining nut.
5. Loosen the tie-rod end retaining nut.
6. Use a tie-rod end puller to loosen the tie-rod end taper in the steering arm.
7. Remove the tie-rod end retaining nut and remove the tie-rod end from the steering arm.
8. Count the number of turns required to thread the tie-rod end out of the tie-rod sleeve.

   Number of turns required to remove the tie-rod end from the tie-rod sleeve

   ____

   Describe the effect of worn, loose outer tie-rod ends on steering quality.

   ____

   ____

9. Install the new tie-rod end in the tie-rod sleeve using the same number of turns recorded in step 8.

10. Push the tie-rod end ball stud fully into the steering arm opening. Only the threads on the tie-rod end ball stud should be visible above the steering arm surface.

Is the taper on the tie-rod end ball stud visible above the steering arm surface?
☐ Yes ☐ No

If the answer to this question is yes, state the necessary repairs required to correct this problem.

____

____

Instructor check ________________________________

11. With the tie-rod end ball stud pushed fully upward into the steering arm, measure the distance from the center of the ball stud to the outer end of the tie-rod sleeve.

Distance from the center of the tie-rod end ball stud to the outer end of the tie-rod sleeve

____

12. If this distance is not the same as recorded in step 3, remove the tie-rod end ball stud from the steering arm, and rotate the tie-rod end until this distance is the same as recorded in step 3.

13. Install the tie-rod end ball stud retaining nut, and tighten this nut to the specified torque.

Specified ball stud nut torque ____________

Actual ball stud nut torque ____________

WARNING: Never loosen a tie-rod end ball stud nut to align the openings in the ball stud and nut to allow cotter pin installation. This action may cause the nut to loosen during operation of the vehicle, and this will result in excessive steering free play. Complete loss of steering control will occur if the nut comes off the tie-rod end ball stud, and this may cause a collision.

14. Install a new cotter pin through the tie-rod end ball stud and nut openings, and bend the cotter pin legs separately around this nut.

15. Tighten the nut on the outer tie-rod sleeve clamp bolt to the specified torque. Be sure the slot in the tie-rod sleeve is positioned away from the opening in the clamp.

16. Measure the front wheel toe with a toe bar.

Specified front wheel toe ____________

Actual front wheel toe ____________

Explain the type of front tire wear that is caused by improper front wheel toe.

____

Instructor's Response ______________________________

____

____

Power Steering Pump Diagnosis and Service

10

Upon completion and review of this chapter, you should be able to:

- Check power steering belt condition and adjust belt tension.
- Diagnose power steering belt problems.
- Check power steering fluid level and add fluid as required.
- Drain and flush power steering system.
- Bleed air from power steering system.
- Perform power steering pump pressure test.
- Check power steering pump fluid leaks.
- Remove and replace power steering pumps, and inspect pump mounts.
- Remove and replace power steering pump pulleys.
- Remove and replace power steering pump integral reservoirs.
- Remove, replace, and check flow control valve and pressure relief valve.
- Remove, replace, and check power steering pump rotating components.
- Remove and replace power steering pump seals and O-rings.
- Check, remove, and replace power steering lines.

Power steering pump diagnosis and service is very important to maintain vehicle safety and driver convenience. If a badly worn power steering pump belt is undetected, the belt may suddenly break while the driver is completing a turn. Under this condition, steering effort is greatly increased, and this may result in a collision. Therefore, the power steering belt should be inspected at regular intervals. A loose power steering belt may cause hard steering intermittently, and this condition requires increased driver steering effort, which reduces driver comfort and convenience. Therefore, one of the first checks when diagnosing a power steering system is to inspect the belt condition and test the belt tension.

POWER STEERING PUMP BELT SERVICE

Checking Belt Condition and Tension

Power steering belt condition and tension are extremely important for satisfactory power steering pump operation. A loose belt causes low pump pressure and hard steering. The steering wheel may jerk and surge during a turn if the power steering pump belt is loose. A loose, dry, or worn belt may cause squealing and chirping noises, especially during engine acceleration and cornering.

The power steering pump belt should be checked for tension, cracks, oil-soaking, worn or glazed edges, tears, and splits (Figure 10-1). If any of these conditions are present, belt replacement is necessary.

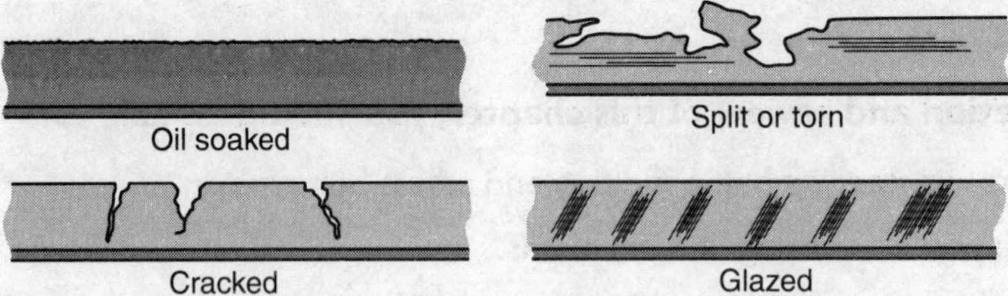

FIGURE 10-1 *Defective belt conditions.*

Since the friction surfaces are on the sides of a **V-type belt**, wear occurs in this area. If the belt edges are worn, the belt may be rubbing on the bottom of the pulley. This condition requires belt replacement. Belt tension may be checked by measuring the belt deflection. Press on the belt with the engine stopped to measure the belt deflection, which should be 1/2 inch per foot of free span. The belt tension may be checked with a **belt tension gauge** placed over the belt (Figure 10-2). The tension on the gauge should equal the vehicle manufacturer's specifications.

If the belt requires tightening, follow this procedure:

> **CAUTION:** Do not pry on the pump reservoir with a pry bar. This action may damage the reservoir.

1. Loosen the power steering pump bracket or tension adjusting bolt.
2. Loosen the power steering pump mounting bolts.
3. Check the bracket and pump mounting bolts for wear. If these bolts or bolt openings in the bracket or pump housing are worn, replacement is necessary.

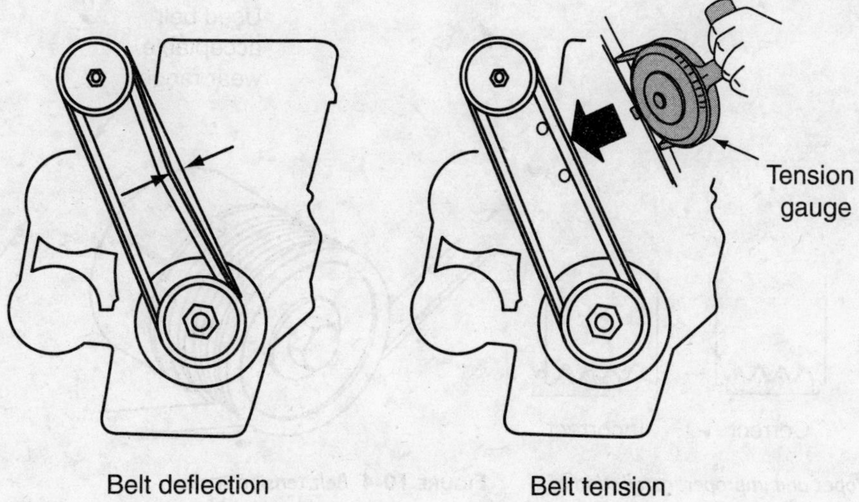

FIGURE 10-2 *Methods of checking belt tension.*

4. Pry against the pump ear and hub with a pry bar to tighten the belt. Some pump brackets have a 1/2-inch square opening in which a breaker bar may be installed to move the pump and tighten the belt.
5. Hold the pump in the position described in step 4, and tighten the bracket or tension adjusting bolt.
6. Recheck the belt tension with the tension gauge. If the belt does not have the specified tension, repeat steps 1 through 5.
7. Tighten the tension adjusting bolt and the mounting bolts to the manufacturer's specified torque.

Some power steering pumps have a **ribbed V-belt** (or **serpentine belt**). Many ribbed V-belts have an automatic tensioning pulley; therefore, a tension adjustment is not required. The ribbed V-belt should be checked to make sure it is installed properly on each pulley in the belt drive system (Figure 10-3). The tension on a ribbed V-belt may be checked with a belt tension gauge in the same way as the tension on a V-belt.

Many ribbed V-belts have a spring-loaded tensioner pulley that automatically maintains belt tension. As the belt wears or stretches, the spring moves the tensioner pulley to maintain the belt tension. Some of these tensioners have a belt length scale that indicates the new belt range and used belt range (Figure 10-4). If the indicator on the tensioner is out of the used belt length range, belt replacement is required. Many belt tensioners have a 1/2-inch drive opening in which a ratchet or flex handle may be installed to move the tensioner pulley off the belt during belt replacement (Figure 10-5).

Belt pulleys must be properly aligned to minimize belt wear. The edges of the pulleys must be in line when a straightedge is placed on the pulleys (Figure 10-6). Repeated belt failure may be caused by a misaligned power steering pump pulley or by extremely high pump pressure caused by a sticking pressure relief valve or a continual or intermittent restriction in the high pressure hose.

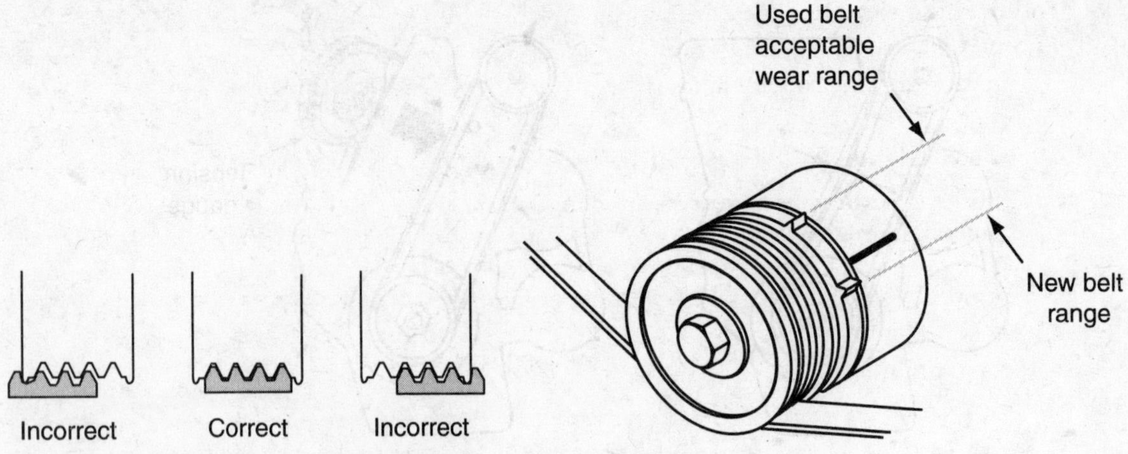

FIGURE 10-3 *Proper and improper installation of ribbed V-belt on a pulley.*

FIGURE 10-4 *Belt tension scale.*

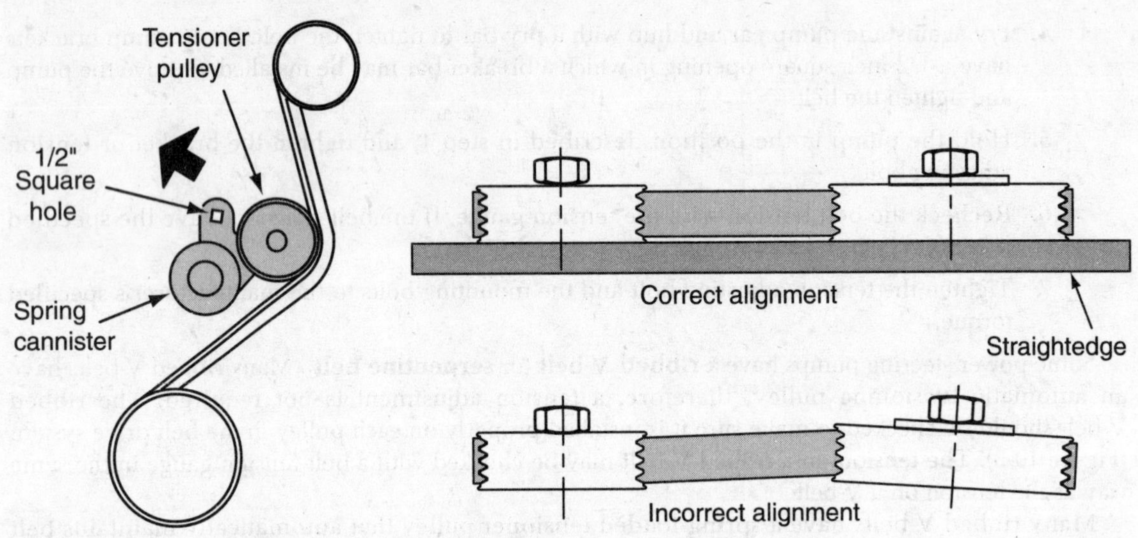

FIGURE 10-5 *One-half inch drive opening in the tensioner pulley.*

FIGURE 10-6 *Checking pulley alignment.*

POWER STEERING PUMP FLUID SERVICE

Fluid Level Inspection

Most car manufacturers recommend power steering fluid or automatic transmission fluid in power steering systems. Always use the type of power steering fluid recommended in the vehicle manufacturer's service manual. If the power steering fluid level is low, **steering effort** is increased and may be erratic. A low fluid level may cause a growling noise in the power steering pump. Some car manufacturers now recommend checking the power steering pump fluid level with the fluid at an ambient temperature of 176°F (80°C).

Follow these steps to check the power steering fluid level:

1. With the engine idling at 1,000 rpm or less, turn the steering wheel slowly and completely in each direction several times to boost the fluid temperature (Figure 10-7).
2. If the vehicle has a remote power steering fluid reservoir, check for foaming in the reservoir, which indicates low fluid level or air in the system.
3. Observe the fluid level in the remote reservoir. This level should be at the hot full mark. Shut off the engine, and remove dirt from the neck of the reservoir with a shop towel. If the power steering pump has an integral reservoir, the level should be at the hot level on the dipstick. When an external reservoir is used, the dipstick is located in the external reservoir (Figure 10-8).

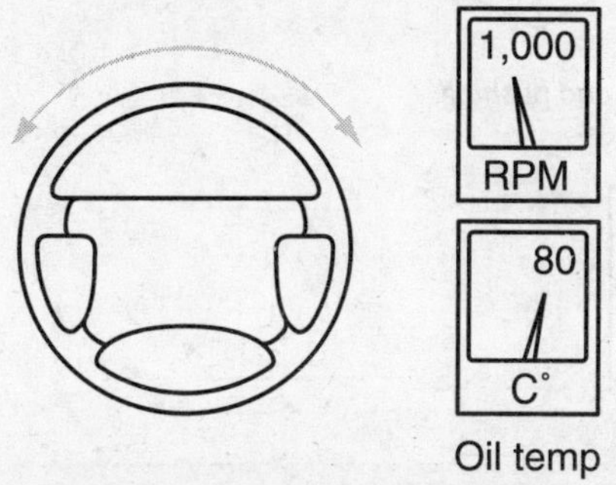

FIGURE 10-7 *Boosting fluid temperature.*

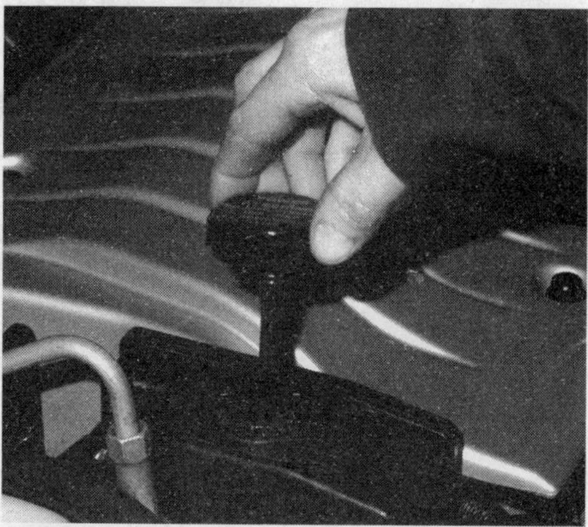

FIGURE 10-8 *Power steering pump dipstick.*

4. Pour the required amount of the car manufacturer's recommended power steering fluid into the reservoir to bring the fluid level to the hot full mark on the reservoir or dipstick with the engine idling.

Power Steering System Draining and Flushing

If the power steering fluid is contaminated with moisture, dirt, or metal particles, the system must be drained and new fluid installed.

Follow these steps to drain and flush the power steering system:

1. Lift the front of the vehicle with a floor jack and install safety stands under the suspension. Lower the vehicle onto the safety stands, and remove the floor jack.
2. Remove the return hose from the **remote reservoir** that is connected to the steering gear. Place a plug on the reservoir outlet and position the return hose in an empty drain pan (Figure 10-9).
3. With the engine idling, turn the steering wheel fully in each direction and stop the engine (Figure 10-10).
4. Fill the reservoir to the hot full mark with the manufacturer's recommended fluid.

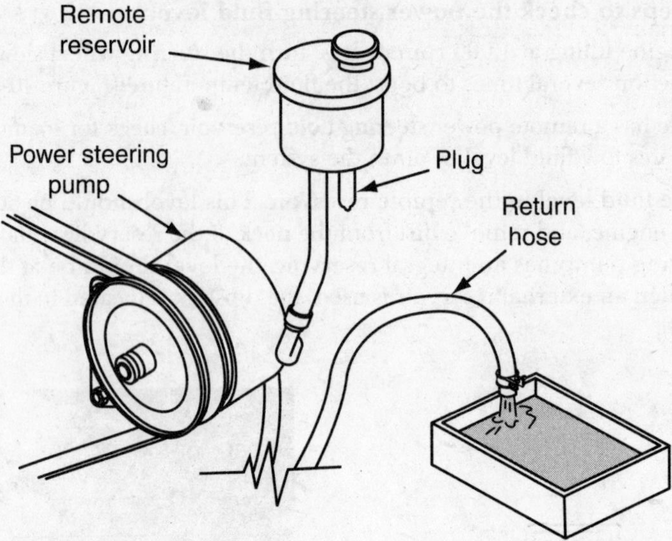

FIGURE 10-9 *Return hose installed in drain pan for power steering draining and flushing.*

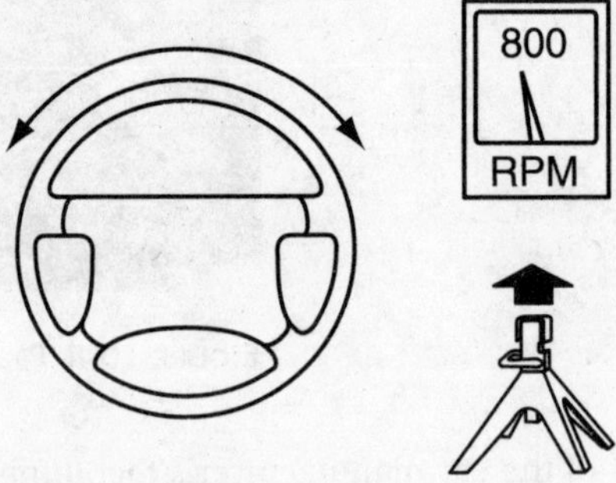

FIGURE 10-10 *Draining fluid from the power steering system.*

5. Start the engine, and run the engine at 1,000 rpm while observing the return hose in the drain pan. When fluid begins to discharge from the return hose, shut the engine off.
6. Repeat steps 4 and 5 until there is no air in the fluid discharging from the return hose.
7. Remove the plug from the reservoir and reconnect the return hose. Bleed the power steering system.

Bleeding Air from the Power Steering System

When air is present in the power steering fluid, a growling noise may be heard in the pump and steering effort may be increased or erratic.

When a power steering system has been drained and refilled, follow this procedure to remove air from the system:

1. Fill the power steering pump reservoir as outlined previously.

2. With the engine running at 1,000 rpm, turn the steering wheel fully in each direction three or four times (Figure 10-11). Each time the steering wheel is turned fully to the right or left, hold it there for 2 to 3 seconds before turning it in the other direction.
3. Check for foaming of the fluid in the reservoir. When foaming is present, repeat steps 1 and 2.
4. Check the fluid level with the engine running and be sure it is at the hot full mark. Shut off the engine, and make sure the fluid level does not increase more than 0.020 in. (5 mm) (Figure 10-12).

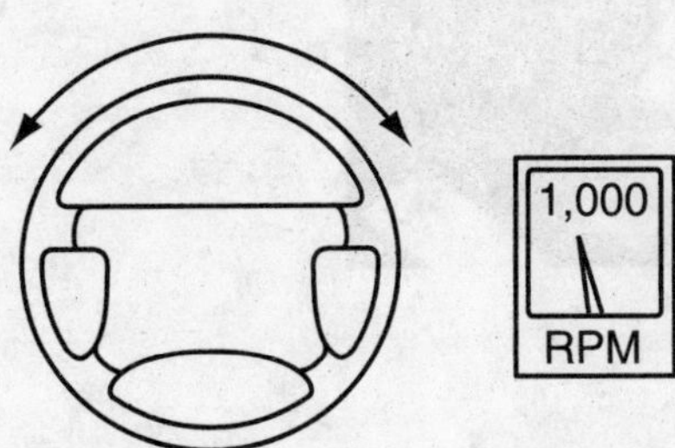

FIGURE 10-11 *Turning the steering wheel slowly to bleed air from the power steering system.*

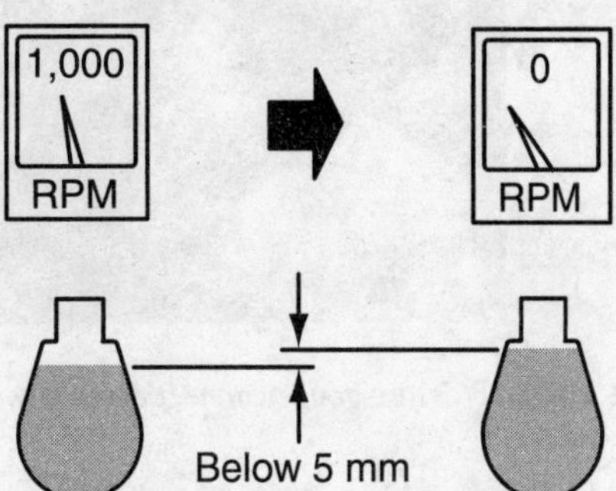

FIGURE 10-12 *Power steering fluid level after bleeding.*

POWER STEERING PUMP DIAGNOSIS

Power Steering Pump Pressure Test

Since there are some variations in power steering pump pressure test procedures and pressure specifications, the vehicle manufacturer's test procedures and specifications must be used. If the power steering pump pressure is low, steering effort is increased. Erratic power steering pump pressure causes variations in steering effort, and the steering wheel may jerk as it is turned. Since a power steering pump will never develop the specified pressure if the belt is slipping, the belt tension must be checked and adjusted, if necessary, prior to a pump pressure test.

The following is a typical power steering pressure test procedure:

1. With the engine stopped, disconnect the pressure line from the power steering pump and connect the gauge side of the **pressure gauge** to the pump outlet fitting. Connect the valve side of the gauge to the pressure line (Figure 10-13).
2. Start the engine, and turn the steering wheel fully in each direction two or three times to bleed air from the system (Figure 10-14). Be sure the fluid level is correct and the fluid temperature is at least 176°F (80°C). A thermometer may be inserted in the pump reservoir fluid to measure the fluid temperature.

WARNING: During the power steering pump pressure test with the engine idling, close the pressure gauge valve for no more than 10 seconds because excessive pump pressure may cause power steering hoses to rupture, resulting in personal injury.

FIGURE 10-13 *Pressure gauge connection to power steering pump.*

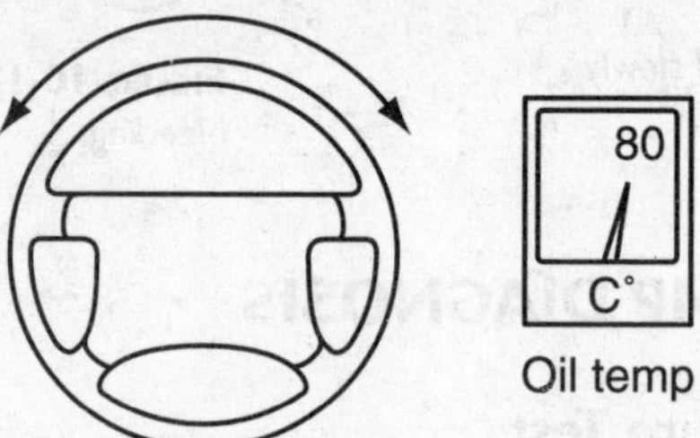

FIGURE 10-14 *Bleeding air from the power steering pump system and checking fluid temperature.*

WARNING: Do not allow the fluid to become too hot during the power steering pump pressure test. Excessively high fluid temperature reduces pump pressure. Wear protective gloves, and always shut the engine off before disconnecting gauge fittings, because the hot fluid may cause burns.

3. With the engine idling, close the pressure gauge valve for no more than 10 seconds, and observe the pressure gauge reading (Figure 10-15). Turn the pressure gauge valve to the fully open position. If the pressure gauge reading does not equal the vehicle manufacturer's specifications, repair or replace the power steering pump.
4. Inspect the power steering pump pressure with the engine running at 1,000 rpm and 3,000 rpm, and record the pressure difference between the two readings (Figure 10-16). If the pressure difference between the pressure readings at 1,000 rpm and 3,000 rpm does not equal the vehicle manufacturer's specifications, repair or replace the **flow control valve** in the power steering pump.
5. With the engine running, turn the steering wheel fully in one direction and observe the steering pump pressure while holding the steering wheel in this position (Figure 10-17). If the pump pressure is less than the vehicle manufacturer's specifications, the steering gear housing has an internal leak and should be repaired or replaced.

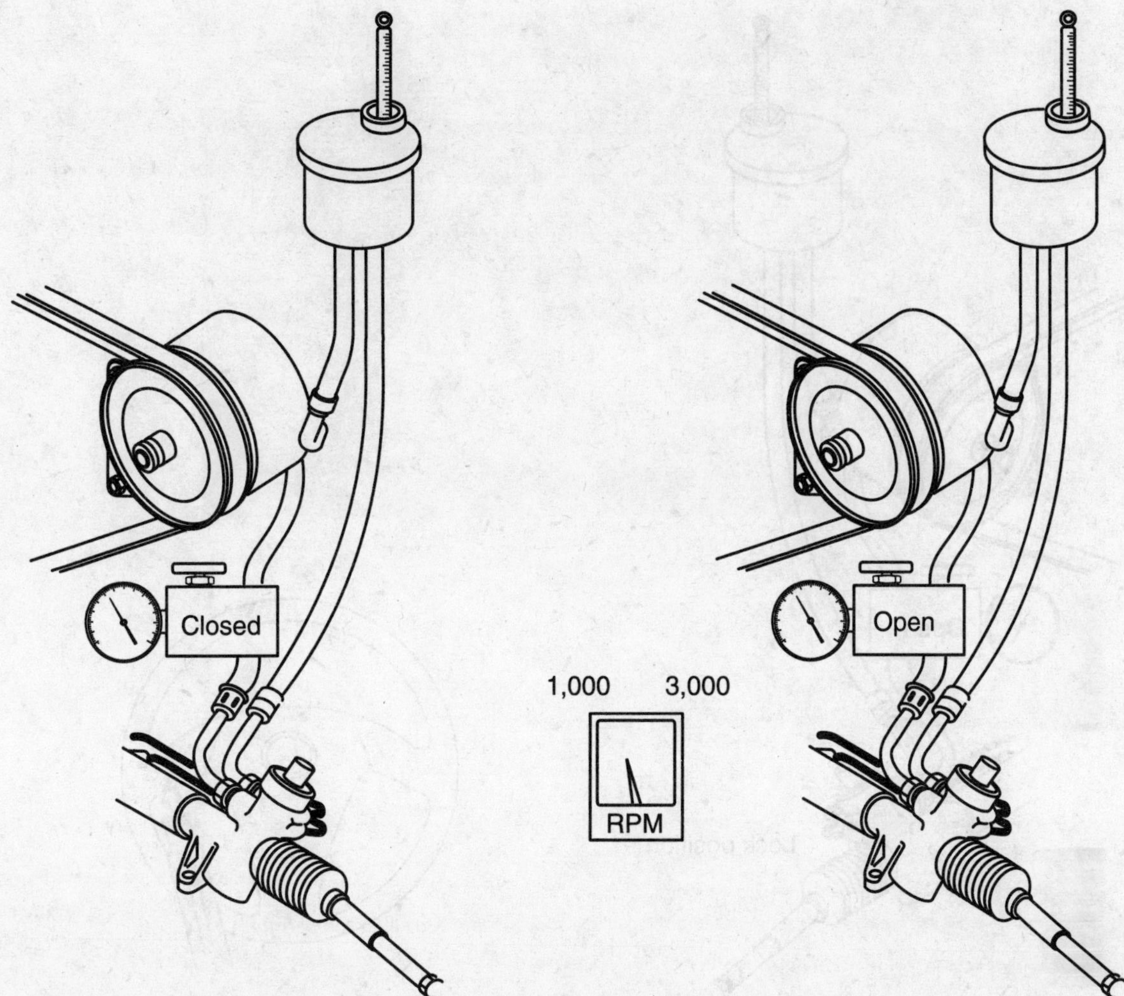

FIGURE 10-15 *Power steering pump pressure test with pressure gauge valve closed.*

FIGURE 10-16 *Power steering pump pressure test at 1,000 and 3,000 rpm.*

6. Be sure the front tire pressure is correct and center the steering wheel with the engine idling. Connect a spring scale to the steering wheel and measure the steering effort in both directions (Figure 10-18). If the power steering pump pressure is satisfactory and the steering effort is more than the vehicle manufacturer's specifications, the power steering gear should be repaired. Photo Sequence 10 shows a typical procedure for pressure testing a power steering pump.

Power Steering Pump Oil Leak Diagnosis

The possible sources of power steering pump oil leaks are the driveshaft seal, reservoir O-ring seal, high-pressure outlet fitting, and the dipstick cap. If leaks occur at any of the seal locations, seal replacement is necessary. When a leak is present at the high-pressure outlet fitting, tighten this fitting to the specified torque (Figure 10-19). If the leak still occurs, replace the O-ring seal on the fitting and retighten the fitting.

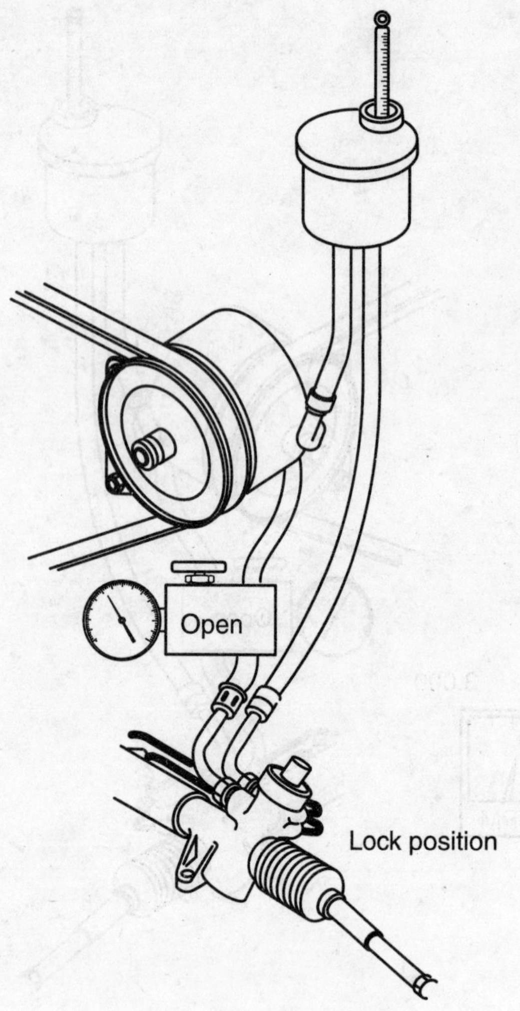

FIGURE 10-17 *Power steering pump pressure test with the front wheels turned fully in one direction.*

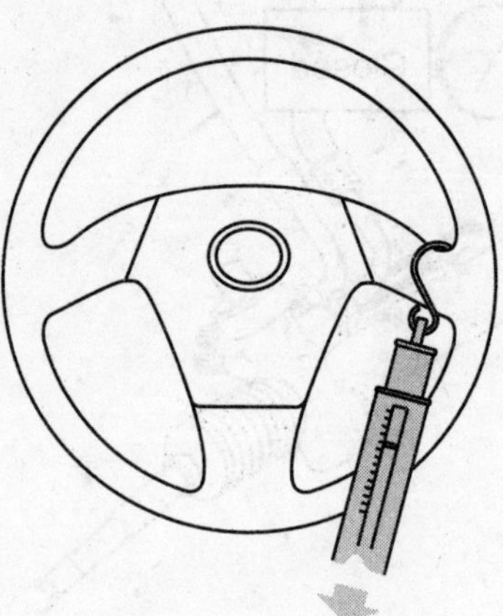

FIGURE 10-18 *Steering effort measurement.*

POWER STEERING PUMP SERVICE

Power Steering Pump Replacement

> **WARNING:** If the vehicle has been driven recently, the pump, hoses, and fluid could be extremely hot. Use caution when handling components to avoid burns.

If a growling noise is present in the power steering pump after the fluid level is checked and air has been bled from the system, the pump bearings or other components are defective and pump replacement or repair is required. When the power steering pump pressure is lower than specified, pump replacement or repair is necessary.

PHOTO SEQUENCE 10
TYPICAL PROCEDURE FOR PRESSURE TESTING A POWER STEERING PUMP

P10-1 *Connect the pressure gauge to the power steering pump.*

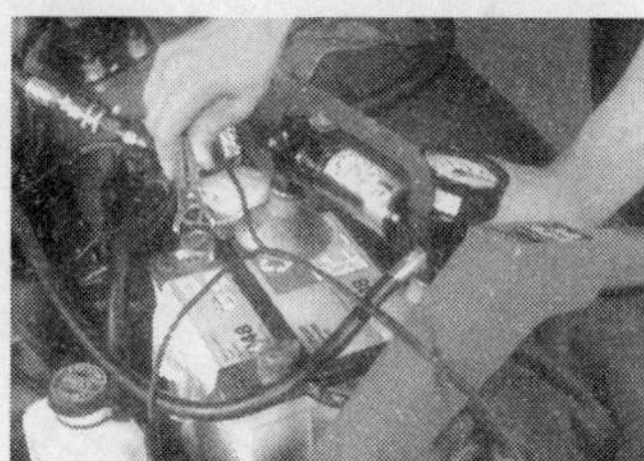

P10-2 *Connect a tachometer to the ignition system.*

P10-3 *Look up the vehicle manufacturer's specified power steering pump pressure in the service manual.*

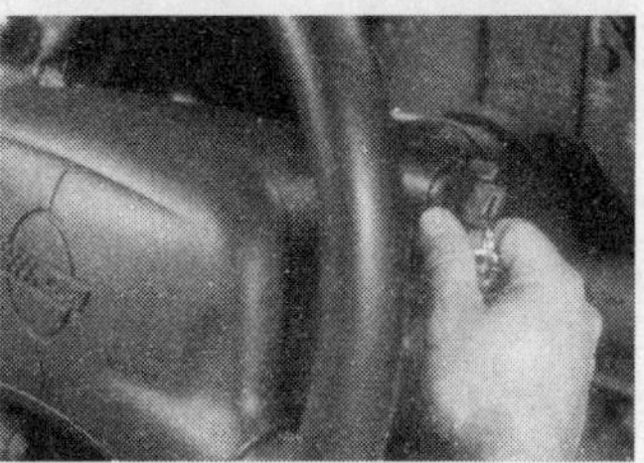

P10-4 *Start the engine, and turn the steering wheel from lock to lock three times to bleed air from the system and heat the power steering fluid.*

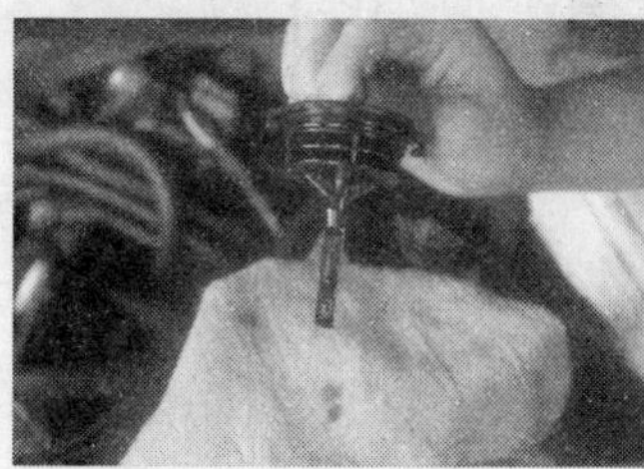

P10-5 *Check the power steering fluid level, and add fluid as required.*

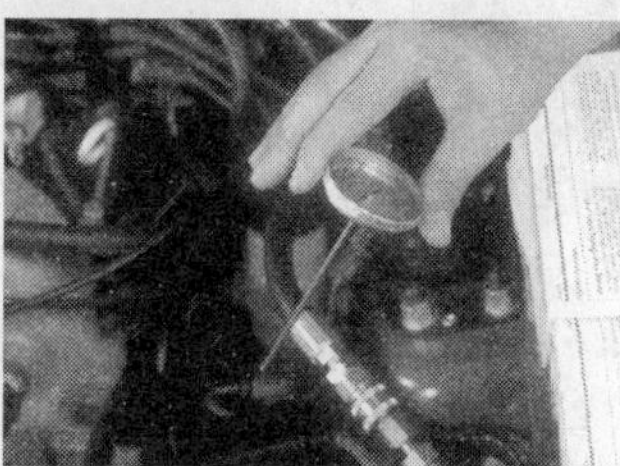

P10-6 *Place a thermometer in the power steering fluid reservoir. Be sure the fluid temperature is at least 176°F (80°C).*

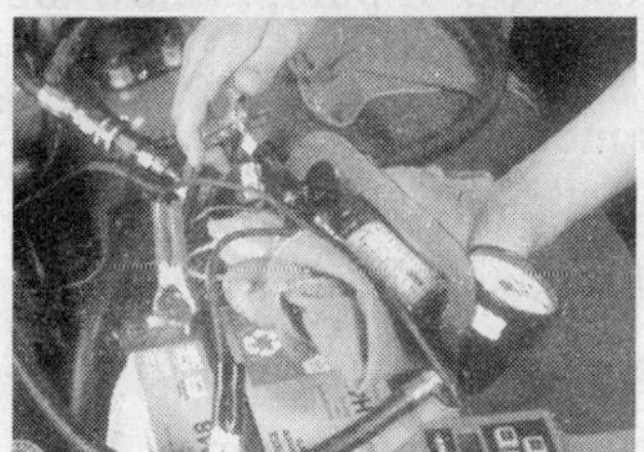

P10-7 *With the engine idling, close the pressure gauge valve for no more than 10 seconds. Observe and record the pressure gauge reading.*

P10-8 *Check and record the power steering pump pressure at 1,000 rpm.*

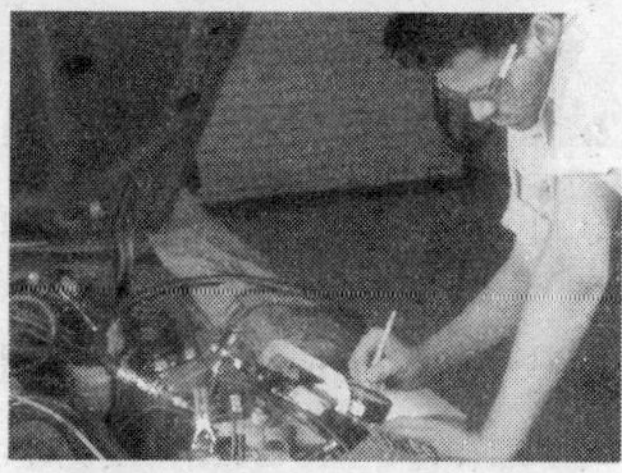

P10-9 *Check and record the power steering pump pressure at 3,000 rpm.*

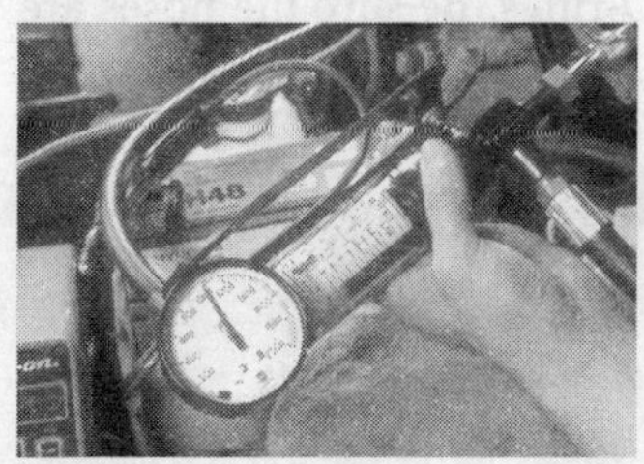

P10-10 *Check and record the power steering pump pressure with the steering wheel turned fully in one direction and the engine idling.*

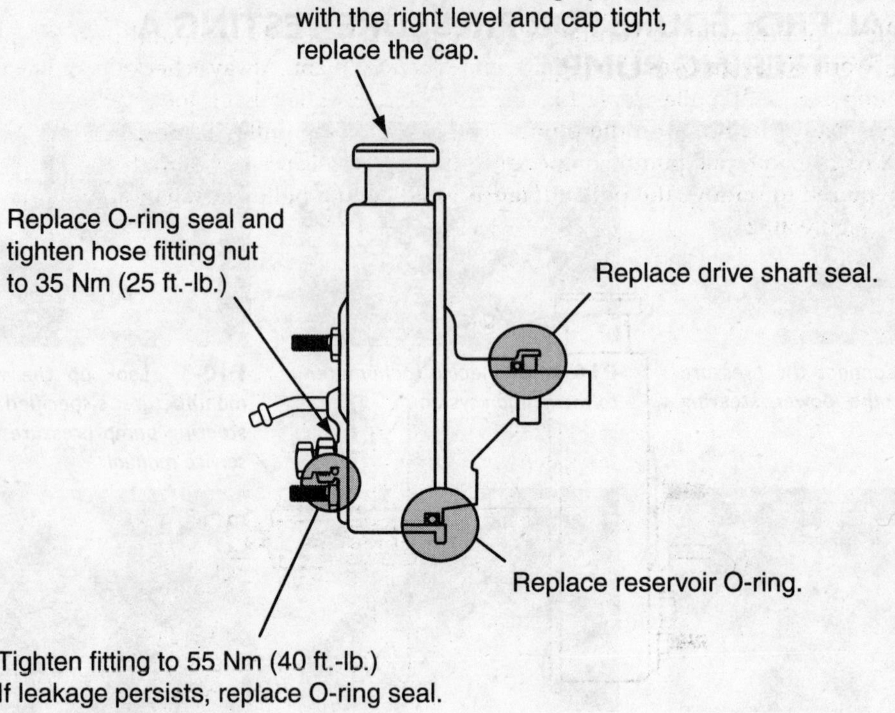

FIGURE 10-19 *Power steering pump oil leak diagnosis.*

To replace the power steering pump, proceed as follows:

1. Disconnect the power steering return hose from the remote reservoir or pump. Allow the fluid to drain from this hose into a drain pan. Discard the used fluid.
2. Loosen the bracket or belt tension adjusting bolt and the pump mounting bolt.
3. Loosen the belt tension until the belt can be removed. On some cars, it is necessary to lift the vehicle on a hoist and gain access to the power steering pump from underneath the vehicle.
4. Remove the hoses from the pump and cap the pump fittings and hoses.
5. Remove the belt tension adjusting bolt and the mounting bolt, and remove the pump.
6. Check the pump mounting bolts and bolt holes for wear. Worn bolts must be replaced. If the bolt mounting holes in the pump are worn, pump replacement is necessary.
7. Reverse steps 1 through 5 to install the power steering pump. Tighten the belt as described previously, and tighten the pump mounting and bracket bolts to the manufacturer's specifications. If O-rings are used on the pressure hose, replace the O-rings. Be sure the hoses are not contacting the exhaust manifold, catalytic converter, or exhaust pipe during or after pump replacement.
8. Fill the pump reservoir with the manufacturer's recommended power steering fluid and bleed air from the power steering system as described earlier.

Power Steering Pump Pulley Replacement

If the pulley wobbles while it is rotating, the pulley is probably bent, and pulley replacement is necessary. Worn pulley grooves also require pulley replacement. Always check the pulley for cracks. If this condition is present, pulley replacement is essential. A pulley that is loose on the pump shaft must be replaced. Never hammer on the pump drive shaft during pulley removal or replacement. This action will damage internal pump components. If the pulley is pressed onto the pump shaft, a special puller is required to remove the pulley (Figure 10-20), and a pulley installation tool is used to install the pulley (Figure 10-21).

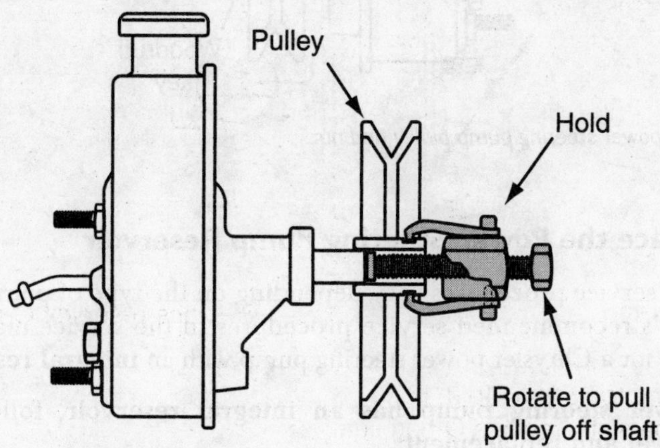

FIGURE 10-20 *Press-on power steering pump pulley removal.*

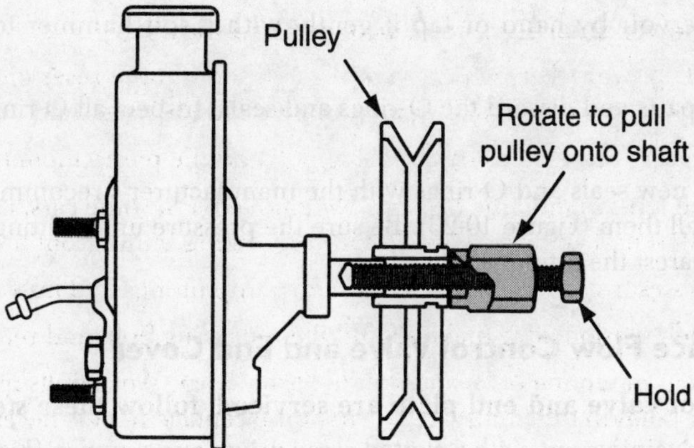

FIGURE 10-21 *Press-on power steering pump pulley installation.*

If the power steering pump pulley is retained with a nut, mount the pump in a vise. Always tighten the vise on one of the pump mounting bolt surfaces. Do not tighten the vise with excessive force. Use a special holding tool to keep the pulley from turning, and loosen the pulley nut with a box end wrench (Figure 10-22). Remove the nut, pulley, and **woodruff key**. Inspect the pulley, shaft, and woodruff key for wear. Be sure the key slots in the shaft and pulley are not worn. Replace all worn components.

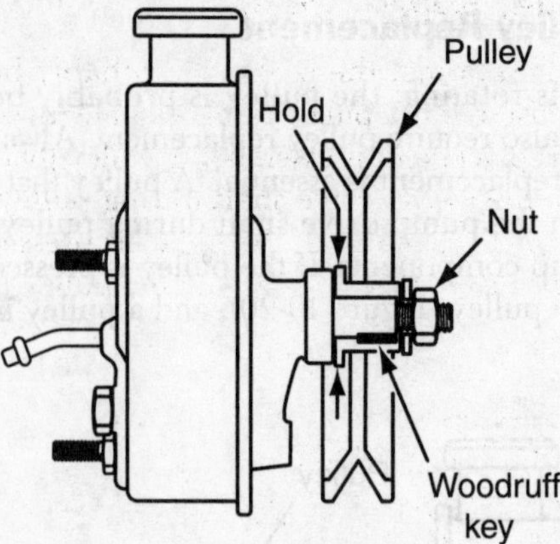

FIGURE 10-22 *Removing power steering pump pulley and nut.*

Remove and Replace the Power Steering Pump Reservoir

Power steering pump service procedures vary depending on the type of pump. Always follow the vehicle manufacturer's recommended service procedures in the service manual. The following service procedures are for a Chrysler power steering pump with an **integral reservoir**.

When the power steering pump has an integral reservoir, follow these steps for reservoir removal and replacement:

1. Remove the filler cap and drain the oil from the reservoir.
2. Remove the two studs and the fitting from the rear of the reservoir.
3. Rock the reservoir by hand or tap it gently with a soft hammer to remove it from the housing.
4. Clean all the parts and discard the O-rings and seals. Inspect all O-ring and seal surfaces for damage.
5. Lubricate the new seals and O-rings with the manufacturer's recommended power steering fluid and install them (Figure 10-23). Be sure the pressure union fitting O-ring is installed in the groove nearest the fitting hex head.

Remove and Replace Flow Control Valve and End Cover

When the flow control valve and end plate are serviced, follow these steps:

1. Remove the retaining ring with a slotted screwdriver and a punch (Figure 10-24).
2. Remove the flow control valve, end cover, spring, and magnet. Inspect the flow control valve for burrs. Remove minor burrs with **crocus cloth** and clean the flow control valve in solvent. Damaged or worn flow control valves must be replaced. Inspect the end cover sealing surface for damage. Inspect the pump driveshaft for corrosion and damage. Remove corrosion with crocus cloth (Figure 10-25). Clean the magnet with a shop towel.
3. Clean all parts and lubricate the end cover with power steering fluid.
4. Install the end cover, retaining ring, and related components.

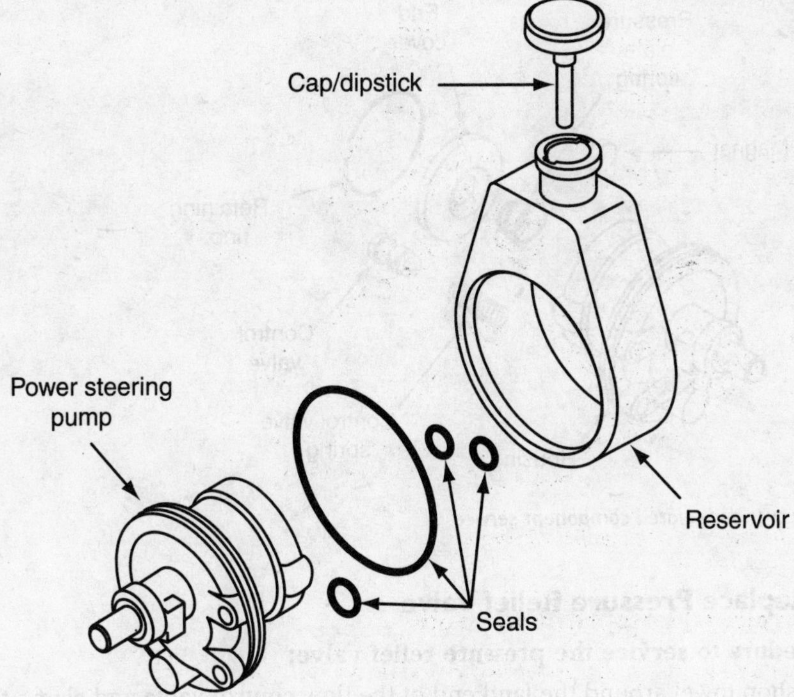

FIGURE 10-23 *Integral power steering pump reservoir seal and O-ring.*

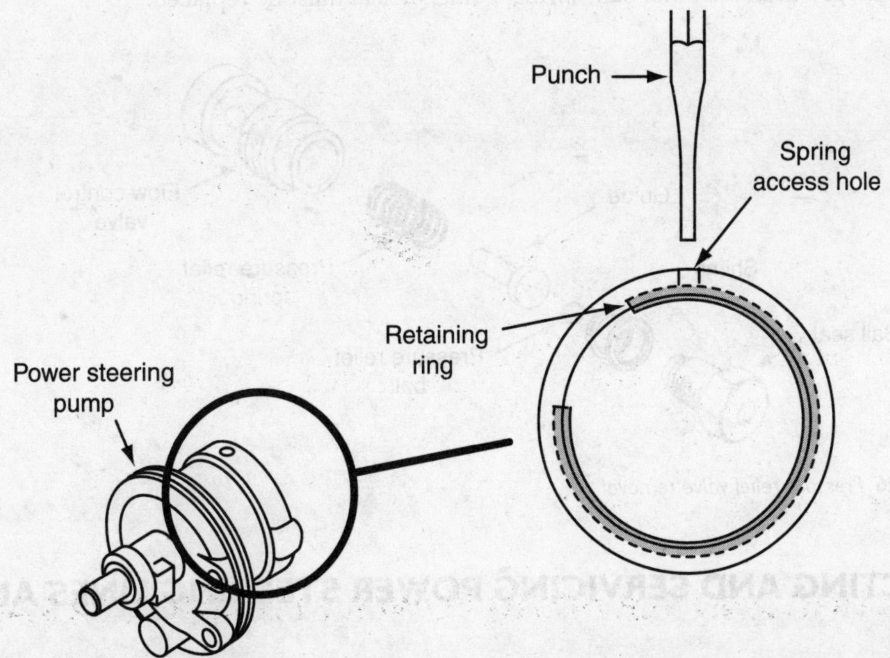

FIGURE 10-24 *Retaining ring removal.*

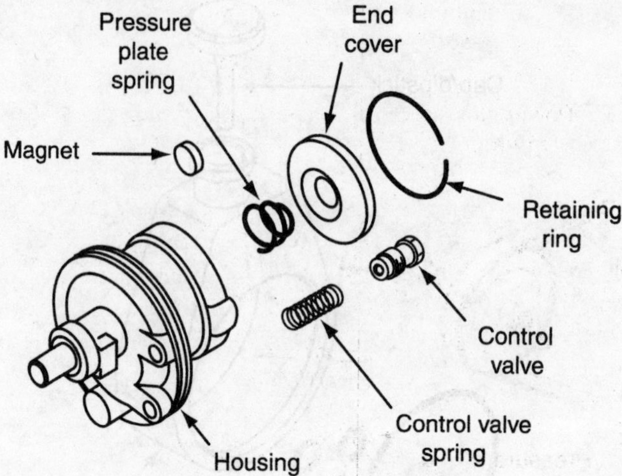

FIGURE 10-25 *End cover and related component service.*

Remove and Replace Pressure Relief Valve

Follow this procedure to service the pressure relief valve:

1. Wrap a shop towel around the land end of the flow control valve and clamp this end in a soft-jawed vise. Be very careful not to mark valve lands.
2. Remove the hex-head ball seat (Figure 10-26). Clean the components in solvent. A worn or damaged pressure relief ball, spring, guide, or seat must be replaced.

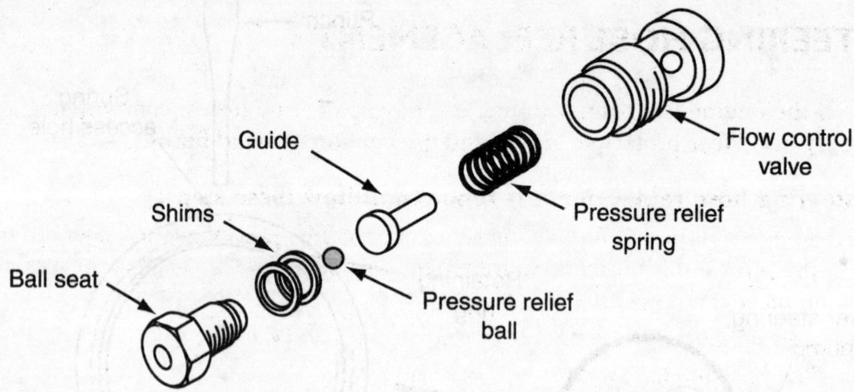

FIGURE 10-26 *Pressure relief valve removal.*

INSPECTING AND SERVICING POWER STEERING LINES AND HOSES

Power steering lines should be inspected for leaks, dents, sharp bends, cracks, and contact with other components. Lines and hoses must not rub against other components. This action could wear a hole in

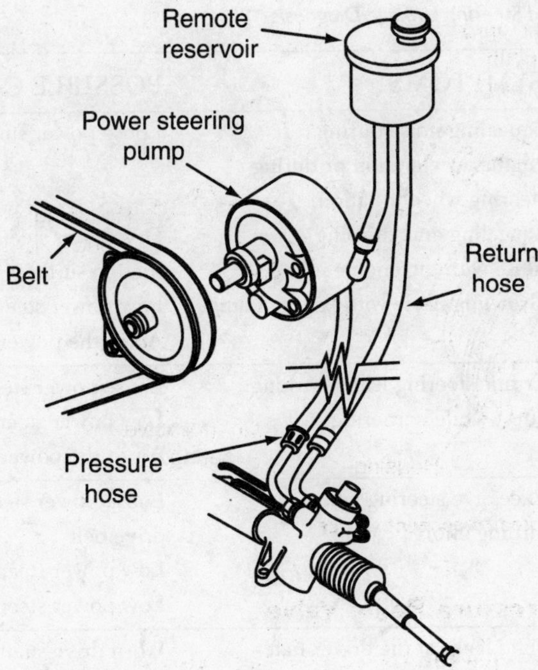

FIGURE 10-27 *Power steering hoses and lines.*

the line or hose. Many high-pressure power steering lines are made from high-pressure steel-braided hose with molded steel fittings on each end (Figure 10-27).

POWER STEERING HOSE REPLACEMENT

WARNING: If the engine has been running, the power steering hoses, components, and fluid may be extremely hot. Wear protective gloves and use caution to avoid burns.

When power steering hose replacement is required, follow these steps:

1. With the engine stopped, remove the return hose at the power steering gear, and allow the fluid to drain from this hose into a drain pan. On some cars, the vehicle must be lifted on a hoist to replace the power steering hoses.
2. Loosen and remove all hose fittings from the pump and steering gear.
3. Remove all hose-to-chassis clips.
4. Remove the hoses from the chassis and cap the pump and steering gear fittings.
5. If O-rings are used on the hose ends, install new O-rings.
6. Reverse steps 1 through 4 to install the power steering hoses. Tighten all fittings to the manufacturer's specified torque. Be sure all hose-to-chassis clips are in place. Do not position hoses where they rub on other components.
7. Fill the pump reservoir to the full mark with the manufacturer's recommended fluid. Bleed air from the power steering system, as mentioned previously in this chapter. Check the fluid level in the reservoir and add fluid as required.

Refer to Table 10-1 for steering colum and steering linkage diagnosis

TABLE 10-1 *Steering Column and Steering Linkage Diagnosis*

PROBLEM	SYMPTOMS	POSSIBLE CAUSES
Underhood noise	Squealing noise during engine acceleration or during steering wheel rotation	Loose power steering pump belt
	Squealing and chirping noise with the engine idling	Dry power steering pump belt friction surfaces
	Growling noise with engine idling	Low power steering fluid level Air in the power steering fluid
Improper steering wheel turning effort	Erratic steering wheel turning effort while cornering	Loose power steering pump belt Low power steering fluid level Air in the power steering fluid
	Excessive steering wheel turning effort	Loose power steering pump drive belt Low power steering fluid level Low power steering pump pressure
Power steering pump fluid leaks	Fluid leaks at the drive shaft behind the pulley	Worn drive shaft seal
	Fluid leaks between the reservoir and the housing	Leaking reservoir O-ring
	Fluid leaks at the back of the reservoir	Leaking O-ring seals or pump-to-line fittings
Rapid power steering belt wear	Power steering belt wears out prematurely	Misalignment of power steering pump pulley, and other pulleys driven by the same belt
		Excessive power steering belt tension

CASE STUDY

The owner of a Dodge Magnum with a 5.7 L turbocharged engine requested a price on a power steering gear replacement. The service writer questioned the owner regarding the reason for the steering gear replacement, and discovered that the problem was intermit-tent hard steering. Further discussion with the owner also revealed that the car had been taken to another automotive service center, and the owner was informed that her car required a steering gear replacement. The owner was now looking for a second opinion.

The technician road tested the vehicle and found no indication of hard steering. The owner was asked about the exact driving conditions when the hard steering was experienced, and the answer to this question provided the solution to the problem. The owner indicated that the hard steering was usually experienced while cornering and always on a rainy day. Once this information was revealed, the technician suspected a problem with the power steering belt, because a wet belt slips more easily. A check of the power steering belt indicated the belt was oil soaked from engine oil leaks and was also slightly loose. The power steering belt was replaced and adjusted, and the owner was informed that the engine oil leaks should be corrected or the belt would become oil soaked again.

A short while later, after a rain, the owner brought the car to the shop to have the engine oil leaks repaired. The owner reported that the belt corrected the hard steering problem. In this situation, a brief discussion about the customer's complaint led to accurate diagnosis of the problem, and because of this accurate diagnosis, the shop gained a steady customer.

SERVICE TIP

- During rainy or wet conditions, a loose power steering belt, which causes low power steering pump pressure and increased steering effort, may be more noticeable because the belt becomes wet and slips more easily.

REVIEW QUESTIONS

1. While discussing power steering belt adjustment:
Technician A says the tension on a power steering pump V-belt should be checked with a tension gauge. *Technician B* says that some ribbed V-belts have an automatic tensioning pulley that eliminates the need for tension adjustments.
Who is correct?
A. A only
B. B only
C. Both A and B
D. Neither A nor B

2. While discussing power steering belt adjustment:
Technician A says that a power steering pump V-belt should be tightened with a pry bar installed against the pump reservoir. *Technician B* says a loose power steering pump V-belt may cause the steering wheel to jerk while turning.
Who is correct?
A. A only
B. B only
C. Both A and B
D. Neither A nor B

3. While discussing power steering fluid level checking:
Technician A says foaming in the remote reservoir may indicate air in the power steering system. *Technician B* says many car manufacturers recommend checking the power steering fluid level with the fluid warmed up.
Who is correct?
A. A only
B. B only
C. Both A and B
D. Neither A nor B

4. While discussing the steering pump pressure test:
Technician A says the pressure gauge and valve should be connected in the power steering pump return hose to check pump pressure. *Technician B* says the pressure gauge valve should be closed for 30 seconds during the power steering pump pressure test.
Who is correct?
A. A only
B. B only
C. Both A and B
D. Neither A nor B

5. While discussing power steering system draining, flushing, refilling, and bleeding: *Technician A* says the return hose from the remote reservoir should be disconnected at the remote reservoir to drain the fluid. *Technician B* says the return hose should be loosened at the remote reservoir with the engine running to bleed air from the power steering system.
Who is correct?
A. A only **C.** Both A and B
B. B only **D.** Neither A nor B

6. A vehicle experiences excessive, erratic steering effort. The most likely cause of this problem is:
A. Underinflated and worn front tires.
B. Power steering pump V-belt pump bottomed in the pulley.
C. Worn power steering pump mountings.
D. Continual low power steering pump pressure.

7. A power steering system has the specified pressure with the pressure gauge valve closed or with the pressure gauge valve open and the engine running at 1,000 and 3,000 rpm. The power steering pump pressure is lower than specified with the front wheels turned fully in either direction. The cause of this problem could be:
A. A defective steering gear.
B. A stuck flow control valve.
C. A stuck pressure relief valve.
D. Worn pump vanes and cam ring.

8. All of these statements about power steering pump pulley replacement are true EXCEPT:
A. If the pulley is retained with a nut, a woodruff key prevents pulley rotation on the shaft.
B. If the pulley is pressed onto the shaft, a special puller must be used to remove the pulley.
C. If the pulley is pressed onto the shaft, a soft hammer may be used to drive the pulley onto the shaft when reinstalling the pulley.
D. If the pulley is misaligned with the engine running, the power steering pump mountings may be worn.

9. A power steering pump has the specified pressure with the pressure gauge valve closed. However, with this valve open, the pump does not have the specified pressure difference between the pressure readings at 1,000 and 3,000 rpm. The cause of this problem could be:
A. A sticking pressure relief valve.
B. A sticking flow control valve.
C. A slipping pump belt.
D. A misaligned pump pulley.

10. A power steering pump has repeated belt failures. The power steering pump V-belt tension and pulley alignment are satisfactory, and the V-belt is not bottomed in the pulley. The most likely cause of this problem is:
A. A pressure relief valve sticking open.
B. Worn pulley friction surfaces on the pulley.
C. Worn thrust plate in the power steering pump.
D. An intermittent restriction in the high-pressure hose.

CHALLENGE QUESTIONS

1. A vehicle has intermittent excessive steering effort.
Technician A says inspect the fluid because it probably has air in it. *Technician B* says inspect the belt because it is probably slipping.
Who is correct?
A. A only **C.** Both A and B
B. B only **D.** Neither A nor B

2. While discussing power steering pump leaks:
Technician A says leaks at the driveshaft seal will leave a wet and oily pump pulley backside. *Technician B* says leaks at the driveshaft seal may leave oil on the hood pad above the pump.
Who is correct?
A. A only **C.** Both A and B
B. B only **D.** Neither A nor B

3. A vehicle has continual excessive steering effort, but there is no noise and the fluid level in the reservoir is correct.
Technician A says the cause of the problem could be a stuck flow control valve. *Technician B* says the cause of the problem could be air in the power steering fluid.
Who is correct?
A. A only **C.** Both A and B
B. B only **D.** Neither A nor B

4. There is air in the power steering fluid. To correct this problem, you should:
A. With the engine running, crack the pressure line at the pump to release trapped air.
B. With the engine running, turn the steering wheel full left and right.
C. With the engine running, drain all fluid from the system and refill.
D. With the engine stopped, raise wheels and remove the return hose from the gear. Turn the steering wheel full left and right. Refill the reservoir and replace the return hose.

5. All of the following are true EXCEPT:
A. A loose belt may cause the steering wheel to jerk.
B. If V-belt edges are worn, the belt may be stretched or the wrong width.
C. An oil-soaked V-belt may slip only in wet weather.
D. When air is in the fluid, the fluid will never reach operating temperature.

JOB SHEET 31

Name ______________________________ Date ______________

DRAINING AND FLUSHING POWER STEERING SYSTEM

Upon completion of this job sheet, you should be able to drain and flush a power steering system.

ASE Correlation

This job sheet is related to ASE Automotive Suspension and Steering Task: *Flush, fill, and bleed power steering systems.*

Tools and Materials

Drain pan
Specified type of power steering fluid
Floor jack
Safety stands

Describe the Vehicle Being Worked On:

Year __________ Make ______________________ Model ______________
VIN ______________________ Engine type and size ______________

Procedure

Task Completed

1. Describe the steering problems and noises that occur when there is air in the power steering system.
____
____
____
____
2. Lift the front of the vehicle with a floor jack and install safety stands under the suspension. Lower the vehicle onto the safety stands, and remove the floor jack. ☐
3. Remove the return hose from the remote reservoir that is connected to the steering gear. Place a plug on the reservoir outlet and position the return hose in an empty drain pan. ☐
4. With the engine idling, turn the steering wheel fully in each direction and stop the engine. ☐
5. Fill the reservoir to the hot full mark with the manufacturer's recommended fluid.

   Specified type of power steering fluid ______________________

   Power steering reservoir filled to the specified level with the proper power steering fluid? ☐ Yes ☐ No

   Instructor check ____

Task Completed

☐ **6.** Start the engine, and run the engine at 1,000 rpm while observing the return hose in the drain pan. When fluid begins to discharge from the return hose, shut the engine off.

7. Repeat steps 4, 5, and 6 until there is no air in the fluid discharging from the return hose.

Have steps 4, 5, and 6 been repeated? ☐ Yes ☐ No

Instructor check ______________________

8. Remove the plug from the reservoir and reconnect the return hose.

Is the return hose connected and tightened? ☐ Yes ☐ No

Instructor check.______________________

☐ **9.** Fill the power steering pump reservoir to the specified level.

10. With the engine running at 1,000 rpm, turn the steering wheel fully in each direction three or four times. Each time the steering wheel is turned fully to the right or left, hold it there for 2 to 3 seconds before turning it in the other direction.

Number of times the steering wheel was turned fully in each direction ________

11. Check for foaming of the fluid in the reservoir. When foaming is present, repeat steps 8 and 9.

Is foaming present in the power steering pump reservoir? ☐ Yes ☐ No

Have steps 8 and 9 been repeated? ☐ Yes ☐ No

Instructor check ______________________

☐ **12.** Check the fluid level and be sure it is at the hot full mark.

☐ **13.** Raise vehicle with a floor jack, remove safety stands, and lower vehicle.

14. Explain how you know that all the air has been bled from the power steering system.

____

____

____

____

Instructor's Response ______________________

____

____

JOB SHEET 32

Name ______________________________ Date ______________

TESTING POWER STEERING PUMP PRESSURE

Upon completion of this job sheet, you should be able to test power steering pump pressure.

ASE Correlation

This job sheet is related to ASE Automotive Suspension and Steering Task: *Perform power steering pump pressure and flow tests; determine needed repairs.*

Tools and Materials

Specified type of power steering fluid
Power steering pressure test gauge
Thermometer

Describe the Vehicle Being Worked On:

Year __________ Make ________________ Model ______________
VIN ____________________ Engine type and size ______________

Procedure

Task Completed

1. With the engine stopped, disconnect the pressure line from the power steering pump. ☐
2. Connect the gauge side of the pressure gauge to the pump outlet fitting. Connect the valve side of the gauge to the pressure line. ☐

   Is the power steering pressure gauge properly connected? ☐ Yes ☐ No

   Are all power steering gauge fittings tightened to the specified torque?
   ☐ Yes ☐ No
3. Start the engine and turn the steering wheel fully in each direction two or three times to bleed air from the system. ☐
4. Install a thermometer in the pump reservoir fluid to measure the fluid temperature. Be sure the fluid level is correct and the fluid temperature is at least 176°F (80°C).

   Is the power steering fluid at the specified level? ☐ Yes ☐ No

   Is the power steering fluid at the proper temperature? ☐ Yes ☐ No

   Instructor check ______________________________

WARNING: During the power steering pump pressure test with the engine idling, close the pressure gauge valve for no more than 10 seconds because excessive pump pressure may cause power steering hoses to rupture, resulting in personal injury.

WARNING: Do not allow the fluid to become too hot during the power steering pump pressure test. Excessively high fluid temperature reduces pump pressure. Wear protective gloves, and always shut the engine off before disconnecting gauge fittings, because the hot fluid may cause burns.

Task Completed

5. With the engine idling, close the pressure gauge valve for no more than 10 seconds, and observe the pressure gauge reading. Turn the pressure gauge valve to the fully open position. If the pressure gauge reading does not equal the vehicle manufacturer's specifications, repair or replace the power steering pump.

   Specified power steering pump pressure with pressure gauge valve closed ______

   Actual power steering pump pressure with the pressure gauge valve closed ______

   Recommended power steering pump service.

   ______

6. Check the power steering pump pressure with the engine running at 1,000 rpm and 3,000 rpm. Record the pressure difference between the two readings.

   Specified power steering pump pressure at 1,000 rpm ______

   Specified power steering pump pressure at 3,000 rpm ______

   Actual power steering pump pressure at 1,000 rpm ______

   Actual power steering pump pressure at 3,000 rpm ______

   Recommended power steering pump service. ______

   ______

7. With the engine running, turn the steering wheel fully in one direction. Observe the steering pump pressure while holding the steering wheel in this position.

   Specified power steering pump pressure with the steering wheel turned fully in one direction ______

   Actual power steering pump pressure with the steering wheel turned fully in one direction ______

   Recommended power steering service.

   ______

8. Be sure the front tire pressure is correct, and center the steering wheel with the engine idling. Connect a spring scale to the steering wheel, and measure the steering effort in both directions.

   Specified force required to turn the steering wheel to the right ______

   Specified force required to turn the steering wheel to the left ______

   Actual force required to turn the steering wheel to the right ______

   Actual force required to turn the steering wheel to the left ______

   List all the required power steering service and explain the reasons why this service is necessary.

   ______

   ______

   ______

Instructor's Response ______

______

______

JOB SHEET 33

Name ______________________________ Date ______________________

MEASURE AND ADJUST POWER STEERING BELT TENSION AND ALIGNMENT

Upon completion of this job sheet, you should be able to measure and adjust power steering belt tension and alignment.

ASE Correlation

This job sheet is related to ASE Automotive Suspension and Steering Task: *Inspect, adjust tension and alignment, and replace power steering pump belt(s).*

Tools and Materials

Belt tension gauge
Pry bar

Describe the Vehicle Being Worked On:

Year ____________ Make ____________________ Model ______________
VIN ______________________ Engine type and size ______________________

Procedure

Task Completed

1. Describe the power steering problems and noises that occur when the power steering pump belt is loose.
____
____
____
____

2. Inspect the power steering belt for fraying, oil soaking, wear on friction surfaces, cracks, glazing, and splits. ☐
   Belt condition: ☐ Satisfactory ☐ Unsatisfactory

3. With the engine stopped, press on the belt at the longest belt span to measure the belt deflection which should be 1/2 inch per foot of free span. ☐
   Length of belt span where belt deflection is measured ____________________
   Amount of belt deflection ____________________
   Belt tension: ☐ Satisfactory ☐ Unsatisfactory

4. Install a belt tension gauge over the belt in the center of the longest span to measure the belt tension.
   Specified belt tension ____________________
   Actual belt tension ____________________

Task Completed

☐ **5.** Loosen the power steering pump bracket or tension adjusting bolt.

☐ **6.** Loosen the power steering pump mounting bolts.

☐ **7.** Remove the power steering belt.

☐ **8.** Check the bracket and pump mounting bolts for wear.

Power steering pump mounting bolt holes and bolt condition:
☐ Satisfactory ☐ Unsatisfactory

Power steering pump bracket and bracket bolt condition:
☐ Satisfactory ☐ Unsatisfactory

List the required power steering pump and bracket service and explain the reasons for your diagnosis.

____

____

____

____

☐ **9.** Install the new power steering pump belt over all the pulleys.

☐ **10.** Pry against the pump ear and hub with a pry bar to tighten the belt. Some pump brackets have a 1/2-inch square opening in which a breaker bar may be installed to move the pump and tighten the belt.

☐ **11.** Hold the pump in the position described in step 9 and tighten the bracket or tension adjusting bolt.

12. Recheck the belt tension with the tension gauge.

Specified power steering belt tension ______________

Actual power steering pump belt tension ______________

13. Tighten the tension adjusting bolt and the mounting bolts to the manufacturer's specified torque.

Specified power steering pump mounting bolt torque ______________

Actual power steering pump mounting bolt torque ______________

Specified power steering pump bracket or tension adjusting bolt torque ______________

Actual power steering pump bracket or tension adjusting bolt torque ______________

14. Check alignment of the power steering pump pulley in relation to the other pulleys surrounded by the power steering belt.

Power steering pump pulley alignment: ☐ Satisfactory ☐ Unsatisfactory

Explain the service required to align the power steering pump pulley with other related pulleys and give the reasons for your diagnosis.

____

____

Instructor's Response ____

____

____

RECIRCULATING BALL STEERING GEAR DIAGNOSIS AND SERVICE

11

Upon completion and review of this chapter, you should be able to:

- Diagnose power recirculating ball steering gear problems.
- Remove and replace power recirculating ball steering gears.
- Adjust worm shaft thrust bearing preload in power recirculating ball steering gears.
- Adjust sector lash in power recirculating ball steering gears.
- Diagnose and repair oil leaks in power recirculating ball steering gears.
- Disassemble, repair, and reassemble power recirculating ball steering gears.

Steering gear and linkage inspection and service is extremely important to maintain vehicle safety! For example, if a vehicle has excessive steering wheel free play, this problem should be diagnosed and corrected as soon as possible. If the excessive steering wheel free play is caused by a loose sector shaft lash or worm bearing preload adjustments, follow the proper adjustment procedure to correct the problem. However, if this problem is caused by worn tie-rod ends or loose steering gear mounting bolts, these conditions create a safety hazard. If a worn tie-rod end becomes disconnected, or the steering gear becomes disconnected from the frame, the result is a complete loss of steering control. This condition may cause a collision resulting in vehicle damage and/or personal injury.

POWER RECIRCULATING BALL STEERING GEAR DIAGNOSIS

If the steering gear is noisy, check these items:

1. Loose pitman shaft lash adjustment–may cause a rattling noise when the steering wheel is turned.
2. Cut or worn dampener O-ring on the valve spool–when this defect is present, a squawking noise is heard during a turn.
3. Loose steering gear mounting bolts.
4. Loose or worn flexible coupling or steering shaft U-joints.

A hissing noise from the power steering gear is normal if the steering wheel is at the end of its travel, or when the steering wheel is rotated with the vehicle standing still. If the steering wheel jerks or surges when the steering wheel is turned with the engine running, check the power steering pump belt condition and tension. When excessive kickback is felt on the steering wheel, check the poppet valve in the steering gear.

When the steering is loose, check these defects:

1. Air in the power steering system. To remove the air, fill the power steering pump reservoir and rotate the steering wheel fully in each direction several times.
2. Loose pitman lash adjustment.
3. Loose worm shaft thrust bearing preload adjustment.
4. Worn flexible coupling or universal joint.
5. Loose steering gear mounting bolts.
6. Worn steering gears.

A complaint of hard steering while parking could be caused by one of these defects:

1. Loose or worn power steering pump belt.
2. Low oil level in the power steering pump.
3. Excessively tight steering gear adjustments.
4. Defective power steering pump with low-pressure output.
5. Restricted power steering hoses.
6. Defects in the steering gear such as:
   (a) Pressure loss in the cylinder because of scored cylinder, worn piston ring, or damaged backup O-ring.
   (b) Excessively loose spool in the valve body.
   (c) Defective or improperly installed gear check poppet valve.

POWER RECIRCULATING BALL STEERING GEAR REPLACEMENT

When the power steering gear is replaced, proceed as follows:

1. Disconnect the hoses from the steering gear and cap the lines and fittings to prevent dirt from entering the system.
2. Remove the pitman arm nut and washer and mark the pitman arm in relation to the shaft with a center punch. Use a puller to remove the pitman arm.
3. Disconnect the steering shaft from the worn shaft.
4. Remove the steering gear mounting bolts and remove the steering gear from the chassis (Figure 11-1).

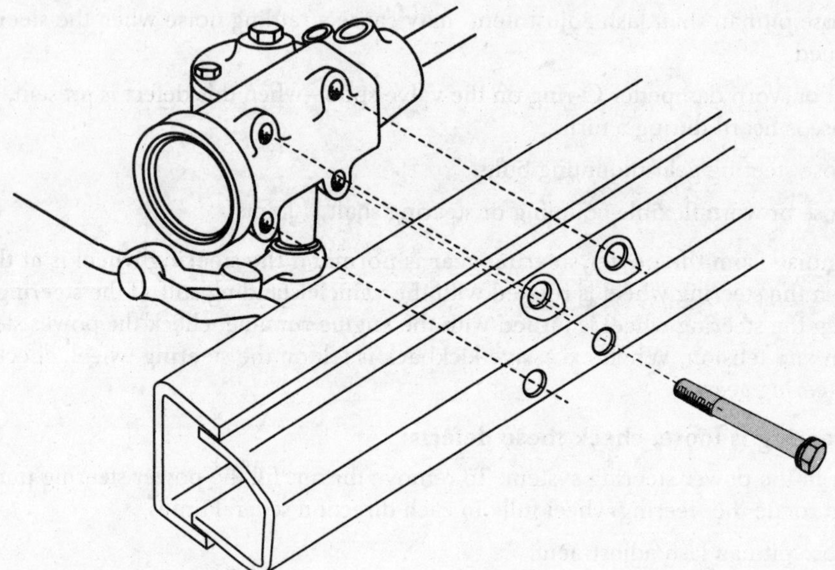

FIGURE 11-1 *Removing steering gear from the chassis.*

5. Reverse steps 1 through 4 to install the steering gear. All bolts must be tightened to the specified torque. Be sure the pitman arm is installed in the original position.

CAUTION: Hard steel bolts can be used for steering gear mounting. Ribs on the bolt head indicate the bolt hardness. Harder bolts have five, six, or seven ribs on the bolt heads. Never substitute softer steel bolts in place of the harder original bolts, because these softer bolts may break, allowing the steering gear box to detach from the frame and resulting in a loss of steering control.

CAUTION: When the steering linkage is disconnected from the gear, do not turn the steering wheel hard against the stops. This action may damage internal steering gear components.

WARNING: The steering gear is often mounted near the exhaust system components. Wear protective gloves when working on a steering gear located near the exhaust system.

POWER RECIRCULATING BALL STEERING GEAR ADJUSTMENTS

Worm Shaft Thrust Bearing Preload Adjustment

A loose worm shaft thrust **bearing preload** adjustment or sector lash adjustment causes excessive **steering wheel free play** and steering wander. The power recirculating ball steering gear adjustment procedures may vary depending on the vehicle make and model year. Always follow the vehicle manufacturer's recommended procedure in the service manual.

When the worm shaft thrust bearing preload adjustment is performed, use this procedure:

1. Remove the worm shaft thrust bearing adjuster plug locknut with a hammer and brass punch (Figure 11-2).

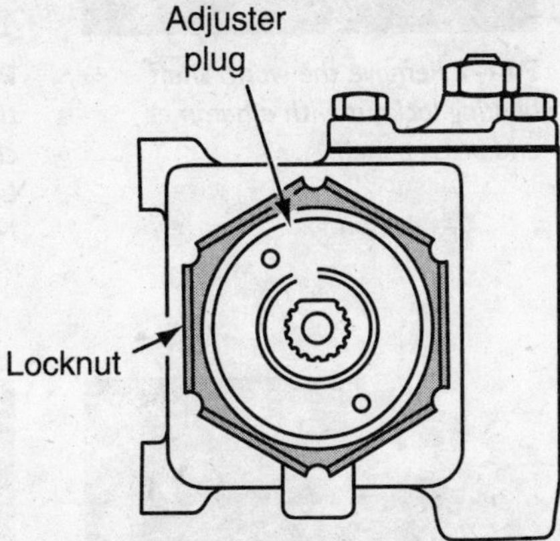

FIGURE 11-2 *Removing worm shaft thrust bearing adjuster plug locknut.*

2. Turn this adjuster plug inward, or clockwise, until it bottoms, and tighten the plug to 20 ft.-lb. (27 Nm).
3. Place an index mark on the steering gear housing next to one of the holes in the adjuster plug (Figure 11-3).
4. Measure 0.50 in. (13 mm) counterclockwise from the index mark, and place a second index mark at this position (Figure 11-4).
5. Rotate the adjuster plug counterclockwise until the hole in the adjuster plug is aligned with the second index mark placed on the housing (Figure 11-5).
6. Install and tighten the adjuster plug locknut to the specified torque.

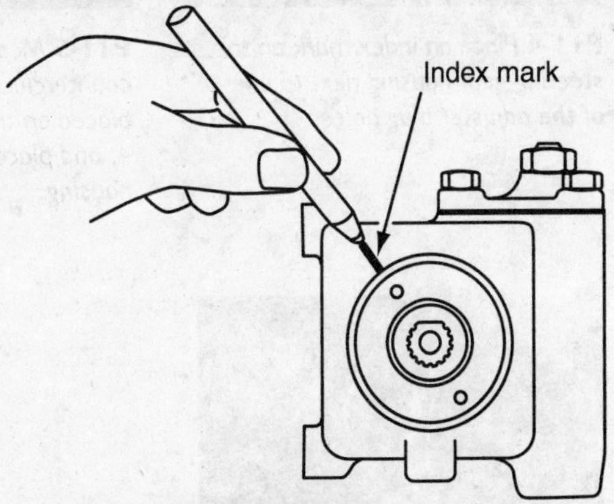

FIGURE 11-3 *Placing index mark on steering gear housing opposite one of the adjuster plug holes.*

Photo Sequence 11 shows a typical procedure for performing a worm shaft bearing preload adjustment.

PHOTO SEQUENCE 11
TYPICAL PROCEDURE FOR PERFORMING A WORM SHAFT BEARING PRELOAD ADJUSTMENT

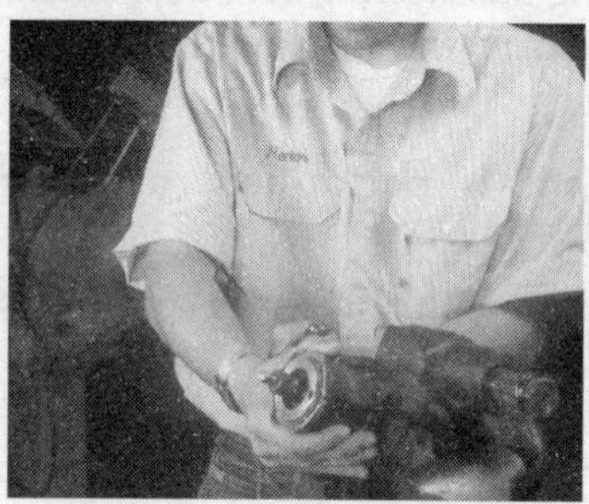

P11-1 *Retain the steering gear in a vise.*

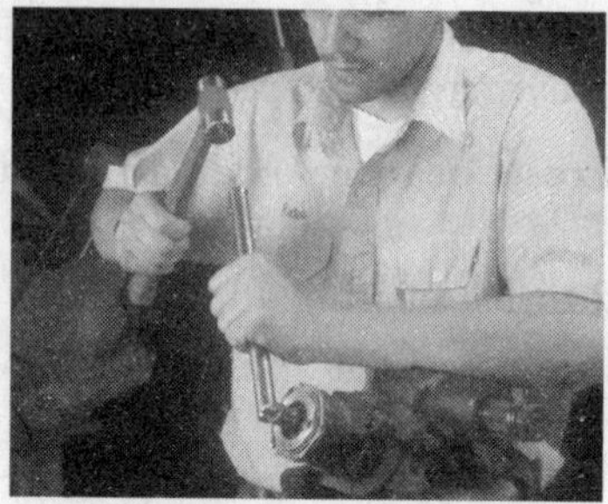

P11-2 *Remove the worm shaft bearing locknut with a hammer and brass punch.*

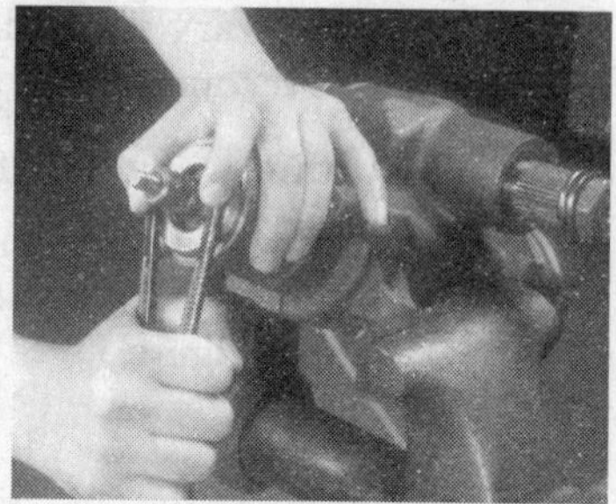

P11-3 *Use the proper tool to turn the worm shaft adjuster plug clockwise until it bottoms, and tighten this plug to 20 ft.-lb. (27 Nm).*

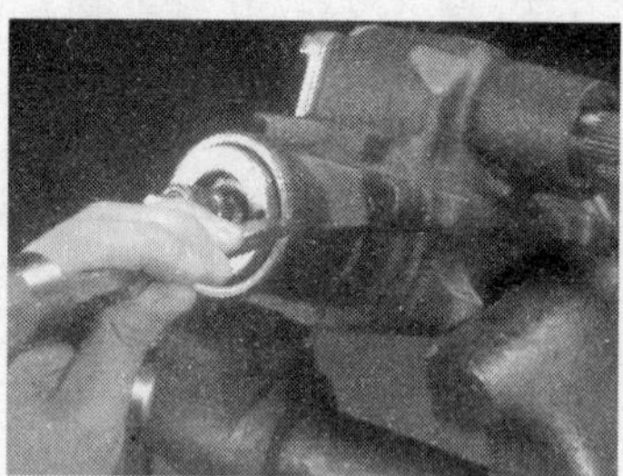

P11-4 *Place an index mark on the steering gear housing next to one of the adjuster plug holes.*

P11-5 *Measure 0.50 in. (13 mm) counterclockwise from the mark placed on the housing in step P11-4, and place a second mark on the housing.*

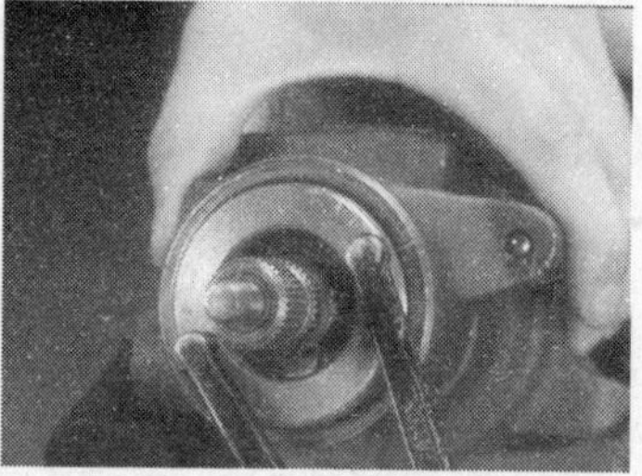

P11-6 *Rotate the worm shaft adjuster plug counterclockwise until the adjuster plug hole is aligned with the second mark placed on the housing.*

P11-7 *Install and tighten the worm shaft adjuster plug locknut.*

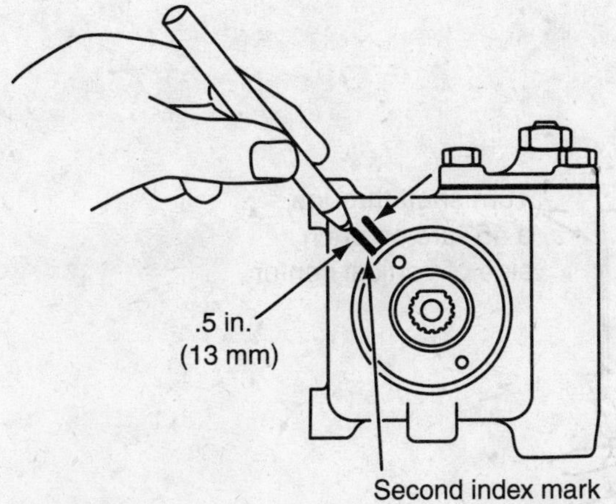

FIGURE 11-4 *Measuring 0.50 in. (13 mm) counter-clockwise from the index mark on the steering gear housing.*

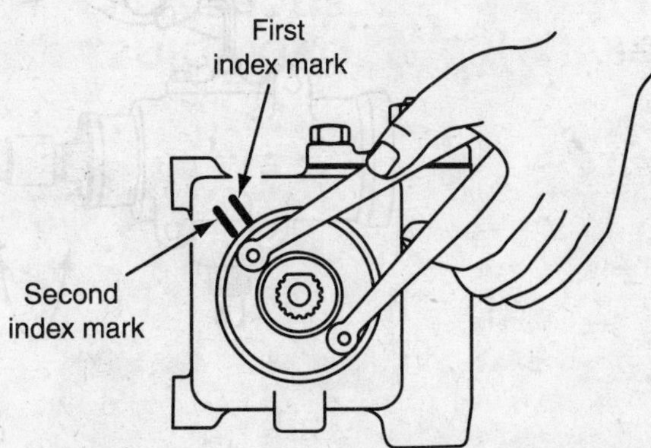

FIGURE 11-5 *Aligning adjuster plug hole with the second index mark placed on steering gear housing.*

Pitman Sector Shaft Lash Adjustment

When the **sector shaft lash** adjustment is too loose, steering wheel free play is excessive, which causes **vehicle wander** when the vehicle is driven straight ahead. A loose sector shaft lash adjustment decreases driver **road feel**. If the sector lash adjustment is too tight, steering effort is increased, especially with the front wheels in the straight-ahead position.

When the pitman sector shaft lash adjustment is performed, proceed as follows:

1. Rotate the stub shaft from stop to stop and count the number of turns.
2. Starting at either stop, turn the stub shaft back one-half of the total number of turns. In this position, the flat on the stub shaft should be facing upward (Figure 11-6), and the master spline on the pitman shaft should be aligned with the pitman shaft backlash adjuster screw (Figure 11-7).

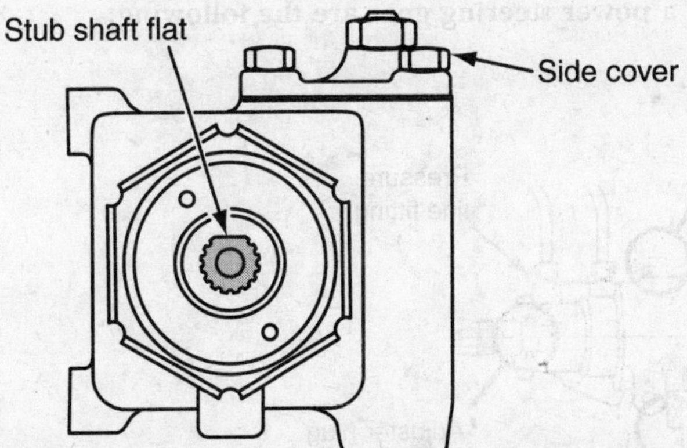

FIGURE 11-6 *Stub shaft flat facing upward and parallel with the side cover.*

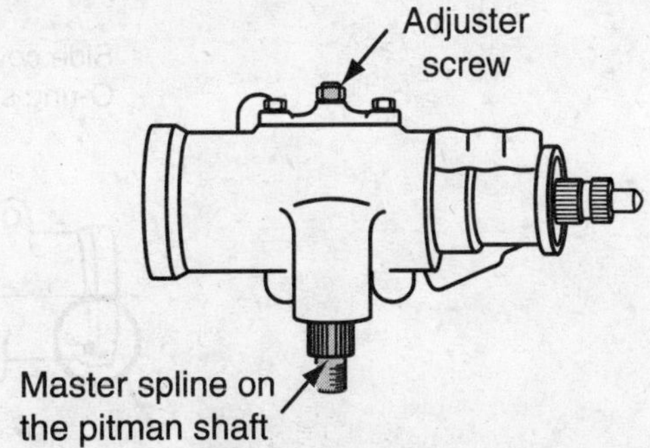

FIGURE 11-7 *Pitman shaft master spline aligned with the pitman backlash adjuster screw.*

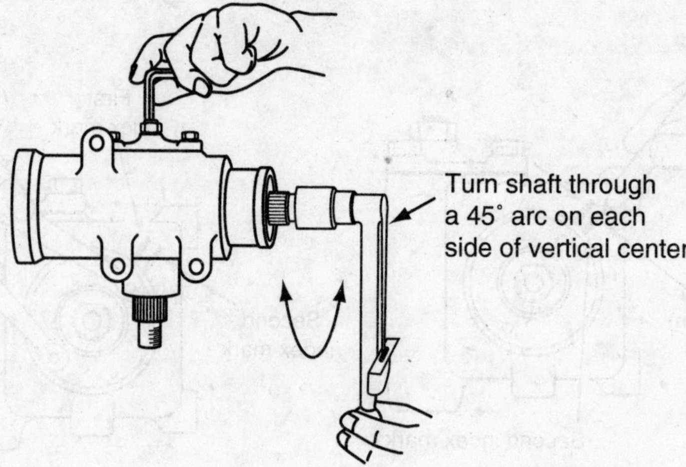

FIGURE 11-8 *Measuring wormshaft turning torque to adjust pitman backlash adjuster screw.*

3. Loosen the locknut and turn the pitman shaft backlash adjuster screw fully counter-clockwise, and then turn it clockwise one turn.
4. Use an inch-pound torque wrench to turn the stub shaft through a 45° arc on each side of the position in step 2. Read the over-center torque as the stub shaft turns through the center position (Figure 11-8).
5. Continue to adjust the pitman shaft adjuster screw until the torque is 6 to 10 in.-lb. (0.6 to 1.2 Nm) more than the torque in step 4.
6. Hold the pitman shaft adjuster screw in this position, and tighten the locknut to the specified torque.

POWER RECIRCULATING BALL STEERING GEAR OIL LEAK DIAGNOSIS

Five locations where oil leaks may occur in a power steering gear are the following:

1. Side cover O-ring seal (Figure 11-9)

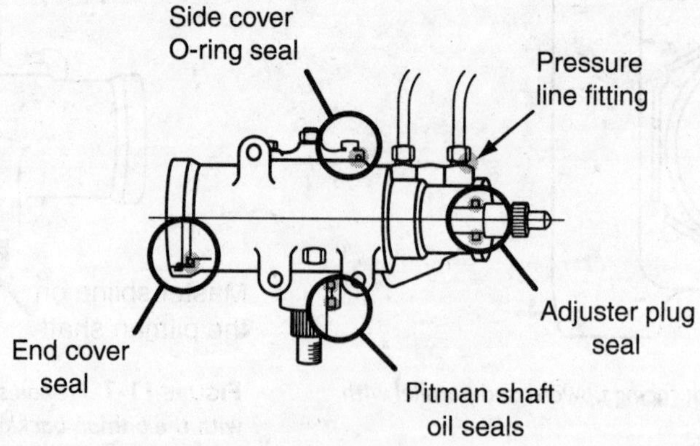

FIGURE 11-9 *Power recirculating ball steering gear oil leak locations.*

2. Adjuster plug seal
3. Pressure line fitting
4. Pitman shaft oil seals
5. End cover seal

If an oil leak is present at any of these areas, complete or partial steering gear disassembly and seal or O-ring replacement is necessary.

POWER RECIRCULATING BALL STEERING GEAR SEAL REPLACEMENT

Side Cover O-Ring Replacement

Prior to any disassembly procedure, clean the steering gear with solvent or in a parts washer. The steering gear service procedures vary depending on the make of gear. Always follow the vehicle manufacturer's recommended procedure in the service manual.

Following is a typical side cover O-ring replacement procedure:

1. Loosen the pitman backlash adjuster screw locknut and remove the side cover bolts. Rotate the pitman backlash adjuster screw clockwise to remove the cover from the screw (Figure 11-10).

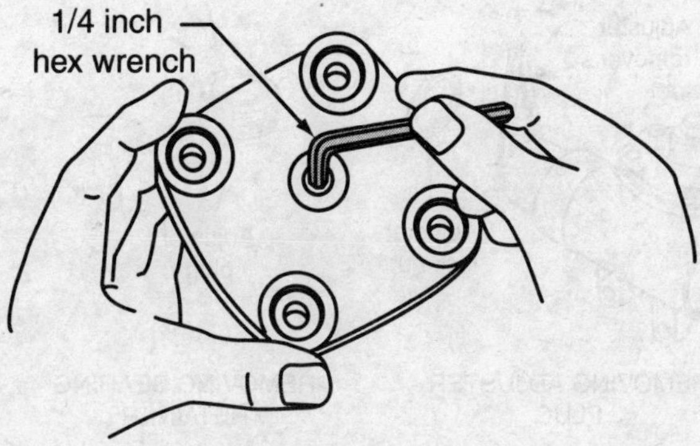

FIGURE 11-10 *Removing steering gear side cover.*

2. Discard the O-ring and inspect the side cover matching surfaces for metal burrs and scratches.
3. Lubricate a new O-ring with the vehicle manufacturer's recommended power steering fluid and install the O-ring.
4. Rotate the pitman backlash adjuster screw counterclockwise into the side cover until the side cover is properly positioned on the gear housing. Turn this adjuster screw fully counterclockwise and then one turn clockwise. Install and tighten the side cover bolts to the specified torque. Adjust the pitman sector shaft lash as explained earlier.

End Plug Seal Replacement

Follow these steps for end plug seal replacement:

1. Insert a punch into the access hole in the steering gear housing to unseat the retaining ring, and remove the ring (Figure 11-11).
2. Remove the end plug and seal.
3. Clean the end plug and seal contact area in the housing with a shop towel.
4. Lubricate a new seal with the vehicle manufacturer's recommended power steering fluid, and install the seal.
5. Install the end plug and retaining ring.

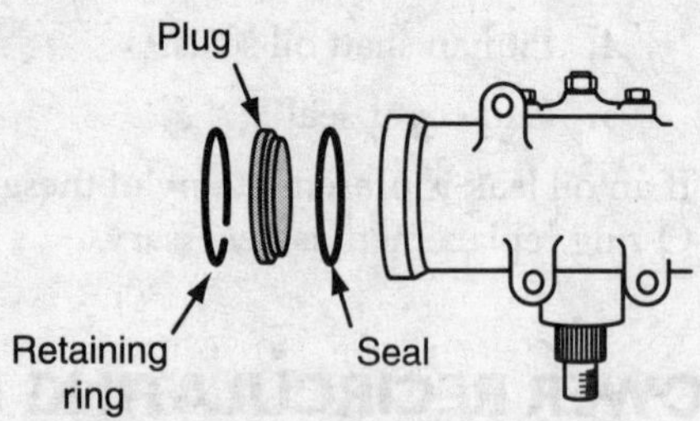

FIGURE 11-11 *Removing steering gear end plug, retaining ring, and seal.*

Worm Shaft Bearing Adjuster Plug Seal and Bearing Replacement

Follow these steps for worm shaft bearing adjuster plug seal and bearing service:

1. Remove the adjuster plug locknut, and use a special tool to remove the adjuster plug.
2. Use a screwdriver to pry at the raised area of the bearing retainer to remove this retainer from the adjuster plug (Figure 11-12).

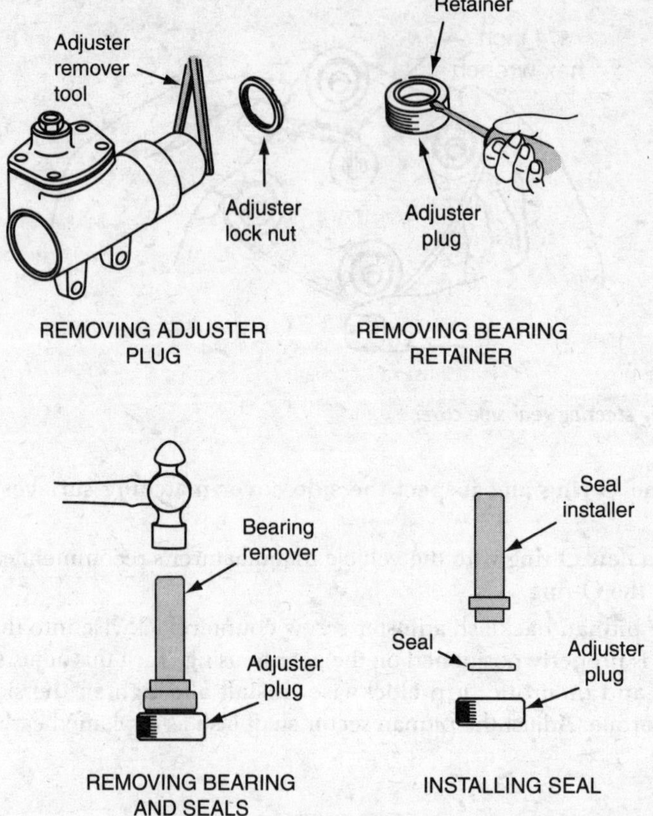

FIGURE 11-12 *Removing and replacing worm shaft adjuster plug, bearing, and seal.*

3. Place the adjuster plug face down on a suitable support, and use the proper driver to remove the needle bearing, dust seal, and lip seal.

CAUTION: The bearing identification number must face the driving tool to prevent bearing damage during installation.

4. Place the adjuster plug face up on a suitable support, and use the proper driver to install the needle bearing dust seal and lip seal.
5. Install the bearing retainer in the adjuster plug, and lubricate the bearing and seal with the vehicle manufacturer's recommended power steering fluid.
6. Install the adjuster plug and locknut, and adjust the worm shaft bearing preload as discussed previously.

TABLE 11-1 *Steering gear DIAGNOSIS*

PROBLEM	SYMPTOMS	POSSIBLE CAUSES
Excessive steering wheel free play	Steering wander when driving straight ahead	Loose worm shaft preload adjustment Losse sector lash adjustment Loose steering gear mounting bolts Worn steering linkage components Worn flexible coupling or universal joint in steering shaft.
Excessive steering effort	Excessive steering wheel turning effort when turning a corner or parking	Lack of steering gear lubricant Tight worm shaft bearing preload adjustment Tight sector lash ajdustment
Underhood noise	Rattling noise when driving over road irregularities	Worn flexible coupling or universal joint in steering shaft Loose steering gear mounting bolts
	Squawking noise while turning a corner	Cut or worn dampener O-ring on spool valve.
Erratic steering effort	Erratic steering effort when turning a corner	Low power steering fluid level Air in power steering system Worn, damaged worm shaft, ball nut, or sector teeth

CASE STUDY

The owner of a 2005 Chervolet Silverado truck complained about increased and somewhat erratic steering effort. The service writer asked the customer about the conditions when this problem occurred, and the customer said that the condition was always present. During a road test, the technician discovered that the customer's description of the problem was accurate.

The technician checked the power steering fluid level and made a careful check of the belt tension and condition without finding any problems. Next, the technician checked the power steering pump pressure and found it to be normal. A check of the power steering hoses did not reveal any hose restrictions.

The technician removed and disassembled the steering gear and found a severely scored cylinder bore in the gear housing. The ball nut piston ring was also worn and scored. A replacement steering gear was installed, and the system filled with the manufacturer's recommended power steering fluid. A road test indicated the new gear worked satisfactorily.

SERVICE TIP

- When tightening the pitman backlash adjuster screw locknut, it is very important to hold the pitman arm lash adjuster screw with a screwdriver to prevent this screw from turning. If the pitman lash adjuster screw turns when the locknut is tightened, the adjustment is changed.

REVIEW QUESTIONS

1. While discussing power recirculating ball steering gear diagnosis:
Technician A says excessive steering wheel free play may be caused by a worm shaft bearing preload adjustment that is tighter than normal. *Technician B* says excessive steering wheel free play may be caused by loose steering gear mounting bolts.
Who is correct?
A. A only **C.** Both A and B
B. B only **D.** Neither A nor B

2. While discussing power recirculating ball steering gear service:
Technician A says steering wander may be caused by a loose sector lash adjustment. *Technician B* says a loose sector lash adjustment may cause reduced feel of the road.
Who is correct?
A. A only **C.** Both A and B
B. B only **D.** Neither A nor B

3. While discussing power recirculating steering gear diagnosis:
Technician A says the sector lash adjustment is performed with the worm shaft halfway between the centered position and the full-right position. *Technician B* says the worm shaft bearing preload adjustment is performed before the sector lash adjustment.
Who is correct?
A. A only **C.** Both A and B
B. B only **D.** Neither A nor B

4. A power recirculating ball steering gear has a rattling noise while driving the vehicle. The most likely cause of this problem is:
A. Low power steering fluid level.
B. Worn flexible coupling in the steering shaft.
C. Loose worm bearing preload adjustment.
D. Leaking pitman shaft seal.

5. A power recirculating ball steering gear has a fluid leakage problem, and fluid appears on the top of the gear. *Technician A* says the side cover O-ring seal may be leaking. *Technician B* says the high pressure line fitting on the gear may be leaking. Who is correct?
A. A only
B. B only
C. Both A and B
D. Neither A nor B

6. A power recirculating ball steering gear has excessive kickback on the steering wheel. The most likely cause of this problem is:
A. A loose sector lash adjustment.
B. A loose worm shaft bearing preload adjustment.
C. A defective poppet valve in the steering gear.
D. A worn pitman shaft bearing.

7. All of these statements about power recirculating ball steering gear defects are true EXCEPT:
A. A worn steering shaft U-joint may cause a growling noise when turning the front wheels.
B. Excessive steering effort may be caused by a defective power steering pump.
C. Excessive steering effort may be caused by a scored steering gear cylinder.
D. Steering wheel jerking when turning may be caused by a slipping power steering belt.

8. When adjusting on a power recirculating ball steering gear:
A. The worm shaft bearing adjuster plug should be bottomed and then backed off until the specified worm shaft turning torque is obtained.
B. The sector lash adjustment screw should be tightened one turn before the worm shaft bearing preload is adjusted.
C. The pitman shaft backlash adjuster screw is turned fully counterclockwise and then one turn clockwise prior to the backlash adjustment.
D. The pitman shaft is positioned one-half turn from the fully right or left position prior to the pitman shaft backlash adjustment.

9. A power recirculating ball steering gear experiences excessive steering effort while parking. The most likely cause of this problem is:
A. A restricted high-pressure steering hose.
B. A misaligned power steering belt.
C. A leaking pitman shaft seal.
D. Excessive torque on the worm shaft adjuster plug locknut.

10. A power recirculating ball steering gear experiences hard steering for a short time after the vehicle sits overnight. The most likely cause of this problem is:
A. Excessively tight worm bearing preload adjustment.
B. A scored cylinder and worn piston ring in the steering gear.
C. A restricted power steering return hose.
D. A binding U-joint in the steering shaft.

CHALLENGE QUESTIONS

1. A car with a power recirculating ball steering gear has excessive steering kickback, and a preliminary inspection shows no abnormal wear in the linkage. Which of the following could be the cause of the problem?
A. Worn gear piston or bore.

B. Slipping pump belt.
C. Worn pump poppet valve.
D. Sticking valve spool.

2. The complaint is loss of power assist, but there is no mention of any associated noise. All of the following could cause this problem EXCEPT:
A. Low fluid.
B. Improperly inflated tires.
C. Broken pump belt.
D. Steering column misalignment.

3. While discussing steering problems:
Technician A says a "jerky" steering wheel and a "clunking" noise could indicate worn steering column U joints. *Technician B* says lack of assist and a "growling" noise in a fluid-filled steering pump could indicatea hose or pump internal restriction.
Who is correct?
A. A only **C.** Both A and B
B. B only **D.** Neither A nor B

4. A vehicle with a power recirculating ball steering system requires much higher than normal steering effort, especially in the parking lot.
Technician A says the cause of the problem is a worn pitman shaft seal. *Technician B* says the cause of the problem is a worn worm shaft thrust bearing.
Who is correct?
A. A only **C.** Both A and B
B. B only **D.** Neither A nor B

5. The complaint is excessive steering wheel free play. All of the following could cause this problem EXCEPT:
A. Loose worm shaft bearing preload.
B. Worn steering gears.
C. Steering gear column misalignment.
D. Worn flex coupling or U joint.

JOB SHEET 34

Name_________________________________ Date____________

POWER RECIRCULATING BALL STEERING GEAR OIL LEAK DIAGNOSIS

Upon completion of this job sheet, you should be able to diagnose oil leaks in a power recirculating ball steering gear.

ASE Correlation

This job sheet is related to ASE Automotive Suspension and Steering Task: *Diagnose power steering gear (non-rack and pinion type) noises, binding, uneven turning effort, looseness, hard steering, and fluid leakage problems; determine needed repairs.*

Tools and Materials

Modern vehicle with a power recirculating ball steering gear.

Describe the Vehicle Being Worked On:

Year ___________ Make ____________________ Model ____________________

VIN ____________________ Engine type and size ____________________

Procedure

Task Completed

1. Place fender, seat, and floor mat covers on the vehicle. ☐
2. Clean the outside of the steering gear.
3. Be sure the power steering pump reservoir is filled to the proper level with the specified fluid.
4. Start the engine and observe the power steering gear while an assistant turns the steering wheel fully in each direction several times. Turn off the ignition switch.
5. If the power steering gear is leaking fluid on the lower side, raise the front of the vehicle with a floor jack and support the front suspension on safety stands positioned at the specified vehicle lift points. Repeats steps 2–4.
6. List the fluid leak locations on the power steering gear.

   ____

   ____

7. State the necessary repairs to correct the power steering gear leaks.

   ____

   ____

Instructor's Response ____

____

____

JOB SHEET 35

Name ______________________________ Date ______________

ADJUST POWER RECIRCULATING BALL STEERING GEAR WORM SHAFT THRUST BEARING PRELOAD, STEERING GEAR REMOVED

Upon completion of this job sheet, you should be able to adjust worm shaft thrust bearing preload on power recirculating ball steering gears.

ASE Correlation

This job sheet is related to ASE Automotive Suspension and Steering Task: *Adjust worm shaft thrust bearing preload and sector lash on power recirculating ball steering gears.*

Tools and Materials

Torque wrench, in.-lb.

Describe the Vehicle Being Worked On:

Year __________ Make ______________ Model ______________
VIN ____________________ Engine type and size ______________
Make of steering gear ______________________________

Procedure

Task Completed

1. Remove the worm shaft thrust bearing adjuster plug locknut with a hammer and brass punch. ☐
2. Turn this adjuster plug inward, or clockwise, until it bottoms and tighten the plug to 20 ft.-lb. (27 Nm).

   Actual worm shaft adjuster plug locknut torque ______________
3. Place an index mark on the steering gear housing next to one of the holes in the adjuster plug.

   Is an index mark placed on steering gear housing beside one of the adjuster plug holes?

   ☐ Yes ☐ No

   Instructor check ______________________________
4. Measure 0.50 in. (13 mm) counterclockwise from the index mark, and place a second index mark at this position.

   Is a second index mark placed 0.50 in. (13 mm) counterclockwise from the first index mark?

   ☐ Yes ☐ No

   Instructor check ______________________________

Task Completed

5. Rotate the adjuster plug counterclockwise until the hole in the adjuster plug is aligned with the second index mark placed on the housing.

   Is the hole in adjuster plug properly aligned with second index mark?
   ☐ Yes ☐ No

   Instructor check ______________________________

6. Install and tighten the adjuster plug locknut to the specified torque.

   Specified adjuster plug locknut torque ______________________________

   Actual adjuster plug locknut torque ______________________________

Instructor's Response ______________________________

____

____

JOB SHEET 36

Name ______________________________ Date ______________

ADJUST POWER RECIRCULATING BALL STEERING GEAR SECTOR LASH, STEERING GEAR REMOVED

Upon completion of this job sheet, you should be able to adjust sector lash on power recirculating ball steering gears.

ASE Correlation

This job sheet is related to ASE Automotive Suspension and Steering Task: *Adjust worm shaft bearing preload and sector lash on power recirculating ball steering gears.*

Tools and Materials

Torque wrench, in.-lb.

Describe the Vehicle Being Worked On:

Year ____________ Make ______________________ Model ________________
VIN ______________________ Engine type and size ____________________
Make of steering gear ____

Procedure

Task Completed

1. Rotate the worm shaft from stop to stop and count the number of turns.

   Total number of worm shaft turns from stop to stop ____________________

2. Starting at either stop, turn the worm shaft back two-thirds of the total number of turns.

   Number of worm shaft turns from fully right or fully left to position the worm shaft properly prior to sector lash adjustment ______________

   Explain the reason for placing the worm shaft in this position prior to the sector lash adjustment.

   ____

   ____

   ____

3. In this position, the flat on the worm shaft should be facing upward, and the master spline on the pitman shaft should be aligned with the pitman shaft backlash adjuster screw.

   Is the worm shaft flat properly positioned? ☐ Yes ☐ No

   Is the master spline on the pitman shaft properly positioned? ☐ Yes ☐ No

   If the answer is no to either of the above questions, state the necessary corrective action.

   ____

   ____

Task Completed

4. Turn the pitman shaft backlash adjuster screw fully counterclockwise, and then turn it clockwise one turn.

   Is the pitman shaft backlash adjuster screw properly positioned? ☐ Yes ☐ No

   Instructor check ______________________

5. Use an inch-pound torque wrench to turn the worm shaft through a 45° arc on each side of the position in step 2. Read the over-center torque as the worm shaft turns through the center position.

   Stub shaft turning torque ______________________

6. Continue to adjust the pitman shaft adjuster screw until the torque is 6 to 10 in.-lb. (0.6 to 1.2 Nm) more than the torque in step 5.

   Final worm shaft turning torque after adjustment ______________________

7. Hold the pitman shaft adjuster screw in this position and tighten the locknut to the specified torque.

   Specified pitman shaft adjuster screw locknut torque ______________________

   Actual pitman shaft adjuster screw locknut torque

   ____

Instructor's Response ______________________

____

____

Rack and Pinion Steering Gear Diagnosis and Service

12

Upon completion and review of this chapter, you should be able to:

- Perform a manual or power rack and pinion steering gear inspection.
- Remove and replace manual or power rack and pinion steering gears.
- Disassemble, inspect, repair, and reassemble manual rack and pinion steering gears.
- Adjust manual rack and pinion steering gears.
- Diagnose manual rack and pinion steering systems.
- Diagnose oil leaks in power rack and pinion steering gears.
- Disassemble, inspect, and repair power rack and pinion steering gears.
- Adjust power rack and pinion steering gears.
- Diagnose Magnasteer.
- Diagnose electronic power steering systems.

Proper rack and pinion steering gear operation is essential to maintain vehicle safety and reduce driver fatigue. Such steering gear conditions as looseness and excessive steering effort may contribute to a loss of steering control, resulting in a vehicle collision. Worn steering gear mountings may cause improper wheel alignment and **bump steer**. Improper wheel alignment increases tire tread wear, and bump steer may increase driver fatigue. Excessive steering gear looseness or high steering effort also contribute to driver fatigue. Therefore, in the interest of vehicle safety and driver alertness, rack and pinion steering gear diagnosis and service are extremely important.

MANUAL OR POWER RACK AND PINION STEERING GEAR ON-CAR INSPECTION

The wear points are reduced to four in a rack and pinion steering gear. These wear points are the inner and outer tie-rod ends on both sides of the rack and pinion assembly (Figure 12-1).

The first step in manual or power rack and pinion steering gear diagnosis is a very thorough inspection of the complete steering system. During this inspection, all steering system components

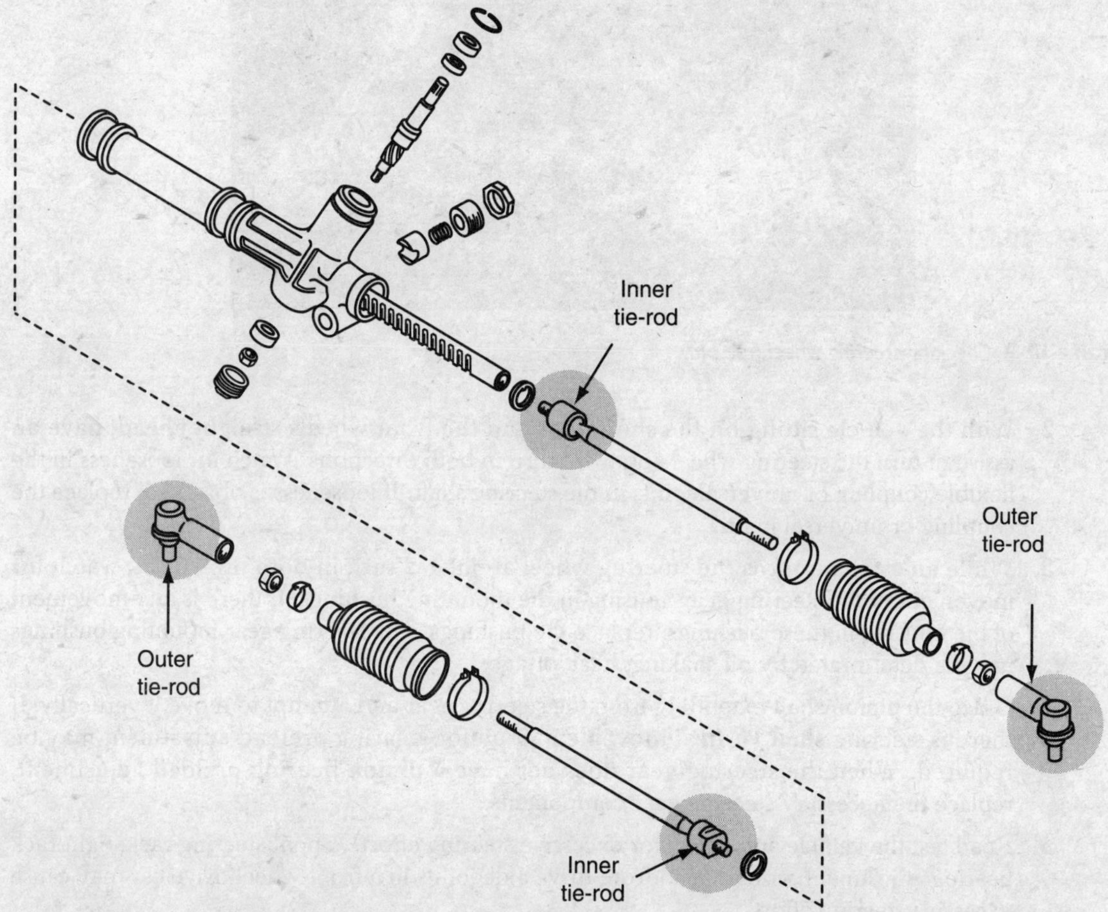

FIGURER 12-1 *Wear points at the inner and outer tie-rod ends in a rack and pinion steering gear.*

such as the inner and outer tie-rod ends, **bellows boots,** mounting bushings, couplings or universal joints, ball joints, tires, and **steering wheel free play** must be checked.

Follow these steps for manual or power rack and pinion steering gear inspection:

1. With the front wheels straight ahead and the engine stopped, rock the steering wheel gently back and forth with light finger pressure (Figure 12-2). Measure the maximum steering wheel free play. The maximum specified steering wheel free play on some vehicles is 1.18 in. (30 mm). Always refer to the vehicle manufacturer's specifications in the service manual. Excessive steering wheel free play indicates worn steering components.

FIGURE 12-2 *Checking steering wheel free play.*

2. With the vehicle sitting on the shop floor and the front wheels straight ahead, have an assistant turn the steering wheel about 1/4 turn in both directions. Watch for looseness in the flexible coupling or universal joints in the steering shaft. If looseness is observed, replace the coupling or universal joint.
3. While an assistant turns the steering wheel about 1/2 turn in both directions, watch for movement of the steering gear housing in the mounting bushings. If there is any movement of the housing in these bushings, replace the bushings. The steering gear mounting bushings may be deteriorated by oil soaking, heat, or age.
4. Grasp the pinion shaft extending from the steering gear and attempt to move it vertically. If there is steering shaft vertical movement, a pinion bearing preload adjustment may be required. When the steering gear does not have a pinion bearing preload adjustment, replace the necessary steering gear components.
5. Road test the vehicle and check for excessive steering effort. A bent steering rack, tight rack bearing adjustment, or damaged front drive axle joints in a front-wheel-drive car may cause excessive steering effort.
6. Visually inspect the bellows boots for cracks, splits, leaks, and proper clamp installation. Replace any boot that indicates any of these conditions. If the boot clamps are loose or

improperly installed, tighten or replace the clamps as necessary. Since the bellows boots protect the inner tie-rod ends and the rack from contamination, boot condition is extremely important. Boots should be inspected each time under-car service such as oil and filter change or chassis lubrication is performed.

7. Loosen the inner bellows boot clamps and move each boot toward the outer tie-rod end until the inner tie-rod end is visible. Push outward and inward on each front tire, and watch for movement in the inner tie-rod end. If any movement or looseness is present, replace the inner tie-rod end. An alternate method of checking the inner tie-rod ends is to squeeze the bellows boots and grasp the inner tie-rod end socket. Movement in the inner tie-rod end is then felt as the front wheel is moved inward and outward. Hard plastic bellows boots may be found on some applications. With this type of bellows boot, remove the ignition key from the switch to lock the steering column and push inward and outward on the front tire while observing any lateral movement in the tie-rod. When lateral movement is observed, replace the inner tie-rod end.

WARNING: Bent steering components must be replaced. Never straighten steering components, because this action may weaken the metal and result in sudden component failure, serious personal injury, and vehicle damage.

8. Grasp each outer tie-rod end and check for vertical movement. While an assistant turns the steering wheel 1/4 turn in each direction, watch for looseness in the outer tie-rod ends. If any looseness or vertical movement is present, replace the tie-rod end. Check the outer tie-rod end seals for cracks and proper installation of the nuts and cotter pins. Cracked seals must be replaced. Inspect the tie-rods for a bent condition. Bent tie-rods or other steering components must be replaced. Do not attempt to straighten these components.

MANUAL OR POWER RACK AND PINION STEERING GEAR REMOVAL AND REPLACEMENT

The replacement procedure is similar for manual or power rack and pinion steering gears. This removal and replacement procedure varies depending on the vehicle. On some vehicles, the front crossmember or engine support cradle must be lowered to remove the rack and pinion steering gear. Always follow the vehicle manufacturer's recommended procedure in the service manual.

The following is a typical rack and pinion steering gear removal and replacement procedure:

1. Place the front wheels in the straight-ahead position and remove the ignition key from the ignition switch to lock the steering wheel. Place the driver's seat belt through the steering wheel to prevent wheel rotation if the ignition switch is turned on (Figure 12-3). This action maintains the clock spring electrical connector or spiral cable in the centered position on air-bag-equipped vehicles.
2. Lift the front end with a floor jack, and place safety stands under the vehicle chassis. Lower the vehicle onto the safety stands. Remove the left and right fender apron seals (Figure 12-4).
3. Place punch marks on the lower universal joint and the steering gear pinion shaft so they may be reassembled in the same position (Figure 12-5). Loosen the upper universal joint bolt, remove the lower universal joint bolt, and disconnect this joint.

FIGURE 12-3 *Driver's seat belt wrapped around the steering wheel to prevent wheel rotation.*

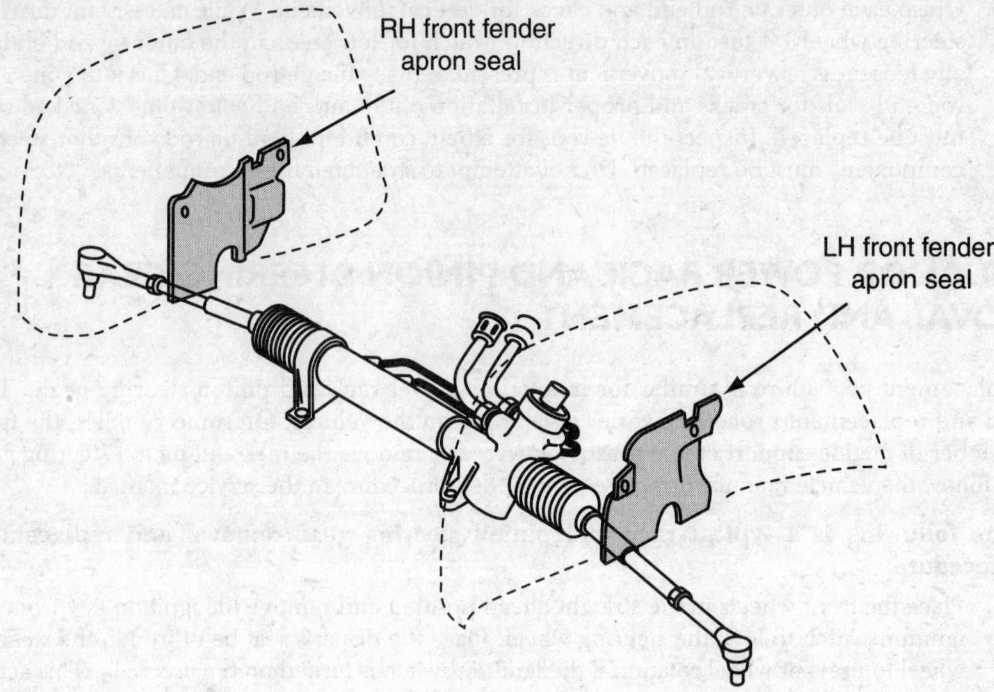

FIGURE 12-4 *Left and right fender apron seals.*

4. Remove the cotter pins from the outer tie-rod ends. Loosen, but do not remove, the tie-rod end nuts. Use a tie-rod end puller to loosen the outer tie-rod ends in the steering arms (Figure 12-6). Remove the tie-rod end nuts and remove the tie-rod ends from the arms.
5. Use the proper wrenches to disconnect the high-pressure hose and the return hose from the steering gear (Figure 12-7). This step is not required on a manual steering gear.

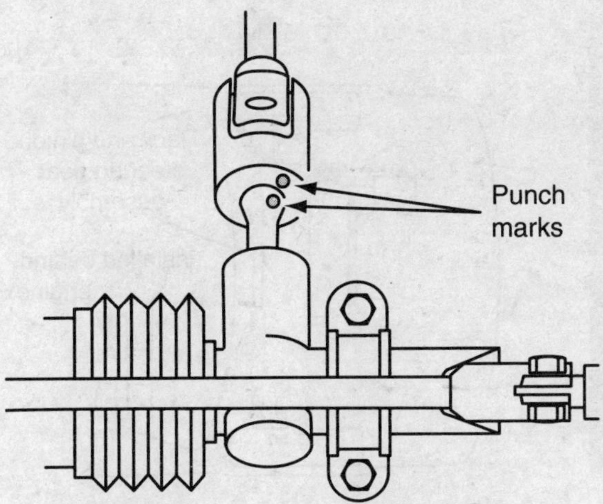

FIGURE 12-5 *Punch marks on universal joint and pinion shaft.*

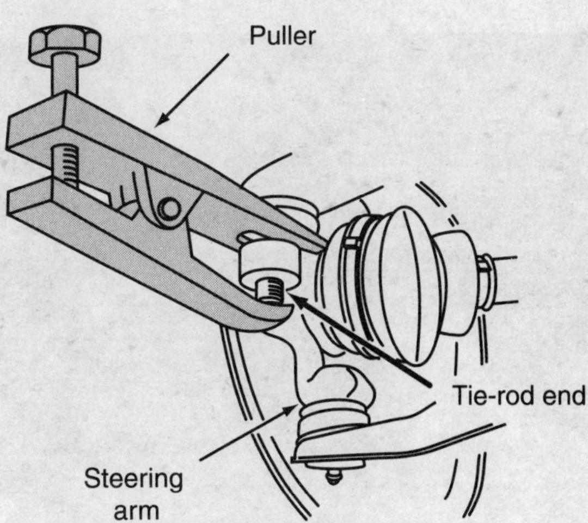

FIGURE 12-6 *Removing outer tie-rod ends.*

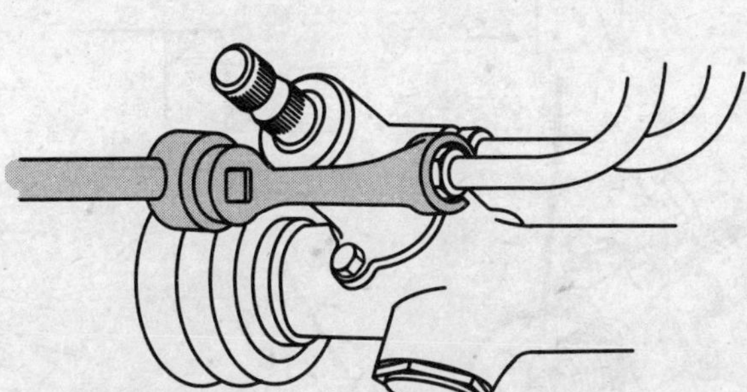

FIGURE 12-7 *Removing high-pressure and return hoses from steering gear.*

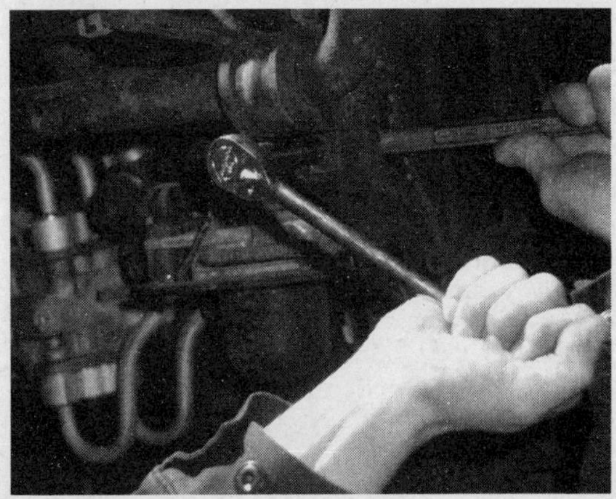

FIGURE 12-8 *Removing stabilizer bar mounting bolts.*

6. Remove the four stabilizer bar mounting bolts (Figure 12-8).
7. Remove the steering gear mounting bolts (Figure 12-9).
8. Remove the steering gear assembly from the right side of the car (Figure 12-10).
9. Position the right and left tie-rods the specified distance from the steering gear housing (Figure 12-11). Install the steering gear through the right fender apron.
10. Install the pinion shaft in the universal joint with the punch marks aligned. Tighten the upper and lower universal joint bolts to the specified torque.
11. Install the steering gear mounting bolts and tighten these bolts to the specified torque.
12. Install the stabilizer bar mounting bolts and torque these bolts to specifications.
13. Install and tighten the high-pressure and return hoses to the specified torque. (This step is not required on a manual rack and pinion steering gear.)

FIGURE 12-9 *Removing steering gear mounting bolts.*

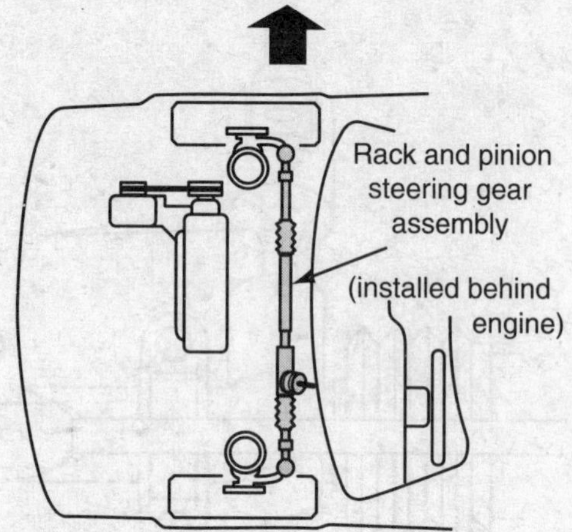

FIGURE 12-10 *Removing steering gear from the car.*

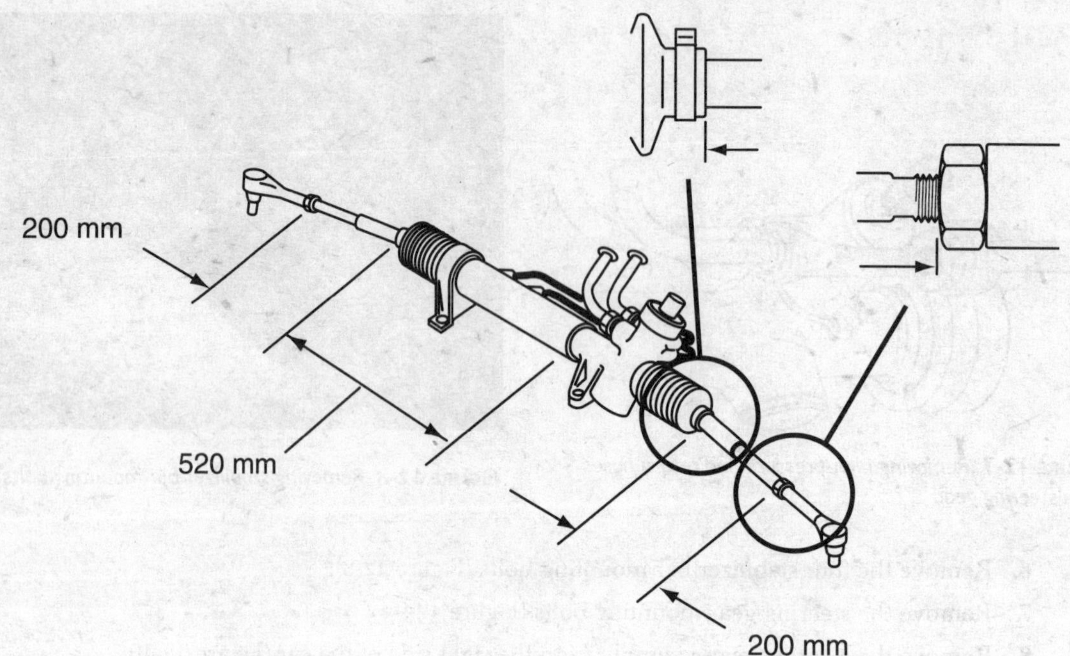

FIGURE 12-11 *Right and left tie-rod position in relation to the steering gear housing prior to installation.*

CAUTION: Do not loosen the tie-rod end nuts to align cotter pin holes. This action causes improper torquing of these nuts.

14. Install the outer tie-rod ends in the steering knuckles, and tighten the nuts to the specified torque. Install the cotter pins in the nuts.
15. Check the front wheel toe and adjust as necessary. Tighten the outer tie-rod end jam nuts to the specified torque, and tighten the outer bellows boot clamps.
16. Install the left and right fender apron seals, and lower the vehicle with a floor jack.

17. Fill the power steering pump reservoir with the vehicle manufacturer's recommended power steering fluid and bleed the air from the power steering system. (Refer to Chapter 10 for these tasks. This step is not required on a manual rack and pinion steering gear.)
18. Road test the vehicle and check for proper steering gear operation and steering control.

MANUAL RACK AND PINION STEERING GEAR DIAGNOSIS AND SERVICE

Manual Rack and Pinion Steering Gear Tie-Rod Service

Follow these steps for manual rack and pinion steering gear disassembly:

1. Clamp the center of the steering gear housing in a **soft-jaw vise.** Do not apply excessive force to the vise.
2. Insert a short piece of wire through each outer tie-rod end cotter pin hole and connect a pull scale to this wire. Pull upward on the scale to check the tie-rod articulation effort (Figure 12-12). If this effort is not within specifications, replace the inner tie-rod end.
3. Mark the outer tie-rod and jam nut position with masking tape wrapped around the tie-rod threads next to the jam nut, or place a dab of paint on the jam nut and tie-rod threads (Figure 12-13). Loosen the jam nuts and remove the outer tie-rod ends.

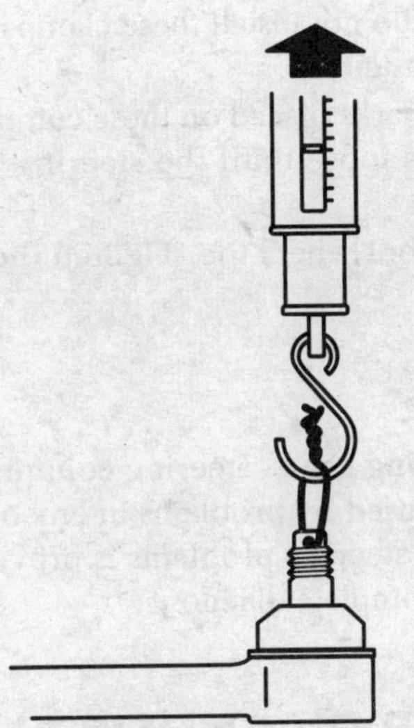

FIGURE 12-12 *Measuring inner tie-rod end articulation effort.*

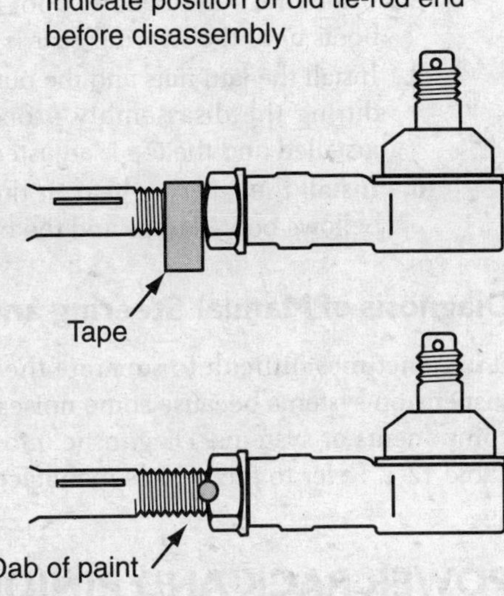

FIGURE 12-13 *Marking outer tie-rod end and jam nut position.*

4. Remove the inner and outer bellows boot clamps and pull the bellows boots from the tie-rods.
5. Hold the rack in a soft-jaw vise and straighten the lock plate where it is bent over the inner tie-rod end (Figure 12-14). Hold the rack with a wrench, and use the proper size wrench to remove the inner tie-rod end from the rack (Figure 12-15). A jam nut is used in place of the lock ring on some inner tie-rod ends, and a roll pin retains some inner tie-rod ends to the rack. Various inner tie-rod socket removal procedures are required depending on the socket design.

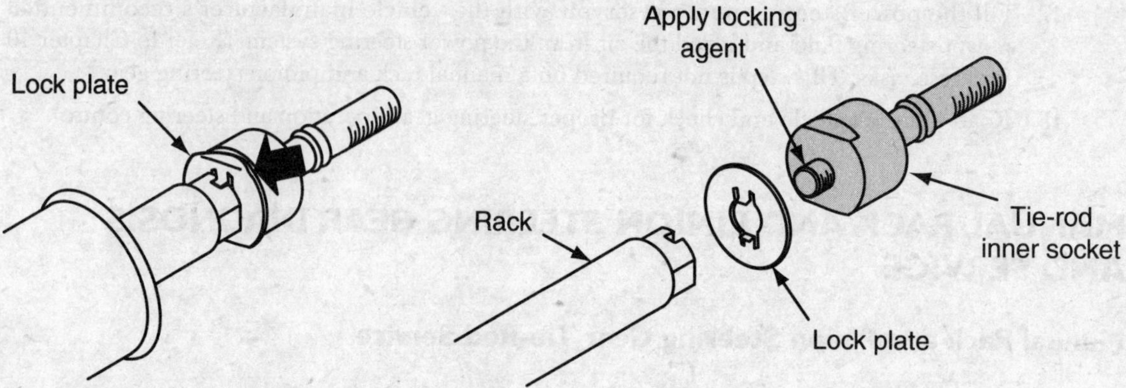

FIGURE 12-14 *Straightening lock plate where it is bent over the inner tie-rod end.*

FIGURE 12-15 *Removing inner tie-rod end from the rack.*

6. Rotate the inner tie-rod ends onto the rack until they bottom. Install the inner tie-rod pins, or stake these ends as required. Always use a wooden block to support the opposite side of the rack and inner tie-rod end while staking. If jam nuts are located on the inner tie-rod ends, be sure they are tightened to the specified torque.
7. Place a large bellows boot clamp over each end of the gear housing. Install the bellows boots, and be sure the boots are seated in the housing and the tie-rod undercuts. Install and tighten the large inner boot clamps.
8. Install the outer bellows boot clamps on the tie-rods, but do not install these clamps on the boots until the steering gear is installed and the toe is adjusted.
9. Install the jam nuts and the outer tie-rod ends. Align the marks placed on these components during the disassembly procedure. Leave the jam nuts loose until the steering gear is installed and the toe is adjusted.
10. Install the steering gear in the vehicle and check the front wheel toe. Tighten the outer bellows boot clamps and the outer tie-rod end jam nuts.

Diagnosis of Manual Steering and Suspension Systems

It is sometimes difficult to separate the diagnosis of manual steering gears, steering columns, and suspension systems because some noises and symptoms may be caused by problems in any of these components or systems. Diagnostic information on three common steering problems is provided in Table 12-1. Refer to the vehicle manufacturer's service manual for complete diagnosis.

POWER RACK AND PINION STEERING GEAR DIAGNOSIS AND SERVICE

Oil Leak Diagnosis

WARNING: If the engine has been running for a length of time, power steering gears, pumps, lines, and fluid may be very hot. Wear eye protection and protective gloves when servicing these components.

TABLE 12-1 *Diagnosis of Manual Steering Gears, Suspension Systems, and Steering Columns*

CONDITION	POSSIBLE CAUSE	CORRECTION
Loose steering	1. Steering linkage connections loose	1. Tighten as required.
	2. Steering linkage ball stud rubber deteriorated	2. Replace as required.
	3. Pitman arm-to-steering-gear attaching nut loose	3. Tighten to specifications.
	4. Flex coupling-to-steering-gear attaching bolt loose	4. Tighten the bolt to specifications.
	5. Intermediate shaft-to-steering-column-shaft attaching bolt loose	5. Tighten the bolt to specifications.
	6. Flex coupling damaged or worn	6. Replace as required.
	7. Front and/or rear suspension components loose, damaged, or worn	7. Tighten or replace as required.
	8. Steering gear adjustment set too low	8. Check the steering gear adjustment and readjust as required.
Noise: Knock, clunk, rapping, squeaking noise when turning	1. Steering wheel-to-steering-column shroud interference	1. Adjust or replace as required.
	2. Lack of lubrication where speed control brush contacts steering wheel pad	2. Lubricate as required.
	3. Steering column mounting bolts loose	3. Tighten the bolt to specifications.
	4. Intermediate shaft-to-steering-column-shaft attaching bolt loose	4. Tighten the bolt to specifications.
	5. Flex coupling-to-steering-gear attaching bolt loose	5. Tighten the bolt to specifications.
	6. Steering gear mounting bolts loose	6. Tighten the bolt to specifications.
	7. Tires rubbing or grounding out against body or chassis	7. Adjust/replace as required.
	8. Front suspension components loose, worn, or damaged	8. Tighten or replace as required.
	9. Steering linkage ball stud rubber deteriorated	9. Replace as required.
	10. Normal lash between sector gear teeth and ball nut gear teeth when the steering gear is in the off-center position permits gear tooth chuckle noise while turning on rough road surfaces	10. This is a normal condition and cannot be eliminated.

TABLE 12-1 *Diagnosis of Manual Steering Gears, Suspension Systems, and Steering Columns (continued)*

CONDITION	POSSIBLE CAUSE	CORRECTION
Vehicle pulls/drifts to one side *Note*: This condition cannot be caused by the manual steering gear.	1. Vehicle overloaded or unevenly loaded	1. Correct as required.
	2. Improper tire pressure	2. Adjust air pressure as required.
	3. Mismatched tires and wheels	3. Install correct tire and wheel combination.
	4. Unevenly worn tires	4. Replace as required (check for cause).
	5. Loose, worn, or damaged steering linkage	5. Tighten or replace as required.
	6. Steering linkage stud not centered within the socket	6. Repair or replace as required.
	7. Bent spindle or spindle arm	7. Repair or replace as required.
	8. Broken and/or sagging front and/or rear suspension springs	8. Replace as required.
	9. Loose, bent, or damaged suspension components	9. Tighten or replace as required.
	10. Bent rear axle housing	10. Replace as required.
	11. Excessive camber/caster split (excessive side-to-side variance in the caster/camber settings)	11. Adjust camber/caster split as required.
	12. Improper toe setting	12. Adjust as required.
	13. Front wheel bearings out of adjustment	13. Adjust as required.
	14. Investigate tire variance (conicity for radial tires and unequal circumference for bias-ply and belted bias-ply tires)	14. Repair or replace as required.

If power steering fluid leaks from the cylinder end of the power steering gear, the outer rack seal is leaking (Figure 12-16).

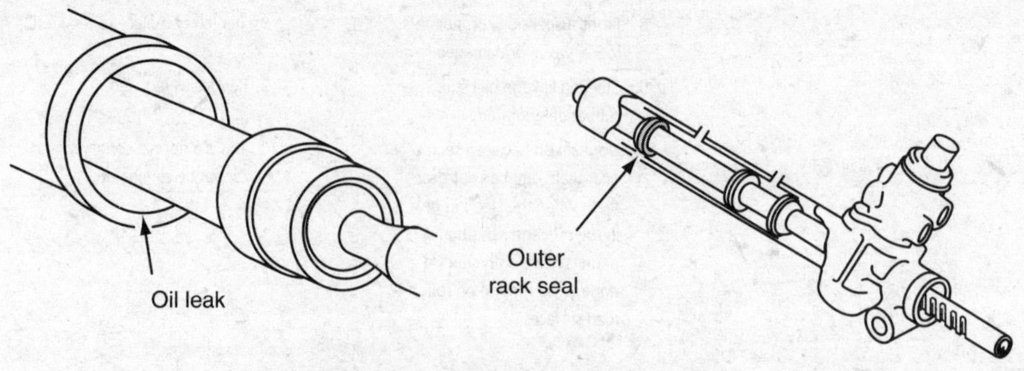

FIGURE 12-16 *Oil leak diagnosis at outer rack seal.*

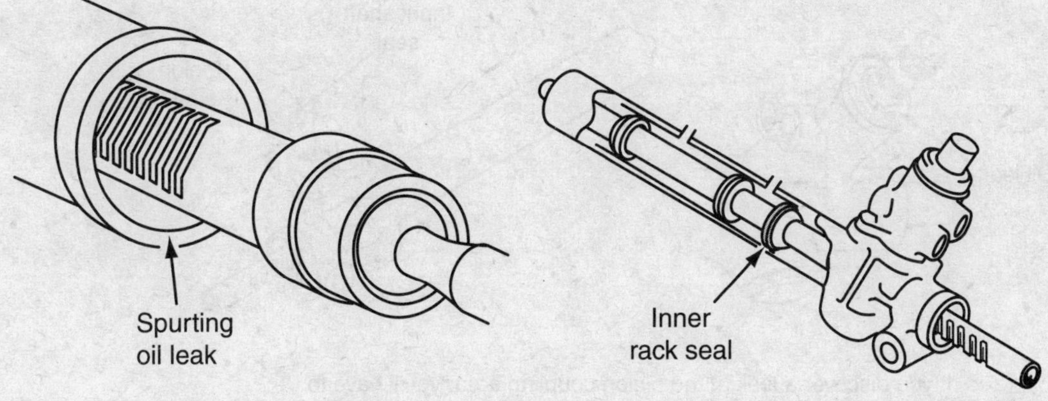

FIGURE 12-17 *Inner rack seal leak diagnosis.*

The inner rack seal is defective if oil leaks from the pinion end of the housing when the rack reaches the left internal stop (Figure 12-17). An oil leak at one rack seal may result in oil leaks from both boots because the oil may travel through the breather tube between the boots.

If an oil leak occurs at the pinion end of the housing and this leak is not influenced when the steering wheel is turned, the pinion seal is defective (Figure 12-18).

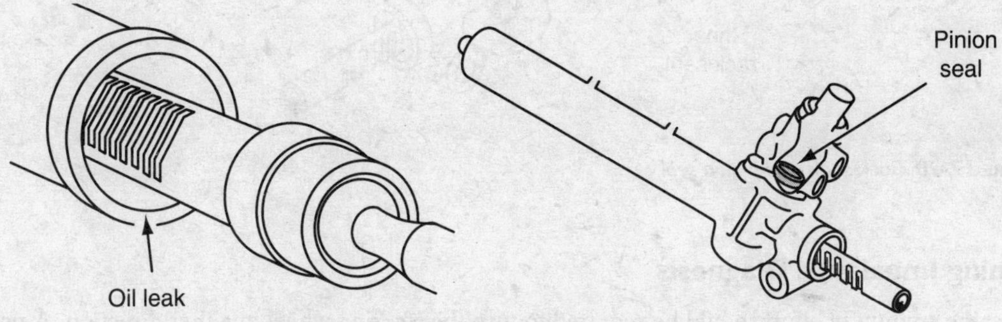

FIGURE 12-18 *Pinion seal leak diagnosis.*

If an oil leak occurs in the pinion coupling area, the input shaft seal is leaking (Figure 12-19). This seal and the pinion seal will require replacement because the pinion seal must be replaced if the pinion is removed.

When the rack is removed, the inner and outer rack seals and the pinion seal must be replaced (Figure 12-20). If oil leaks occur at fittings, these fittings must be torqued to the manufacturer's specifications. If the leak is still present, the line and fitting should be replaced. Leaks in the lines or hoses require line or hose replacement.

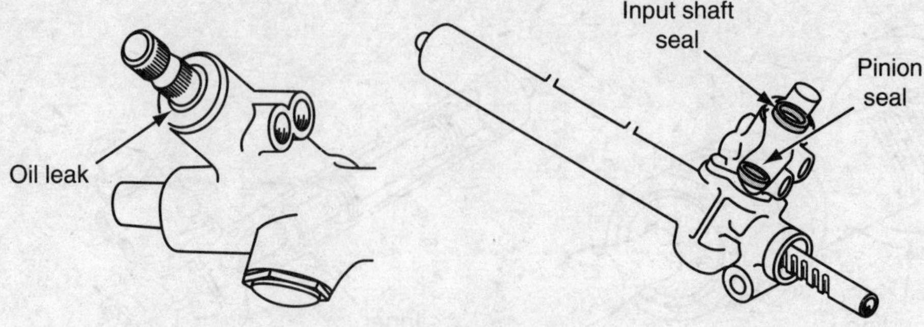

FIGURE 12-19 *Oil leak diagnosis on pinion coupling area.*

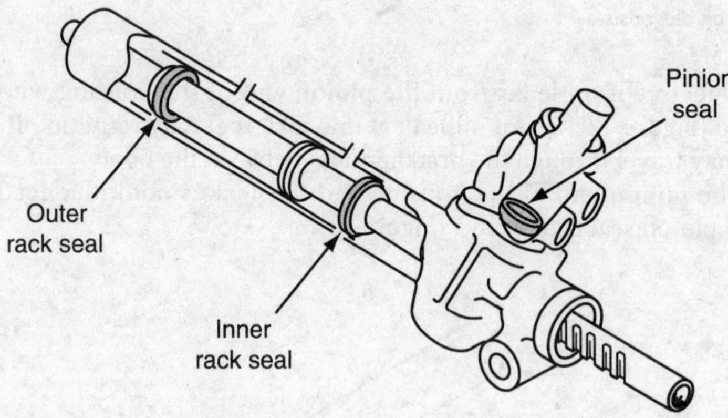

FIGURE 12-20 *Rack seals and pinion seal.*

Turning Imbalance Diagnosis

The same amount of effort should be required to turn the steering wheel in either direction. A pressure gauge connected to the high-pressure hose should indicate the same pressure when the steering wheel is turned in each direction. **Steering effort imbalance** or lower power assist in each direction may be caused by defective rack seals (Figure 12-21). Steering effort imbalance or low power assist in both directions may also be caused by defective rotary valve rings and seals or restricted hoses and lines (Figure 12-22).

Power Rack and Pinion Steering Gear Tie-Rod and Rack Bearing Service

1. Install a holding tool on the steering gear housing, and clamp this tool in a vise (Figure 12-23).
2. Mark the outer tie-rod ends, jam nuts, and tie-rods (Figure 12-24). Loosen the jam nuts and remove the tie-rod ends and jam nuts.

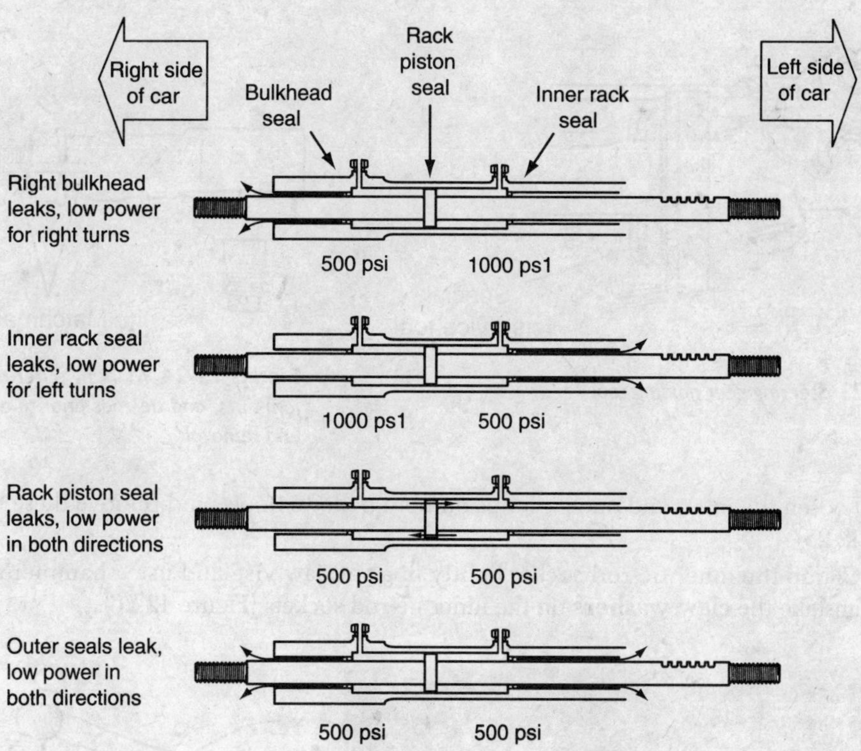

FIGURE 12-21 *Effect of defective rack seals on steering effort imbalance and low power assist.*

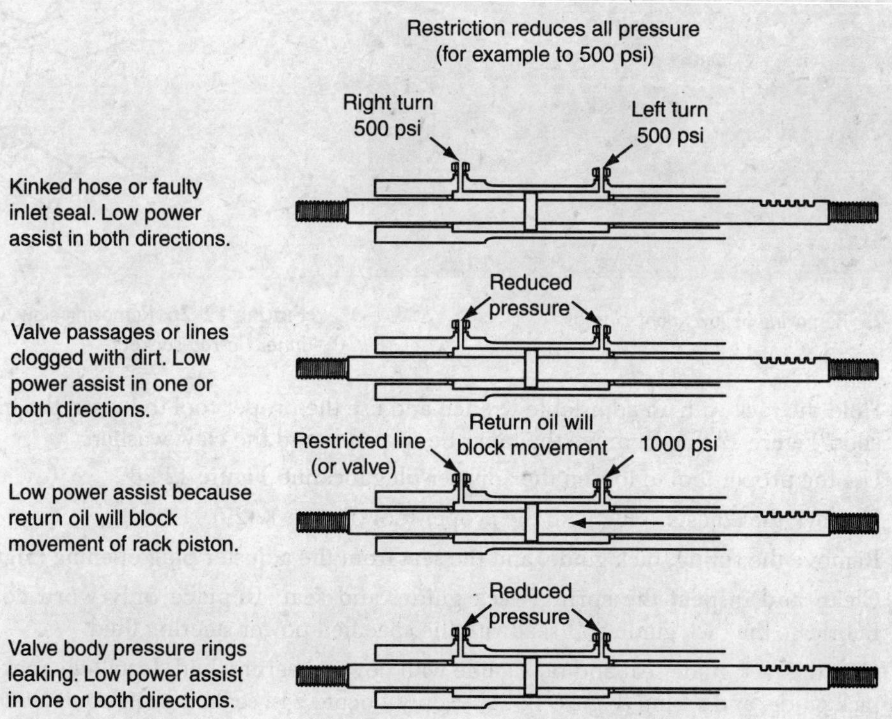

FIGURE 12-22 *Effect of worn rotary valve rings and seals or restricted lines or hoses on steering effort.*

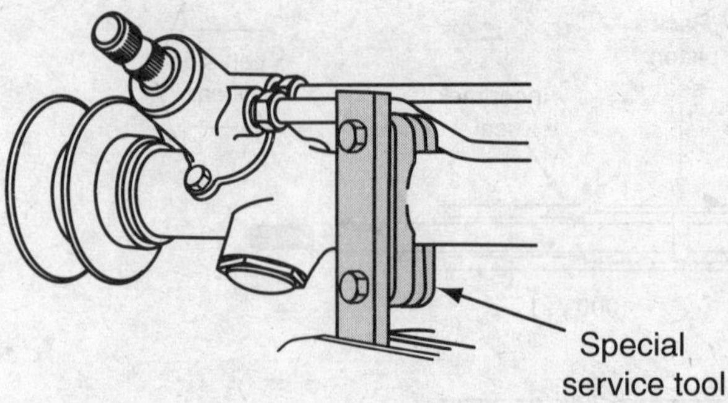

FIGURE 12-23 *Steering gear holding tool.*

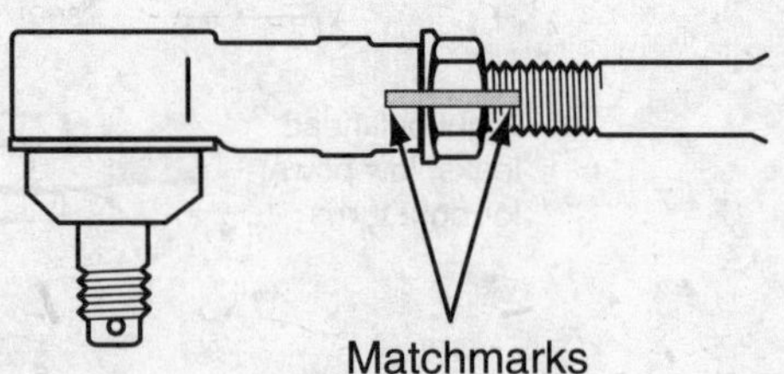

FIGURE 12-24 *Marking outer tie-rod ends, jam nuts, and tie-rods prior to outer tie-rod end removal.*

3. Loosen the inner and outer clamps on both bellows boots, and remove these boots (Figure 12-25).
4. Clamp the inner tie-rod socket lightly in a soft-jaw vise and use a hammer and chisel to unstake the **claw washers** on the inner tie-rod sockets (Figure 12-26).

FIGURE 12-25 *Removing bellows boot clamps.*

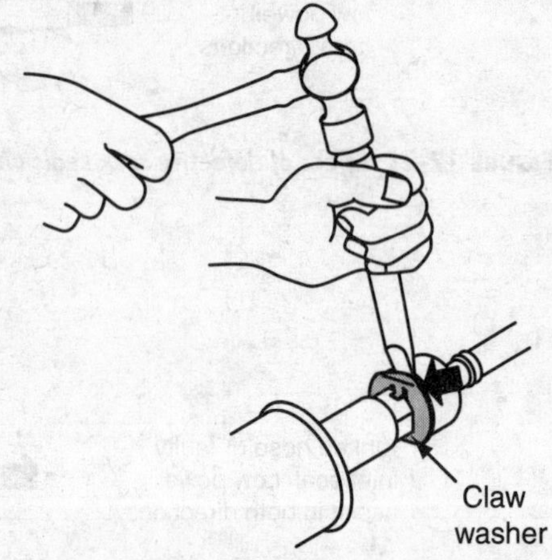

FIGURE 12-26 *Removing claw washers from inner tie-rod sockets.*

5. Hold the rack with an adjustable wrench and use the proper tool to loosen the inner tie-rod ends (Figure 12-27). Remove the inner tie-rod ends and the claw washers.
6. Use the proper tool to loosen the adjuster plug locknut (Figure 12-28).
7. Remove the adjuster plug with the proper tool (Figure 12-29).
8. Remove the spring, rack guide, and the seat from the adjuster plug opening (Figure 12-30).
9. Clean and inspect the spring, rack guide, and seat. Replace only worn components. Lubricate the rack guide and seat with the specified power steering fluid.
10. Coat the rack guide seat and rack guide with power steering fluid. Install the rack guide seat, rack guide, and spring (Figure 12-31). Apply Loctite 242 sealant or its equivalent to the first two or three threads on the rack spring cap. Install the rack spring cap and tighten it to the specified torque (Figure 12-32).

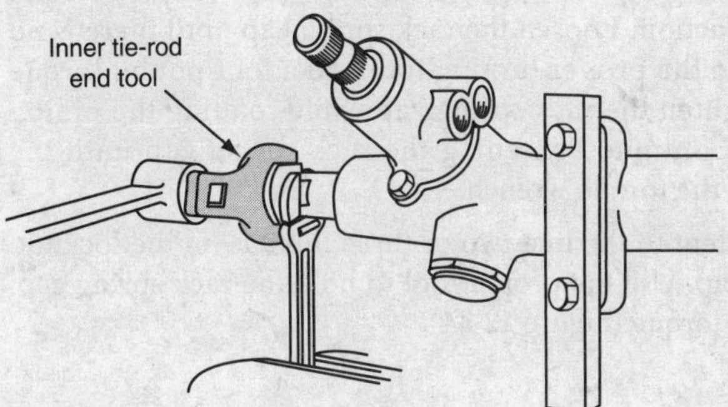

FIGURE 12-27 *Loosening inner tie-rod ends.*

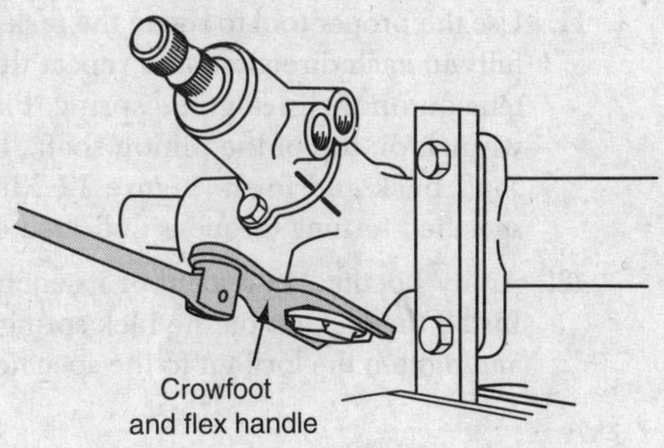

FIGURE 12-28 *Loosening adjuster plug locknut.*

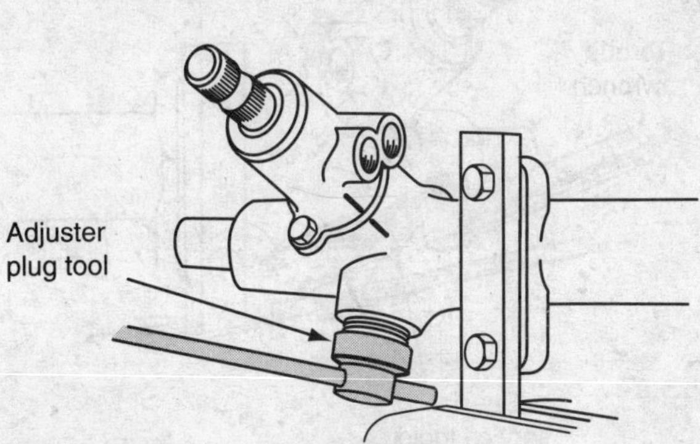

FIGURE 12-29 *Removing adjuster plug.*

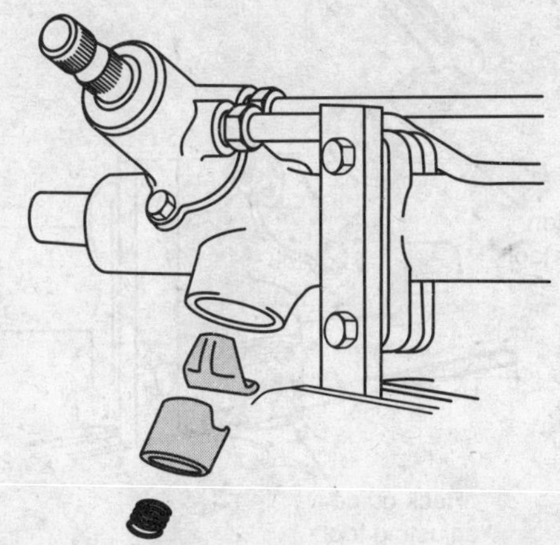

FIGURE 12-30 *Removing spring, rack guide, and seat.*

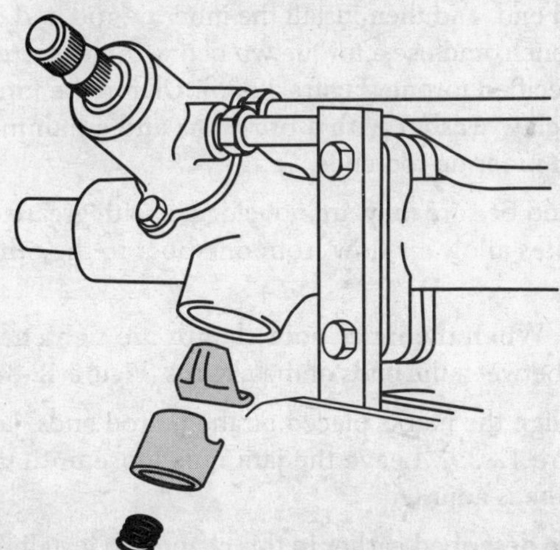

FIGURE 12-31 *Installing rack guide seat, rack guide, and spring.*

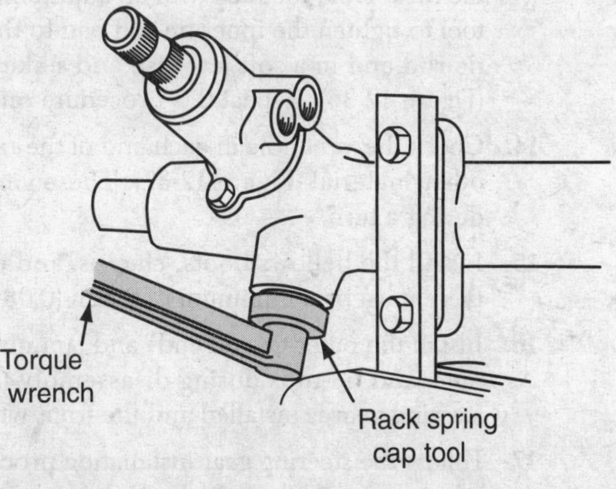

FIGURE 12-32 *Installing rack spring cap.*

11. Use the proper tool to rotate the rack spring cap 12° counterclockwise. Turn the pinion shaft fully in each direction, and repeat this action. Loosen the rack spring cap until there is no tension on the rack guide spring. Place the proper turning tool and a foot-pound torque wrench on top of the pinion shaft. Tighten the rack spring cap while rotating the pinion shaft back and forth (Figure 12-33). Continue tightening the rack spring cap until the specified turning torque is indicated on the torque wrench.
12. Apply Loctite 242 sealant or its equivalent to the first two or three threads on the locknut. Install the locknut on the rack spring cap. Use the proper tool to hold the rack spring cap, and tighten the locknut to the specified torque (Figure 12-34).

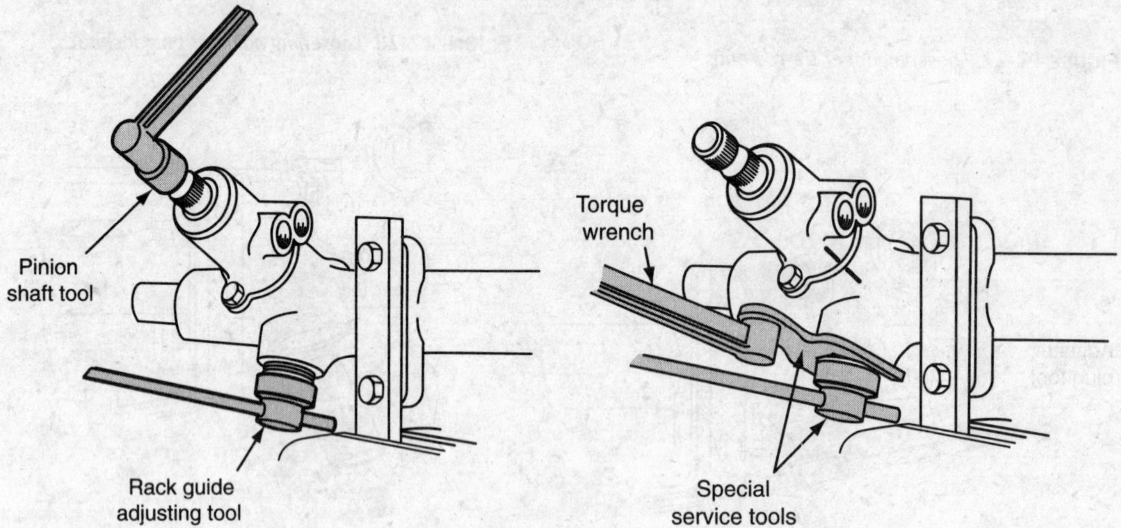

FIGURE 12-33 *Adjusting pinion shaft turning torque.*

FIGURE 12-34 *Tightening locknut on rack spring cap.*

13. Install a new claw washer on the inner tie-rod end, and then install the inner tie-rod end on the rack. Hold the rack with an adjustable wrench, and use a torque wrench with the correct tool to tighten the inner tie-rod end to the specified torque (Figure 12-35). Clamp the inner tie-rod end in a soft-jaw vise and stake the claw washer with a brass bar and a hammer (Figure 12-36). Repeat this procedure on both inner tie-rod ends.
14. Check the vent hole in each end of the rack and be sure they are not clogged with grease or other material (Figure 12-37). These vent holes allow air flow from one boot to the other during a turn.
15. Install the bellows boots, clamps, and clips. When the inner boot clamps are tightened, there must be a minimum of 2 mm (0.08 in.) between the ends of the clamps (Figure 12-38).
16. Install the outer tie-rod ends and jam nuts. Align the marks placed on the tie-rod ends, jam nuts, and tie-rods during disassembly (Figure 12-39). Leave the jam nuts loose until the steering gear is installed and the front wheel toe is adjusted.
17. Follow the steering gear installation procedure described earlier in this chapter to install the steering gear in the vehicle. Tighten all fasteners to the specified torque. (See Chapter 10 for power steering pump filling and bleeding procedure.) Check the front wheel toe and tighten the outer tie-rod end jam nuts to the specified torque. Tighten the outer bellows boot clamps. Road test the vehicle and check for proper steering operation and control.

FIGURE 12-35 *Tightening inner tie-rod end on the rack.*

FIGURE 12-36 *Staking claw washer on inner tie-rod end.*

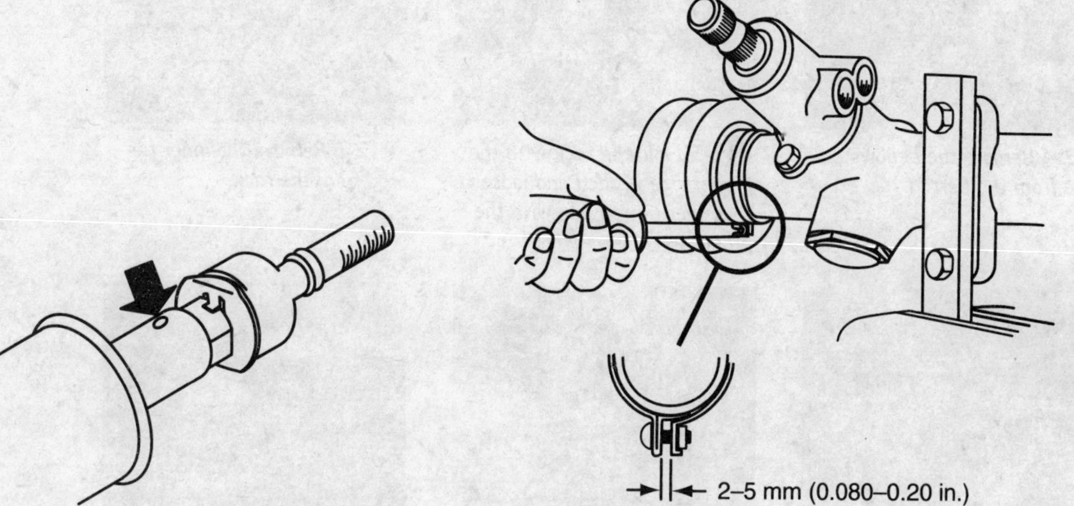

FIGURE 12-37 *Rack vent holes must be open.*

FIGURE 12-38 *Minimum clearance between boot clamp ends.*

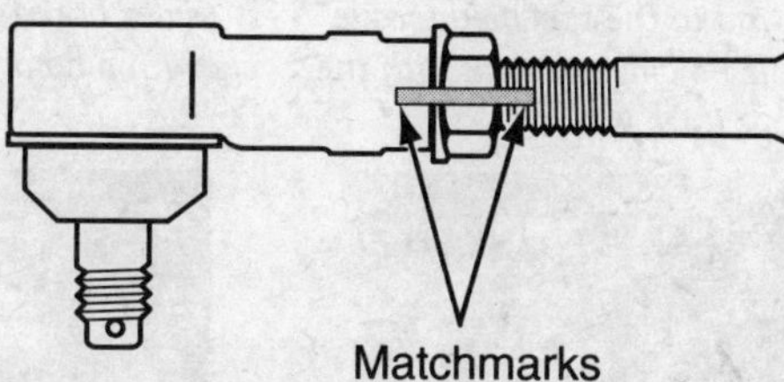

FIGURE 12-39 *Aligning marks on the outer tie-rod ends, jam nuts, and tie-rods.*

Photo Sequence 12 shows a typical procedure for removing and replacing an inner tie-rod end on a power rack and pinion steering gear.

PHOTO SEQUENCE 12
TYPICAL PROCEDURE FOR REMOVING AND REPLACING INNER TIE-ROD END, POWER RACK AND PINION STEERING GEAR

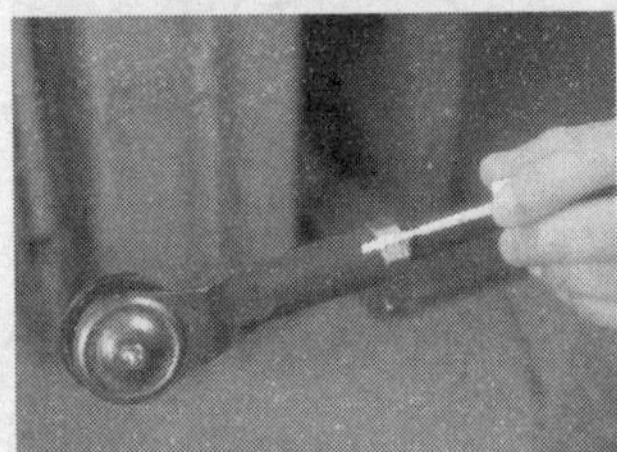

P12-1 *Place an index mark on the outer tie-rod end, jam nut, and tie-rod.*

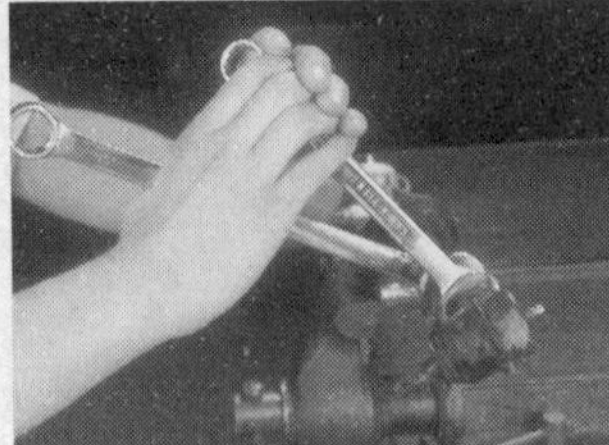

P12-2 *Loosen the jam nut and remove the outer tie-rod end and jam nut.*

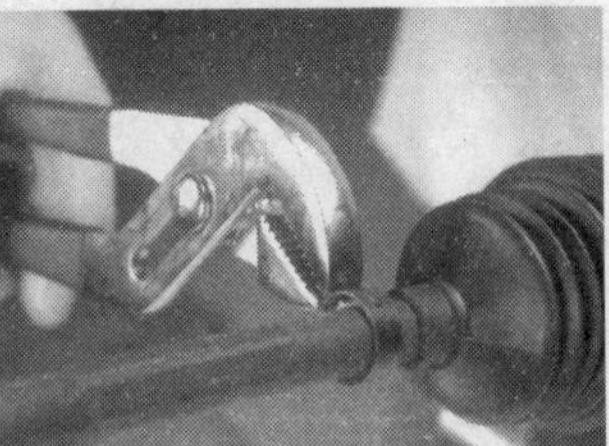

P12-3 *Remove the inner and outer boot clamps.*

P12-4 *Remove the bellows boot from the tie-rod.*

P12-5 *Hold the rack with the proper size wrench and loosen the inner tie-rod end with the proper wrench.*

P12-6 *Remove the inner tie-rod from the rack.*

P12-7 *Be sure the shock damper ring is in place on the rack.*

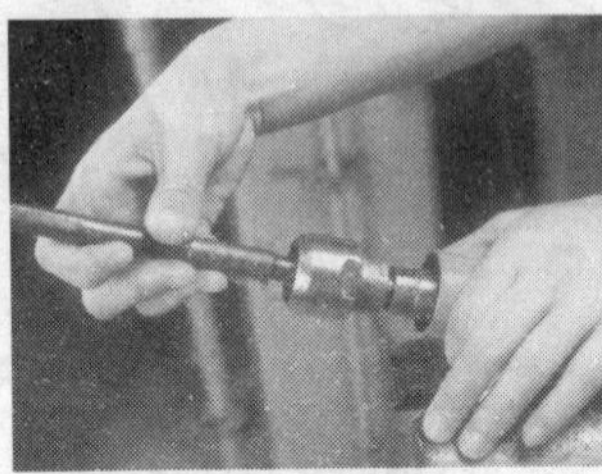

P12-8 *Install the inner tie-rod on the rack, and tighten the tie-rod to the specified torque while holding the rack with the proper size wrench.*

P12-9 *Support the inner tie-rod on a vise, and stake both sides of the inner tie-rod joint with a hammer and punch.*

P12-10 *Use a feeler gauge to measure the clearance between the rack and the inner tie-rod joint housing stake.*

P12-11 *Install the bellows boot and new clamps.*

P12-12 *Install the jam nut and outer tie-rod end with the index marks aligned.*

DIAGNOSIS OF POWER STEERING, STEERING COLUMN AND SUSPENSION SYSTEMS

Some power steering problems may be caused by defects in the steering gear, pump, or column. For example, heavy steering effort may be caused by a defective power steering pump, damaged rack

TABLE 12-2 *Power Steering System, Steering Column, and suspension system Diagnosis*

CONDITION	POSSIBLE CAUSE	CORRECTION
Wander: The vehicle wanders side to side on the roadway when it is driven straight ahead, while the steering wheel is held in a firm position. Evaluation should be conducted on a level road (little road crown).	1. Loose/worn tie-rod ends or ball socket	1. Replace tie-rod end or tie-rod assembly.
	2. Inner ball housing loose or worn	2. Replace tie-rod assemblies.
	3. Gear assembly loose crossmember	3. Tighten the two mounting nuts to specification.
	4. Excessive yoke clearance	4. Adjust yoke clearance.
	5. Loose suspension struts or ball joints	5. Tighten or replace as required.
	6. Column intermediate shaft connecting bolts loose	6. Tighten bolts to specification at gear and column.
	7. Column intermediate shaft joints loose or worn	7. Replace intermediate shaft assembly.
	8. Improper wheel alignment	8. Set alignment to specification.
	9. Tire size and pressure	9. Check tire sizes and adjust tire pressure.
	10. Vehicle unevenly loaded or overloaded	10. Adjust load.
	11. Steering gear mounting insulators and/or attachment bolts loose or damaged	11. Replace insulators and/or attachment nuts and bolts. Tighten to specification.
	12. Steering gear adjustments	12. Refer to steering gear section of *Shop Manual*.
	13. Front end misaligned	13. Check and align to specifications.
	14. Worn front end parts or wheel bearings	14. Inspect and replace affected parts.
	15. Unbalanced or badly worn steering gear control valve	15. Inspect and replace affected parts.
Pulls to one side: The vehicle tends to pull to one side when driven on a level surface.	1. Improper tire pressure	1. Adjust tire pressure.
	2. Improper tire size or different type	2. Replace as required.
	3. Vehicle unevenly or excessively loaded	3. Adjust load.
	4. Improper wheel alignment	4. Adjust as required.
	5. Damaged front suspension components	5. Refer to front suspension section of Shop Manual.
	6. Damaged rear suspension components	6. Refer to rear suspension section of Shop Manual.
	7. Steering gear valve effort out of balance	7. Place transmission in Neutral while driving and turn engine off (coasting). — If vehicle does not pull, replace the steering gear

Table 12-2 *Power Steering System, Steering Column, and suspension system Diagnosis (continued)*

CONDITION	POSSIBLE CAUSE	CORRECTION
		valve assembly. Refer to steering gear section of Shop Manual. — If vehicle does drift: • Cross-switch front tire/wheel assemblies. • If vehicle pulls to opposite side, cross-switch tire/wheel assemblies that were on the rear to the same on the front. • If vehicle pull direction is not changed, check front suspension components and wheel alignment.
	8. Front and rear brakes operation	8. Adjust if necessary.
	9. Bent rear axle housing, or damaged or sagging springs in the front and/or rear suspension	9. Replace if necessary.
	10. Loose/worn shock absorber or suspension attaching fasteners in rear suspension.	10. Tighten all attaching fasteners to specification.

piston and ring, or misalignment of the steering column. Diagnostic information on common power steering problems is provided in Table 12-2. Refer to the vehicle manufacturer's service manual for more complete diagnosis.

DIAGNOSIS OF MAGNASTEER SYSTEMS

The most common customer complaints on Magnasteer systems are continually heavy or light steering effort. When diagnosing a Magnasteer system, the first step is to visually inspect the system. Be sure the power steering fluid level is correct, and check the power steering belt tension. Inspect the wiring harness connected to the actuator solenoid in the steering gear.

CAUTION: Always be sure the ignition switch is off when connecting or disconnecting the scan tool. Computer system and/or scan tool damage may occur if the ignition switch is on when connecting or disconnecting the scan tool from the data link connector (DLC).

If the visual inspection does not locate any defects, connect a scan tool to the DLC near the steering column under the dash (Figure 12-40). Turn the ignition switch on and select the Electronic Brake and Traction Control Module (EBTCM) on the scan tool menu. If there is an electrical defect in the actuator solenoid, connecting wires, or EBTCM, Diagnostic Trouble Code (DTC) C1241 will be displayed on the scan tool. To locate the exact cause of this DTC, perform voltmeter tests on the actuator solenoid and connecting wires. A detailed diagnostic chart is included in the vehicle manufacturer's service manual.

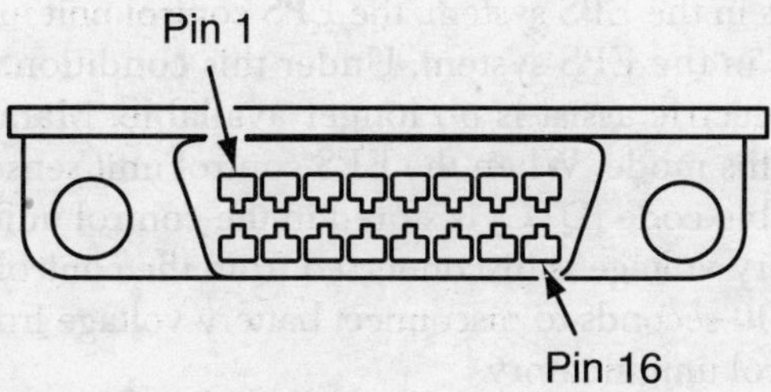

FIGURE 12-40 *Data link connector (DLC) on-board diagnostic II (OBD-II) system.*

If the customer complains about continually heavy or light steering and there are no defects in the Magnasteer system, reprogramming of the system may be required.

To reprogram the system, follow these steps:

1. Connect the scan tool to the DLC.
2. Select Magnasteer and Recalibration on the scan tool.
3. Respond to the VIN query on the scan tool. If the displayed VIN is incorrect, enter the correct VIN.
4. When Factory Standard Calibration Will Be Used For This VIN appears on the scan tool, press Enter on the scan tool to install factory calibration.
5. When calibration is complete, disconnect the scan tool.

DIAGNOSIS OF RACK-DRIVE ELECTRONIC POWER STEERING

When the ignition switch is turned on, in a vehicle with **rack-drive electronic power steering** electronic power steering (EPS) light in the instrument panel should be illuminated (Figure 12-41). This EPS light action proves the bulb and related circuit are functioning normally. When the engine starts, the EPS light is turned off by the EPS control unit if there are no electrical defects in the EPS system. The EPS light should remain off while the engine is running.

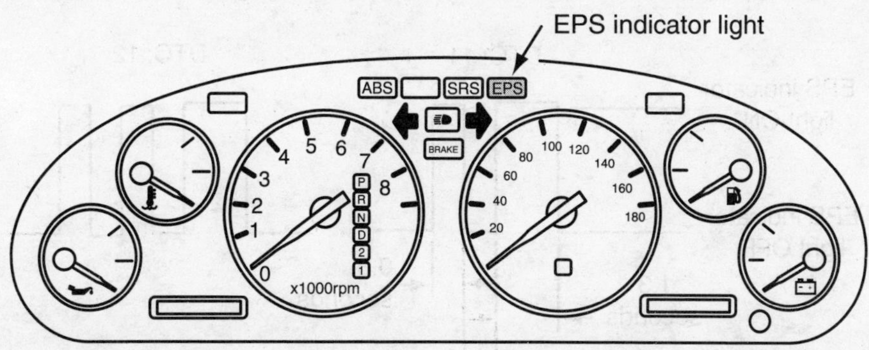

FIGURE 12-41 *Electronic power steering (EPS) warning light.*

If an electrical defect occurs in the EPS system, the EPS control unit turns on the EPS light to alert the driver that a defect exists in the EPS system. Under this condition, the EPS control unit shuts down the EPS system, and electric assist is no longer available. Manual steering with increased steering effort is provided in this mode. When the EPS control unit senses an electrical defect in the EPS system, a diagnostic trouble code (DTC) is stored in the control unit memory. The EPS control unit memory is erased if battery voltage is disconnected from the control unit. The 7.5 ampere clock fuse may be disconnected for 10 seconds to disconnect battery voltage from the EPS control unit and erase the DTCs from the control unit memory.

If the EPS light is on with the engine running, shut the ignition switch off and disconnect the clock fuse for 10 seconds; then road test the car to determine if the EPS light comes back on. If the EPS light comes on again with the engine running, proceed with the diagnosis. Locate the two-wire EPS service check connector under the glove box. With the ignition switch off, connect a special jumper wire to the service check connector (Figure 12-42). This connects the two wires together in the service check connector. When the ignition switch is turned on, the EPS light begins to flash DTCs. Each DTC is indicated by a long light flash or flashes followed by a short flash or flashes. For example, DTC 11 is one long flash followed by a short flash, and DTC 12 is one long flash followed by two short flashes (Figure 12-43). If more than one DTC is stored in the EPS control unit memory, these DTCs are

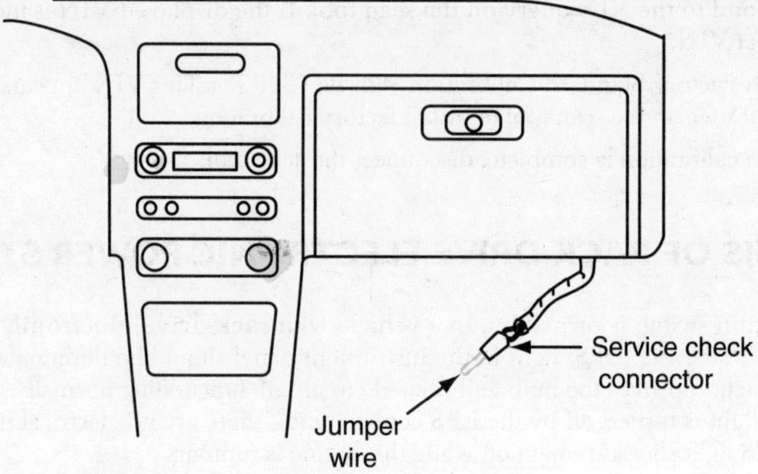

FIGURE 12-42 *EPS system service check connector and special jumper wire.*

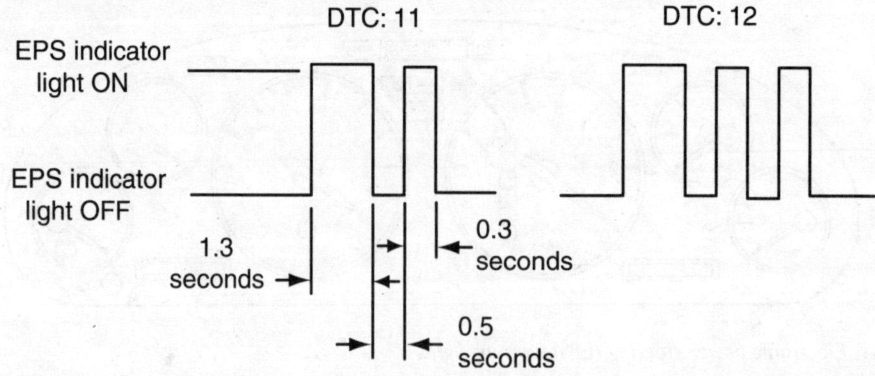

FIGURE 12-43 *DTC 11 is one long flash followed by a short flash, and DTC 12 is one long flash followed by two short flashes.*

flashed in numerical order. The DTC sequence continues until the ignition switch is turned off. Be sure to remove the special jumper wire after the ignition switch is turned off.

All the possible DTCs in the EPS system are provided in Figure 12-44. A DTC indicates a defect in a certain area. For example, DTC 11 indicates high or low voltage from the torque sensor. The defect may be in the sensor itself, or the problem could be in the connecting wires from the sensor to the control unit. Tests usually have to be performed with a voltmeter or ohmmeter to locate the exact cause of the defect. Detailed diagnostic charts are provided in the car manufacturer's service manual.

Diagnostic trouble code (DTC)	EPS indicator light	Description/symptom	Diagnostic period			After detecting for system	Reset	
			Individual diagnosis	Individual diagnosis	Regular diagnosis		Individual diagnosis	Individual diagnosis
—	O	EPS indicator light does not come on when ignition is switched ON						17-27
—	O	EPS indicator light does not go off after engine is started				System OFF		17-29
3	O	A problem with the current sensor offset	O			^		17-36
4	O	A problem with the current sensor offset	O	O		^	O	
5	O	A problem with the current sensor fixed		O		^	O	
6	O	A problem with the current sensor fixed		O		^	O	
11	O	A problem the high voltage with or low voltage of the torque sensor (TRQ1 and TRQ2)		O		^	O	17-31
12	O	A problem with the voltage for torque sensor (TRQ3)		O		^	O	
13	O	A problem with the average of voltage on TRQ1 and TRQ2		O		^	O	
14	O	A problem with the 2.5-V reference voltage		O		^	O	
21	O	A problem with the circuit for the input motor voltage in the EPS control unit	O	O	O	^	O	17-36
22	O	A problem with the lower current			O	^	O	
23	O	A problem with the circuit for check function in the EPS control unit	O	O		^	O	
24	O	The fail-safe relay or power relay is stuck ON	O			^	O	
25	O	The lower FET is stuck ON	O			^	O	
26	O	The upper FET is stuck ON	O			^	O	
31	O	A problem with the voltage for IG1	O	O		^	O	—
33	O	A problem with the average of VSS1 and VSS2			O	^	O	17-38
34	O	A problem with the CPU in the EPS control unit	O	O	O	^	O	Replace EPS control unit

- Initial diagnosis: Performed right after the engine starts until the EPS indicator light goes off.
- Regular diagnosis: Continuously performed (under some conditions) after the EPS indicator goes off and engine is running.
- Individual part/system diagnosis: Diagnoses a specific part/system under its operating conditions.
- CPU: Central Processing Unit.

FIGURE 12-44 *DTC list for EPS system.*

DIAGNOSIS OF COLUMN-DRIVE ELECTRONIC POWER STEERING

When diagnosing a **column-drive EPS**, the first step is to verify the customer complaint. Road test the vehicle if necessary to be sure the complaint is identified. The next step is to perform a visual inspection of the EPS using the following steps:

1. Inspect all EPS electrical connections for corrosion or looseness including ground connections.
2. Inspect EPS wiring for damaged insulation.
3. Be sure the vehicle is equipped with the vehicle manufacturer's specified tire and wheel sizes.
4. Inspect the steering column and EPS components for collision damage.
5. Be sure the battery is fully charged and that the battery connections are clean and tight.
6. Check all the EPS fuses.
7. Inspect the vehicle for aftermarket accessories such as stereo equipment that could affect the EPS operation if they are improperly installed.
8. Search for service bulletins related to the EPS complaint.

Repair any problems discovered during the visual inspection. If the visual inspection did not locate any problems, perform a diagnostic system check using the following procedure:

1. Be sure the ignition switch is off, and connect a scan tool to the data link connector (DLC) under the left side of the dash.
2. Turn on the ignition switch, and select Vehicle DTC Information on the scan tool. If the scan tool displays No Comm. From Any Computer, repair the data link communication problem by referring to the appropriate diagnostic procedure in the vehicle manufacturer's service manual.
3. Be sure the engine cranks and starts properly.
4. Turn on the ignition switch with the engine stopped, and select List All DTCs on the scan tool.
5. Record all DTCs displayed on the scan tool. Check for DTCs from other computer systems that may affect the EPS system. For example, a DTC representing the VSS is displayed as a PCM DTC, but this sensor signal is transmitted on the data links to the PSCM and affects EPS operation.

Repair the causes of the DTCs displayed on the scan tool. Some typical EPS DTCs are:

1. C0460 steering position sensor
2. C0475 electric steering motor circuit
3. C0545 steering wheel torque input sensor
4. C0870 PSCM voltage range performance

In these **On-Board Diagnostic II (OBD II)** DTCs the first letter C indicates the DTC is related to a chassis problem. If the second digit in the DTC is a 0, the DTC is a universal Society of Automotive Engineers (SAE) code. When the second digit in the DTC is a 1, a vehicle manufacturer's code is indicated. The third digit in the DTC indicates the sub-system to which the DTC belongs, and the last two digits indicate the specific area where the fault exists. A complete list of DTCs is provided in the vehicle manufacturer's service manual. Some scan tools provide an explanation of each DTC indicating the area where the problem is located. A DTC indicates only the area in which a problem exists. Voltmeter and ohmmeter tests may be required to test the circuit and locate the exact cause of the problem. The vehicle manufacturer's service manual also provides a detailed diagnostic procedure for each DTC. Always follow these diagnostic procedures when diagnosing the cause of a DTC.

Scan Tool Data Display

The scan tool also displays the following EPS data which are very helpful when diagnosing EPS defects:

1. Battery voltage – The scan tool displays 6.5 V to 16.5 V as sensed at the power steering control module.
2. Calculated system temperature – The ambient temperature up to 275° F (135° C) as sensed by an internal temperature sensor in the PSCM.
3. Motor command – The amount of EPS assist motor current commanded by the PSCM.
4. Steering shaft torque – The amount of torque being applied to the steering column shaft. A positive value indicates a right turn, and a negative number indicates a left turn.
5. Steering position sensor voltage 1 – The amount of steering position sensor voltage from the sensor signal 1 circuit. The voltage range is 0 V to 5 V as the steering wheel is turned.
6. Steering position sensor voltage 2 – The amount of steering position sensor voltage from the sensor signal 2 circuit. The voltage range is 0 V to 5 V as the steering wheel is turned.
7. Steering tuning – The scan tool displays 1 or 2 depending on the vehicle. Steering tuning 1 is for 4-cylinder engines, and steering tuning 2 is for 6-cylinder engines. Steering tuning 3 is for the extended sedan.
8. Steering wheel position – The scan tool displays from 562° to –562° indicating the number of degrees the steering wheel has been turned for the center position. A positive number indicates a right turn, and a negative number indicates a left turn.
9. Torque sensor signal 1 – The scan tool displays 0.25 V to 4.75 V indicating the voltage from the steering shaft torque sensor 1 circuit.
10. Torque sensor signal 2 – The scan tool displays 0.25 V to 4.75 V indicating the voltage from the steering shaft torque sensor 2 circuit.
11. Vehicle speed – The actual vehicle speed from 0 to 158 mph (255 km/h).

Steering Position Sensor Calibration

If the PSCM or steering column is replaced, use the scan tool to calibrate the center position of the steering wheel position sensor as follows:

1. Be sure the ignition switch is off, and connect the scan tool to the DLC.
2. Turn on the ignition switch, but do not start the engine.
3. Turn the steering wheel from lock-to-lock and count the number of turns. From the fully left or fully right position, turn the steering wheel back toward the center position one-half the total number of turns.
4. Select Special Functions on the scan tool.
5. Select Steering Position Sensor Calibration on the scan tool and press the enter key. The scan tool screen indicates Calibration in Progress during the calibration procedure.
6. When the calibration process is completed, and the scan tool displays Calibration Completed, press the exit key.
7. Use the scan tool to clear any DTCs.
8. Turn off the ignition switch and disconnect the scan tool.

Torque Sensor Calibration

If the PSCM or steering column is replaced, a scan tool must be used to perform a center position calibration for the steering shaft torque sensor as described in the following steps:

1. Be sure the ignition switch is off, and connect the scan tool to the DLC.

2. Turn on the ignition switch, but do not start the engine.
3. Turn the steering wheel from lock-to-lock and count the number of turns. From the fully left or fully right position, turn the steering wheel back toward the center position one-half the total number of turns.
4. After the steering wheel is centered, remove your hands or any other objects from the steering wheel. Be sure the suspension is relaxed, and that no uneven force is applied to the steering system.
5. Select Special Functions on the scan tool.
6. Select Torque Sensor Calibration on the scan tool and press the enter key. The scan tool screen indicates Calibration in Progress during the calibration procedure.
7. When the calibration process is completed, and the scan tool displays Calibration Completed, press the exit key.
8. Use the scan tool to clear any DTCs.
9. Turn off the ignition switch and disconnect the scan tool.

If the PSCM and motor assembly is removed from the steering column, inspect the steering column assist mechanism input shaft for the rotor isolator bumper (Figure 12-45). If present, the isolator bumper should be removed from the input shaft, and this bumper must be installed in the rotor isolator in the PSCM and motor assembly. Remove any debris from the steering column assist mechanism housing, but do not remove the remaining grease on the steering column assist mechanism input shaft.

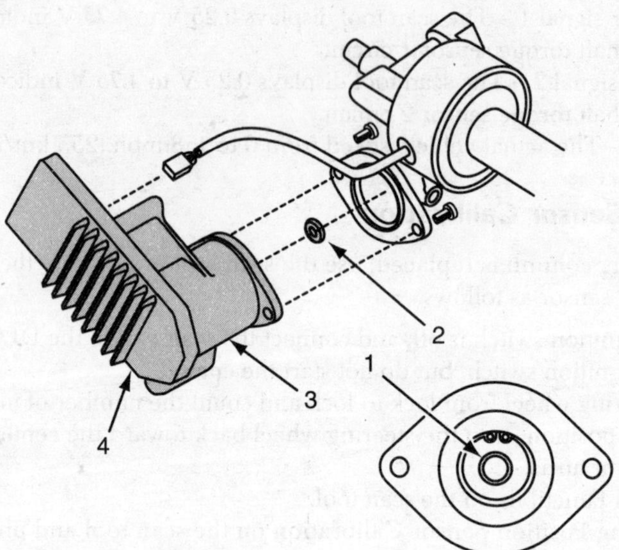

Figure 12-45 *Removing and replacing the PSCM and motor assembly.*

Steering Tuning Selection

If the PSCM is replaced, these steps must be followed to perform a steering tuning procedure:

1. Be sure the ignition switch is off, and connect the scan tool to the DLC.
2. Turn on the ignition switch, but do not start the engine.
3. Select Special Functions on the scan tool.
4. Select Steering Tuning Selection on the scan tool and press the enter key. The scan tool screen indicates Selection in Progress during the selection procedure.

5. When the selection process is completed, and the scan tool displays Selection Completed, press the exit key.
6. Use the scan tool to clear any DTCs.
7. Turn off the ignition switch and disconnect the scan tool.

CASE STUDY

A customer complains about excessive steering effort on a 2004 Cadillac CTS. The technician road tested the car and found no evidence of hard steering. Further questioning of the customer revealed that the problem only occurred when the engine was first started in the morning after the car had been parked all night. The service writer informed the customer that the car would have to be parked overnight in the shop and then diagnosed the following morning. The customer complied with this request.

Prior to starting the engine the next morning, the technician connected a power steering pressure test gauge in series with the high-pressure hose. When the engine was started, the technician discovered the steering effort was very high, and the steering felt much like manual steering while the steering wheel was turned. However, the power steering pump pressure on the pressure gauge was higher than specified. Once the steering wheel was turned in one direction, the steering effort quickly decreased to normal. Since the power steering pump pressure was higher than specified, the technician concluded the pump and drive belt must be in satisfactory condition. The technician also reasoned that other causes of excessive steering effort, such as binding in the steering column or flexible coupling, would be constant. Therefore, the technician decided that the problem must be in the steering gear.

After receiving the customer's approval to remove and inspect the steering gear, the gear was removed and disassembled. The technician found the rack cylinder was severely ridged and scored in the center area, and the Teflon ring on the rack piston was badly worn. The customer was advised that the steering gear required replacement. A replacement steering gear was installed, and the system was flushed and refilled with power steering fluid. When the engine was started, the steering effort and the power steering pump pressure were normal.

SERVICE TIPS

- To provide equal turning effort in both directions, the rack must be centered with the front wheels straight ahead.
- A common problem with power rack and pinion steering gears is excessive steering effort when the car is first started after sitting overnight. The steering effort becomes normal, however, after the steering wheel is turned several times. This problem usually indicates severe scoring where the pinion sealing rings contact the pinion housing. Steering gear replacement is required to correct this problem.
- In some power rack and pinion steering gears, the inner tie-rod ends are staked after they are installed on the rack (refer to Photo Sequence 12 later in this chapter). In other power rack and pinion steering gears, a pin retains the inner tie-rod ends to the rack, and this pin must be removed before the inner tie-rod ends are removed. When the inner tie-rod ends are replaced, a new retaining pin must be installed.
- A scored cylinder surface in the steering gear housing may cause temporary excessive steering effort after the car sits overnight.

- Some generic scan tools do not have the capability to reprogram computers.
- If the special jumper wire is left in the EPS service connector and the engine is started, the malfunction indicator light (MIL) for the engine computer system is illuminated.
- If DTC 33 is set in the EPS control unit memory, the EPS system remains functional, but the EPS light is illuminated.
- When connecting certain scan tools to controller area network (CAN) or local area network (LAN) data link systems, a CANdi module must be connected in series between the scan tool and the DLC. Always refer to the vehicle manufacturer's recommended procedure.
- After the ignition switch is turned off, wait 25 seconds before performing any procedures that require disconnecting the vehicle battery. If this precaution is not observed, the PSCM memory may be erased. This precaution also applies to torque sensor calibration and steering tuning selection.
- The combination steering wheel position sensor and steering shaft torque sensor are not serviced separately; the steering column and these two sensors are replaced as an assembly. The PSCM and motor can be replaced as an assembly separate from the steering column.

Review Questions

1. While discussing steering wheel free play:
Technician A says excessive steering wheel free play may be caused by a worn outer tie-rod end. *Technician B* says excessive steering wheel free play may be caused by loose steering gear mounting bushings.
Who is correct?
A. A only **C.** Both A and B
B. B only **D.** Neither A nor B

2. While discussing steering effort:
Technician A says a tight rack bearing adjustment may cause excessive steering effort. *Technician B* says a loose inner tie-rod end may cause excessive steering effort.
Who is correct?
A. A only **C.** Both A and B
B. B only **D.** Neither A nor B

3. While discussing steering gear removal and replacement on air-bag-equipped vehicles:
Technician A says the steering column should be locked in the centered position to prevent air bag deployment. *Technician B* says the rack should be centered in the housing prior to steering gear installation.
Who is correct?
A. A only **C.** Both A and B
B. B only **D.** Neither A nor B

4. While discussing power rack and pinion steering gear adjustment:
Technician A says the self-locking nut on the pinion shaft should be rotated to adjust the pinion shaft bearing preload. *Technician B* says the rack spring cap should be rotated to obtain the specified turning torque on the pinion shaft.
Who is correct?
A. A only **C.** Both A and B
B. B only **D.** Neither A nor B

5. While discussing manual rack and pinion steering gear lubrication:
Technician A says the pilot bearing should be lubricated with anhydrous calcium grease. *Technician B* says the rack and rack teeth should be coated with lithium-based grease.
Who is correct?
A. A only **C.** Both A and B
B. B only **D.** Neither A nor B

6. All of these statements about diagnosing and servicing power rack and pinion steering gears are true EXCEPT:
A. The inner rack seal may be defective if oil leaks from the pinion end of the housing when the rack reaches the left inner stop.
B. A leaking rack piston seal causes increased steering effort in one direction.
C. Leaking Teflon rings on the rotary valve may increase steering effort in both directions.
D. If the pinion shaft is removed, the pinion seal and the input shaft seal must be replaced.

7. When diagnosing and servicing power rack and pinion steering gears:
A. The rack should not be held when the outer tie-rod ends are loosened on the rack.
B. In some steering gears, claw washers lock the tie-rods in position on the rack.
C. A straightedge must be used to check the rack for a bent condition.
D. Bent tie-rods may be straightened in a hydraulic press and then reinstalled.

8. When diagnosing and servicing power rack and pinion steering gears:
A. Teflon rings on the rack piston may be expanded by heating them with a propane torch.
B. A bent rack may cause excessive steering wheel free play.
C. A compressing tool may be used to compress the Teflon rings on the rotary valve prior to installation.
D. A scored cylinder surface in the steering housing may cause excessive steering wheel kickback.

9. When diagnosing electronic power steering (EPS) systems:
A. The EPS system enters the diagnostic mode when the ignition switch is cycled three times in a 5-second interval.
B. If the EPS warning light is on with the engine shut off and the ignition switch on, there is a defect in the EPS system.
C. The EPS warning light flashes diagnostic trouble codes (DTCs) in numerical order.
D. The EPS control unit memory has the capability to store only one DTC.

10. When diagnosing electronic power steering (EPS) systems:
A. The DTCs may be erased from the EPS control unit by disconnecting the stop light fuse for 10 seconds.
B. A DTC indicates the exact cause of an electrical defect in the EPS system.
C. If a DTC is stored in the EPS control unit memory, the EPS system is usually inoperative and manual steering is available.
D. In the EPS diagnostic mode if the EPS warning light provides two long flashes followed by two short flashes, code 2 is indicated.

CHALLENGE QUESTIONS

1. While discussing power rack and pinion steering gears:
Technician A says inner rack seal leaks can cause power rack and pinion steering to turn easier in one direction than another. *Technician B* says a hissing noise is normal when the steering is turned to the limit on either side.

Who is correct?

A. A only **C.** Both A and B

B. B only **D.** Neither A nor B

2. Wandering or poor straight-ahead tracking may be caused by all of the following EXCEPT:

A. Worn or loose rack mounting bushings.

B. Rack piston seal leaks.

C. Steering gear off-center.

D. Loose or worn tie-rod ends.

3. A customer says his front-wheel-drive car with power rack and pinion steering is hard to steer for several minutes the first time the car is driven during the day.

Technician A says the cause of the problem could be a plugged spool valve spring. *Technician B* says the cause of the problem could be a scored steering gear cylinder.

Who is correct?

A. A only **C.** Both A and B

B. B only **D.** Neither A nor B

4. A front-wheel-drive car requires very heavy steering effort in the parking lot but seems not too bad on the highway. Tire pressure is fine. After checking the fluid and finding the level is OK, you should:

A. Check the engine idle speed.

B. Look for steering system leaks.

C. Check the tie-rod ends.

D. Inspect the rack for damage.

5. *Technician A* says an oil leak at one rack seal may result in oil leaking from both boots. *Technician B* says the inner rack seal is defective if oil leaks from the pinion end of the housing when the rack reaches the left internal stop.

Who is correct?

A. A only **C.** Both A and B

B. B only **D.** Neither A nor B

JOB SHEET 37

Name ______________________________ Date ______________

INSPECT MANUAL OR POWER RACK AND PINION STEERING GEAR AND TIE-RODS

Upon completion of this job sheet, you should be able to inspect manual or power rack and pinion steering gears and tie-rods.

ASE Correlation

This job sheet is related to ASE Automotive Suspension and Steering Task: *Inspect and replace inner tie-rod ends and related components on rack and pinion steering gears.*

Tools and Materials

Tape measure

Describe the Vehicle Being Worked On:

Year __________ Make ______________ Model ____________
VIN ____________ Engine type and size ____________
Make of steering gear ______________________

Procedure

Task Completed

1. With the front wheels straight ahead and the engine stopped, rock the steering wheel gently back and forth with light finger pressure, and measure the maximum steering wheel free play with a tape measure.

   Specified steering wheel free play ______________________

   Actual steering wheel free play ______________________

   State the necessary repairs to correct steering wheel free play.

   ____

   ____

   ____

   ____

2. With the vehicle sitting on the shop floor and the front wheels straight ahead, have an assistant turn the steering wheel about 1/4 turn in both directions. Watch for looseness in the steering shaft and the flexible coupling or universal joints.

   Looseness in U-joints or flexible coupling: ☐ Satisfactory ☐ Unsatisfactory

   Looseness in steering shaft: ☐ Satisfactory ☐ Unsatisfactory

   State the necessary repairs and explain the reasons for your diagnosis.

   ____

   ____

   ____

   ____

Task Completed

3. While an assistant turns the steering wheel about 1/2 turn in both directions, watch for movement of the steering gear housing in the mounting bushings.

   Looseness in steering gear mounting bushings: ☐ Satisfactory ☐ Unsatisfactory

   State the necessary repairs and explain the reasons for your diagnosis.

   ____
   ____
   ____
   ____

4. Grasp the pinion shaft extending from the steering gear and attempt to move it vertically. If there is steering shaft vertical movement, a pinion bearing preload adjustment may be required. When the steering gear does not have a pinion bearing preload adjustment, replace the necessary steering gear components.

   Excessive pinion shaft vertical endplay: ☐ Satisfactory ☐ Unsatisfactory

   State the necessary repairs and explain the reasons for your diagnosis.

   ____
   ____
   ____
   ____

5. Road test the vehicle and check for excessive steering effort. A bent steering rack, tight rack bearing adjustment, or damaged front drive axle joints in front-wheel-drive cars may cause excessive steering effort.

   Steering effort: ☐ Satisfactory ☐ Excessive

   State the necessary repairs and explain the reasons for your diagnosis.

   ____
   ____
   ____
   ____

6. Visually inspect the bellows boots for cracks, splits, leaks, and proper clamp installation. Replace any boot that indicates any of these conditions.

   Condition of tie-rod bellows boots and clamps:

   Left side boot: ☐ Satisfactory ☐ Unsatisfactory

   Right side boot: ☐ Satisfactory ☐ Unsatisfactory

   State the necessary repairs and explain the reasons for your diagnosis.

   ____
   ____
   ____
   ____

Task Completed

7. Loosen the inner bellows boot clamps and move each boot toward the outer tie-rod end until the inner tie-rod end is visible. Push outward and inward on each front tire, and watch for movement in the inner tie-rod end. An alternate method of checking the inner tie-rod ends is to squeeze the bellows boots and grasp the inner tie-rod end socket. Movement in the inner tie-rod end is then felt as the front wheel is moved inward and outward. Hard plastic bellows boots may be found on some applications. With this type of bellows boot, remove the ignition key from the switch to lock the steering column, and push inward and outward on the front tire while observing any lateral movement in the tie-rod.

Condition of inner tie-rod ends:

Left side inner tie-rod end: ☐ Satisfactory ☐ Unsatisfactory

Right side inner tie-rod end: ☐ Satisfactory ☐ Unsatisfactory

State the necessary repairs and explain the reasons for your diagnosis.

____

____

____

____

WARNING: Bent steering components must be replaced. Never straighten steering components because this action may weaken the metal and result in sudden component failure, serious personal injury, and vehicle damage.

8. Grasp each outer tie-rod end and check for vertical movement. While an assistant turns the steering wheel 1/4 turn in each direction, watch for looseness in the outer tie-rod ends. Check the outer tie-rod end seals for cracks and proper installation of the nuts and cotter pins. Cracked seals must be replaced. Inspect the tie-rods for a bent condition.

tie-rod and outer tie-rod end condition:

Left side tie-rod and outer tie-rod end condition: ☐ Satisfactory ☐ Unsatisfactory

Right side tie-rod and outer tie-rod end condition: ☐ Satisfactory ☐ Unsatisfactory

List the necessary repairs and explain the reasons for your diagnosis.

____

____

____

____

Instructor's Response ________________________________

____

____

JOB SHEET 38

Name ______________________________ Date ______________

REMOVE AND REPLACE MANUAL OR POWER RACK AND PINION STEERING GEAR

Upon completion of this job sheet, you should be able to remove and replace manual or power rack and pinion steering gears.

ASE Correlation

This job sheet is related to ASE Automotive Suspension and Steering Task List: *Remove and replace power rack and pinion steering gears on vehicles with air bags or other steering wheel-mounted controls. Inspect and replace steering gear mounting bushings and brackets.*

Tools and Materials

Floor jack
Safety stands
Outer tie-rod end puller
Tape measure
Torque wrench
Power steering fluid

Describe the Vehicle Being Worked On:

Year ____________ Make ______________ Model ______________
VIN ________________________ Engine type and size ______________

Procedure

Task Completed

1. Place the front wheels in the straight-ahead position and remove the ignition key from the ignition switch to lock the steering wheel. Place the driver's seat belt through the steering wheel to prevent wheel rotation if the ignition switch is turned on. This action maintains the clock spring electrical connector or spiral cable in the centered position on air-bag-equipped vehicles.

   Are the front wheels straight ahead and steering wheel locked? ☐ Yes ☐ No

   Instructor check ______________________________

2. Lift the front end with a floor jack and place safety stands under the vehicle chassis. Lower the vehicle onto the safety stands. Remove the left and right fender apron seals.

   Is the chassis properly supported on safety stands? ☐ Yes ☐ No

   Are the fender apron seals removed? ☐ Yes ☐ No

   Instructor check ______________________________

3. Place punch marks on the lower universal joint and the steering gear pinion shaft so they may be reassembled in the same position.

   Are the pinion shaft and U-joint punchmarked? ☐ Yes ☐ No

   Instructor check ______________________________

Task Completed

4. Loosen the upper universal joint bolt, remove the lower universal joint bolt, and disconnect this joint.

   Is the U-joint disconnected from pinion shaft? ☐ Yes ☐ No

   Instructor check ____________________

5. Remove the cotter pins from the outer tie-rod ends. Loosen, but do not remove, the tie-rod end nuts.

   Are the outer tie-rod end nuts loosened? ☐ Yes ☐ No

   Instructor check ____________________

6. Use a tie-rod end puller to loosen the outer tie-rod ends in the steering arms. Remove the tie-rod end nuts and remove the tie-rod ends from the arms.

   Are the outer tie-rod ends removed from the steering arms? ☐ Yes ☐ No

   Instructor check ____________________

7. Use the proper wrenches to disconnect the high-pressure hose and the return hose from the steering gear. (This step is not required on a manual steering gear.)

   Are the high-pressure and return hoses disconnected from the steering gear?

   ☐ Yes ☐ No

   Instructor check ____________________

8. Remove the four stabilizer bar mounting bolts.

   Are the stabilizer mounting bolts removed? ☐ Yes ☐ No

   Instructor check ____________________

9. Remove the steering gear mounting bolts.

   Are the steering gear mounting bolts removed? ☐ Yes ☐ No

   Instructor check ____________________

☐ 10. Remove the steering gear assembly from the right side of the car.

11. Position the right and left tie-rods the specified distance from the steering gear housing. Measure this distance with a tape measure.

    Are the right and left tie-rods positioned at equal distances from the steering gear housing? ☐ Yes ☐ No

    Instructor check ____________________

☐ 12. Install the steering gear through the right fender apron.

13. Install the pinion shaft in the universal joint with the punch marks aligned. Tighten the upper and lower universal joint bolts to the specified torque.

    Are the punch marks on the pinion shaft and U-joint properly aligned?

    ☐ Yes ☐ No

    Instructor check ____________________

    Specified U-joint bolt torque ____________________

    Actual U-joint bolt torque ____________________

    Instructor check ____________________

Task Completed

14. Install the steering gear mounting bolts and tighten these bolts to the specified torque.

Specified steering gear mounting bolt torque ____________________

Actual steering gear mounting bolt torque ____________________

15. Install the stabilizer bar mounting bolts and torque these bolts to specifications.

Specified stabilizer mounting bolt torque ____________________

Actual stabilizer mounting bolt torque ____________________

16. Install and tighten the high-pressure and return hoses to the specified torque. (This step is not required on a manual rack and pinion steering gear.)

Specified high-pressure and return hose fitting torque ____________________

Actual high-pressure and return hose fitting torque ____________________

CAUTION: Do not loosen the tie-rod end nuts to align the cotter pin holes. This action causes improper torquing of these nuts.

17. Install the outer tie-rod ends in the steering knuckles, and tighten the nuts to the specified torque. Install the cotter pins in the nuts.

Specified outer tie-rod end nut torque ____________________

Actual outer tie-rod end nut torque ____________________

Are the cotter pins properly installed? ☐ Yes ☐ No

18. Tighten the outer tie-rod end jam nuts to the specified torque; then tighten the outer bellows boot clamps.

Specified outer tie-rod end jam nut torque ____________________

Actual outer tie-rod end jam nut torque ____________________

Are the bellows boot clamps properly installed and tightened? ☐ Yes ☐ No

Instructor check ____________________

19. Install the left and right fender apron seals; then lower the vehicle with a floor jack. ☐

20. Fill the power steering pump reservoir with the vehicle manufacturer's recommended power steering fluid, and bleed air from the power steering system. (This step is not required on a manual rack and pinion steering gear.)

Is the power steering pump reservoir filled to the specified level with the proper power steering fluid? ☐ Yes ☐ No

Is the air bled from the power steering system? ☐ Yes ☐ No

21. Perform a front wheel toe measurement, and adjust the toe as required.

Toe satisfactory ☐ Yes ☐ No

Toe adjustment performed ☐ Yes ☐ No

Instructor check ____________________

22. Road test the vehicle and check for proper steering gear operation and steering control.

Steering operation: ☐ Satisfactory ☐ Unsatisfactory

If the steering operation in unsatisfactory, state the necessary repairs and explain the reason for your diagnosis.

____

____

____

Instructor's Response ____

____

____

JOB SHEET 39

Name ______________________________ Date ______________

DIAGNOSE POWER RACK AND PINION STEERING GEAR OIL LEAKAGE PROBLEMS

Upon completion of this job sheet, you should be able to diagnose power rack and pinion steering gear oil leakage problems.

ASE Correlation

This job sheet is related to ASE Automotive Suspension and Steering Task: *Diagnose vibration, noises, looseness, hard steering, and fluid leaks in power rack and pinion steering gears.*

Tools and Materials

Power steering fluid

Describe the Vehicle Being Worked On:

Year __________ Make ____________________ Model ______________

VIN ______________________ Engine type and size ________________

Procedure

WARNING: If the engine has been running for a length of time, power steering gears, pumps, lines, and fluid may be very hot. Wear eye protection and protective gloves when servicing these components.

Task Completed

1. Be sure the power steering reservoir is filled to the specified level with the proper power steering fluid. ☐
2. Be sure the power steering fluid is at normal operating temperature. If necessary, rotate the steering wheel several times from lock-to-lock to bring the fluid to normal operating temperature.

   Is the power steering reservoir filled to the specified level? ☐ Yes ☐ No

   Is the power steering fluid at normal temperature? ☐ Yes ☐ No

   Instructor check ________________________________
3. Inspect the cylinder end of the steering gear for oil leaks.

   Oil leaks at cylinder end of the power steering gear:

   ☐ Satisfactory ☐ Unsatisfactory

   If there are oil leaks in this area, state the necessary repairs and explain the reasons for your diagnosis.

   ____

   ____

   ____
4. Inspect the steering gear for oil leaks at the pinion end of the housing with the engine running and the steering wheel turned so the rack is against the left internal stop.

   Oil leaks at the pinion end of the steering gear with the rack against the left inner stop:

   ☐ Satisfactory ☐ Unsatisfactory

Task Completed

If there are oil leaks in this area, state the necessary repairs and explain the reasons for your diagnosis.

SERVICE TIP: An oil leak at one rack seal may result in oil leaks from both boots because the oil may travel through the breather tube between the boots.

5. Inspect the pinion end of the power steering gear housing for oil leaks with the steering wheel turned in either direction.

Oil leak at the pinion end of the housing with the steering wheel turned in either direction: ☐ Satisfactory ☐ Unsatisfactory

If there are oil leaks in the area, state the necessary repairs and explain the reasons for your diagnosis.

6. Inspect the pinion coupling area for oil leaks.

Oil leaks in the pinion coupling area: ☐ Satisfactory ☐ Unsatisfactory

If there are oil leaks in the area, state the necessary repairs and explain the reasons for your diagnosis.

7. Inspect all the lines and fittings on the steering gear for oil leaks as an assistant turns the wheels with the engine running.

Oil leaks at steering gear fittings: ☐ Satisfactory ☐ Unsatisfactory

Oil leaks in steering gear hoses and lines: ☐ Satisfactory ☐ Unsatisfactory

If there are oil leaks in the power steering fittings, lines, or hoses, state the necessary repairs and explain the reasons for your diagnosis.

8. With the engine running, turn the steering wheel fully in each direction and check the steering effort.

Steering effort in both directions: ☐ Normal ☐ Excessive

If the steering effort is not equal in both directions, state the direction in which steering effort is highest: ☐ Right ☐ Left

If the steering effort is excessive or unequal, state the necessary repairs and explain the reason for your diagnosis.

Instructor's Response

ELECTRONIC FOUR-WHEEL STEERING DIAGNOSIS AND SERVICE

13

Upon completion and review of this chapter, you should be able to:

- Perform a preliminary inspection on a four-wheel steering (4WS) system.
- Perform a trouble code diagnosis on a 4WS system with the ignition switch on.
- Perform a trouble code diagnosis on a 4WS system with the engine running.
- Remove and replace the rear steering actuator.
- Remove and replace the tie-rod ends on the rear steering actuator.
- Remove and replace tie-rods and boots on the rear steering actuator.
- Remove and replace the rear main steering angle sensor.
- Remove and replace the rear sub steering angle sensor.

Diagnosis, service, and adjustments on 4WS systems must be performed precisely as explained in the vehicle manufacturer's service manual. On some systems inaccurate sensor adjustments may cause improper rear wheel steering operation, and this may result in reduced steering control. Always follow the diagnostic, service, and adjustment procedures carefully and accurately!

PRELIMINARY INSPECTION

Prior to any four-wheel steering diagnosis, the following concerns should be considered:

1. Have any suspension modifications been made that would affect steering?
2. Are the tire sizes the same as specified by the vehicle manufacturer?
3. Are the tires inflated to the pressure specified by the vehicle manufacturer?
4. Is the power steering belt adjusted to the vehicle manufacturer's specified tension?
5. Is the power steering pump reservoir filled to the proper level with the type of fluid specified by the vehicle manufacturer?
6. Is the engine idling at the speed specified by the vehicle manufacturer? Is the idle speed steady?
7. Is the steering wheel original equipment?
8. Is the battery fully charged?
9. Are all electrical connections clean and tight?
10. Is there any damaged electrical wiring in the system?
11. Are the rear wheel steering fuses in satisfactory condition?
12. Are there any damaged or worn rear steering gear or rear axle components?
13. Is the Service 4 Wheel Steer indicator illuminated in the instrument panel cluster?

QUADRASTEER DIAGNOSIS

Fast, accurate Quadrasteer diagnosis is very important when correcting steering complaints. If the preliminary inspection does not indicate any problems, the next step in Quadrasteer diagnosis is to perform a diagnostic system check using these steps:

1. With the ignition switch off, connect a scan tool to the DLC under the dash.
2. Turn on the ignition switch, and select Rear Wheel Steering Control Module on the scan tool. If the scan tool does not communicate with this module, check the scan tool electrical connection and the data links. Be sure the scan tool communicates with all the other modules on the vehicle.
3. Access the Class 2 Power Mode on the scan tool, and rotate the ignition switch through all positions while observing the scan tool. The engine may start with the ignition switch in the Start position. The ignition switch position displayed on the scan tool should match the actual ignition switch position.
4. Select the Display DTCs function on the scan tool and then select Rear Wheel Steering Control Module to display the DTCs related to the 4WS system. Select all the other modules on the vehicle, and display any DTCs stored in these modules. Record all DTCs.

5. Are there any DTCs beginning with a U? These DTCs relate to data link problems and must be repaired before proceeding with 4WS diagnosis.
6. Does the scan tool display DTC B1000? This DTC indicates an internal defect in the body control module (BCM), and causes the BCM to refuse all additional inputs. The Quadrasteer system depends on some inputs from the BCM. Therefore, 4WS operation is affected by this BCM problem.

Rear Wheel Steering Data Display

Select Rear Wheel Steering and Data Display on the scan tool. Observe the data displayed on the scan tool and illustrated in Figure 13-1 and Figure 13-2. Compare the displayed data to the vehicle manufacturer's specified data. Repair the cause of any incorrect data.

Operating conditions: Ignition ON/Engine ON

Scan tool parameter	Data List	Units displayed	Typical data value
2 wheel steer mode lamp	Output	On/Off	Varies
4 wheel steer mode lamp	Output	On/Off	Varies
4WS-Tow mode lamp	Output	On/Off	Varies
8-digit GM part number	ID information	Numerical	Varies
Actual rear wheel steering angle	Data display	Degrees	0° to 12°
Base model part number	ID information	Numerical	Varies
Battery voltage	Data display	Voltage	9.0-16.0 volts
Calibration part number	ID information	Numerical	Varies
Calibration S/W suffix	ID information	Numerical	Varies
Digital SWPS phase A	Data display	High/Low	Varies
Digital SWPS phase B	Data display	High/Low	Varies
Hall sensor reference	Data display	Voltage	12 volts
Ignition 3	Data display	Voltage	9.0-16.0 volts

FIGURE 13-1 *Rear wheel steering data.*

Operating conditions: Ignition ON/Engine ON

Scan tool parameter	Data List	Units displayed	Typical data value
Ign. cycles since last fault	Data display	Counts	Counts
Marker pulse	Data display	High/Low	1
Motor current	Data display	Amps	20-50A typical 0 to 85A max.
Motor relay commanded state	Data display	On/Off	Varies
Motor relay feedback state	Data display	On/Offg	Varies
Rear steer mode actual	Data display	2WS,4WS,4WS tow	Varies
Rear steer mode requested	Data display	2WS,4WS,4WS tow	Varies
Rear steer position 1	Data display	Voltage	.25 to 4.75 volts
Rear steer position 2	Data display	Voltage	.25 to 4.75 volts
Rear steer select switch	Data display	On/Off	Off
Rear wheel centering 1	Data display	Voltage	2.5 volts
Rear wheel centering 2	Data display	Voltage	2.5 volts
Requested rear steer angle	Data display	Degrees	0° to 12°
Sensor supply voltage	Data display	Voltage	4.97 volts
Steering wheel angle	Data display	Degrees	-609° to +609°
Steering wheel angle (TBC)	Data display	Degrees	.25 to 4.75 volts
Steering wheel sensor signal	BCM data	Voltage	Varies
Vehicle speed	Data display	km/h (mph)	

FIGURE 13-2 *Rear wheel steering data (continued).*

Compare the incorrect data to the DTCs recorded previously. If any DTCs and incorrect data are from the same component, repair this component or the related circuit.

Rear Wheel Steering DTC Interpretation

The possible 4WS system DTCs and causes are the following:

1. B3593 – The mode select switch 5 V reference circuit is open, shorted to ground, or shorted to voltage.
2. C0000 – The vehicle speed sensor, related circuit, or Class 2 data links are defective.
3. C0253 – The steering wheel position sensor phase A and phase B voltage signals may be out of the valid alignment range, or the steering wheel position marker pulse points may not be occurring at the proper time in relation to steering wheel rotation (Figure 13-3). The steering wheel position sensor analog voltage may be out of the valid alignment range (Figure 13-4), the rear wheel position sensor analog voltage may be out of the valid alignment range, or a valid Learn Wheel Alignment Procedure may not have been performed.

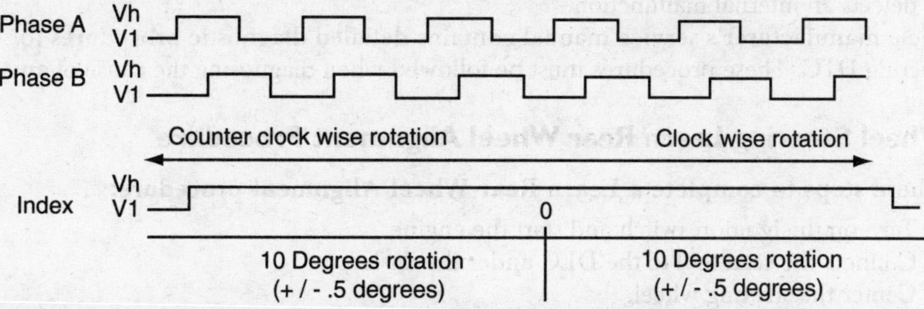

FIGURE 13-3 *Steering wheel position sensor phase A, phase B, and marker pulse signals.*

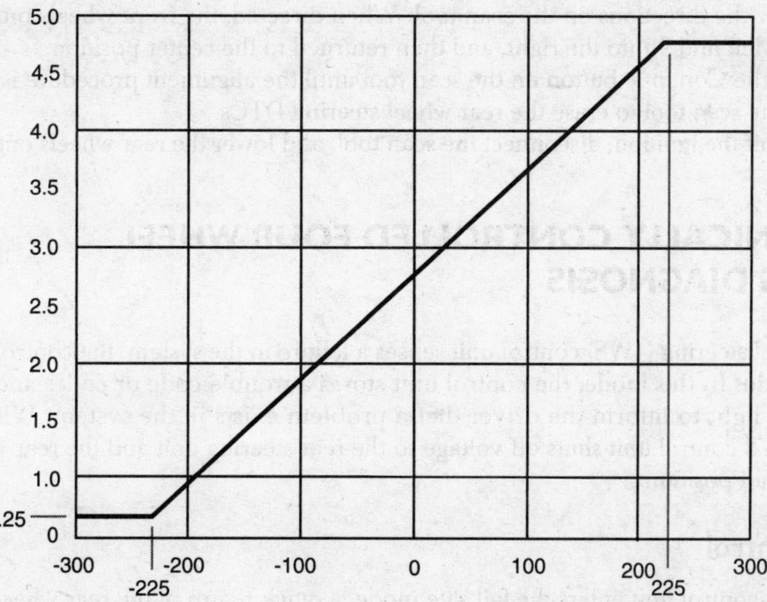

FIGURE 13-4 *Steering wheel position sensor analog voltage.*

4. C0455 – The steering wheel position sensor phase A, phase B, or marker pulse signals are defective or the related circuits are open, or shorted to ground or voltage. This DTC may also be caused by a fault that sets a BCM DTC C0472 or C0473.
5. C0472 or C0473 – The BCM detects the analog steering wheel position sensor circuit is open or shorted to ground or voltage.
6. C0522 – The rear wheel position sensor position 1 or position 2 signals are defective, the 5 V reference circuit to this sensor is open or shorted, or the sensor ground circuit is open.
7. C0527 – The Hall Effect switches in the rear steering gear actuator motor are defective, the voltage supply to these switches is open, or the ground circuit is open.
8. C0532 – The rear wheel position sensor and the actual rear wheel position varies by more than 1.4°.
9. C0533 – The shorting relay in the rear steering actuator motor is stuck open or closed.
10. C0538 – The rear steering motor electrical circuit is open, or shorted to ground or voltage.
11. C0543 – The difference between the commanded rear wheel steering position and the actual rear wheel steering position exceeds 3°.
12. C0550 – When the ignition switch is turned on, the rear wheel steering control module detects an internal malfunction.

The vehicle manufacturer's service manual contains detailed diagnostic procedures for each rear wheel steering DTC. These procedures must be followed when diagnosing the cause of any DTC.

Rear Wheel Steering Learn Rear Wheel Alignment Procedure

Follow these steps to complete a Learn Rear Wheel Alignment procedure:

1. Turn on the ignition switch and start the engine.
2. Connect the scan tool to the DLC under the dash.
3. Center the steering wheel.
4. Lift the rear of the vehicle so the rear tires are a few inches off the shop floor. Be sure the chassis is securely supported on safety stands, and the rear wheels are centered.
5. Select the Learn Alignment menu on the scan tool.
6. Follow the directions on the scan tool. When directed, the front wheels must be turned 90° to the left and 90° to the right, and then returned to the center position.
7. Press the Continue button on the scan tool until the alignment procedure is completed.
8. Use the scan tool to erase the rear wheel steering DTCs.
9. Shut off the ignition, disconnect the scan tool, and lower the rear wheels onto the shop floor.

ELECTRONICALLY CONTROLLED FOUR-WHEEL STEERING DIAGNOSIS

If the four-wheel steering (4WS) control unit senses a failure in the system, the control unit switches to a **fail-safe mode**. In this mode, the control unit stores a trouble code or codes and illuminates the 4WS indicator light to inform the driver that a problem exists in the system. When this mode is entered, the 4WS control unit shuts off voltage to the rear steering unit and the rear wheels remain in the straight-ahead position.

Damper Control

When the 4WS control unit enters the fail-safe mode, a quick return of the rear wheels to the straight-ahead position would adversely affect steering under certain steering wheel and rear wheel positions.

TABLE 13-1 *Quadrasteer Diagnosis*

PROBLEM	SYMPTOMS	POSSIBLE CAUSES
Inoperative rear wheel steer system	Rear wheels do not steer when front wheels are turned	Open fuse(s) related to 4WS system Defect in data links Defective BCM Defective input sensor(s) Defective rear wheel steering gear
Repeated blowing of fuse(s) related to 4WS system	Inoperative rear wheel steering system	Grounded or shorted circuit in related fuse circuit
Improper 4WS operation	Steering wheel position sensor phase A, phase B, marker pulse, and steering wheel position analog voltage signals are out of alignment with steering wheel rotation; DTC C0253 displayed	Defective steering wheel position sensor Learn Rear Wheel Alignment procedure not performed after component replacement

To prevent this action, the 4WS control unit energizes the damper relay when it enters the fail-safe mode. The rear steering actuator motor is spun by the steering shaft movement as this shaft is moved to the centered position by centering spring force. This action causes the motor armature to act as a voltage generator. The voltage generated by the armature is fed back through the damper relay to the motor armature. Under this condition, the motor rotation is slowed and the return spring slowly moves the rear steering shaft to the straight-ahead position. Without the action of the damper relay, the return spring would move the rear steering shaft quickly to the straight-ahead position.

Trouble Code Diagnosis

Road Test

The 4WS control unit stores a fault code and illuminates the 4WS indicator light if a defect occurs in the system, even if the defect is temporary. Always ask the customer about the conditions that caused the 4WS indicator light to come on, and duplicate this condition during a road test. If the 4WS light is not illuminated during the road test, the system is satisfactory electronically and does not require further electronic diagnosis. The troubleshooting procedures in the vehicle manufacturer's service manual assume that the problem is present at the time of diagnosis.

Trouble Code Display with Ignition Switch On

CAUTION: When diagnosing a computer system, never connect or ground any terminals unless instructed to do so in the vehicle manufacturer's service manual. This action may damage electronic components.

CAUTION: When diagnosing a computer system, never disconnect or connect any computer system component with the ignition switch on unless instructed to do so in the vehicle manufacturer's service manual. This action may damage the computer or system components.

CAUTION: When performing electronic diagnosis on a vehicle equipped with an air bag, most vehicle manufacturers recommend turning the ignition switch off, disconnecting the negative battery cable, and waiting one minute before proceeding with electronic component diagnosis or service.

CAUTION: When performing electronic diagnosis on a vehicle equipped with an air bag, follow all the service precautions recommended in the vehicle manufacturer's service manual. If these precautions are not followed, electronic components may be damaged.

Always follow the exact 4WS service and diagnostic procedures in the vehicle manufacturer's service manual. These procedures vary depending on the make and year of the vehicle.

The following are typical procedures for a Honda Prelude. These procedures should be avoided until after the diagnosis is complete because any of these procedures will erase trouble codes:

1. Disconnect the battery terminals.
2. Disconnect the 4WS control unit connector.
3. Remove the number 43 clock-radio 10-A fuse from the underhood fuse/relay box.

Follow these steps to obtain the trouble codes:

1. Remove the dual-terminal **service check connector** located behind the center console, and connect the two terminals in this connector with a jumper wire (Figure 13-5).

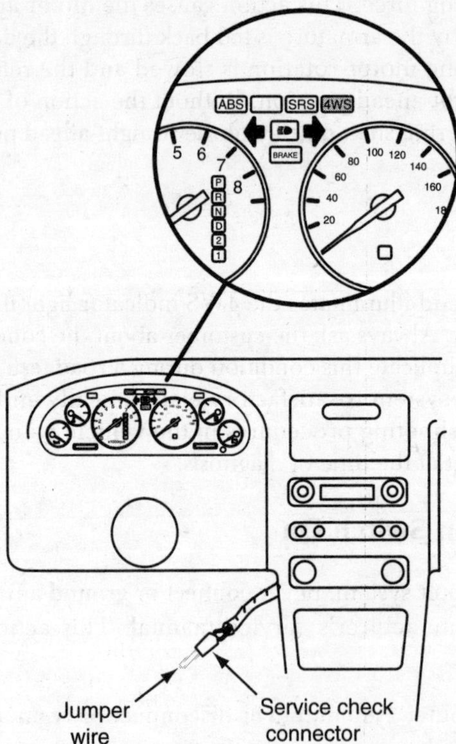

FIGURE 13-5 *Dual-terminal service check connector positioned behind the center console.*

2. Turn on the ignition switch, but do not start the engine.
3. Observe the 4WS indicator light to read the trouble codes. Three longer flashes followed by a brief pause and one quicker flash indicates code 31. The codes are given in numerical order.
4. Record the fault codes.

Trouble Code Display with Engine Running

The 4WS control unit actually contains two processing units that are referred to as the main and sub processing units. Each processing unit can store a maximum of 10 trouble codes. If the trouble code diagnosis is performed with the engine running, the code display indicates whether the codes are stored in the main or sub processor.

When the service connector terminals are connected with a jumper wire and the engine is started, the 4WS indicator light follows this sequence if there are trouble codes in the main and sub processors:

1. Blinks quickly once when the ignition switch is turned on
2. Pauses for 3 seconds
3. Displays codes stored in the main processor
4. Pauses for 1.6 seconds
5. Blinks quickly for 3 seconds to indicate a separation between the main and sub processor codes
6. Pauses for 1.6 seconds
7. Displays codes stored in the sub processor
8. Pauses for 3 seconds, and then repeats the cycle (Figure 13-6)

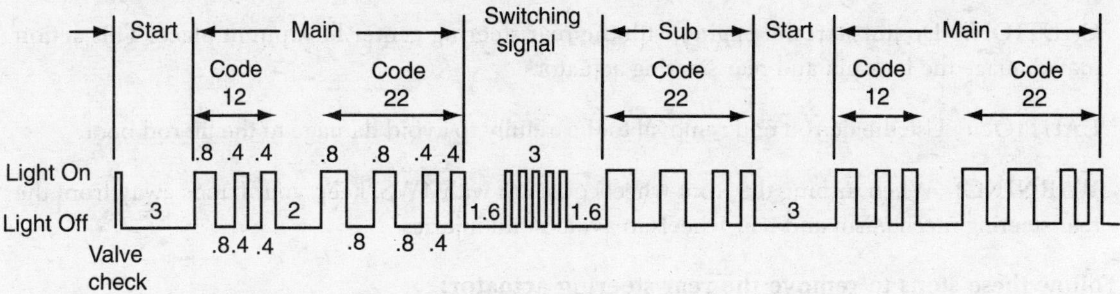

FIGURE 13-6 *Trouble codes in main and sub processors obtained with engine running.*

Main Steering Angle Sensor Trouble Code

If a defect occurs in the main steering angle sensor system, the clock-radio 10-A fuse must be disconnected to cancel the 4WS indicator light. When defects occur in other parts of the electronic 4WS system, the 4WS indicator light is cancelled when the ignition switch is turned off. However, the 4WS indicator light is illuminated again when the ignition switch is turned on, and the 4WS control unit detects the problem again.

Trouble Codes Representing Temporary Driving Conditions

Codes 70, 71, 73, and 74 represent problems resulting from abnormal or harsh driving conditions (Figure 13-7). When the 4WS control unit detects one of these problems, it does not illuminate the 4WS indicator light, but these codes are flashed during the diagnostic procedure.

DTC	OPERATION	4WS INDICATOR LIGHT
70	The ignition is turned from Off to On while driving.	On
71	The car is driven aggressively with the driver and three passengers on board, or the steering wheel is turned with a rear wheel blocked by a curb, etc.	—
73	The engine is started while quick-charging the battery.	—
74	Driving the car with the parking brake On.	On 5 minutes after detection

FIGURE 13-7 *Codes that represent problems caused by abnormal or harsh driving conditions.*

REAR STEERING ACTUATOR SERVICE

Rear Steering Actuator Removal

CAUTION: Many steering service and diagnostic procedures require the installation of the rear steering center lock pin in the rear steering actuator to lock this unit in the centered position. If this lock pin is not installed, diagnosis will be inaccurate.

CAUTION: Do not start the engine with the rear steering center lock pin in place. This action may damage the lock pin and rear steering actuator.

CAUTION: Use the tie-rod end removal tool carefully to avoid damage to the tie-rod boot.

WARNING: When turning the front wheels on a car with 4WS, keep your hands away from the rear steering mechanism and rear wheels to avoid hand injuries.

Follow these steps to remove the rear steering actuator:

1. Raise the vehicle on a hoist or lift the rear of the vehicle with a floor jack, and support the chassis with safety stands placed in the vehicle manufacturer's recommended locations.
2. Remove the cotter pin and nut from each tie-rod end.
3. Install a 12-millimeter (mm) nut on each tie-rod end until the nuts are flush with the tie-rod stud.
4. Install the special tool on the tie-rod end, and with the tool arms parallel, tighten the screw on the tool to loosen the tie-rod end (Figure 13-8). Repeat the procedure on both tie-rod ends.

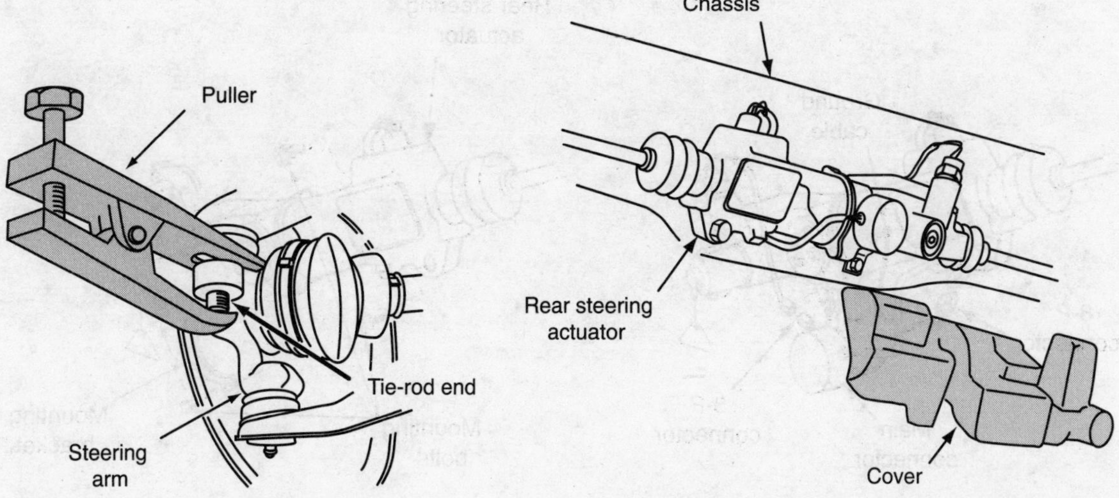

FIGURE 13-8 *Removing a tie-rod end with a special tool.*

FIGURE 13-9 *Removing the rear steering actuator cover.*

5. Remove the nuts from the tie-rods and remove the tie-rods from the steering arms.
6. Remove the rear steering actuator cover (Figure 13-9).
7. Remove the cap bolt and washer and install the **rear steering center lock pin** (Figure 13-10).

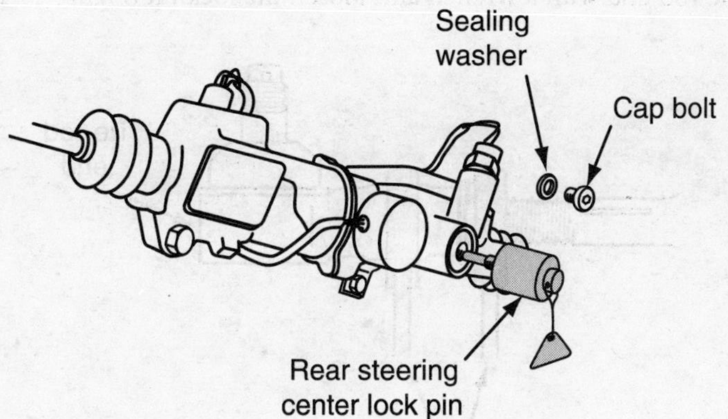

FIGURE 13-10 *Removing the cap bolt and washer, and installing the rear steering center lock pin.*

8. Remove the ground cable connector and all wiring harness connectors on the rear steering actuator (Figure 13-11).
9. Remove the four mounting bolts and bracket, and remove the rear steering actuator (Figure 13-12).

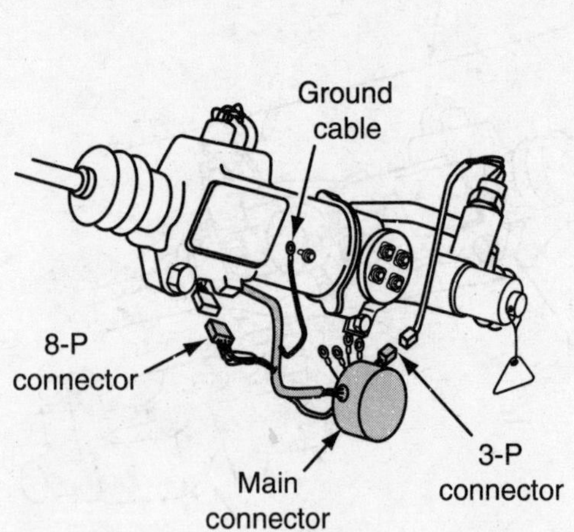

FIGURE 13-11 *Removing the ground cable connector and all wiring harness connectors on the rear steering actuator.*

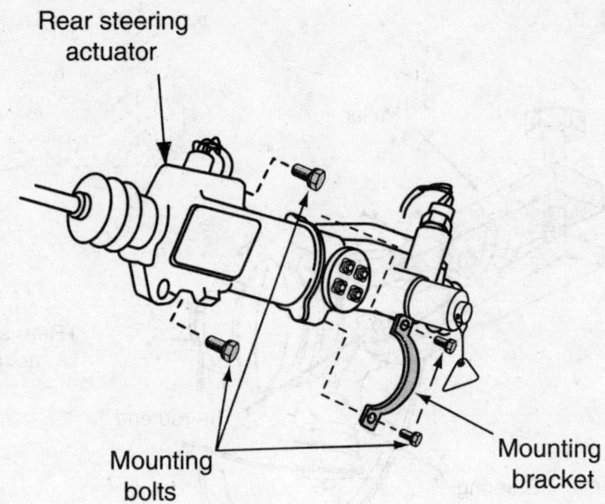

FIGURE 13-12 *Removing the four mounting bolts, bracket, and rear steering actuator.*

Tie-Rod and Tie-Rod End Removal

Follow these steps for tie-rod and tie-rod end removal:

1. Mark the relative position of the tie-rod end, locknut, and tie-rod with a wax marker.
2. Hold the tie-rod end with a wrench and loosen the locknut (Figure 13-13).

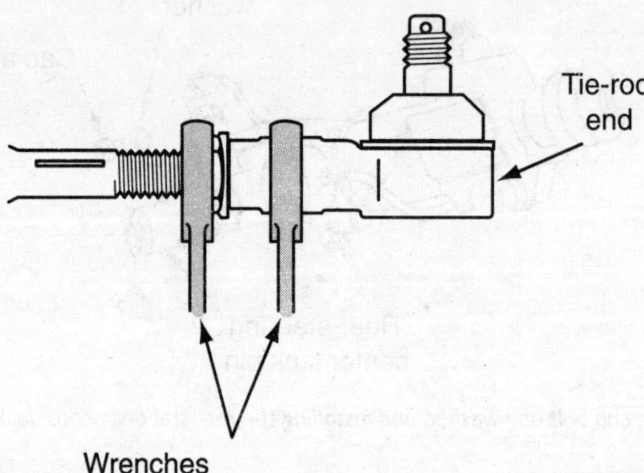

FIGURE 13-13 *Loosening the tie-rod end locknut.*

3. Remove the tie-rod end.
4. Remove the boot bands and clamps from the inner tie-rod ends (Figure 13-14).
5. Place the flat side of the rack holding tool toward the actuator housing and drive the special rack holding tool between the actuator housing and the stop washer with a soft hammer (Figure 13-15).

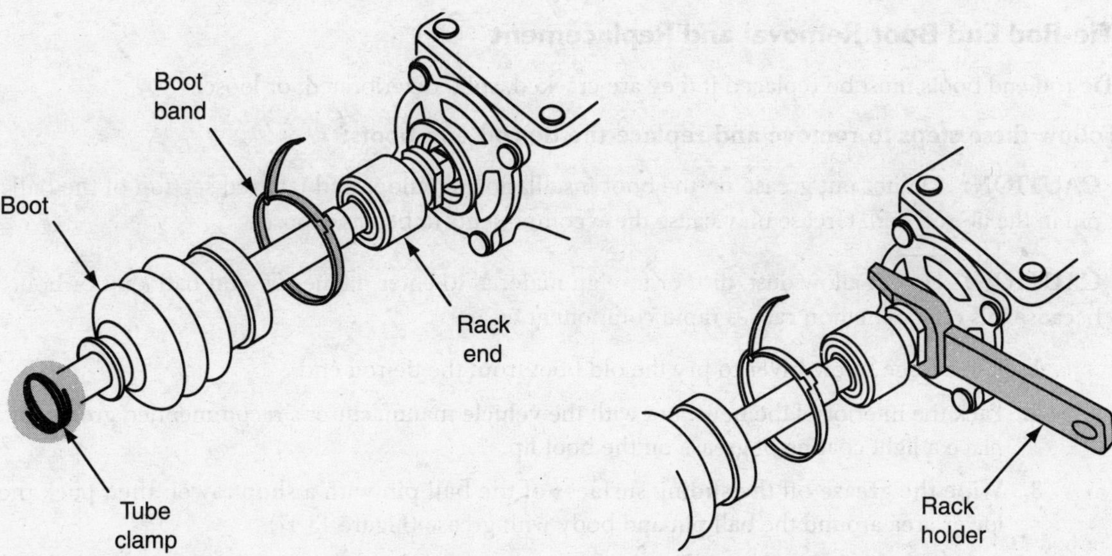

FIGURE 13-14 *Removing boot bands and clamps from the inner tie-rod end.*

FIGURE 13-15 *Installing the special rack holding tool between the actuator housing and the stop washer.*

6. Straighten the tabs on the tie-rod lock washer.
7. Hold the shaft screw with the holding tool and loosen the tie-rod with a wrench (Figure 13-16).
8. Thread the tie-rod off the shaft screw and repeat this procedure on each tie-rod end.

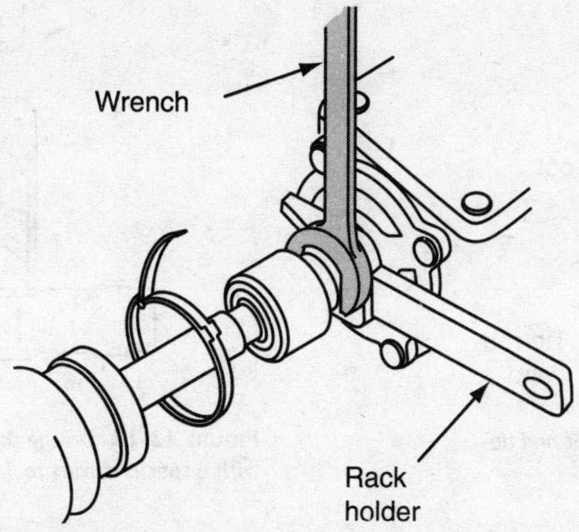

FIGURE 13-16 *Removing the tie-rod from the shaft screw.*

Tie-Rod End Boot Removal and Replacement

Tie-rod end boots must be replaced if they are cracked, split, deteriorated, or loose.

Follow these steps to remove and replace the tie-rod end boots:

CAUTION: Do not put grease on the boot installation shoulder and tapered section of the ball pin in the tie-rod end. Grease may cause these components to become loose.

CAUTION: Do not allow dust, dirt, or foreign material to enter the tie-rod end ball joint or boot because this contamination causes rapid component wear.

1. Use a large screwdriver to pry the old boot from the tie-rod end.
2. Pack the interior of the new boot with the vehicle manufacturer's recommended grease and place a light coating of grease on the boot lip.
3. Wipe the grease off the sliding surfaces of the ball pin with a shop towel; then pack the lower area around the ball pin and body with grease (Figure 13-17).
4. Use the special driving tool to install the new boot on the tie-rod end (Figure 13-18).
5. Wipe any grease from the tapered section of the ball pin with a shop towel. Apply sealant around the lower edge of the boot and tie-rod body.

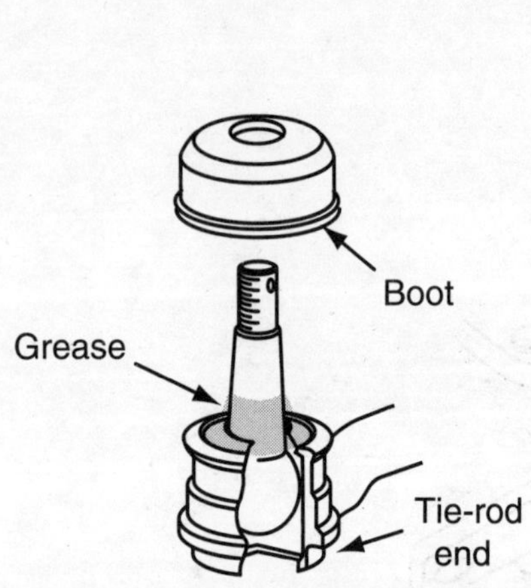

FIGURE 13-17 *Packing the boot and tie-rod end with grease.*

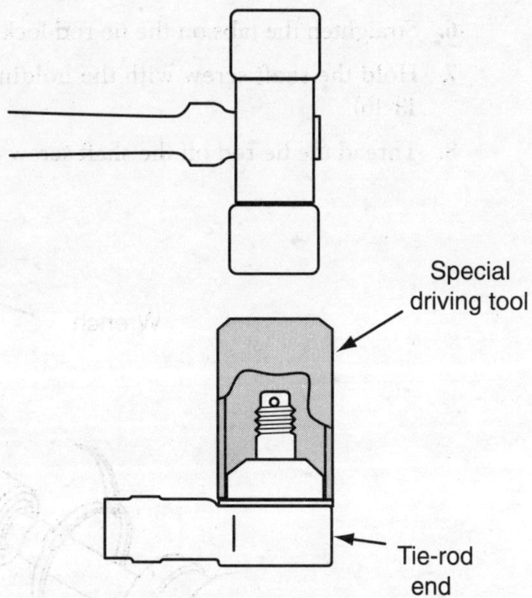

FIGURE 13-18 *Driving the boot onto the tie-rod end with a special driving tool.*

Installation of Tie-Rods and Tie-Rod Ends

CAUTION: Never apply axial impact or rotational force to the shaft screw in the rear steering actuator. Either of these actions may cause internal actuator damage.

Inner tie-rod boots must be replaced if they are cracked, split, deteriorated, or damaged.

Follow these steps for tie-rod and tie-rod end installation:

1. Install the tie-rod ends so the marks on the tie-rod ends, nuts, and tie-rods are aligned, and tighten the tie-rod nuts to the specified torque.
2. Screw each inner tie-rod onto the shaft screw while holding the lock washer so its tabs are in the inner tie-rod end. The stop washer must be installed on the shaft screw with the chamfered side facing outward (Figure 13-19).
3. Drive the special holding tool between the actuator housing and the stop washer with a soft hammer (Figure 13-20).

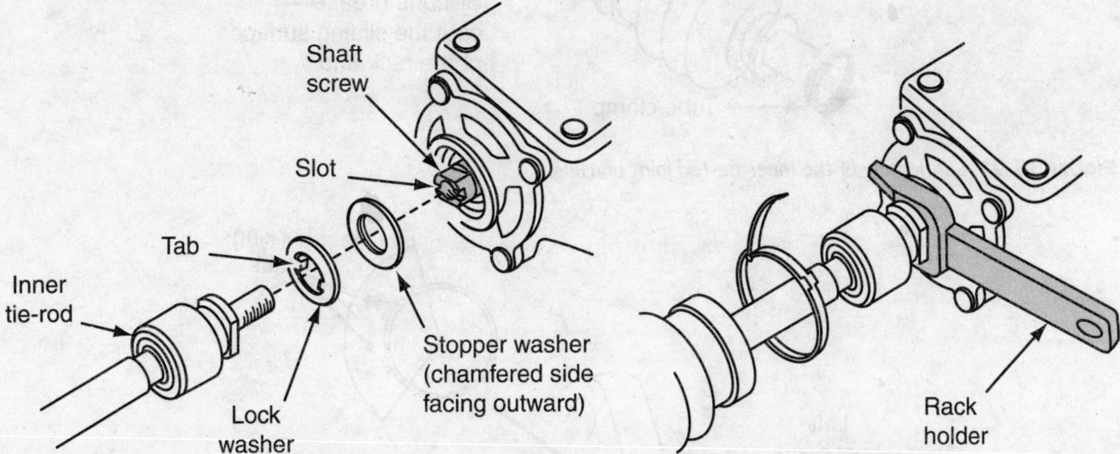

FIGURE 13-19 *Installing the inner tie-rod end on the shaft screw.*

FIGURE 13-20 *Installing the special tool to hold the shaft screw while tightening the inner tie-rod end.*

4. Hold the shaft screw with the holding tool and tighten the inner tie-rod end to the specified torque.
5. Bend the lock washer tabs against the flat on the inner tie-rod end.
6. Remove the special holding tool and apply silicone grease to the sliding surface of the tie-rod (Figure 13-21). Place a light coating of silicone grease inside the tie-rod boot.
7. Apply the vehicle manufacturer's recommended grease to the circumference of the inner tie-rod joint housing.
8. Install the boots on the actuator housing; then install the boot bands with the locking tabs properly positioned in relation to the actuator housing (Figure 13-22).

CAUTION: While staking the boot clamps, be careful not to damage the inner tie-rod boots.

9. Tighten the boot bands and bend both sets of locking tabs over the band (Figure 13-23). Tap lightly on the doubled-over portion of the band to reduce its height and stake the locking tabs firmly.

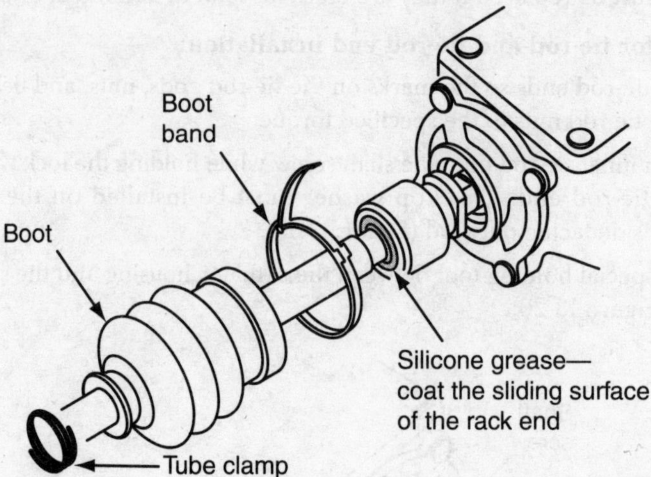

FIGURE 13-21 *Lubricating of the inner tie-rod joint housing.*

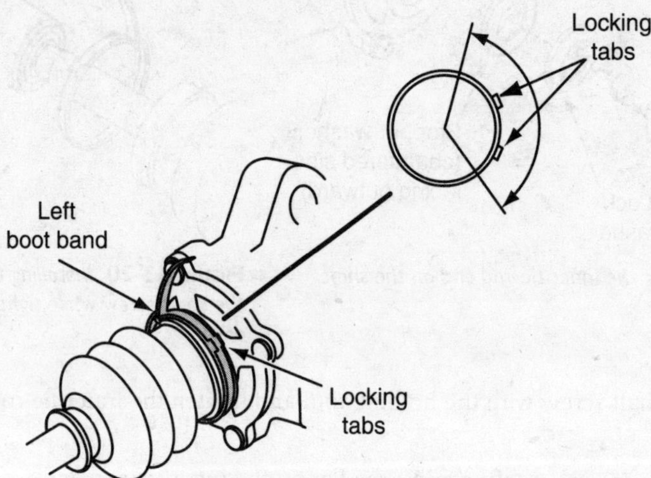

FIGURE 13-22 *Proper boot band position in relation to the actuator housing.*

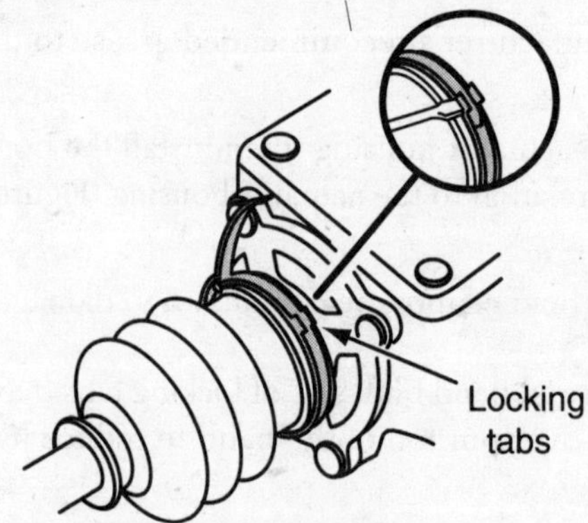

FIGURE 13-23 *Tightening and staking the inner tie-rod boot clamps.*

Remove and Replace Rear Steering Actuator Sensors

Follow these steps to remove and replace the rear sub steering angle sensor and the rear main steering angle sensor:

1. Loosen the rear sub steering angle sensor locknut and rotate the sensor to thread it out of the housing (Figure 13-24). Discard the sensor O-ring.
2. Remove the two mounting bolts in the rear main steering angle sensor, and then remove the sensor from the actuator housing (Figure 13-25). Note the position of the dowel pins, and discard the O-ring.

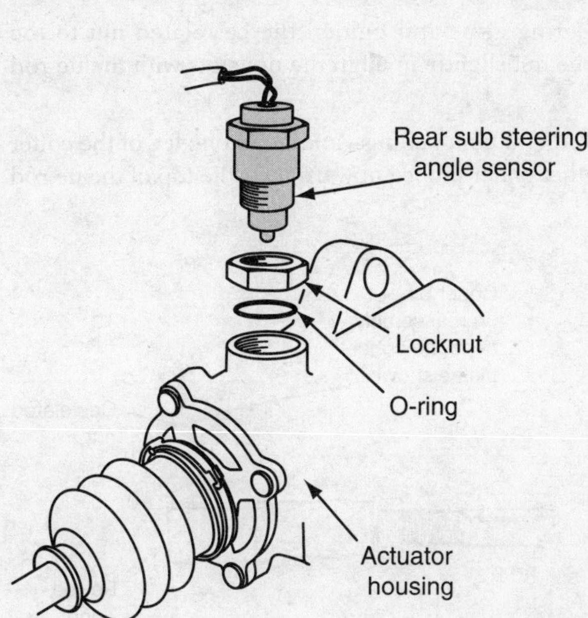

FIGURE 13-24 *Removing the rear sub steering angle sensor.*

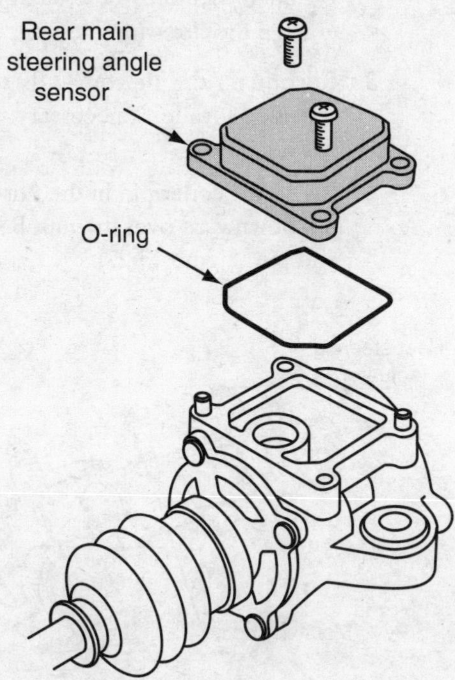

FIGURE 13-25 *Removing the rear main steering angle sensor.*

3. Install the locknut and a new O-ring on the rear sub steering angle sensor.
4. Place a light coating of grease on the O-ring and install the sensor in the actuator housing.
5. Rotate the sensor until it touches the tapered shaft and back it out one-half turn. Tighten the locknut finger tight. Final adjustment of the rear sub steering angle sensor is completed with the actuator installed in the vehicle.
6. Place a light coating of grease on the rear main steering angle sensor O-ring and install this O-ring on the sensor.
7. Install the rear main steering angle sensor and O-ring in the actuator housing with the dowel pins properly positioned, and tighten the mounting bolts to the specified torque.

Installing Rear Steering Actuator

Follow these steps for rear steering actuator installation:

1. Install the rear steering actuator and the four mounting bolts and bracket. The arrow on the bracket must face upward (Figure 13-26).
2. Tighten the rear steering actuator mounting bolts to the specified torque.

CAUTION: Tighten the castelated nut on the tie-rod ends to the specified torque, and then tighten these nuts enough to align the slots in the nut with the hole in the tie-rod pin. Do not loosen the nut to align the nut slots with the tie-rod pin hole. If this nut is loosened to align the slot with the hole, the tie-rod end may become loose in service.

3. Reconnect the tie-rod ends to the steering arms and tighten the castelated nut to the specified torque. If necessary, tighten the nut slightly to align the nut slots with the tie-rod pin hole.
4. Install the cotter pin in the nut and tie-rod end pin openings, and bend one leg of the cotter pin downward over the nut. Bend the other cotter pin leg upward over the top of the tie-rod end pin (Figure 13-27).

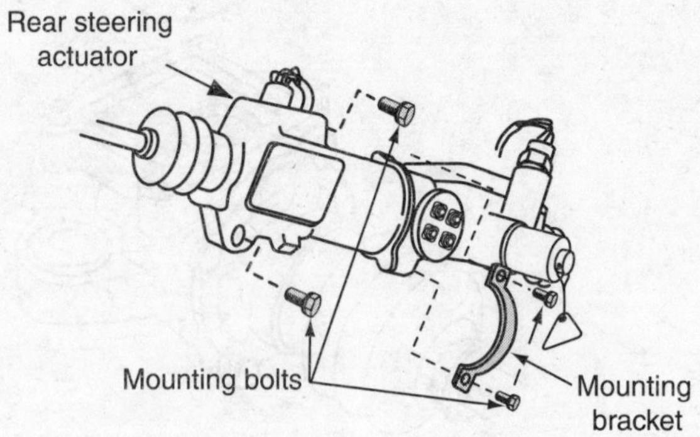

FIGURE 13-26 *Installing the rear steering actuator, four mounting bolts, and bracket.*

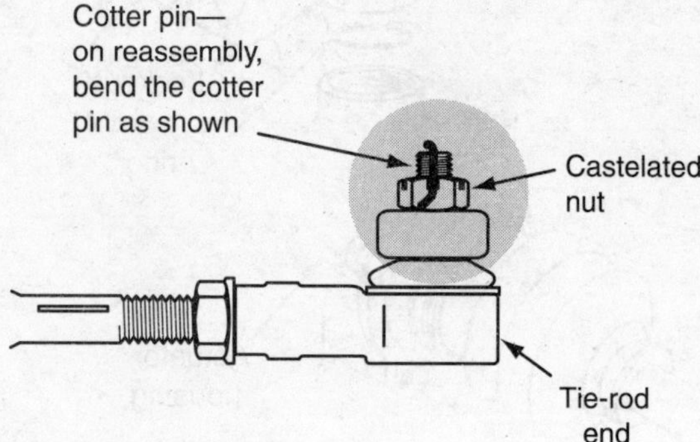

FIGURE 13-27 *Proper installation of cotter pin in the tie-rod end.*

5. Check all the wiring connectors for contamination and clean as necessary. Install all the wiring connectors on the rear steering actuator and tighten all the terminal nuts to the specified torque (Figure 13-28).
6. Install the terminal cover on the rear main steering sensor terminals. Remove the rear steering lock pin and install the cap bolt and washer. Leave the steering actuator cover removed until after the final rear steering actuator adjustments.

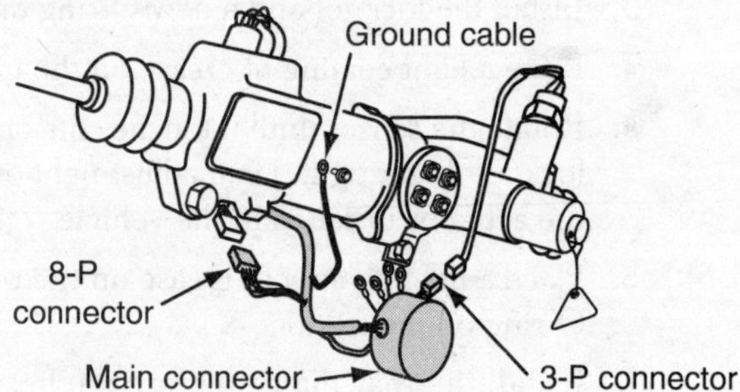

FIGURE 13-28 *Installing wiring connectors on the rear steering actuator.*

Photo Sequence 13 shows a typical procedure for diagnosing an electronically controlled four-wheel steering system.

PHOTO SEQUENCE 13
TYPICAL PROCEDURE FOR DIAGNOSING AN ELECTRONICALLY CONTROLLED FOUR-WHEEL STEERING SYSTEM

P13-1 *Road test the vehicle to check 4WS operation and indicator light.*

P13-2 *Raise the vehicle on a lift, and check all electrical connectors on the front steering gear and rear steering actuator.*

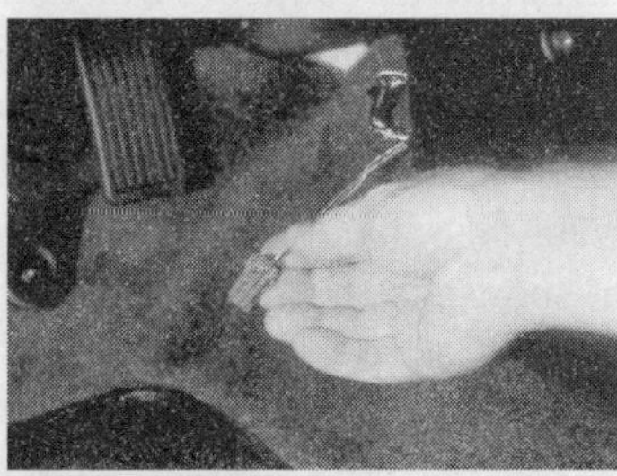

P13-3 *Lower the vehicle and locate the service check connector behind the center console.*

P13-4 *Look up the diagnostic procedure and trouble codes in the car manufacturer's service manual.*

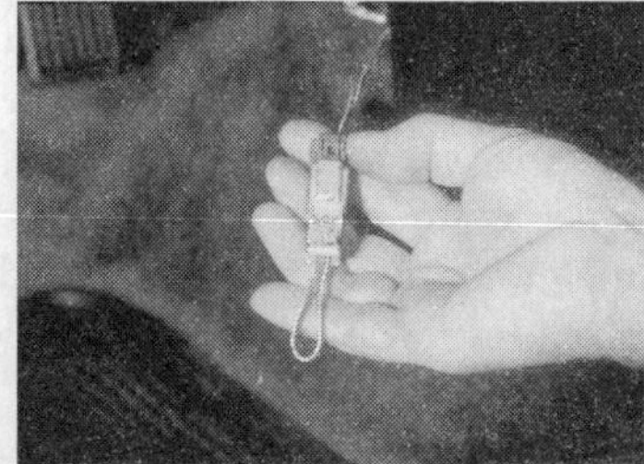

P13-5 *Connect a jumper wire between the terminals in the service check connector.*

P13-6 *Turn on the ignition switch.*

P13-7 *Observe the 4WS indicator light flashes to obtain the fault codes.*

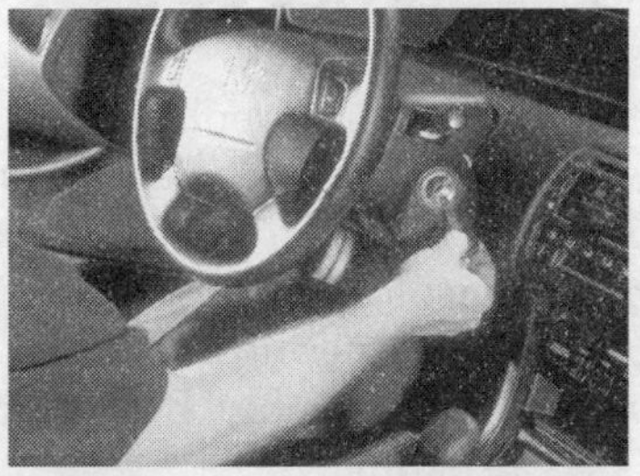

P13-8 *Turn off the ignition switch.*

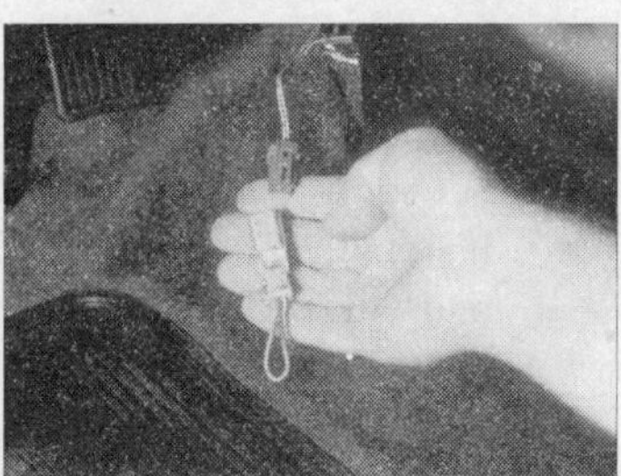

P13-9 *Remove the jumper wire from the service check connector.*

Case Study

A customer complained about the 4WS indicator light coming on intermittently on a Honda Prelude with an electronic 4WS system. The technician asked the customer about any other steering problems, and the customer reported the car steered normally. The technician road-tested the car, but the 4WS light did not come on, which indicated there were no electronic problems in the system. The customer was concerned about a possible safety hazard while driving this vehicle with the 4WS indicator light illuminated. In reply to this concern, the technician explained to the customer about the fail-safe function in the 4WS system and the rear wheels being centered in this mode.

The technician asked the customer about any recent service work completed on the vehicle. In response to this question, the customer replied that the car had been in a rear end collision recently, and when the body work was completed, the 4WS indicator light problem started occurring. The technician informed the customer that a 4WS system diagnosis and inspection should be performed.

Since the 4WS indicator light was not illuminated, the technician concluded that a trouble code diagnosis would probably not provide any diagnostic answers. However, the technician checked the system for codes in case there was a code caused by abnormal or harsh driving, which would not cause the indicator light to be illuminated.

When the technician raised the vehicle on a hoist, it was clearly visible that many of the rear suspension and body parts had been replaced recently. Even the rear steering actuator cover had been replaced. The technician removed the rear steering actuator cover to inspect the wiring on the actuator. All the wiring connectors were inspected, including the terminals on the rear main steering angle sensor. When the technician inspected the rear sub steering angle sensor wiring harness, he found this harness had been punctured by a sharp object near the sensor. The technician probed the sensor wires at the sensor and connected a pair of ohmmeter leads from each wire at the sensor to the corresponding colored wire in the sensor connector. Each wire showed a normal zero-ohm resistance. The technician repeated these ohmmeter connections and wiggled the wires at the damaged location. On one of the wires, the ohmmeter reading went to infinite while wiggling the wires, indicating an intermittent open circuit.

The technician replaced the rear sub steering angle sensor and performed the electronic neutral check and the rear sub steering angle sensor adjustment. During a road test, the 4WS indicator light did not come on.

Service Tips

- If any of the sensors or the control module is replaced in a Quadrasteer system, a Learn Rear Wheel Alignment Procedure must be performed with a scan tool.
- If step 6 is not completed properly, a false steering wheel position sensor DTC may be set in the rear wheel steering control module memory.
- Do not attempt to disassemble the rear steering actuator other than tie-rods, tie-rod ends, and sensors. This actuator is serviced as an assembly. Because individual parts for the actuator are not available, disassembly is a waste of time.
- Hold the special holding tool firmly while loosening the tie- rod to avoid applying rotational force to the shaft screw in the actuator.
- Cover the rear main steering sensor and rear sub steering sensor openings in the actuator housing with masking tape or its equivalent to keep dirt and foreign material out of the actuator housing.

REVIEW QUESTIONS

1. While discussing the fail-safe function:
Technician A says the 4WS indicator light is illuminated during the fail-safe function. *Technician B* says the rear wheels steer normally when the 4WS control unit enters the fail-safe mode.
Who is correct?
A. A only **C.** Both A and B
B. B only **D.** Neither A nor B

2. While discussing the fail-safe function and damper control:
Technician A says the rear wheels move instantly to the centered position when the 4WS control unit enters the fail-safe mode. *Technician B* says the return spring moves the rear wheels away from the centered position.
Who is correct?
A. A only **C.** Both A and B
B. B only **D.** Neither A nor B

3. While discussing trouble code diagnosis:
Technician A says the 4WS system service check connector is located under the driver's seat. *Technician B* says when one of the service check connector terminals is grounded, the 4WSsystem enters the diagnostic mode.
Who is correct?
A. A only **C.** Both A and B
B. B only **D.** Neither A nor B

4. While discussing trouble code diagnosis:
Technician A says many 4WS system trouble codes are cancelled when the ignition switch is turned off. *Technician B* says codes representing problems caused by abnormal or harsh driving conditions do not illuminate the 4WS indicator light.
Who is correct?
A. A only **C.** Both A and B
B. B only **D.** Neither A nor B

5. While discussing rear steering actuator service:
Technician A says the rear steering actuator is a replacement unit except for tie-rods and sensors. *Technician B* says the arrows on the rear steering actuator brackets must face downward.
Who is correct?
A. A only **C.** Both A and B
B. B only **D.** Neither A nor B

6. All of these statements about rear steering actuators and actuator service are true EXCEPT:
A. Axial impact on the shaft screw may damage the actuator.
B. Rotational force on the shaft screw may damage the actuator.
C. The engine may be started with the rear steering lock pin in place.
D. The shaft screw must be held with a special tool while loosening the tie-rods.

7. When diagnosing a Quadrasteer system a DTC B1000 is displayed on the scan tool. The most likely reason for this DTC is:
   A. A defective steering wheel position sensor.
   B. A defective rear wheel steering motor.
   C. An internal defect in the BCM.
   D. An open circuit in the wiring to the rear steering motor.

8. When performing a Learn Rear Wheel Alignment procedure:
   Technician A says the steering wheel must be centered. *Technician B* says during this procedure the front wheels must be lifted off the shop floor.
   Who is correct?
   A. A only **C.** Both A and B
   B. B only **D.** Neither A nor B

9. A DTC representing a data link defect begins with a:
   A. B. **C.** P.
   B. C. **D.** U.

10. A Quadrasteer system is inoperative, and the scan tool indicates a B1000 DTC. This DTC indicates an internal defect in the:
    A. BCM. **C.** 4WS module.
    B. PCM. **D.** IPC module.

CHALLENGE QUESTIONS

1. While discussing electronic 4WS:
   Technician A says jumping the two terminals of the service check connector with the engine off will display DTCs. *Technician B* says jumping the service check connector then starting the engine displays the processor in which the codes are stored.
   Who is correct?
   A. A only **C.** Both A and B
   B. B only **D.** Neither A nor B
2. The Honda Prelude 4WS system uses a main and a sub processing unit, each storing 10 trouble codes. If the 4WS light on the dash blinks quickly and repeatedly for three seconds, it means:
   A. A DTC is stored in the main processor.
   B. A DTC is stored in the sub processor.
   C. The system is moving from the main to the sub processor memory.
   D. A DTC sequence will be repeated.
3. Honda Prelude temporary "abnormal or harsh driving" 4WS DTCs range from ____ to ____.
   A. 07/14 **C.** 17/24
   B. 70/74 **D.** 44/47
4. The Honda Prelude 4WS light has gone on and remains on.
   Technician A says that before performing any diagnostic tests, the 10A fuse for the clock radio should be removed. *Technician B* says to retrieve the DTC, the 4WS control unit connector must be disconnected.

Who is correct?

A. A only
B. B only
C. Both A and B
D. Neither A nor B

5. While discussing electronic 4WS:
Technician A says that after repairing a defect of the main steering angle sensor in the Honda Prelude 4WS system, fuse #43 must be removed to cancel the code. *Technician B* says the battery terminal must be removed to cancel DTCs in parts of the Honda Prelude 4WS system other than the main steering angle sensor.
Who is correct?

A. A only
B. B only
C. Both A and B
D. Neither A nor B

Job Sheet 40

Name ______________________________ Date ______________

RETRIEVE DIAGNOSTIC TROUBLE CODES (DTCS), FOUR-WHEEL STEERING (4WS) SYSTEM

Upon completion of this job sheet, you should be able to retrieve diagnostic trouble codes (DTCs) on four-wheel steering (4WS) systems.

ASE Correlation

This job sheet is related to ASE Automotive Suspension and Steering Task: *Inspect, diagnose, adjust, service, or replace components of electronically controlled steering systems.*

Tools and Materials

Jumper wire

Describe the Vehicle Being Worked On:

Year __________ Make ______________ Model ______________
VIN ______________ Engine type and size ______________

Procedure

Task Completed

1. Be sure the ignition switch is off and remove the dual-terminal service check connector located behind the center console. Connect the two terminals in this connector with a jumper wire.

   Is the jumper wire properly connected? ☐ Yes ☐ No

   Instructor check ______________________________

2. Turn the ignition switch on, but do not start the engine. ☐
3. Observe the 4WS indicator light to read the diagnostic trouble codes (DTCs). Three longer flashes followed by a brief pause and one quicker flash indicates code 31. The codes are given in numerical order. ☐
4. List the DTCs provided with ignition switch on and the engine not running and include the DTC interpretation.

   1. ______________________________
   2. ______________________________
   3. ______________________________

5. Turn the ignition switch off and start the engine while observing the 4WS indicator light in the instrument panel. ☐
6. Does the 4WS indicator light blink once quickly when the ignition switch is turned on?

   4WS light operation: ☐ Satisfactory ☐ Unsatisfactory

   If the 4WS light operation is unsatisfactory, describe the light operation.

   ____

   ____

Task Completed

7. After the quick flash in step 6, did the 4WS indicator light pause for 3 seconds?
4WS light operation: ☐ Satisfactory ☐ Unsatisfactory
If the 4WS light operation is unsatisfactory, describe the light operation.
____
____

8. List the main processor DTCs displayed after the pause in step 7 and include the DTC interpretation.
1. ____
2. ____
3. ____

9. Did the 4WS indicator light pause for 1.6 seconds after the DTCs displayed in step 8?
☐ Yes ☐ No
4WS light operation: ☐ Satisfactory ☐ Unsatisfactory
If the 4WS light operation is unsatisfactory, describe the light operation.
____
____

10. Did the 4WS indicator light blink quickly for three seconds to indicate a separation between the main and sub processor codes? ☐ Yes ☐ No
4WS light operation: ☐ Satisfactory ☐ Unsatisfactory
If the 4WS light operation is unsatisfactory, describe the light operation.
____
____

11. Did the 4WS indicator light pause for 1.6 seconds? ☐ Yes ☐ No
4WS light operation: ☐ Satisfactory ☐ Unsatisfactory
If the 4WS light operation is unsatisfactory, describe the light operation.
____
____

12. List the sub processor DTCs displayed after the pause in step 11, and include the DTC interpretation.
1. ____
2. ____
3. ____

13. Did the 4WS indicator light pause for 3 seconds and then repeat the cycle?
☐ Yes ☐ No
4WS light operation: ☐ Satisfactory ☐ Unsatisfactory
If the 4WS light operation is unsatisfactory, describe the light operation.
____
____

14. On the basis of all the DTCs displayed, state the required diagnostic procedure to locate the exact cause of the defect(s) and explain the reasons for your diagnosis.
____
____

Instructor's Response ____________________________________
____
____

JOB SHEET 41

Name ______________________________ Date ______________

PERFORM A LEARN REAR WHEEL ALIGNMENT PROCEDURE ON A QUADRASTEER SYSTEM

Upon completion of this job sheet, you should be able to perform a Learn Rear Wheel Alignment procedure on a Quadrasteer system.

ASE Correlation

This job sheet is correlated with ASE Automotive Suspension and Steering Task: *Diagnose, inspect, repair, or replace components of variable-assist steering systems.*

Tools and Materials

Vehicle with a Quadrasteer system
Compatible scan tool

Describe the Vehicle Being Worked On:

Year __________ Make ____________________ Model ________________
VIN ______________________ Engine Type and Size ________________

Procedure

Task Completed

1. Turn on the ignition switch and start the engine.

   Engine running, ☐ Yes ☐ No
2. Connect the scan tool to the DLC under the dash.

   Scan tool properly connected to the DLC, ☐ Yes ☐ No
3. Center the steering wheel.

   Steering wheel properly centered, ☐ Yes ☐ No
4. Lift the rear of the vehicle so the rear tires are a few inches off the shop floor. Be sure the chassis is securely supported on safety stands, and the rear wheels are centered.

   Rear wheels raised off the shop floor, ☐ Yes ☐ No

   Chassis properly supported on safety stands, ☐ Yes ☐ No

   Steering wheel centered, ☐ Yes ☐ No
5. Select the Learn Alignment menu on the scan tool.

   Learn Alignment displayed on the scan tool, ☐ Yes ☐ No
6. Follow the directions on the scan tool. When directed, the front wheels must be turned 90° to the left and 90° to the right, and then returned to the center position.

   Steering wheel rotated 90° in each direction, ☐ Yes ☐ No

   Steering wheel centered, ☐ Yes ☐ No

Task Completed

7. Press the Continue button on the scan tool until the Learn Alignment procedure is completed.

   Learn Alignment procedure properly completed, ☐ Yes ☐ No

8. Use the scan tool to erase the rear wheel steering DTCs.

   DTCs erased, ☐ Yes ☐ No

9. Shut off the ignition, disconnect the scan tool, and lower the rear wheels onto the shop floor.

   Ignition shut off and scan tool disconnected, ☐ Yes ☐ No

   Vehicle lowered onto shop floor, ☐ Yes ☐ No

Instructor's Response ____

____

____

Job Sheet 42

Name ______________________________ Date ______________

QUADRASTEER DIAGNOSTIC SYSTEM CHECK

Upon completion of this job sheet, you should be able to perform a Diagnostic System Check on a Quadrasteer System.

ASE Correlation

This job sheet is correlated with ASE Automotive Suspension and Steering Task: *Diagnose, inspect, repair, or replace components of variable-assist steering systems.*

Tools and Materials

Vehicle with a Quadrasteer system
Compatible scan tool

Describe the Vehicle Being Worked On:

Year __________ Make ______________ Model ______________
VIN ________________ Engine Type and Size ______________

Procedure

Task Completed

1. With the ignition switch off, connect a scan tool to the DLC under the dash.

Scan tool properly connected to the DLC, ☐ Yes ☐ No

2. Turn on the ignition switch, and select Rear Wheel Steering Control Module on the scan tool. If the scan tool does not communicate with this module, check the scan tool electrical connection and the data links. Be sure the scan tool communicates with all the other modules on the vehicle.

Proper scan tool communication with rear wheel steering control module and other modules on the vehicle, ☐ Yes ☐ No

3. Access the Class 2 Power Mode on the scan tool, and rotate the ignition switch through all positions while observing the scan tool. The engine may start with the ignition switch in the Start position. The ignition switch position displayed on the scan tool should match the actual ignition switch position.

Actual ignition switch positions match displayed ignition switch positions on the scan tool, ☐ Yes ☐ No

4. Select the Display DTCs function on the scan tool and then select Rear Wheel Steering Control Module to display the DTCs related to the 4WS system. Select all the other modules on the vehicle, and display any DTCs stored in these modules. Record all DTCs.

Rear wheel steering control module DTCs ______________________________

____

DTCs from other modules ______________________________

____

Task Completed ______

5. Are there any DTCs beginning with a U? These DTCs relate to data link problems and must be repaired before proceeding with 4WS diagnosis.

   DTCs beginning with a U ______________________________

6. Does the scan tool display DTC B1000? This DTC indicates an internal defect in the body control module (BCM) and causes the BCM to refuse all additional inputs.

   DTC B1000 displayed, ☐ Yes ☐ No

Instructor's Response ______________________________

____

____

FRAME DIAGNOSIS AND SERVICE

14

Upon completion and review of this chapter, you should be able to:

- Take the necessary precautions to avoid frame damage.
- Diagnose the causes of frame damage.
- Follow safety precautions when measuring and welding frames.
- Visually inspect frames.
- Measure frames with a plumb bob and diagnose frame damage.
- Measure frames with a tram gauge and diagnose frame damage.
- Perform unitized body measurements with a tram gauge.
- Perform unitized body measurements with a dedicated bench system.

Improper frame or unitized body alignment may cause wheel alignment defects, rapid tire tread wear, and reduced directional stability. After collision damage, a unitized body vehicle may be repaired so it has satisfactory cosmetic appearance, but body and wheel alignment defects are still present. These defects may contribute to reduced directional stability, especially during such extreme conditions as hard cornering or severe braking. Therefore, diagnosing and correcting frame and unitized body alignment is very important to restoring vehicle safety! Body shops have mechanical or electronic body and chassis alignment equipment that can help correct improper body alignment.

INDICATIONS OF FRAME DAMAGE

The most common cause of frame damage on cars and light-duty trucks is collision damage. In some cases, the collision damage may be repaired to make the cosmetic appearance of the vehicle satisfactory, but the frame damage may not always be correctable.

When driving the vehicle, some indications of frame damage are:

1. Excessive tire wear when the front suspension alignment angles are correct.
2. Steering pull when the front suspension alignment angles are correct.
3. Steering wheel not centered when driving straight ahead, but the steering wheel was centered in the shop.

FRAME DIAGNOSIS

Preventing Frame Damage

Since frame problems affect wheel alignment, technicians must be able to diagnose frame defects so they are not confused with wheel alignment problems.

Follow these precautions to minimize frame damage:

1. Do not overload the vehicle.
2. Place the load evenly in a vehicle.
3. Do not operate the vehicle on extremely rough terrain.
4. Do not mount equipment such as a snow plow on a vehicle unless the frame is strong enough to carry the additional load and force.

Diagnosis of Frame Problems

Side Sway. The causes of frame side sway are:

1. Collision damage.
2. Fire damage.
3. Use of equipment on the vehicle for which the frame was not designed.

Sag. The causes of frame sag are:

1. Vehicle loads that exceed the load-carrying capacity of the frame.
2. Uneven load distribution.
3. Sudden changes in **section modulus**.

4. Holes drilled in the **frame flange**.
5. Too many holes drilled in the **frame web**.
6. Holes drilled too close together in the frame web.
7. Welds on the frame flange.
8. Cutting holes in the frame with a cutting torch.
9. Cutting notches in the frame rails.
10. A fire involving the vehicle.
11. Collision damage.
12. The use of equipment for which the frame was not designed.

Buckle. The causes of frame buckle are:

1. Collision damage.
2. Using equipment such as a snow plow when the frame was not designed for this type of service.
3. A fire involving the vehicle.

Diamond-Shaped. Diamond-shaped frame damage may be caused by:

1. Collision damage.
2. Towing another vehicle with a chain attached to one corner of the frame.
3. Being towed by another vehicle with a chain attached to one corner of the vehicle frame.

Twist. Frame twist may be caused by:

1. An accident or collision, especially one involving a rollover.
2. Operating the vehicle on extremely rough terrain.

CHECKING FRAME ALIGNMENT

Safety Concerns

While servicing vehicle frames, always wear the proper safety clothing and safety items for the job being performed. This includes proper work clothing, safety goggles, ear protection, respirator, proper gloves, welding shield, and safety shoes (Figure 14-1).

If arc welding is necessary on a vehicle frame, follow these precautions:

1. Remove the negative battery cable before welding (Figure 14-2).
2. Remove the fuel tank before welding (Figure 14-3).
3. Protect the interior and exterior of the vehicle as necessary (Figure 14-4).

Visual Inspection

Prior to frame measurement, the frame and suspension should be visually inspected. Check for wrinkles on the upper flange of the frame, which indicate a sag problem. Visually inspect the lower

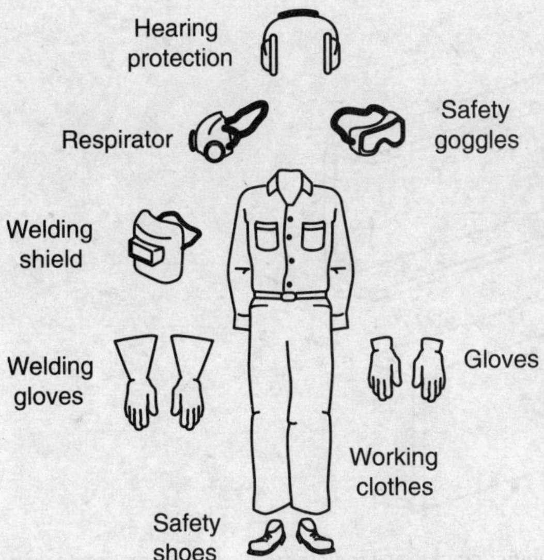

FIGURE 14-1 *Safety items for frame service.*

FIGURE 14-2 *Remove the negative battery cable before arc welding on a vehicle.*

FIGURE 14-3 *Remove the fuel tank before arc welding on a vehicle.*

FIGURE 14-4 *Protect the interior and exterior of the vehicle while arc welding.*

flange for wrinkles, which are definite evidence of buckle. Since suspension or axle problems may appear as frame problems, the suspension components should be inspected for wear and damage. For example, an offset rear axle may appear as a diamond-shaped frame. Check all suspension mounting bushings and inspect leaf-spring shackles and center bolts.

The frame should be inspected for cracks, bends, and severe corrosion. Minor frame bends are not visible, but severe bends may be visible. Straight cracks may occur at the edge of the frame flange, and **sunburst cracks** may radiate from a hole in the frame web or cross member (Figure 14-5).

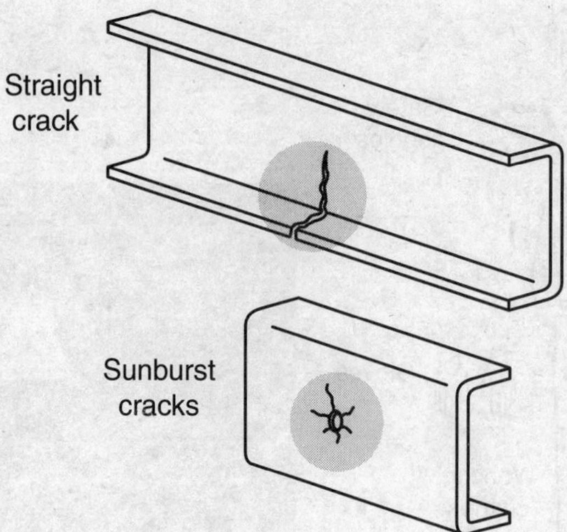

FIGURE 14-5 *Straight cracks may occur in the frame flange; sunburst cracks may radiate from a hole in the frame web or cross member.*

Frame Welding

CAUTION: Always follow the vehicle manufacturer's recommendations in the service manual regarding welding or reinforcing the frame, or mounting additional equipment on the frame. If these recommendations are not followed, the frame may be weakened and damaged.

Follow these steps for a typical frame welding procedure:

1. Remove any components that would interfere with the weld or be damaged by heat.
2. Find the extreme end of the crack and drill a 0.25 in. (6-mm) hole at this point.
3. V-grind the entire length of the crack from the starting point to the drilled hole.
4. The bottom of the crack should be opened 0.062 in. (2 mm) to allow proper weld penetration. A hacksaw blade may be used to open the crack.
5. Arc weld with the proper electrode and welding procedure.

Frame Measurement, Plumb Bob Method

Photo Sequence 14 shows a typical procedure for performing frame measurement using the plumb bob method.

Locating the Frame Centerline. Some vehicle manufacturers recommend measuring the frame with the **plumb bob** method.

Follow these steps to complete a plumb bob measurement for frame damage:

1. Place the vehicle on a level area of the shop floor and use a floor jack to raise the front and rear suspension off the floor. Support the chassis on safety stands at the manufacturer's recommended locations.
2. Suspend a plumb bob at locations 1, 2, 11, and 12 on the inside of the frame web, and allow the plumb bob to almost touch the floor surface (Figure 14-6). Points 1 and 2 are at the

PHOTO SEQUENCE 14
TYPICAL PROCEDURE FOR PERFORMING FRAME MEASUREMENT, PLUMB BOB METHOD

P14-1 *Park the vehicle on a level area of the shop floor.*

P14-2 *Raise the front suspension with a floor jack and lower the chassis onto safety stands positioned at the manufacturer's recommended lifting points.*

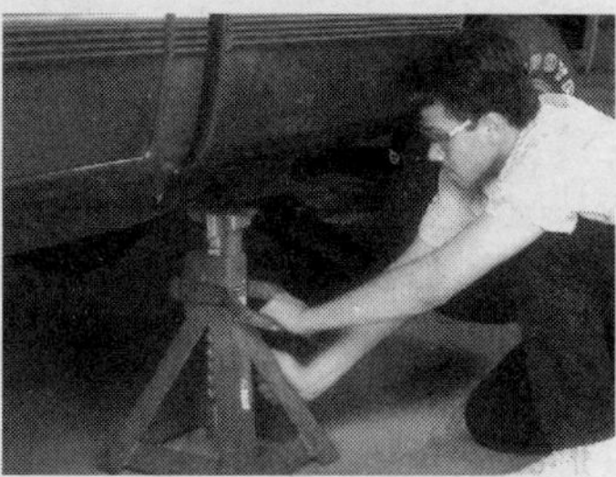

P14-3 *Raise the rear suspension with a floor jack and lower the chassis onto safety stands positioned at the manufacturer's recommended lifting points.*

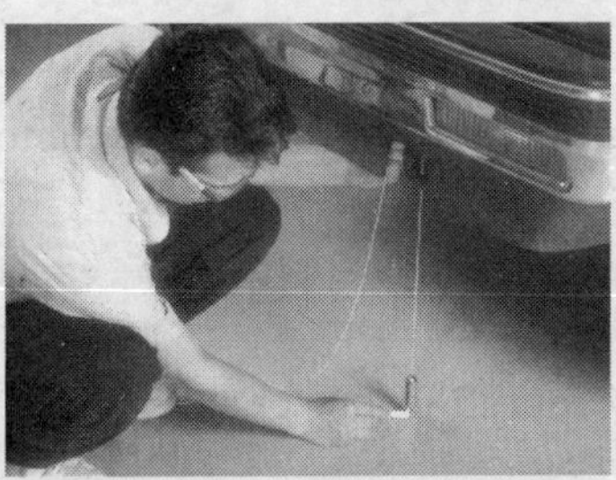

P14-4 *Suspend a plumb bob at the manufacturer's recommended frame measurement locations and place a chalk mark on the floor directly under the plumb bob.*

P14-5 *Use a floor jack to lift the vehicle, remove the safety stands, and lower the vehicle.*

P14-6 *Drive the vehicle away from the chalk-marked area.*

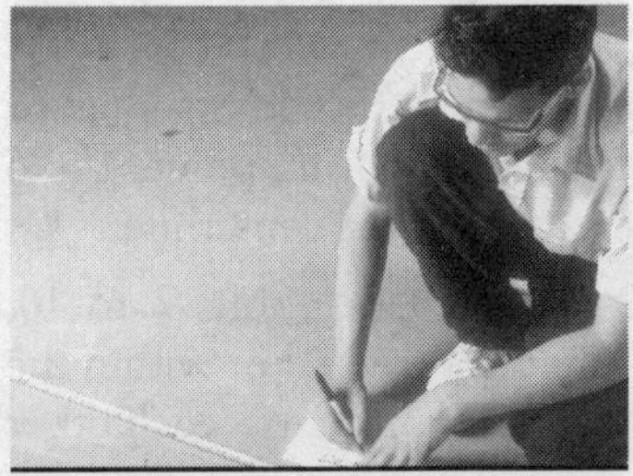

P14-7 *Use a tape measure to measure the vehicle's frame measurements between the chalk marks on the floor.*

P14-8 *Compare the frame measurements obtained with the vehicle manufacturer's specifications in the service manual.*

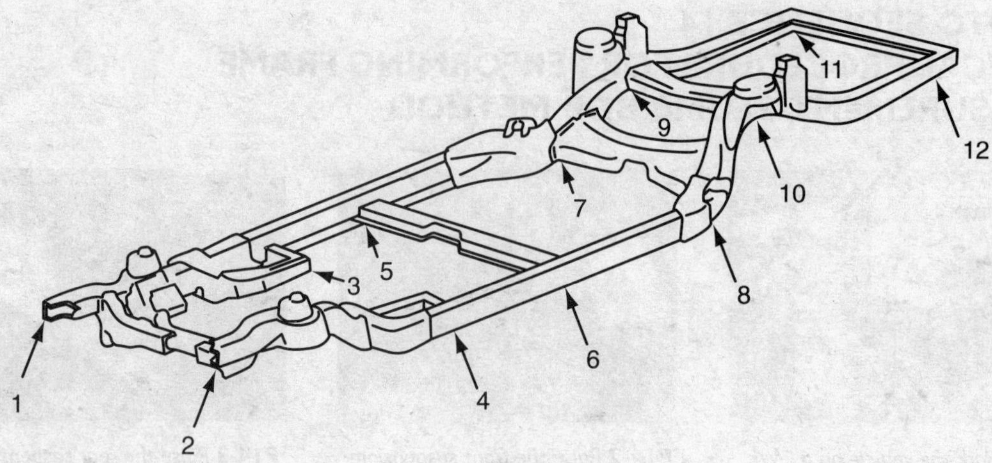

FIGURE 14-6 *Suspend a plumb bob at the locations shown on the frame and mark these locations on the floor with chalk.*

centerline of the slotted hole in each front bumper bracket, and points 11 and 12 are on the inside of the rear frame web. Mark these plumb bob locations on the floor with chalk.

3. Use a plumb bob to transfer points 3 through 10 from the frame to chalk marks on the floor.
4. Raise the vehicle with the floor jack, remove the safety stands, and lower the vehicle onto the floor. Move the vehicle away from the chalk-marked area.
5. Measure the distance between points 1 and 2 with a tape measure, and chalk mark the exact halfway point in this distance. This mark is the frame centerline at the front.
6. Measure the distance between points 11 and 12, and chalk mark the exact center of this measurement. This chalk mark is the frame centerline at the rear.
7. Draw a straight chalk line from the centerline at the front of the frame to the centerline at the rear of the frame. This chalk line is the complete centerline of the frame.

Horizontal Frame Measurements

The procedure used for horizontal frame measurements follows:

1. Measure the distance from the frame centerline to points 3 through 10. Each pair of these points should be equal within 0.125 in. (3 mm). For example, the distance from point 5 to the centerline should be equal to the distance from point 6 to the centerline.
2. Measure diagonally from point 1 to 6 and point 2 to 5. These distances should be equal or within the manufacturer's specified tolerance. Place a straight chalk mark from points 1 to 6 and points 2 to 5. These diagonal lines should cross each other at the frame centerline.
3. Repeat step 2 at all the other diagonal frame measurements, such as points 3 to 10, 4 to 9, 5 to 12, and 6 to 11. All these diagonal measurements should be equal or within the vehicle manufacturer's specified tolerance. Each pair of diagonal lines must cross each other at the vehicle centerline (Figure 14-7).

When such frame problems as side sway, buckle, or a diamond-shaped condition are present, some of the horizontal frame measurements are not within specifications, and some of the diagonal chalk lines do not cross at the frame centerline, depending on the location of the damaged area.

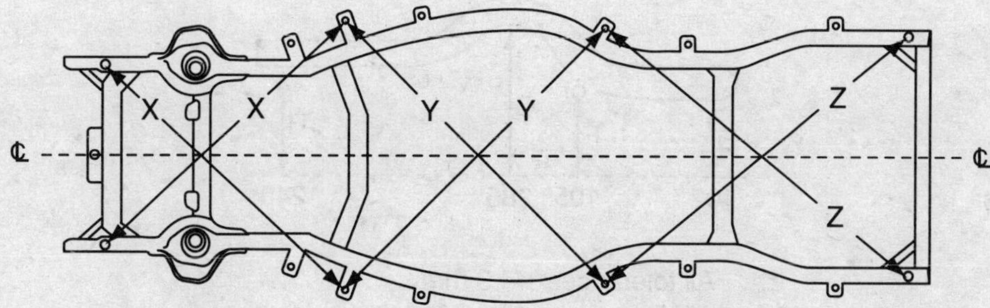

FIGURE 14-7 *Each pair of diagonal measurement lines on the frame must cross each other at the frame centerline.*

Frame Measurement, Tram Gauge Method

A **tram gauge** is a long, straight bar with two adjustable pointers. The distance between the pointers is adjustable, and the height of the pointers is also adjustable (Figure 14-8).

The horizontal frame measurements may be completed with a tram gauge, rather than using the plumb bob method. When measuring a frame, horizontal measurements are completed straight across the frame and diagonally forward and rearward on the frame, as discussed previously.

Vertical measurements from specific locations on the frame to an imaginary standard line are also necessary to detect such conditions as frame sag and twist (Figure 14-9). This imaginary horizontal line used for vertical frame measurements is called the **datum line.**

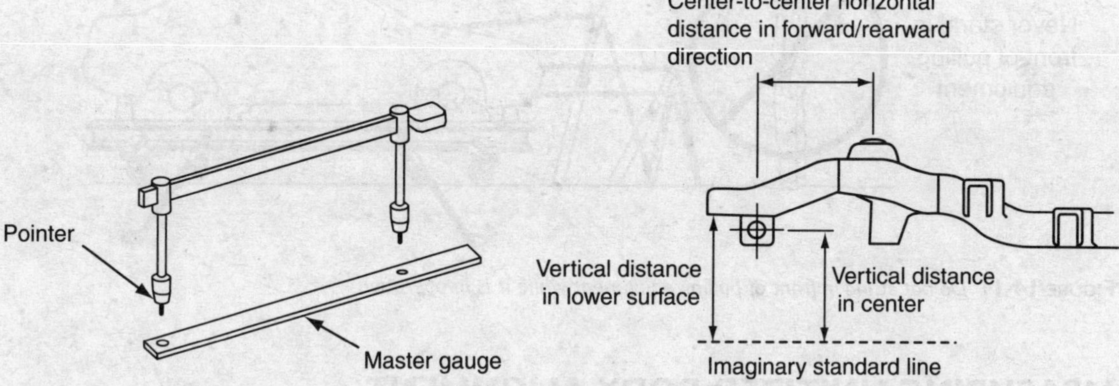

FIGURE 14-8 *Tram gauge for frame measurements.*

FIGURE 14-9 *Horizontal and vertical frame measurements.*

When vertical frame measurements are completed with the tram gauge, the gauge pointers must be set at the manufacturer's specified distance for each frame location (Figure 14-10). With the tram gauge pointers set at the specified height and the gauge properly installed across the frame in the recommended frame openings, the tram gauge should be level if the vertical frame measurements are within specifications. If the frame is twisted, the tram gauge is not level when adjusted to specifications and installed in the twisted area.

To measure frame sag, three tram gauges may be installed at various locations for vertical frame measurement. When viewed from the front or the rear, the tram gauges must be level with each other. If the tram gauge near the center of the frame is lower than the tram gauges at the front and rear of the frame, the frame is sagged.

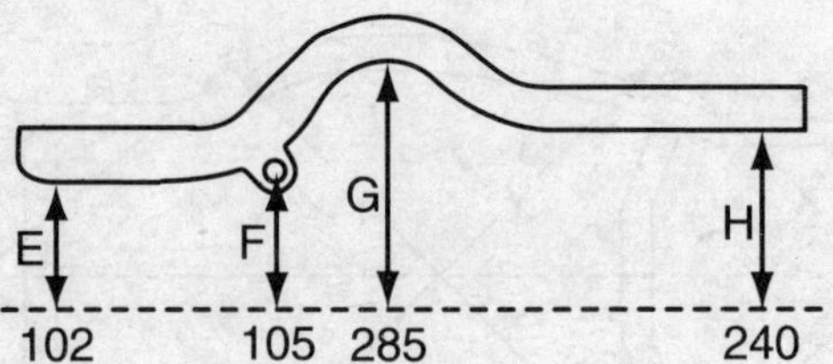

FIGURE 14-10 *Tram gauge setting and locations for vertical frame measurements, rear subframe.*

Frame Straightening

Frame straightening is usually done with special hydraulically operated bending equipment. This equipment must be operated according to the equipment manufacturer's recommended procedures. Since frame straightening is usually done by experienced body technicians, we will not discuss this service in detail. All safety precautions must be observed while operating frame-straightening equipment. Never stand in front of pulling equipment when it is in operation (Figure 14-11).

FIGURE 14-11 *Do not stand in front of pulling equipment while it is in operation.*

MEASURING UNITIZED BODY ALIGNMENT

Tram Gauge

On unitized bodies, a tram gauge may be used to perform such measurements as the upper strut towers (Figure 14-12) and the front cross member (Figure 14-13).

If the underhood body measurements such as the strut tower measurements are not within specifications, the strut towers may not be in the original position. Collision damage may cause the strut towers to move out of the original position. If the strut towers are out of position, the front alignment angles are incorrect.

Because the lower control arms are attached to the cross member or cradle and also to the lower end of the steering knuckle, if the crossmember is moved from the original intended position, front wheel alignment is adversely affected (Figure 14-14). Improper cross member position may be caused

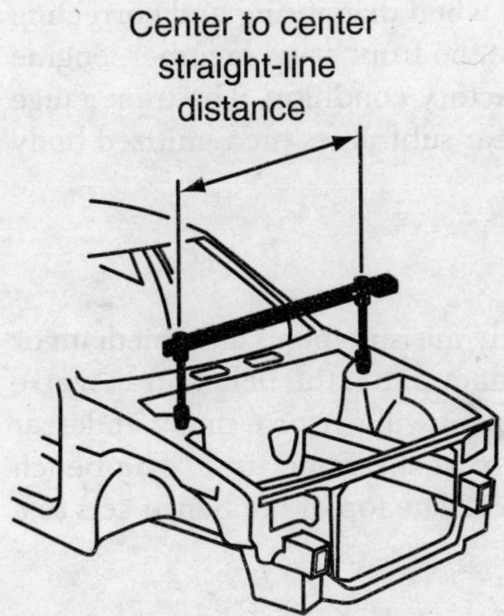

FIGURE 14-12 *Performing an upper strut tower measurement with a tram gauge on a unitized body vehicle.*

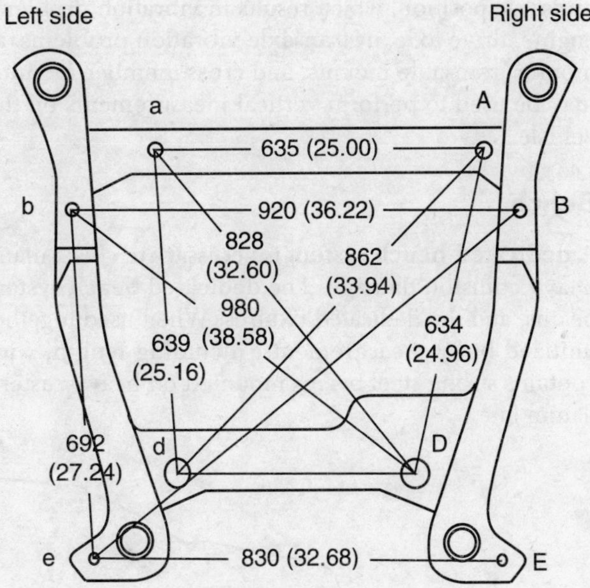

FIGURE 14-13 *Tram gauge measurements on the front cross member of a unitized body vehicle.*

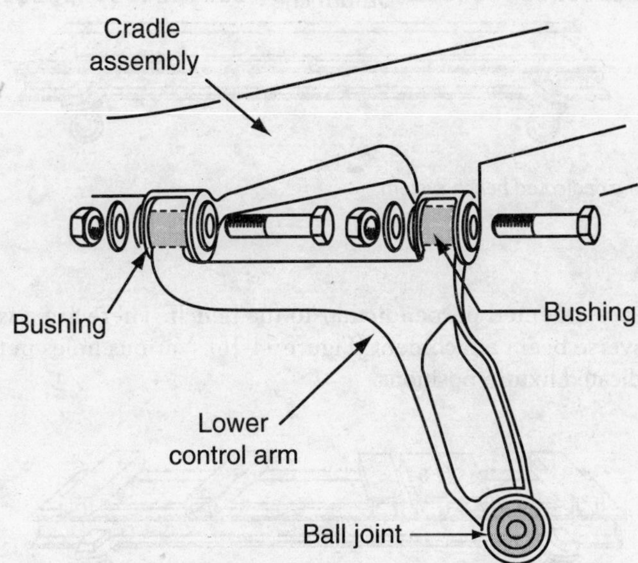

FIGURE 14-14 *Lower control arm-to-cradle attachment.*

by loose, worn cross member mounts or a bent cross member. Improper front wheel alignment may result in excessive front tire tread wear, steering pull, steering wander, and reduced directional stability. When removing a front cross member, always mark the cradle in relation to the chassis so it can be re-installed in the original position.

The engine and transaxle mounts are also connected to the front cross member. Therefore, a bent cross member or improperly positioned cross member mounts may cause improper engine and transaxle position, which results in vibration problems. Therefore, when diagnosing and correcting engine, drive axle, or transaxle vibration problems, always be sure the front cross member, engine mounts, transaxle mounts, and cross member mounts are in satisfactory condition. The tram gauge may be used to perform vertical measurements on the front and rear subframes on a unitized body vehicle.

Bench

A **dedicated bench system** is necessary to check many unitized body measurements after medium or heavy collision damage. The dedicated bench system has three main parts: the bench, transverse beams, and the dedicated fixtures. When used together, this equipment will perform many undercar unitized body measurements, including length, width, and height at the same time. The bench contains strong steel beams mounted on heavy casters (Figure 14-15). The top of the bench acts as a datum line.

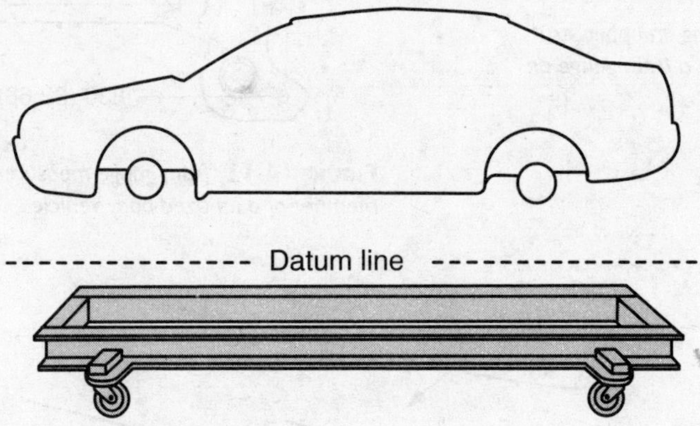

FIGURE 14-15 *Bench from a dedicated bench system.*

Transverse Beams

The transverse beams are mounted perpendicular to the bench. There are a variety of holes in the bench for proper transverse beam attachment (Figure 14-16). Various holes in the transverse beams provide the correct dedicated fixture positions.

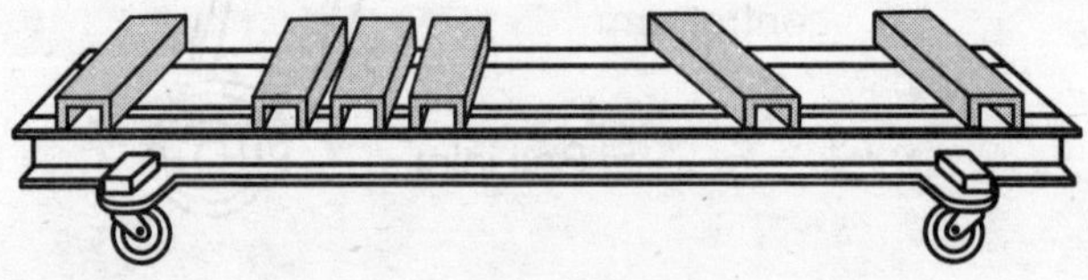

FIGURE 14-16 *Transverse beams placed on the bench.*

Dedicated Fixtures

The dedicated fixtures are specific to the body style being measured (Figure 14-17). These fixtures are bolted to the transverse beams, and the holes in the upper end of the fixtures must be aligned with specific body openings (Figure 14-18).

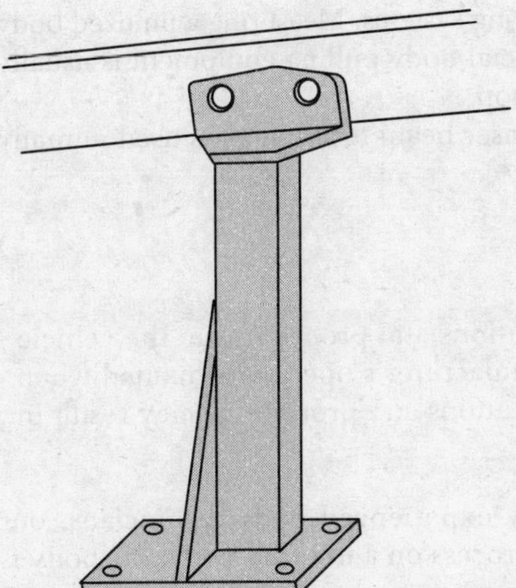

FIGURE 14-17 *Dedicated fixtures are specific to the body style being measured.*

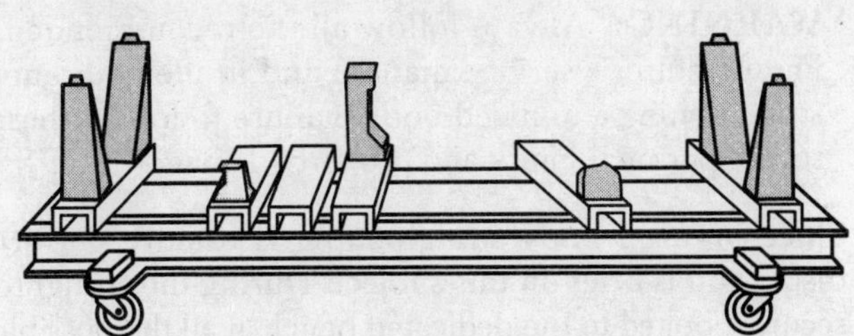

FIGURE 14-18 *Dedicated fixtures are bolted to the transverse beams in specific locations depending on the body style.*

The unitized body must be straightened until the holes in the dedicated fixtures and the body openings are aligned. If the holes in the unitized body are behind and above the dedicated fixture openings, the unitized body must be pulled forward and downward in that area (Figure 14-19).

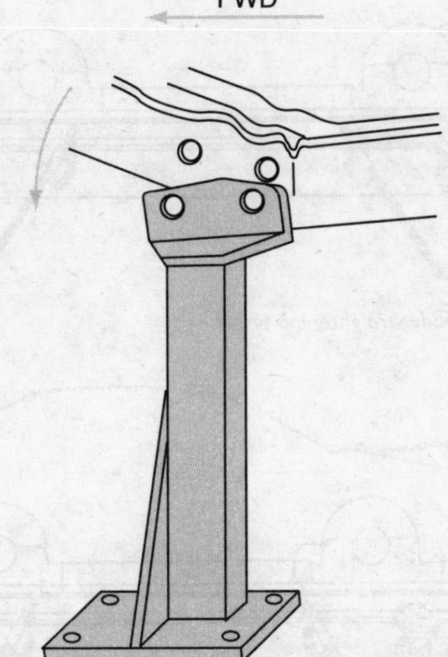

FIGURE 14-19 *When holes in the body are behind and above the openings in the dedicated fixture, the unitized body must be pulled forward and downward in that area.*

Universal benches are now available with computer measuring systems. Measuring a unitized body with a bench system and straightening these bodies with special body pulling equipment is usually done in an autobody shop rather than an automotive repair shop.

Electronic body and chassis alignment equipment using laser beam technology is used in many body shops during collision repair.

Unitized Body Straightening

WARNING: Always follow all the recommended precautions and procedures in the vehicle manufacturer's service manual and in the equipment manufacturer's operator's manual when straightening a unitized body. Failure to follow these precautions and procedures may result in severe personal injury and property damage.

Since unitized body straightening is usually performed by experienced body technicians, our discussion is brief on this subject. During the straightening process on a unitized body, the body is securely bolted to the dedicated bench at all the possible locations except those where misalignment is present. The dedicated bench is securely chained to special holding fixtures in the shop floor. Hydraulically operated pulling equipment is then attached securely to the unitized body to pull the body in the intended direction. **Single-pull** equipment pulls only one location at a time (Figure 14-20), and **multipull** equipment pulls in several locations at the same time (Figure 14-21). The unitized body is pulled until the holes in the body are aligned with the holes in the dedicated fixtures.

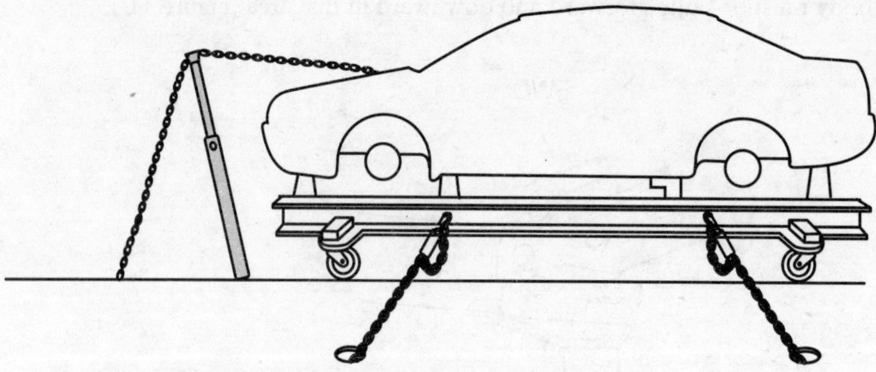

FIGURE 14-20 *Single-pull unitized body straightening system.*

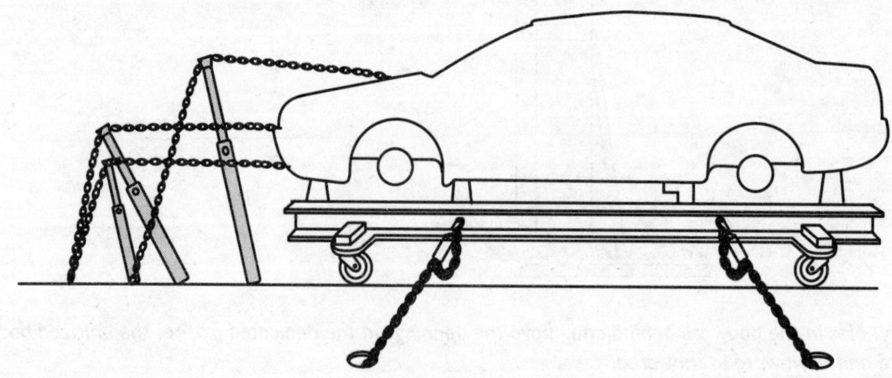

FIGURE 14-21 *Multipull unitized body straightening system.*

TABLE 14-1 *Diagnosing Frame and Body Damage*

PROBLEM	SYMPTOMS	POSSIBLE CAUSES
Excessive front tire tread wear	Front tire tread wear with correct front suspension alignment angles	Frame, front cradle damage
Steering pull when driving straight ahead	Steering pull with correct front and rear alignment angles	Frame, front cradle damage
Steering wheel not centered when driving straight ahead	Steering wheel centered in the shop, but it is not centered when driving straight ahead	Frame, front cradle damage
Improper strut tower tower position	Incorrect front suspension alignment angles, steering pull, tire tread wear	Collision damage
Frame buckle	Wrinkles in frame flanges	Collision damage, vehicle abuse
Improper cradle measurements or position	Incorrect front suspension alignment angles, steering pull, tire tread wear	Collision damage, worn or improperly positioned cradle mounts

CASE STUDY

A customer complained about a vibration problem on an Chryster Concorde with front-wheel drive. Further questioning of the customer revealed that the vibration occurred when accelerating and decelerating at 40 to 60 mph (64 to 96 km/h). During a road test, the technician found the customer's description of the problem was accurate. The car did have a vibration problem at the speed indicated by the customer. While road-testing the car, the technician thought about the causes of this problem and decided the most likely cause of the vibration would be inner front drive axle joints. The technician informed the customer that a drive axle joint inspection was necessary.

The technician raised the vehicle on a hoist and checked the front drive axle joints. He was surprised to discover the inner and outer joints were all in good condition with no cracked boots or looseness. An inspection of the engine cradle indicated the crosspiece at the rear of the cradle was severely damaged near the left side of the cradle. It appeared this crosspiece may have struck an object such as a rock during off-road driving. A check of the cradle mounts indicated the cradle openings were jammed into the rubber mounts on the left side of the cradle. The rubber mounts were bulged at the rear of the cradle openings, indicating the left side of the cradle was driven rearward.

The technician informed the customer that cradle removal, measurement, and possible replacement was necessary. After the customer approved this service operation, the technician removed the cradle and measured it with a tram gauge. The diagonal measurements on the cradle were not within the manufacturer's specifications. Since the cradle was severely distorted, a replacement cradle was installed, and all damaged cradle mounting bushings were replaced. A road test indicated the vibration problem was corrected.

SERVICE TIPS

- If the frame is cracked, frame alignment is often necessary.
- The points on the left and right frame webs must be at the same location on each web for accurate measurements.
- When using a tape measure, avoid twists and bends in the tape to provide accurate readings.
- When the tram gauge is installed on the frame, be sure the pointers are seated properly in the frame openings (Figure 14-22).

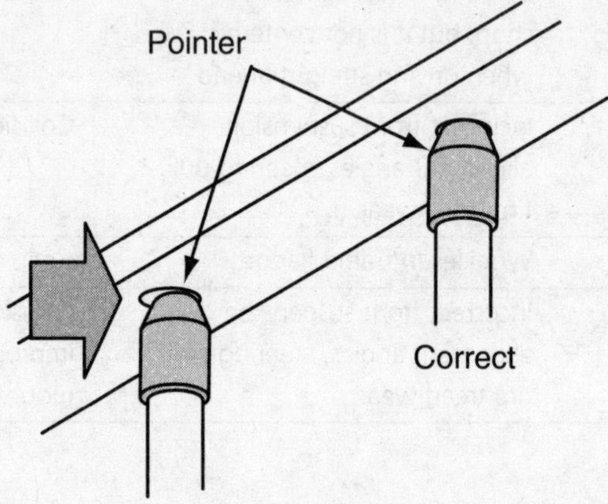

FIGURE 14-22 *Correct and incorrect tram gauge pointer seating in the frame openings.*

REVIEW QUESTIONS

1. While discussing frame sag:
   Technician A says frame sag may be caused by holes drilled in the frame flange. *Technician B* says frame sag may be caused by holes drilled too close together in the frame web.
   Who is correct?
   A. A only **C.** Both A and B
   B. B only **D.** Neither A nor B
2. While discussing frame side sway:
   Technician A says frame side sway may be caused by uneven load distribution. *Technician B* says frame side sway may result from too many holes drilled in the frame web.
   Who is correct?
   A. A only **C.** Both A and B
   B. B only **D.** Neither A nor B
3. While discussing a diamond-shaped frame condition:
   Technician A says this condition may be caused when the vehicle is involved in a fire. *Technician B* says this condition may be caused by towing another vehicle with the chain attached to one corner of the frame.

Who is correct?

A. A only
B. B only
C. Both A and B
D. Neither A nor B

4. When discussing the plumb bob method of frame measurement:
Technician A says the distance from the frame centerline to the same point on each side of the frame should be equal. *Technician B* says diagonal frame measurement lines on each side of the vehicle should cross each other at the frame centerline.
Who is correct?

A. A only
B. B only
C. Both A and B
D. Neither A nor B

5. When discussing vertical frame measurements:
Technician A says the datum line is an imaginary horizontal line parallel to the vehicle frame that is used for vertical frame measurements. *Technician B* says if three tram gauges are properly adjusted and installed at specified locations on the frame, these gauges should be level with each other.
Who is correct?

A. A only
B. B only
C. Both A and B
D. Neither A nor B

6. All of these statements about frame problems are true EXCEPT:
A. Frame sag may be caused by overloading the vehicle.
B. Frame sag may be caused by the use of equipment for which the frame was not designed.
C. Frame buckle may be caused by using a snow plow on the front of the vehicle.
D. A diamond-shaped frame may be caused by operating the vehicle on extremely rough terrain.

7. While diagnosing and inspecting vehicle frames:
A. Wrinkles on the lower frame flange indicate frame buckle.
B. Fire damage may cause frame twist.
C. Unequal vehicle load distribution may cause frame side sway.
D. Frame twist may be caused by cutting notches in the frame flanges.

8. When welding a vehicle frame crack:
A. A 0.25 in. hole should be drilled in the center of the crack.
B. The crack should be V-ground at both ends of the crack.
C. Disconnect the negative battery cable before welding the crack.
D. Use a cutting torch to open the crack for proper weld penetration.

9. While performing unitized body measurements:
A. A dedicated bench system performs measurements on upper strut towers.
B. Fixtures on a dedicated bench system are specific for the vehicle body being straightened.
C. The fixtures are bolted to the bench in a dedicated bench system.
D. The transverse beams on a dedicated bench system are specific for the body being straightened.

10. While inspecting and measuring a front cradle on a front-wheel-drive car:
A. Front wheel alignment angles may be changed by a bent front cradle.
B. Engine mounting position is not affected by a bent front cradle.
C. A bent front cradle has no effect on front drive axle vibration.
D. A bent front cradle may cause premature front wheel bearing failure.

CHALLENGE QUESTIONS

1. When making horizontal frame measurements to determine if the frame or unibody is straight, all of the measurements should be made with reference to which one of the following?
A. Vertical
B. Centerline
C. Horizontal
D. Body bushings

2. A bent front cross member affects all of the following alignments EXCEPT:
A. Centerline.
B. Suspension.
C. Axle.
D. Engine.

3. While discussing frame damage:
Technician A says a possible indication of frame damage is an uncentered steering wheel when driving straight ahead. *Technician B* says suspension alignment may be impossible if the frame is bent.
Who is correct ?
A. A only
B. B only
C. Both A and B
D. Neither A nor B

4. Which of the following makes this statement true? Measurement points of a frame or unibody using a tram gauge are:
A. Seam notches.
B. Calculated by computer.
C. Based on a vertical datum plane.
D. Manufacturer's-specified frame openings.

5. Referring to Figure 14-14:
Technician A says the measurement between "e" and "b" should be no more than ±1.0 in. different from the measurement between "E" and "B." *Technician B* says frame damage problems, such as buckling, can be determined if the measurements between points "e" and "E" are more than ±0.25 in. different than between "b" and "B."
Who is correct?
A. A only
B. B only
C. Both A and B
D. Neither A nor B

JOB SHEET 43

Name ______________________________ Date ______________

FRAME MEASUREMENT, PLUMB BOB METHOD

Upon completion of this job sheet, you should be able to perform frame measurements with a plumb bob.

Tools and Materials

Floor jack
Safety stands
Plumb bob
Chalk

Describe the Vehicle Being Worked On:

Year __________ Make __________ Model __________
VIN ______________ Engine type and size ______________

Procedure

Task Completed

1. Place the vehicle on a level area of the shop floor and use a floor jack to raise the front and rear suspension off the floor. Support the chassis on safety stands at the manufacturer's recommended locations.

Is the vehicle chassis supported securely on safety stands? ☐ Yes ☐ No

Instructor check ______________________________

2. Locate the frame measurement locations in the vehicle manufacturer's service manual. ☐

3. Suspend a plumb bob at each frame measurement location and place a chalk mark on the floor directly below the tip of the plumb bob.

Are all frame measurement locations chalk marked on the shop floor?
☐ Yes ☐ No

Instructor check ______________________________

SERVICE TIP: The measurement points on the left and right frame webs must be at the same location on each web to obtain accurate measurements.

4. Raise the vehicle with the floor jack, remove the safety stands, and lower the vehicle onto the floor. Move the vehicle away from the chalk-marked area. ☐

SERVICE TIP: When using a tape measure, avoid twists and bends in the tape to provide accurate readings.

5. Measure the distance between the two chalk marks directly across from each other at the front of frame, and chalk mark the exact halfway point in this distance. This mark is the frame centerline at the front.

Distance between the two chalk marks directly across from each other at the front of the frame ______________

Midpoint in the distance between the two chalk marks directly across from each other at the front of the frame ______________

Task Completed

6. Measure the distance between the two chalk marks directly across from each other at the rear of the frame, and chalk mark the exact halfway point of this distance. This mark is the frame centerline at the rear.

   Distance between the two chalk marks directly across from each other at the rear of the frame ____________

   Midpoint of the distance between the two chalk marks directly across from each other at the rear of the frame ____________

7. Draw a straight chalk line from the centerline at the front of the frame to the centerline at the rear of the frame. This chalk line is the complete centerline of the frame.

   Is the vehicle centerline chalk marked on shop floor? ☐ Yes ☐ No

   Instructor check ____________

8. Use a tape measure to measure the distance from the frame centerline to all frame measurement points directly opposite each other. Each pair of these points should be equal within 0.125 in. (3 mm).

   Frame measurements between specified measurement locations that are directly opposite each other and the vehicle centerline, starting at the front of the frame:

   A. left side ______ right side ______ difference ______

   B. left side ______ right side ______ difference ______

   C. left side ______ right side ______ difference ______

   D. left side ______ right side ______ difference ______

   Necessary frame repairs:

   ____

   ____

   ____

9. Use a tape measure to complete all diagonal frame measurements at the vehicle manufacturer's recommended locations. These distances should be equal or within the manufacturer's specified tolerances.

   Distances between diagonal frame measurement points:

   Diagonal frame measurements at the front of the frame:

   diagonal A ______ diagonal B ______
   difference between diagonal A and B ______

   Diagonal frame measurements at the center of the frame:

   diagonal C ______ diagonal D ______
   difference between diagonal C and D ______

   Diagonal frame measurements at the rear of the frame:

   diagonal E ______ diagonal F ______
   difference between diagonal E and F ______

   Necessary frame service:

   ____

   ____

   ____

Task Completed

10. Use a long, straight steel bar to place a straight chalk mark between all frame diagonal measurement locations. These diagonal lines should cross each other at the frame centerline. ☐

If all diagonal lines do not cross the frame centerline at the same location, state the required frame repairs.

____

____

Instructor's Response ____

____

____

JOB SHEET 44

Name ______________________________ Date ______________

INSPECT AND MEASURE FRONT CRADLE

Upon completion of this job sheet, you should be able to inspect and measure front cradles.

ASE Correlation

This job sheet is related to ASE Automotive Suspension and Steering Task: *Measure front cradle (subframe) alignment and determine the necessary repairs.*

Tools and Materials

Tram gauge

Describe the Vehicle Being Worked On:

Year __________ Make ________________ Model ______________
VIN ______________________ Engine type and size ____________________

Procedure

Task Completed

1. Raise the vehicle on a lift using the vehicle manufacturer's specified lifting points. ☐
2. Inspect front cradle mounts for looseness, damage, oil soaking, wear, and deterioration.

   Cradle mount condition: right front ______ right rear ______

   left front ______ left rear ______
3. Inspect front cradle for visible bends and damage.

   Front cradle condition indicated in visible inspection:

   ____

   ____

   ____
4. Inspect front cradle alignment.

   Is the front cradle aligning hole(s) properly aligned with the matching hole in the chassis? ☐ Yes ☐ No

   Recommended cradle service:

   ____

   ____

   ____
5. Use a tram gauge to complete all measurements across the width of the cradle starting at the front of the cradle.

   Width measurement A ________

   Specified width measurement A ________

   Width measurement B ________

Task Completed ____________

Specified width measurement B ________

Width measurement C ________

Specified width measurement C ________

Width measurement D ________

Specified width measurement D ________

Width measurement E ________

Specified width measurement E ________

Necessary cradle service:

____

____

6. Use a tram gauge to complete all front-to-rear measurements on the cradle, starting on the left side of the cradle.

Front-to-rear measurement A ________

Specified front-to-rear measurement A ________

Front-to-rear measurement B ________

Specified front-to-rear measurement B ________

Front-to-rear measurement C ________

Specified front-to-rear measurement C ________

Front-to-rear measurement D ________

Specified front-to-rear measurement D ________

Necessary cradle service:

____

____

7. Use a tram gauge to complete all diagonal cradle measurements, starting at the left side of the cradle.

Diagonal measurement A ________

Specified diagonal measurement A ________

Diagonal measurement B ________

Specified diagonal measurement B ________

Diagonal measurement C ________

Specified diagonal measurement C ________

Diagonal measurement D ________

Specified diagonal measurement D ________

Necessary cradle service:

____

____

Instructor's Response ____

____

____

JOB SHEET 45

Name ____ Date ____________________

INSPECT AND WELD VEHICLE FRAME

Upon completion of this job sheet, you should be able to inspect and weld a vehicle frame.

Tools and Materials

Hand pump
Arc welder
Welding hammer
Welding rods

Describe the Vehicle Being Worked On:

Year __________ Make ________________ Model ______________

VIN ____________________ Engine type and size ______________

Procedure

Task Completed

CAUTION: Always wear eye protection while working in the shop, and use the specified eye protection while arc welding to prevent eye injury.

1. Raise the vehicle on a lift using the vehicle manufacturer's specified lifting points. ☐
2. Read the instructions for disconnecting the negative battery cable in the vehicle manufacturer's service manual. These instructions may include connecting a 12-V power source to the cigarette lighter socket to maintain power to computer memories, radio-stereo, and other electronic equipment.

   List the vehicle manufacturer's instructions for disconnecting the negative battery cable.

   ____

   ____

   Have these instructions been completed on the vehicle being serviced?
   ☐ Yes ☐ No

   Instructor check ______________________________
3. If the vehicle is air-bag-equipped, determine the specified waiting period after the negative battery cable is disconnected before performing service work.
   Waiting period __________
4. Disconnect the negative battery cable.

   Is the negative battery cable disconnected? ☐ Yes ☐ No

   Has the specified waiting period been completed before servicing the vehicle?
   ☐ Yes ☐ No

   Instructor check ______________________________
5. Use a hand pump to pump all the fuel from the fuel tank. Place the fuel in the proper fuel safety containers and store this fuel away from the work area and other ignition sources.

   Has all the fuel been pumped from the tank? ☐ Yes ☐ No

Task Completed

Is this fuel placed in proper fuel safety containers and stored away from the work area?
☐ Yes ☐ No

Instructor check ____________________

6. Remove the fuel tank from the vehicle and store the fuel tank away from the work area and other ignition sources.

   Is the fuel tank removed? ☐ Yes ☐ No

   Fuel tank stored away from the work area? ☐ Yes ☐ No

   Instructor check ____________________

7. Protect the interior and exterior of the vehicle from heat or sparks generated by the welding process.

   Are the vehicle's interior and exterior protected? ☐ Yes ☐ No

   Instructor check ____________________

8. Inspect the entire frame for cracks, bends, severe corrosion, and wrinkles in the flanges.

   Defective frame conditions:

   ____

   ____

   ____

9. Remove any components that would interfere with the weld or be damaged by heat.

   Have all components been removed that would interfere with the weld or be damaged by the heat? ☐ Yes ☐ No

   Instructor check ____________________

10. Find the extreme end of the crack and drill a 0.25 in. (6-mm) hole at this point.

    Is a 0.25 in. hole drilled at the end of the crack? ☐ Yes ☐ No

    Instructor check ____________________

11. V-grind the entire length of the crack from the starting point to the drilled hole.

    Is the entire length of the crack V-ground? ☐ Yes ☐ No

    Instructor check ____________________

12. The bottom of the crack should be opened 0.062 in. (2 mm) to allow proper weld penetration. A hacksaw blade may be used to open the crack.

    Is the bottom of the crack open 0.062 in. (2 mm)? ☐ Yes ☐ No

    Instructor check ____________________

13. Arc weld the crack with the electrodes specified by the frame and/or vehicle manufacturer. Complete several passes with the arc weld to fill the crack.

    Is the crack filled with arc weld material? ☐ Yes ☐ No

    Instructor check ____________________

14. Use a pointed welding hammer to remove slag from the exterior of the weld.

    Is the slag removed from the weld? ☐ Yes ☐ No

    Instructor check ____________________

Instructor's Response ____________________

____

____

FOUR WHEEL ALIGNMENT ADJUSTMENTS

15

Upon completion and review of this chapter, you should be able to:

- Adjust front wheel camber on various front suspension systems.
- Adjust front wheel caster on various front suspension systems.
- Correct setback conditions.
- Check and correct front engine cradle position.
- Correct SAI angles that are not within specifications.
- Adjust front wheel toe.
- Center steering wheel.
- Recognize the symptoms of improper rear wheel alignment.
- Diagnose the causes of improper rear wheel alignment.
- Perform rear wheel camber adjustments.
- Perform rear wheel toe adjustments.
- Use a track gauge to measure rear wheel tracking.
- Diagnose rear wheel tracking problems from the track gauge measurements.

Proper front and rear wheel alignment is extremely important because it affects directional stability, tire tread wear, and vehicle safety! Technicians must know how to check front and rear wheel alignment angles and diagnose the causes of steering and alignment problems. It is also essential for technicians to know how to adjust front and rear suspension angles while maintaining vehicle safety. On certain vehicles, some wheel alignment angles are considered non-adjustable by the vehicle manufacturer, but aftermarket suppliers often provide parts kits to provide adjustments on these suspension systems. This chapter provides various adjustment procedures of front and rear suspension alignment angles as summarized in Photo Sequence 16 on page 516.

WHEEL ALIGNMENT PROCEDURE

The proper procedure for front and rear wheel alignment is important since adjusting one wheel alignment angle may change another angle. For example, adjusting front wheel caster changes front wheel toe. The wheel alignment adjustment procedure is especially critical on four-wheel independent suspension systems. A front wheel adjustment procedure is provided in Figure 15-1, and a typical rear wheel adjustment procedure is given in Figure 15-2. Always follow the wheel alignment procedure in the vehicle manufacturer's service manual.

Check tire pressure on both sides.

Check the ride height on both sides.

Measure and adjust both camber and toe of the left side.

Measure and adjust both camber and toe of the right side.

Adjust caster on both sides.

Measure and readjust both camber and toe of the left side.

Measure and readjust both camber and toe of the right side.

FIGURE 15-1 *Front wheel alignment adjustment procedure.*

Check tire pressure on both sides.

Check the ride height on both sides.

Adjust both camber and toe of the left side.

Adjust both camber and toe of the right side.

FIGURE 15-2 *Rear wheel alignment adjustment procedure.*

CAMBER ADJUSTMENT

Shims

Various methods are provided by car manufacturers for camber adjustment. Some car manufacturers provide a shim-type **camber adjustment** between the upper control arm mounting and the inside of

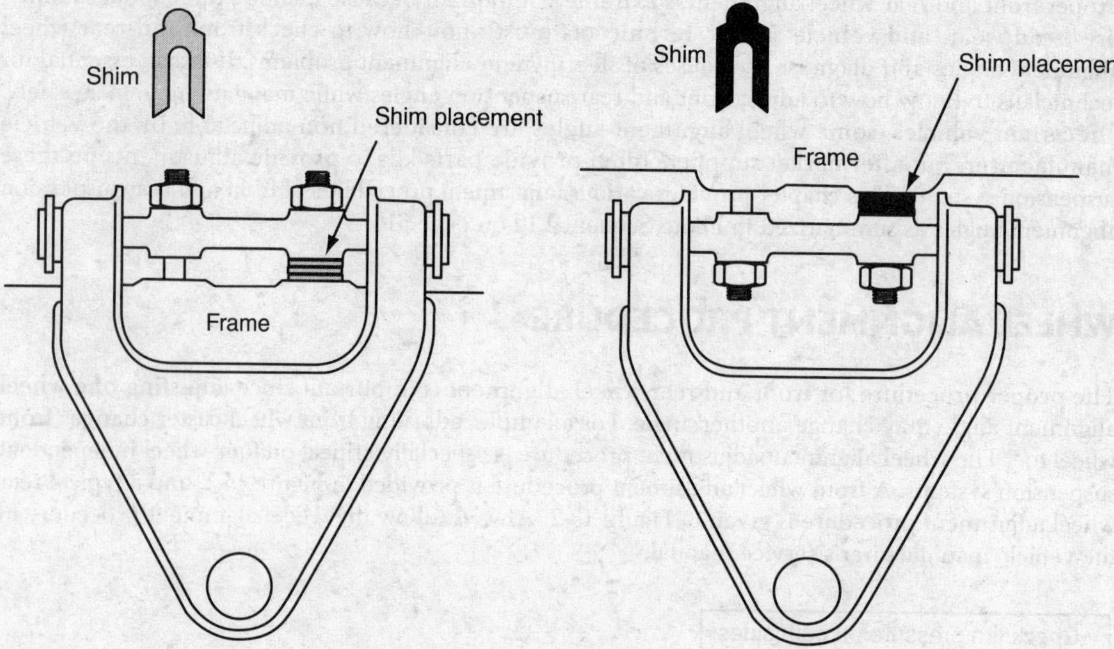

FIGURE 15-3 *Shim-type camber adjustment between upper control arm mounting and the inside of the frame.*

FIGURE 15-4 *Shim-type camber adjustment between upper control arm mounting and the outside of the frame.*

the frame (Figure 15-3). In this type of camber adjustment, increasing the shim thickness moves the camber setting to a more negative position, whereas decreasing shim thickness changes the camber toward a more positive position. Shims of equal thickness should be added or removed on both upper control arm mounting bolts to change the camber setting without affecting the caster setting.

Other vehicle manufacturers provide a shim-type camber adjustment between the upper control arm mounting and the outside of the frame (Figure 15-4). On this shim-type camber adjustment, increasing the shim thickness increases positive camber.

Older vehicles have shim-type camber adjustments, but newer vehicles have eccentric cams for this adjustment.

Eccentric Cams

Some vehicles have **eccentric cams** on the inner ends of the upper control arm to provide camber adjustment (Figure 15-5), whereas other suspension systems have eccentric cams on the inner ends of the lower control arms (Figure 15-6). If the original cam adjustment on the inner ends of the upper control arms does not provide enough camber adjustment, aftermarket upper control arm shaft kits are available that provide an extra 1 1/2° of camber adjustment (Figure 15-7). The suspension adjustments shown in Figures 15-3 through 15-7 are used on rear-wheel-drive cars with short-and-long arm front suspension systems.

Some MacPherson strut front suspension systems on front-wheel-drive cars have a cam on one of the steering-knuckle-to-strut bolts to adjust camber (Figure 15-8). Aftermarket camber adjustment kits that provide 2-1/2° of camber adjustment are available for many MacPherson strut suspension systems (Figure 15-9 and Figure 15-10). Similar camber adjustment kits are available for many cars with

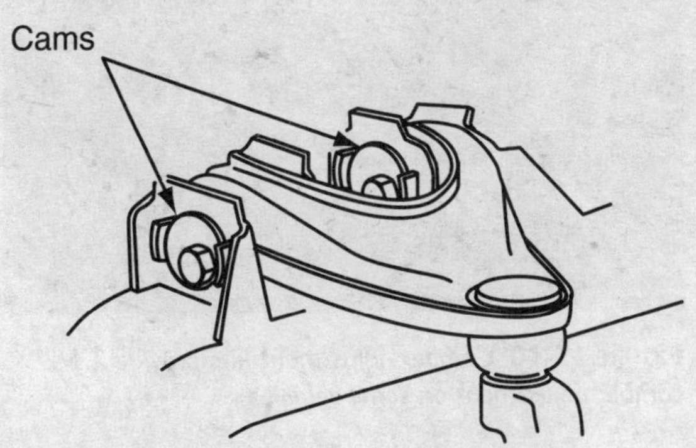

FIGURE 15-5 *Cam adjustment on the inside ends of the upper control arm.*

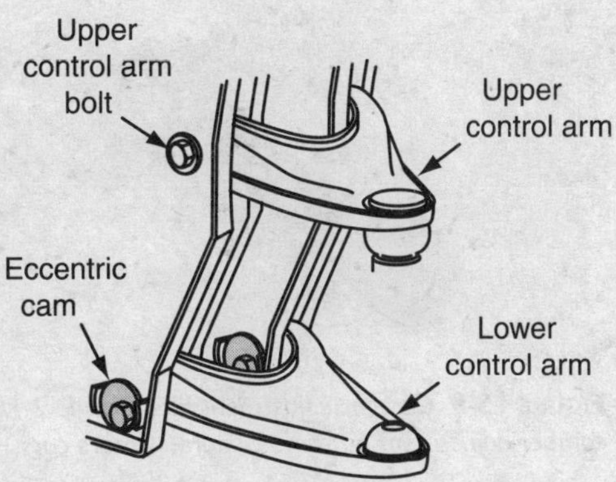

FIGURE 15-6 *Cam adjustment on the inner ends of the lower control arms.*

FIGURE 15-7 *Upper control arm shaft kit provides an extra 1 1/2° camber adjustment.*

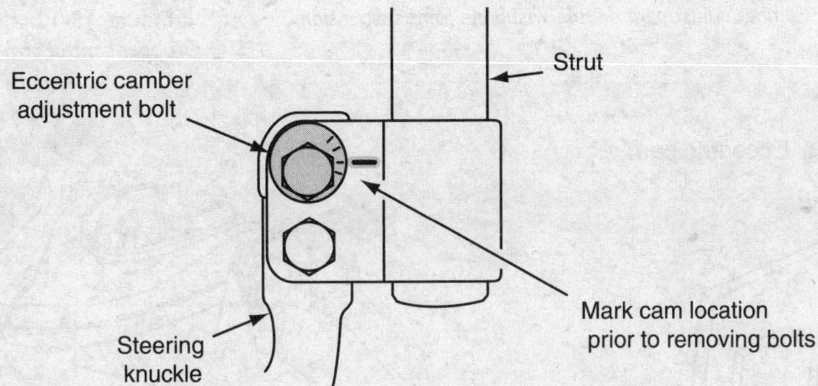

FIGURE 15-8 *Eccentric steering knuckle-to-strut camber adjusting bolt, MacPherson strut front suspension.*

MacPherson strut front suspension systems. On some double-wishbone front suspension systems, a graduated cam on the inner end of the lower control arm provides a camber adjustment (Figure 15-11).

On late model Ford F-150 light-duty truck 4 x 2 front suspension systems, an alignment plate is installed on the upper control arm attaching nuts when the vehicle is manufactured (Figure 15-12). If a camber or caster adjustment is required, remove the control arm attaching nuts one at a time and install eccentric cams behind the adjusting nuts (Figure 15-13). Turn the eccentric cams equally on the front and rear upper control arm attaching nuts to adjust the camber. To increase the positive caster, move the front of the upper control arm outboard and move the rear of the upper control arm inboard (Figure 15-14). If it is necessary to decrease the positive caster, move the front of the upper control arm

FIGURE 15-9 *Camber adjustment kits provide 2 1/2° camber adjustment on some General Motors cars.*

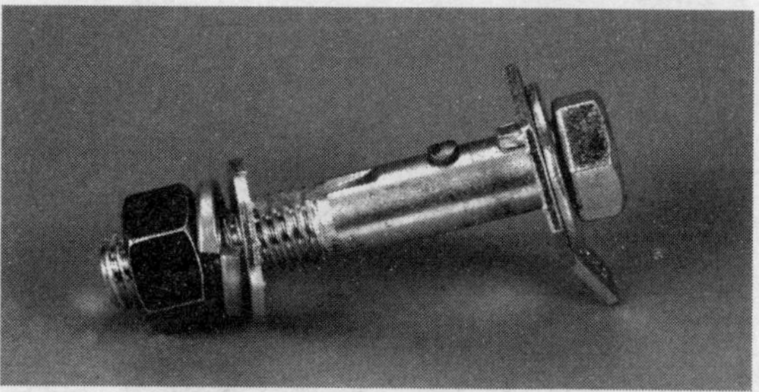

FIGURE 15-10 *Camber adjustment kits provide 2 1/2° camber adjustment on some vehicles.*

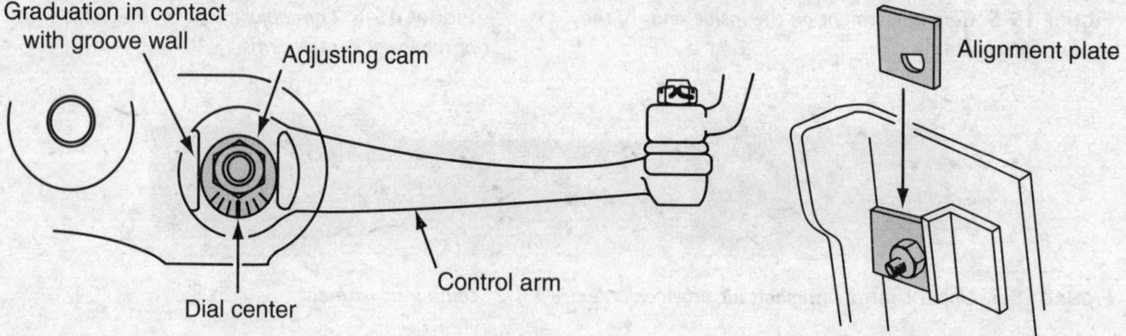

FIGURE 15-11 *Camber adjustment double-wishbone front suspension.*

FIGURE 15-12 *Alignment plate on upper control arm attaching nut.*

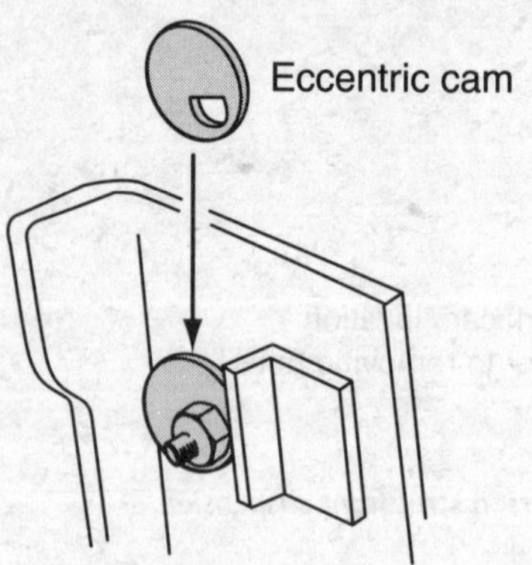

FIGURE 15-13 *Eccentric cam installed behind upper control arm attaching nut.*

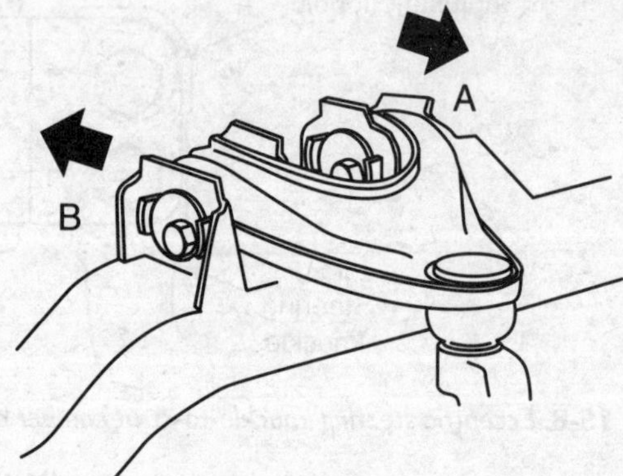

FIGURE 15-14 *To increase the positive caster, move the front of the upper control arm (A) outboard and move the rear of the upper control arm (B) inboard.*

inboard and move the rear of the upper control arm outboard (Figure 15-15). These front suspension systems also have eccentric cams on the lower control arm attaching bolts (Figure 15-16). However, these eccentric cams are only for factory use, and they must not be adjusted in service. When removing the lower control arms, always mark the eccentric cams on the attaching bolts and reinstall these cams in their original position.

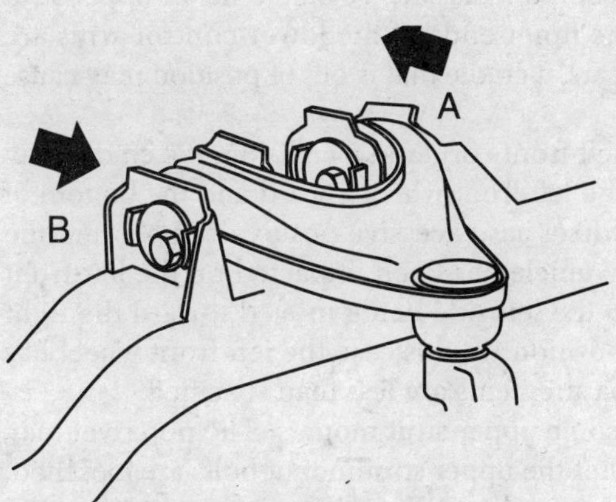

FIGURE 15-15 *To decrease the positive caster move the front of the upper control arm (A) inboard and move the rear of the upper control arm (B) outboard.*

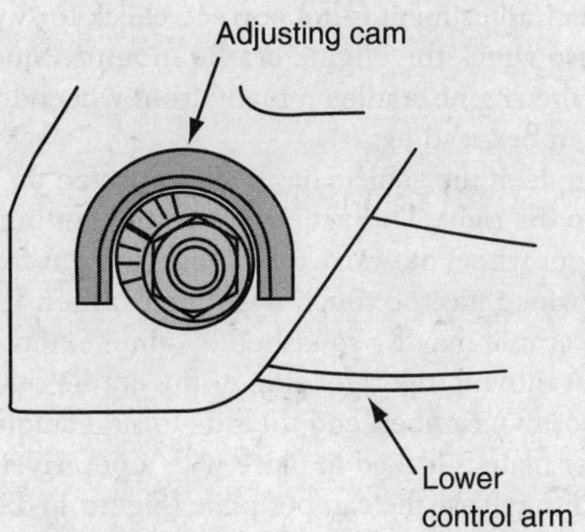

FIGURE 15-16 *Factory-set eccentric cam on lower control arm attaching bolts.*

In some front suspension systems such as on the PT Cruiser, eccentric cams are not installed to provide a camber adjustment. In these suspension systems, the manufacturer supplies slightly undersize strut bracket-to-knuckle attaching bolts which allow a 2° camber adjustment on each side of the front suspension. If a camber adjustment is required, remove the strut bracket-to-knuckle attaching bolts one at a time and install the undersize bolts. Install the nuts snugly on these bolts, but do not torque the nuts. Install each bolt from the rear of the knuckle. With the car on a wheel alignment rack, pull or push the top of the tire to obtain the specified camber. After the camber is set to specifications, tighten the strut bracket-to-knuckle attaching bolts to the specified torque.

Slotted Strut Mounts and Frames

On some MacPherson strut front suspension systems, the upper strut mounts may be loosened and moved inward or outward to adjust camber (Figure 15-17). Other MacPherson strut front suspension systems do not provide a camber adjustment. For these cars, aftermarket manufacturers sell slotted upper strut bearing plates that provide camber adjustment capabilities (Figure 15-18). If the front

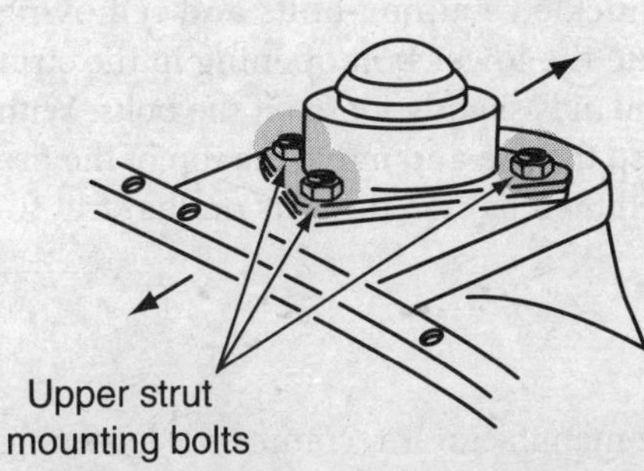

FIGURE 15-17 *The upper strut mounting bolts can be loosened and the mount moved inward or outward to adjust camber on some MacPherson strut front suspension systems.*

FIGURE 15-18 *Slotted upper strut bearing plates provide camber adjustment on some MacPherson strut front suspension systems.*

wheel camber adjustment is not correct, check for worn components such as ball joints or upper strut mounts. Also check the engine cradle mounts. Since the inner ends of the lower control arms are attached to the engine cradle on many front-wheel-drive cars, a cradle that is out of position may cause improper camber readings.

For example, if the vehicle has been impacted on the left-front corner in a collision, the cradle may be shifted to the right. This action moves the bottom of the left-front wheel inward and the bottom of the right-front wheel outward. Therefore, the left-front wheel has excessive positive camber and the right-front wheel has too much negative camber. If the vehicle has been impacted on the left-front corner, the cradle may be squashed to some extent with the left side being moved toward the right side without moving the right side of the cradle out of position. In this case the left front wheel has excessive positive camber, and the side-to-side cradle measurements are less than specified.

A camber plate is locked in place with a pop rivet on some upper strut mounts. The pop rivet may be removed to release the camber plate (Figure 15-19). After the upper strut mount bolts are loosened, the mount may be moved inward or outward to adjust the camber. When the camber is adjusted to the vehicle manufacturer's specification, the strut mount bolts should be tightened to the correct torque and a new pop rivet installed.

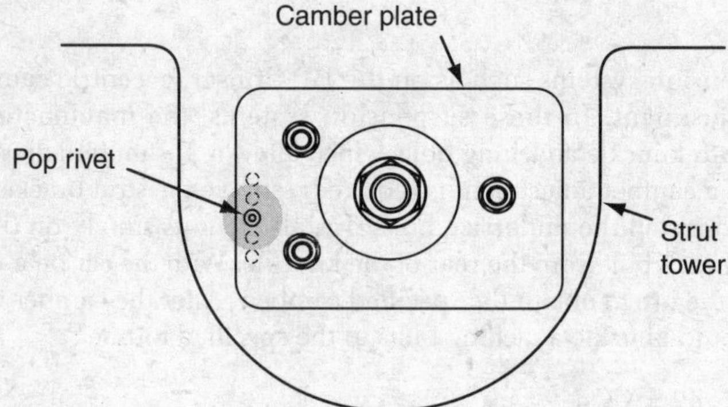

FIGURE 15-19 *Upper strut mount with camber plate and rivet, modified MacPherson strut front suspension.*

On some short-and-long arm front suspension systems, the bolt holes in the frame are elongated for the inner shaft on the upper control arm. When these bolts are loosened, the upper control arm may be moved inward or outward to adjust camber (Figure 15-20).

When a camber adjustment is required on some MacPherson strut front suspensions, the vehicle manufacturer recommends removing the strut-to-steering knuckle retaining bolts and removing the strut from the knuckle. A round file is then used to elongate the lower bolt opening in the strut (Figure 15-21). Reinstall the strut and retaining bolts, but leave the nuts slightly loose on the bolts. With the vehicle in the proper position on the wheel aligner rack, grasp the tire and move the top of the tire inward or outward to obtain the desired camber adjustment, and then tighten the nuts on the strut-to-knuckle bolts to the specified torque.

Special Adjustment Bolts

On other vehicles such as the 2005 Dodge Magnum, the vehicle manufacturer recommends loosening the cradle mounts and shifting the cradle to provide minor camber and/or caster adjustments (Figure 15-22). If the desired camber adjustment cannot be obtained by shifting the cradle, the vehicle manufacturer provides an adjustment bolt package for camber and caster adjustment. These bolts are

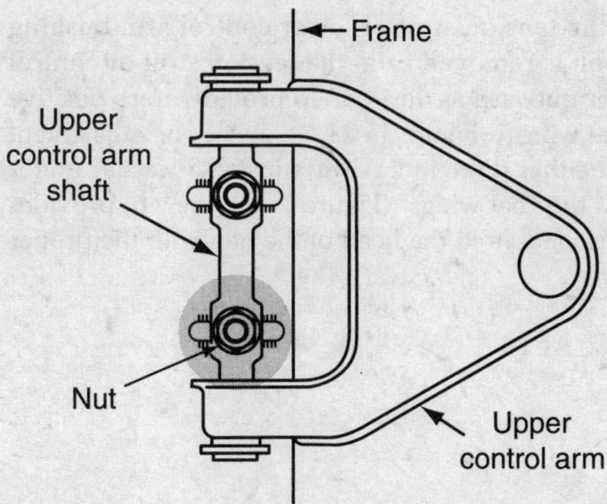

FIGURE 15-20 *Elongated bolt holes for upper control arm shaft bolts provide camber adjustment on some short-and-long arm front suspension systems.*

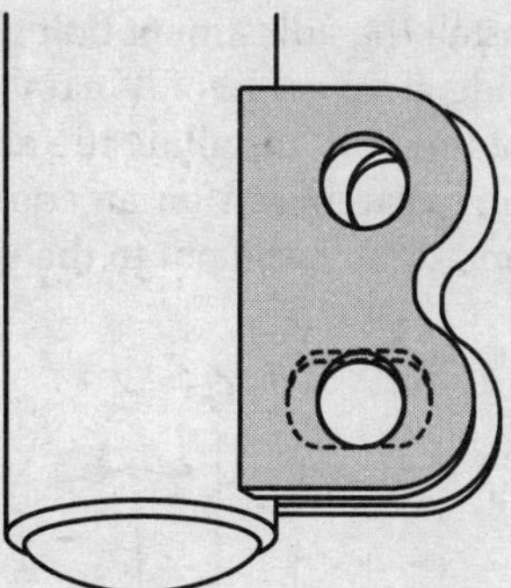

FIGURE 15-21 *Elongated lower strut-to-knuckle bolt hole for camber adjustment.*

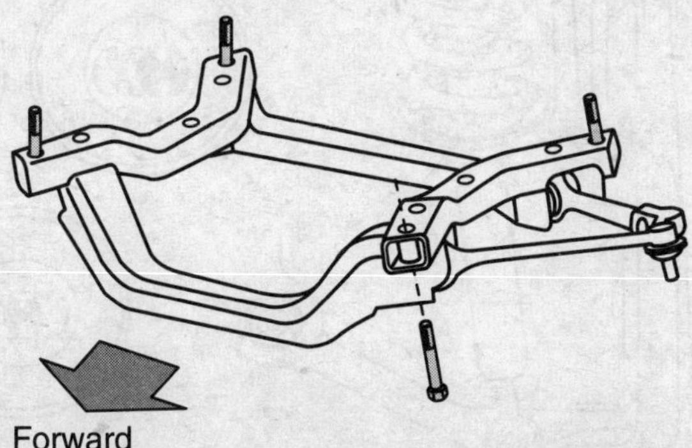

FIGURE 15-22 *Loosening cradle mounting bolts and shifting the cradle to perform minor camber adjustments.*

designed to replace the inboard bolts in the lower control arm and tension strut. To adjust camber use both bolts, and to adjust caster only use a replacement bolt in the tension strut.

The wheel alignment adjustment bolts have offset grooves cut into the length of the bolts (Figure 15-23). The grooves in the adjustment bolts force the bolt to be installed in one or two ways depending on whether more positive or negative camber is required. The bolt grooves work with "bat wing" holes in the lower control arm and tension strut bushings. The original non-grooved bolt is

FIGURE 15-23 *Camber/caster adjustment bolt with offset grooves.*

installed between the "bat wings" in the center of the tension strut or lower control arm bushing opening (Figure 15-24, view C). After the original bolt is removed from the tension strut or control arm, move the control arm or tension strut inward or outward as desired. To provide more positive camber, install the adjustment bolt grooves in the "bat wings" (Figure 15-24, view A). The adjustment bolts provide an average of 3° camber adjustment in either direction. Always install a washer under the head of the bolt. Installing the adjustment bolts in the "bat wings" (Figure 15-24, view b) provides more negative camber. After an adjustment bolt is installed, hold the head of the bolt with the proper size tool, and tighten the nut to the specified torque.

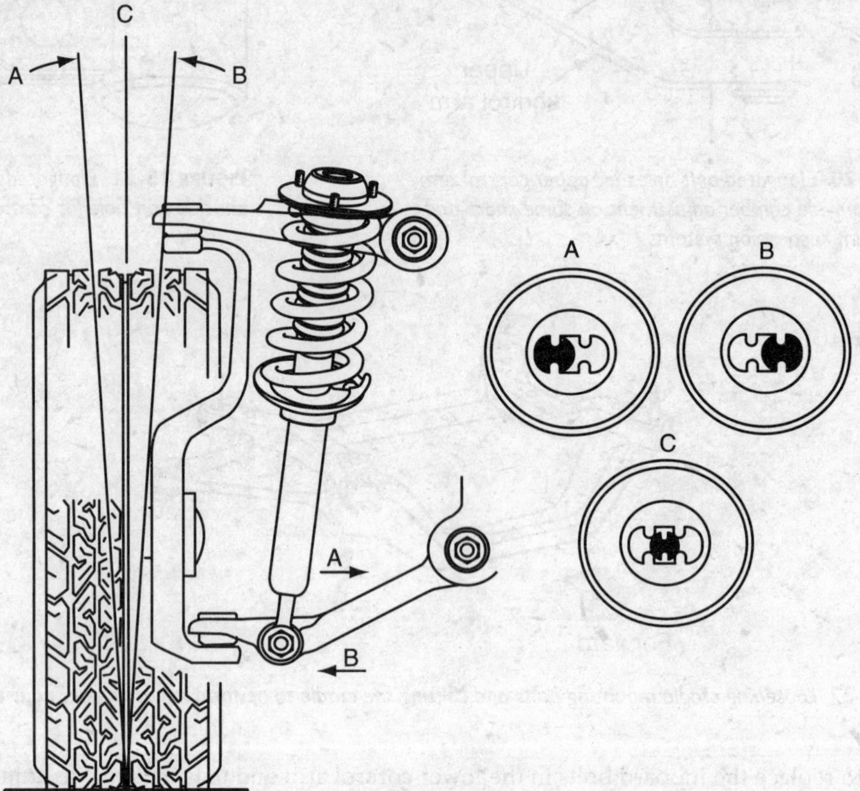

FIGURE 15-24 *Adjustment bolt positions in tension strut or lower control arm bushing to provide camber adjustment.*

CAUTION: After an adjustment bolt is installed, do not attempt to rotate the bolt. This action will damage the "bat wing" in the control arm or tension strut bushing.

To adjust the front wheel caster, follow the same procedure, but install the adjustment bolt only in the tension strut.

Special Tools for Camber Adjustment

Some vehicle manufacturers provide a special tool for adjusting front wheel camber and caster. This tool has threaded projections on each end extending at a right angle from a turnbuckle in the center of the tool. When the turnbuckle is rotated, the tool is lengthened or shortened. The tool is installed into

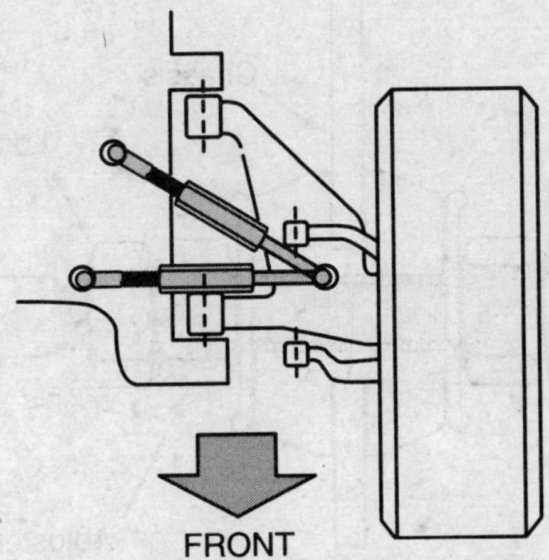

FIGURE 15-25 *Tool installed in lower control arm and chassis openings to adjust camber/caster.*

openings in the lower control arm and the chassis (Figure 15-25). After the bolt is loosened in the inner end of the control arm, the tool can be lengthened or shortened to adjust the camber and/or caster.

Camber Adjustment on Twin I-Beam Front Suspension System

On twin I-beam front suspension systems, a special clamp-type bending tool with a hydraulic jack is used to bend the I beams and change the camber setting. On a twin I-beam front suspension, the clamp and hydraulic jack must be positioned properly to adjust the camber to a more positive setting (Figure 15-26) or a more negative setting (Figure 15-27).

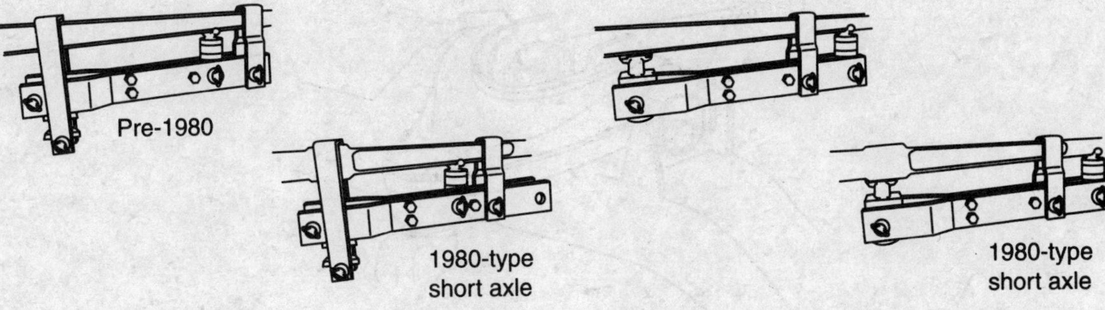

FIGURE 15-26 *Adjusting camber to a more positive setting, twin I-beam front suspension.*

FIGURE 15-27 *Adjusting camber to a more negative setting, twin I-beam front suspension.*

CASTER ADJUSTMENT PROCEDURE

Strut Rod Length Adjustment

On some suspension systems, the nuts on the forward end of the strut rod may be adjusted to lengthen or shorten the strut rod, which changes the caster setting (Figure 15-28). Shorten the strut rod to increase the positive caster.

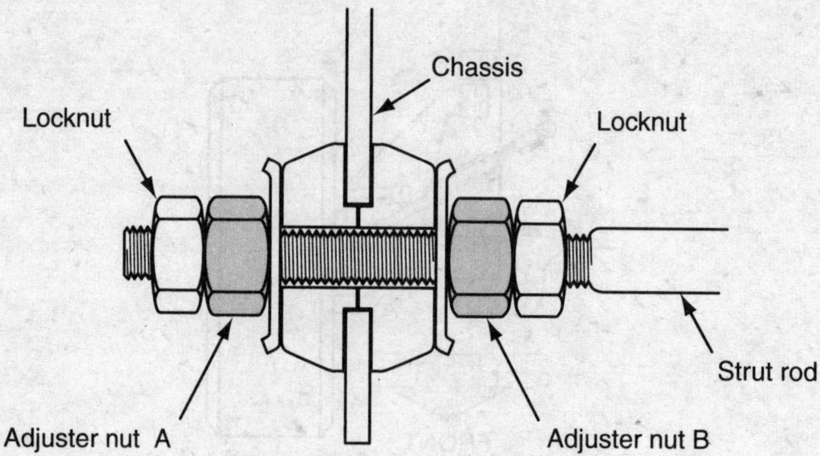

FIGURE 15-28 *Strut rod nuts can be adjusted to lengthen or shorten the strut rod to adjust caster.*

Eccentric Cams

The same eccentric cams on the inner ends of the upper or lower control arms may be used to adjust camber or caster (Figure 15-29). If an eccentric bushing in the outer end of the upper control arm is rotated to adjust camber, this same eccentric also adjusts caster. On some double-wishbone front suspension systems, the pivot adjuster mounting bolt nuts must be loosened under the compliance pivot, and the graduated cam may then be rotated to adjust caster (Figure 15-30).

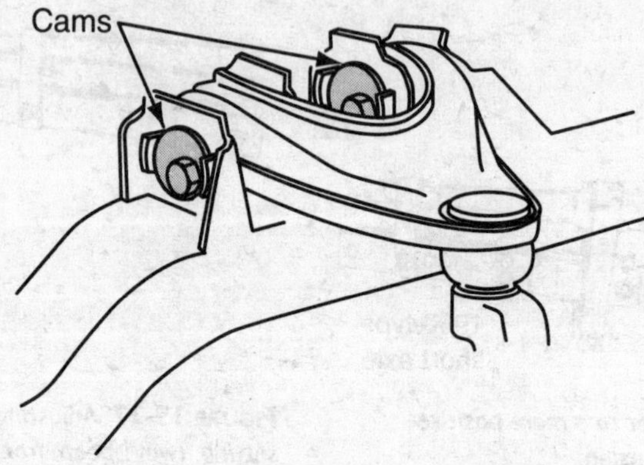

FIGURE 15-29 *Eccentric cams on the inner ends of the upper or lower control arms can be used to adjust camber and caster.*

Slotted Strut Mounts and Frames

If a **caster adjustment** is required and the suspension does not have an adjustment for this purpose, check for worn components such as upper strut mounts and ball joints. Also check the engine cradle mounts. Since the inner ends of the lower control arms are attached to the engine cradle on many front-wheel-drive cars, a cradle that is out-of-position may cause improper caster readings.

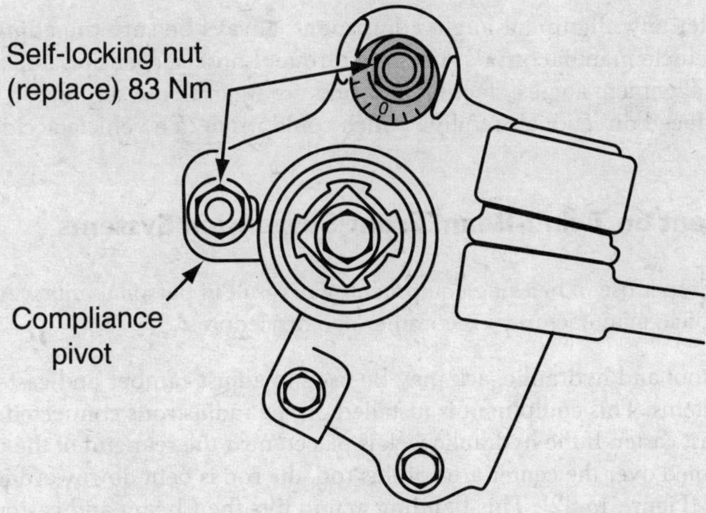

FIGURE 15-30 *Graduated cam for caster adjustment, double-wishbone front suspension.*

The slots in the frame at the upper control arm shaft mounting bolts provide camber and caster adjustment. If the upper strut mount is adjustable on a MacPherson strut suspension, the mount retaining bolts may be loosened and the mount moved forward or rearward to adjust caster.

When a caster adjustment is necessary, some vehicle manufacturers recommend removing the upper strut mount bolts and elongating the bolt hole openings in the strut tower with a round file to provide a caster adjustment (Figure 15-31).

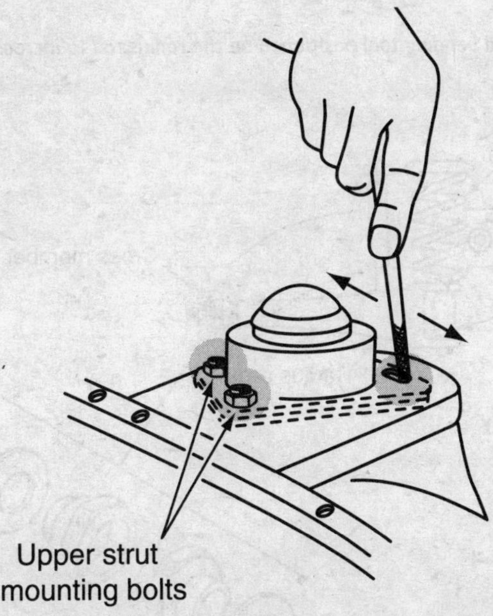

FIGURE 15-31 *Elongating upper strut mount bolt openings to provide caster adjustment.*

WARNING: After any alignment angle adjustment, always be sure the adjustment bolts are tightened to the vehicle manufacturer's specified torque. Loose suspension adjustment bolts will result in improper alignment angles, steering pull, and tire wear. Loose suspension adjustment bolts may also cause reduced directional stability, which could result in a vehicle accident and possible personal injury.

Caster Adjustment on Twin I-Beam Front Suspension Systems

WARNING: Improper use of bending equipment may result in personal injury. Always follow the equipment and vehicle manufacturer's recommended procedures.

The same bending tool and hydraulic jack may be used to adjust camber and caster on twin I-beam front suspension systems. This equipment is installed on the radius rods connected from the I beams to the chassis to adjust caster. If the hydraulic jack is placed near the rear end of the radius rod and the clamp arm is positioned over the center area of this rod, the rod is bent downward in the center when the jack is operated (Figure 15-32). This bending action tilts the I beam and caster line rearward to increase positive caster.

Aftermarket parts manufacturers supply a special radius arm bushing to provide a caster adjustment on some twin I-beam front suspension systems (Figure 15-33).

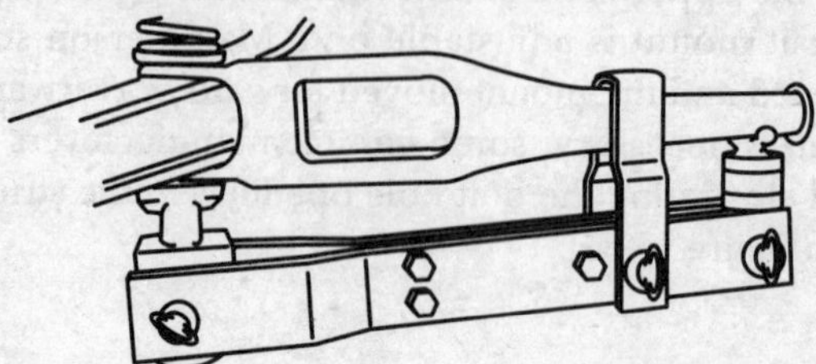

FIGURE 15-32 *Hydraulic jack and bending tool positioned on the radius rod to increase positive caster on a twin I-beam front suspension.*

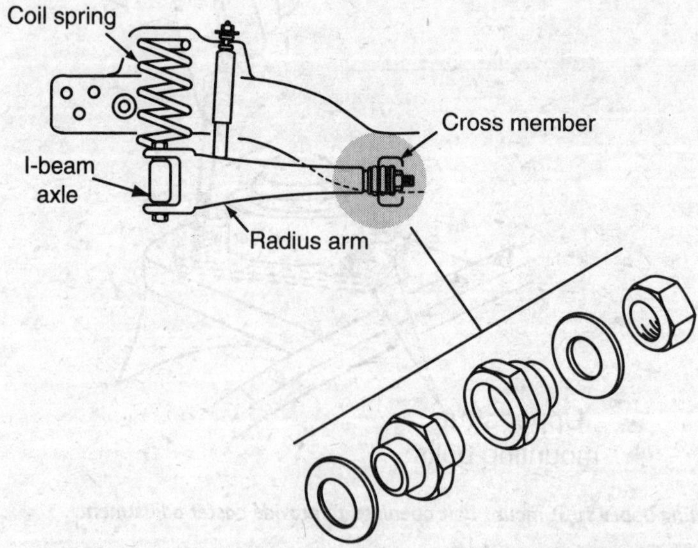

FIGURE 15-33 *Radius arm bushing for caster adjustment on some twin I-beam suspension systems.*

SETBACK MEASUREMENT AND CORRECTION PROCEDURE

Computer wheel aligners have **setback** measuring capabilities on the front wheels. These aligners automatically display setback angles with the other front suspension alignment angles. If a front-wheel-drive vehicle has experienced collision damage on the left front, the left side of the cradle or subframe may be driven rearward (Figure 15-34). This type of collision damage also moves the bottom of the left front strut rearward to a setback condition and shifts the caster to a negative position.

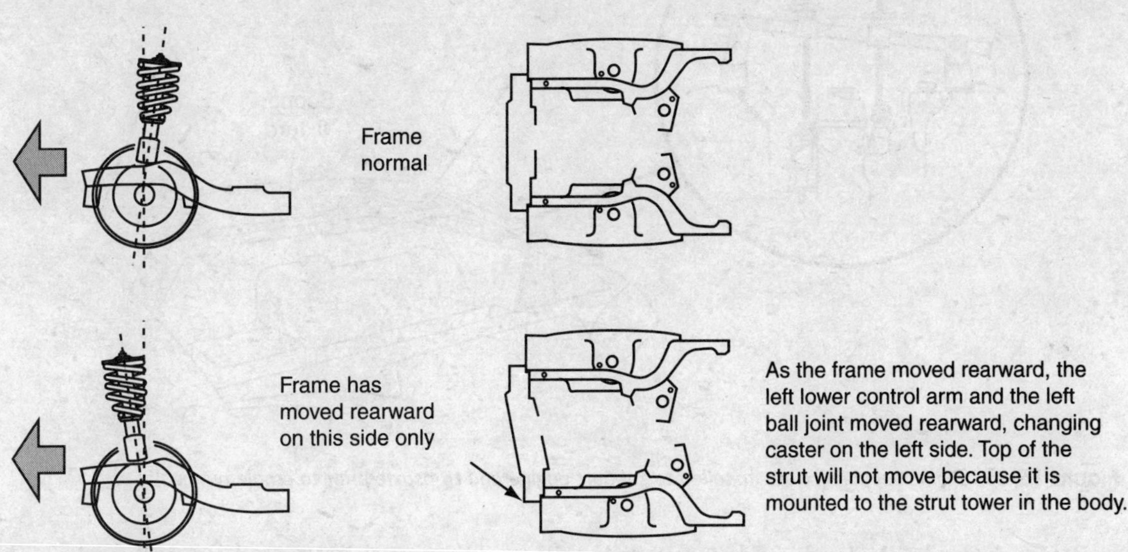

FIGURE 15-34 *Collision damage on the left front moves the cradle and strut rearward to a setback condition and shifts the caster to a negative position.*

CAUTION: If the engine cradle has to be removed or loosened, the engine support fixture must hold the engine in the normal position to prevent damage to the fan shroud, power steering hoses, and other components.

WARNING: Prior to any service operation where the body is going to be moved in relation to the cradle or subframe, the intermediate shaft on the rack and pinion gear must be disconnected. If this shaft is not disconnected, it may be damaged, resulting in loss of steering control, serious vehicle damage, and personal injury.

With this type of collision damage, it may be possible to adjust the caster back to the specified setting, but that does not correct the setback problem. If the caster is adjusted and the setback problem is ignored, the steering may pull to one side while driving straight ahead, especially if the setback condition is severe. The cradle must be straightened and the unitized body must be pulled back to the original measurements to correct this problem. A severely bent, distorted cradle should be replaced.

Collision damage may push a front cradle sideways. This condition may increase the positive camber on one side of the car and move the camber toward a negative position on the opposite side. When this condition is encountered, always inspect and correct the cradle position. If the camber is adjusted in this situation, the steering will not provide proper directional control.

Prior to cradle removal, an engine support fixture must be installed to support the engine and transaxle (Figure 15-35). The engine support fixture must hold the engine in the original position to prevent damage to the power steering hoses or other components.

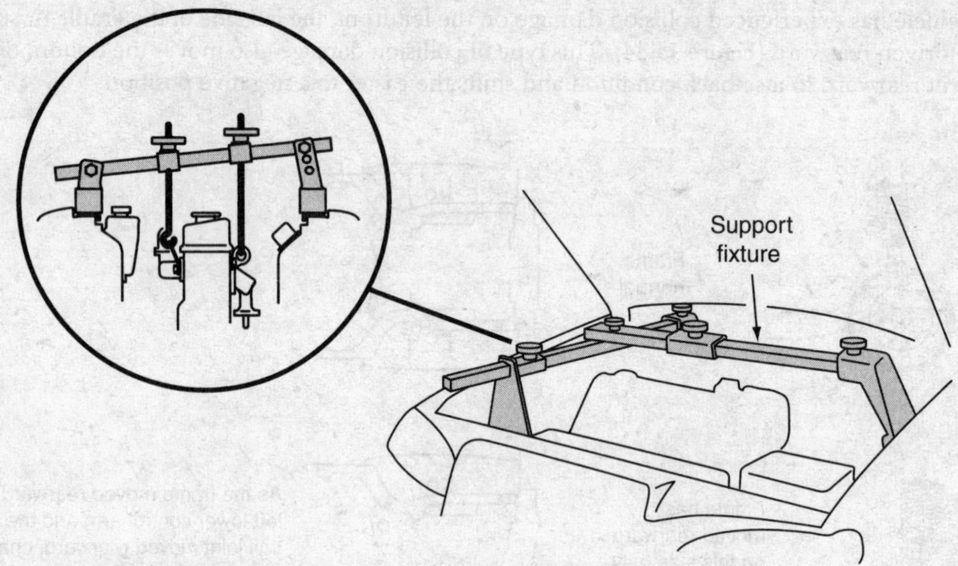

FIGURE 15-35 *Engine support fixture installed to support engine and transaxle prior to cradle removal.*

Before the body is moved in relation to the cradle or subframe, the intermediate shaft on the rack and pinion steering gear must be disconnected to prevent damage to this shaft. Remove all the engine and transaxle mount bolts in the cradle, plus the cradle retaining bolts and insulators to remove the cradle. Perform the front underbody measurements with a tram gauge (Figure 15-36), and pull the unitized body back to these specifications. This pulling operation is usually done in an automotive body shop rather than an automotive repair shop.

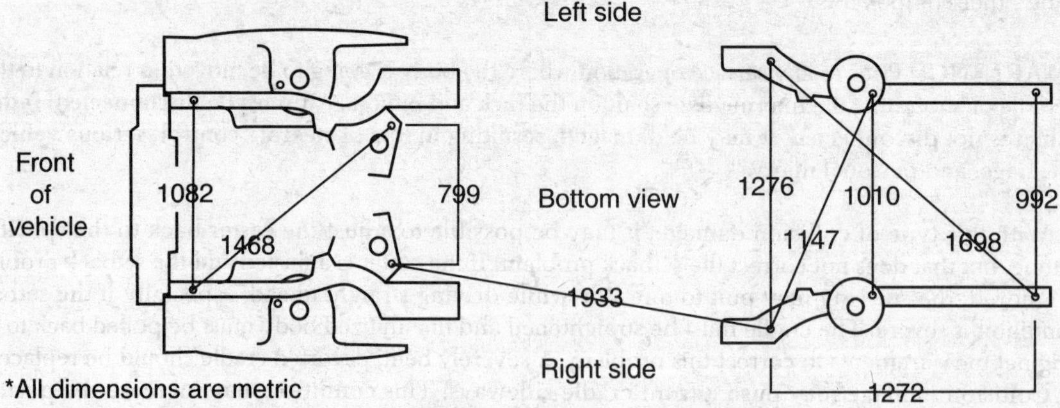

FIGURE 15-36 *Front and rear underbody measurements.*

The cradle must be restored to the specified measurements (Figure 15-37). Inspect all cradle insulators and replace any that are damaged, oil soaked, or worn. When the cradle is replaced, all the insulators must be installed properly, and all the cradle bolts should be aligned with the bolt holes in the body. Alignment hole A in the cradle must be perfectly aligned with the matching alignment hole in the body (Figure 15-38). Observing this alignment hole is a quick way to check cradle position.

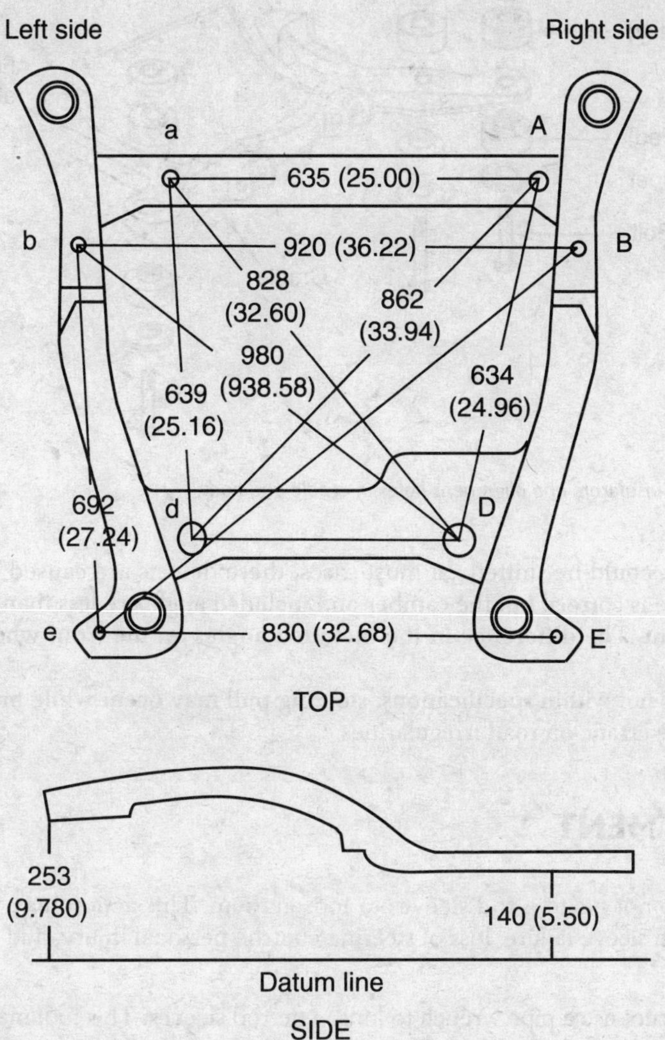

FIGURE 15-37 *Front cradle measurements.*

STEERING AXIS INCLINATION (SAI) CORRECTION PROCEDURE

Steering axis inclination (SAI) is not considered adjustable. If the SAI is not within specifications, the upper strut tower may be out of position, the lower control arm may be bent, or the center cross

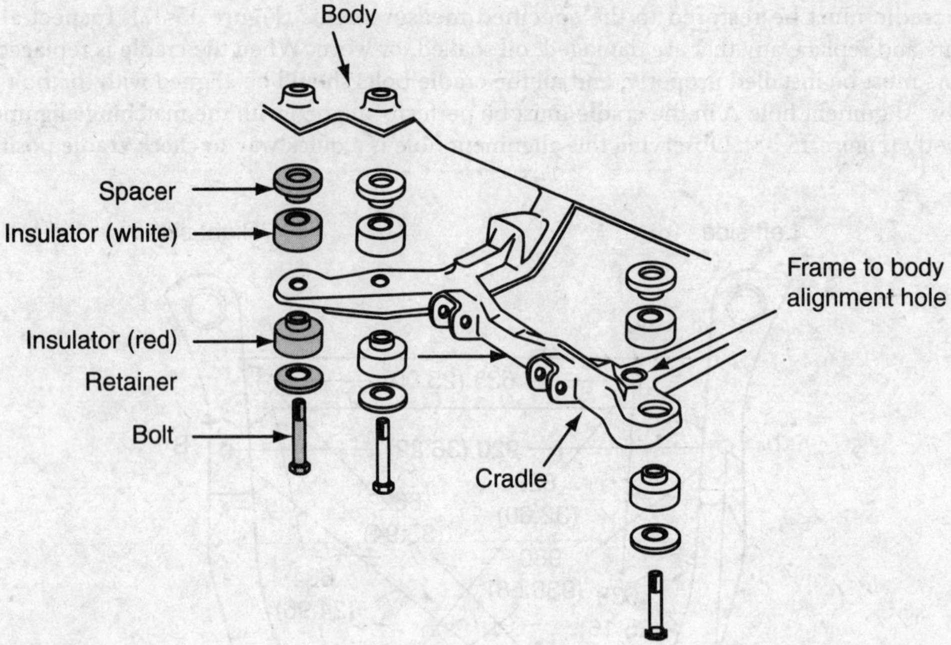

FIGURE 15-38 *Cradle insulators and alignment holes in cradle and body.*

member, or cradle, could be shifted. In most cases, these defects are caused by collision damage. When the SAI angle is correct, but the camber and included angle are less than specified, the strut or spindle may be bent. The difference in the included angles on the front wheels must not exceed 1 1/2°.

When the SAI is not within specifications, steering pull may occur while braking or accelerating and steering may be erratic on road irregularities.

TOE ADJUSTMENT

WARNING: Do not heat tie-rod sleeves to loosen them. This action may weaken the sleeves, resulting in sudden sleeve failure, loss of steering control, personal injury, and vehicle damage.

WARNING: Do not use a pipe wrench to loosen tie-rod sleeves. This tool may crush and weaken the sleeve, causing sleeve failure, loss of steering control, personal injury, and vehicle damage. A tie-rod rotating tool must be used for this job.

When a front wheel toe adjustment is required, apply penetrating oil to the tie-rod adjusting sleeves and sleeve clamp bolts. Loosen the tie-rod adjusting sleeve clamp bolts enough to allow the clamps to partially rotate. One end of each tie-rod sleeve contains a right-hand thread; the opposite end contains a left-hand thread. These threads match the threads on the tie-rod and outer tie-rod end. When the tie-rod sleeve is rotated, the complete tie-rod, sleeve, and tie-rod end assembly is lengthened or shortened. Use a tie-rod sleeve rotating tool to turn the sleeves until the toe-in on each front wheel is equal to one-half the **total toe** specification (Figure 15-39).

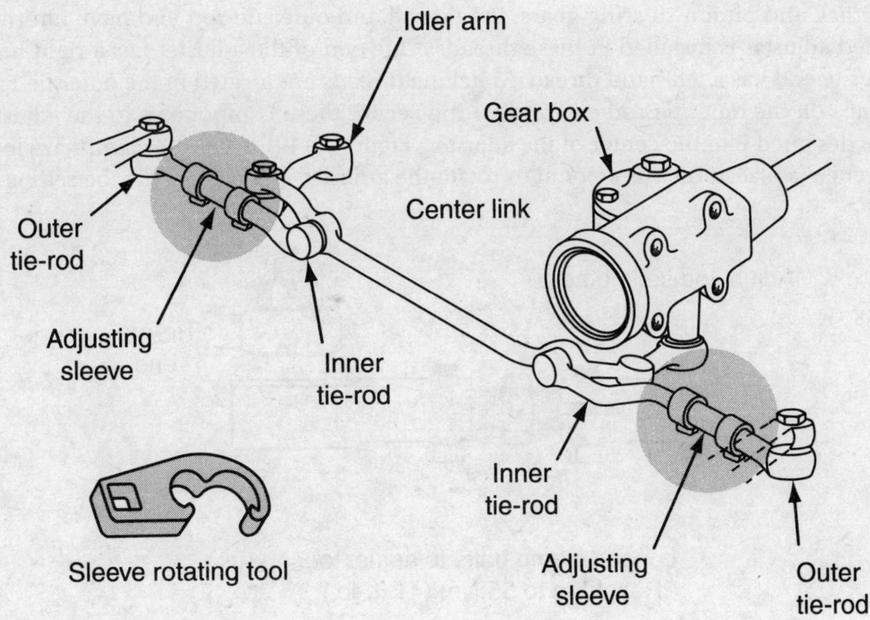

FIGURE 15-39 *Rotating toe-rod sleeves to adjust front wheel toe.*

After the **toe-in** adjustment is completed, the adjusting sleeve clamps must be turned so the openings in the clamps are positioned away from the slots in the adjusting sleeves (Figure 15-40). Replace clamp bolts that are rusted, corroded, or damaged, and tighten these bolts to the specified torque.

On some rack and pinion steering gears, the tie-rod locknut is loosened and the tie-rod is rotated to adjust toe on each front wheel (Figure 15-41). Prior to rotating the tie-rod, the small outer bellows boot clamp should be removed to prevent it from twisting during tie-rod rotation. After the toe-in adjustment, the tie-rod locknut must be torqued to specifications, and the small bellows boot clamp must be reinstalled.

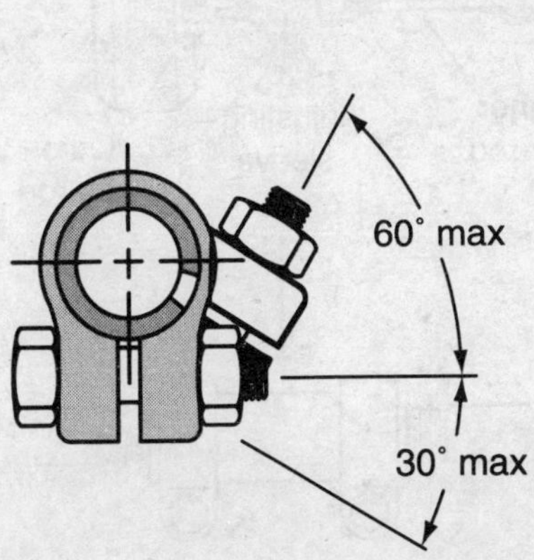

FIGURE 15-40 *Proper tie-rod adjusting sleeve and clamp position.*

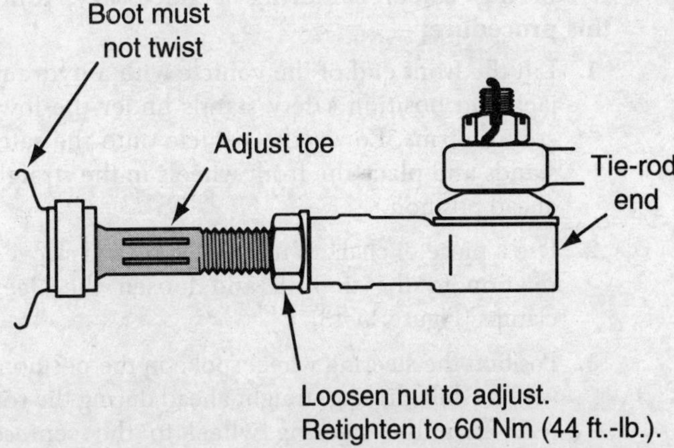

FIGURE 15-41 *Rotating tie-rod to adjust the toe on a rack and pinion steering gear.*

On other rack and pinion steering gears, the tie-rod and outer tie-rod end have internal threads, and a threaded adjuster is installed in these threads. One end of the adjuster has a right-hand thread, and the opposite end has a left-hand thread. Matching threads are located in the outer tie-rod end and tie-rod. Clamps on the outer tie-rod end and tie-rod secure these components to the adjuster. A hex-shaped nut is designed into the center of the adjuster (Figure 15-42). After the clamps are loosened, an open-end wrench is placed on this hex nut to rotate the adjuster and change the toe setting.

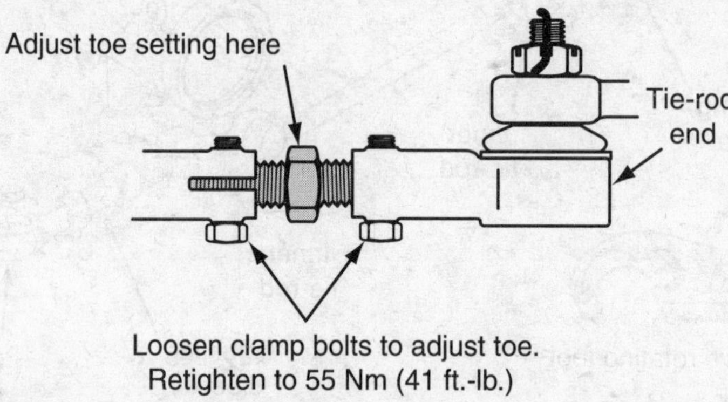

FIGURE 15-42 *Rack and pinion steering gear with externally threaded toe adjuster and internal threads on the tie-rod and outer tie-rod end.*

When the toe-in adjustment is completed, the toe must be set within the manufacturer's specifications with the steering wheel in the centered position. If the steering wheel is not centered, a centering adjustment is required.

STEERING WHEEL CENTERING PROCEDURE

Road test the vehicle and determine if the steering wheel spoke is centered when the vehicle is driven straight ahead.

If steering wheel centering is necessary, follow this procedure:

1. Lift the front end of the vehicle with a hydraulic jack and position safety stands under the lower control arms. Lower the vehicle onto the safety stands and place the front wheels in the straight-ahead position.
2. Use a piece of chalk to mark each tie-rod sleeve in relation to the tie-rod, and loosen the sleeve clamps (Figure 15-43).
3. Position the steering wheel spoke in the position it was in while driving straight ahead during the road test. Turn the steering wheel to the centered position and note the direction of the front wheels.
4. If the steering wheel spoke is low on the left side while driving the vehicle straight ahead, use a

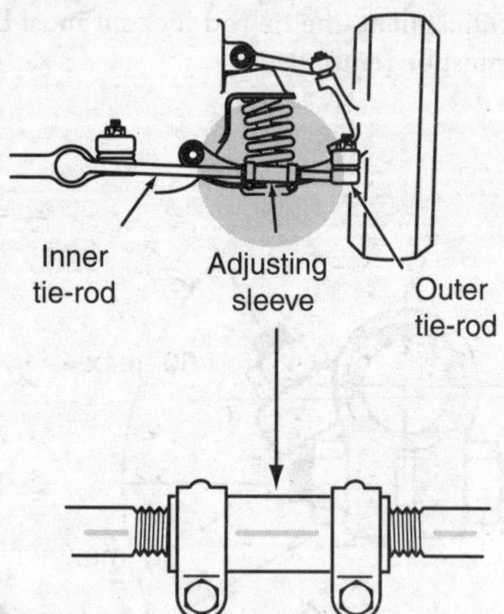

FIGURE 15-43 *Marking toe-rod sleeves in relation to the tie-rods and outer tie-rod ends.*

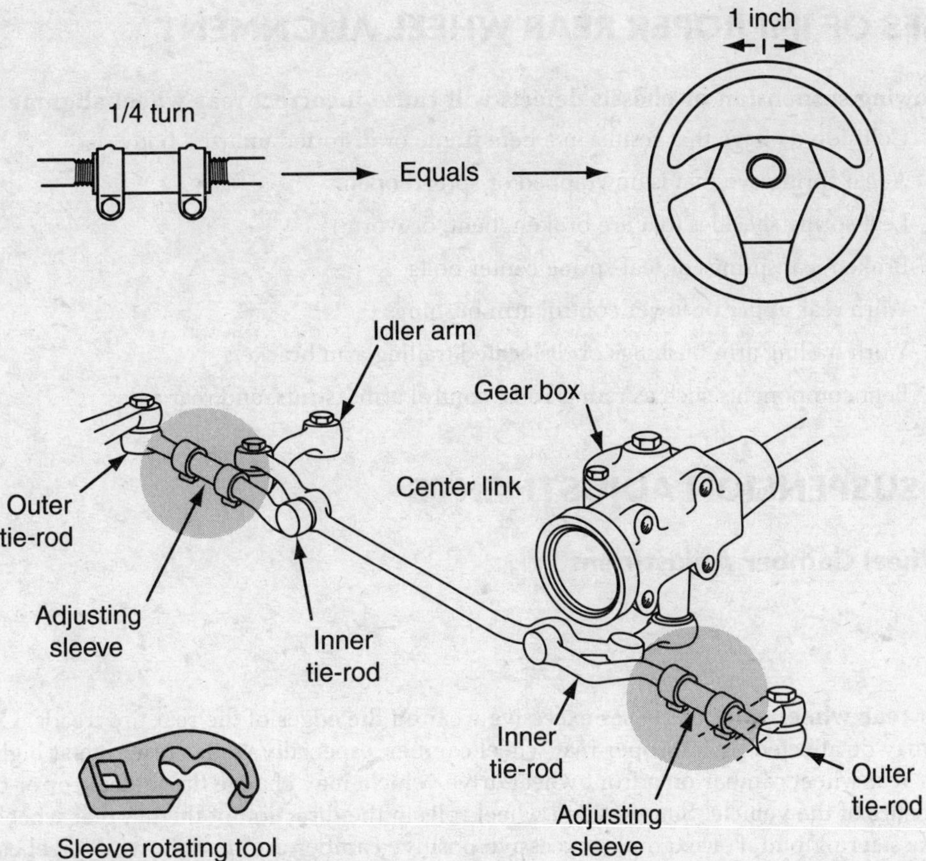

FIGURE 15-44 *Rotating tie-rod sleeves to center steering wheel.*

tie-rod sleeve rotating tool to shorten the left tie-rod and lengthen the right tie-rod (Figure 15-44). One-quarter turn on a tie-rod sleeve moves the steering wheel position approximately one inch. Turn the tie-rod sleeves the proper amount to bring the steering wheel to the centered position. For example, if the steering wheel spoke is two inches off-center, turn each tie-rod sleeve one-half turn.

5. If the steering wheel spoke is low on the right side while driving the vehicle straight ahead, lengthen the left tie-rod and shorten the right tie-rod.
6. Mark each tie-rod sleeve in its new position in relation to the tie-rod. Be sure the sleeve clamp openings are positioned properly, as indicated earlier in this chapter. Tighten the clamp bolts to the specified torque.
7. Lift the front chassis with a floor jack and remove the safety stands. Lower the vehicle onto the shop floor, and check the steering wheel position during a road test.

When all the front suspension alignment angles are adjusted within the manufacturer's specifications, road-test the vehicle. When the vehicle is driven on a relatively smooth, straight road, there should be directional stability with no drift to the right or left, and the steering wheel must be centered.

CAUSES OF IMPROPER REAR WHEEL ALIGNMENT

The following suspension or chassis defects will cause incorrect rear wheel alignment:

1. Collision damage that results in a bent frame or distorted unitized body
2. A leaf-spring eye that is unwrapped or spread open
3. Leaf-spring shackles that are broken, bent, or worn
4. Broken leaf springs or leaf-spring center bolts
5. Worn rear upper or lower control arm bushings
6. Worn trailing arm bushings or dislocated trailing arm brackets
7. Bent components such as radius rods, control arms, struts, and rear axles

REAR SUSPENSION ADJUSTMENTS

Rear Wheel Camber Adjustment

Improper **rear wheel camber** causes excessive wear on the edges of the rear tire treads. Cornering stability may be affected by improper rear wheel camber, especially while cornering at high speeds. Improper rear wheel camber on a front-wheel-drive vehicle may change the understeer or oversteer characteristics of the vehicle. Since a tilted wheel rolls in the direction of the tilt, rear wheel camber may cause steering pull. For example, excessive positive camber on the right rear wheel causes the rear suspension to drift to the right and steering to pull to the left.

Rear suspension adjustments vary depending on the type of suspension system. Some manufacturers of wheel alignment equipment and tools provide detailed diagrams for front and rear wheel alignment adjustments on all makes of domestic and imported vehicles. Our objective is to show a few of the common methods of adjusting rear wheel alignment angles on various types of rear suspension systems.

On some semi-independent rear suspension systems, camber and toe are adjusted by inserting different sizes of shims between the rear spindle and the spindle mounting surface. These shims are retained by the spindle mounting bolts. The shim thickness is changed between the top or bottom of the spindle to adjust camber (Figure 15-45).

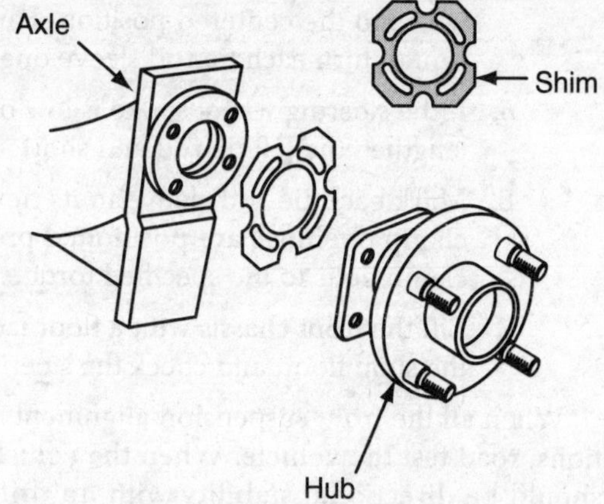

FIGURE 15-45 *Shim adjustment for rear wheel camber, semi-independent rear suspension system.*

Many rear camber shims are now circular and are available in a wide variety of configurations to fit various rear wheels. Some computer wheel aligners indicate the thickness of shim required and the proper shim position. These same shims also adjust rear wheel toe (Figure 15-46).

On some transverse leaf rear suspension systems such as those on a later model Oldsmobile Cutlass Supreme, the spindle must be removed from the strut,

FIGURE 15-46 *Circular shim for rear wheel camber and toe adjustment.*

and the lower strut bolt hole elongated to allow a camber adjustment (Figure 15-47). Once this bolt hole is elongated, assemble the knuckle and strut and leave the retaining bolts loose. The top of the tire and the spindle may be moved outward or inward to adjust camber. After the camber is adjusted to specifications, the strut-to-knuckle nuts must be tightened to the specified torque.

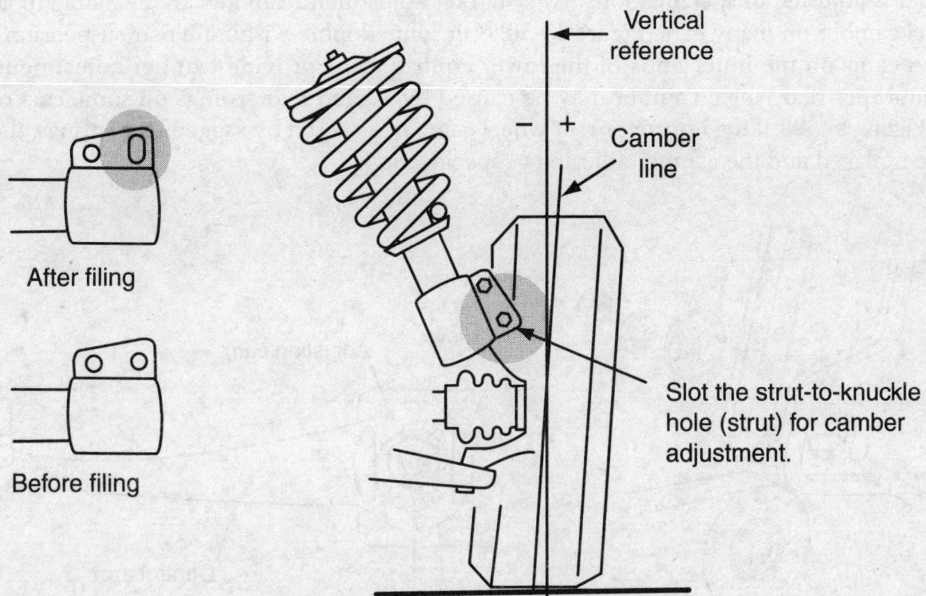

FIGURE 15-47 *Elongating the lower strut bolt hole provides camber adjustment.*

On some independent rear suspension systems with a lower control arm and ball joint, the strut-to-knuckle bolts are loosened and a special camber tool must be installed on the lower strut-to-knuckle bolt and the rear side of the strut (Figure 15-48). Rotate the adjusting bolt in the back of the tool to adjust the camber; then tighten the strut-to-knuckle nuts to the specified torque.

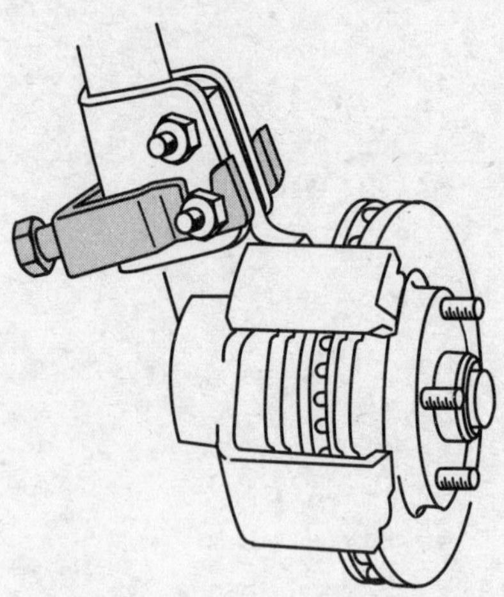

FIGURE 15-48 *Camber adjustment with special tool inserted on rear lower strut-to-knuckle bolt.*

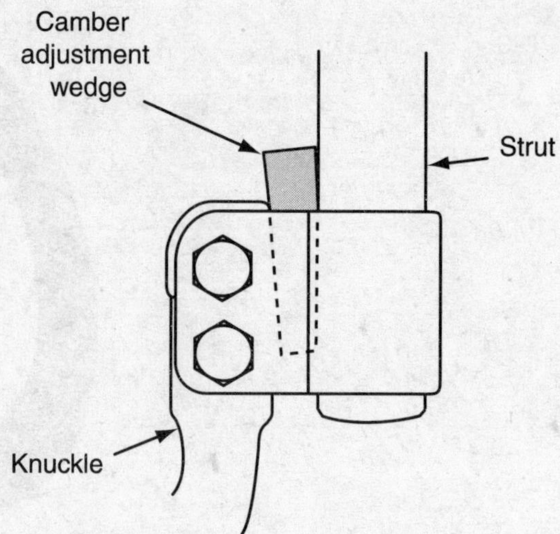

FIGURE 15-49 *Camber adjusting wedge installed between the top of the rear knuckle and strut.*

On other rear suspension systems, a camber adjustment wedge may be installed between the top of the knuckle and the strut to adjust camber (Figure 15-49). The nuts on the strut-to-knuckle bolts must be loosened prior to wedge installation, and these nuts must be tightened to the specified torque after the camber is adjusted to specifications. Aftermarket adjustment cam kits are available to adjust the rear wheel camber on many cars (Figure 15-50). On some double-wishbone rear suspension systems, graduated cams on the inner ends of the lower control arms provide camber adjustment (Figure 15-51). Improper rear wheel camber may be caused by sagged rear springs on some cars or station wagons (Figure 15-52). If the improper rear wheel camber is caused by sagged rear springs, the springs should be replaced and the camber adjusted to specifications.

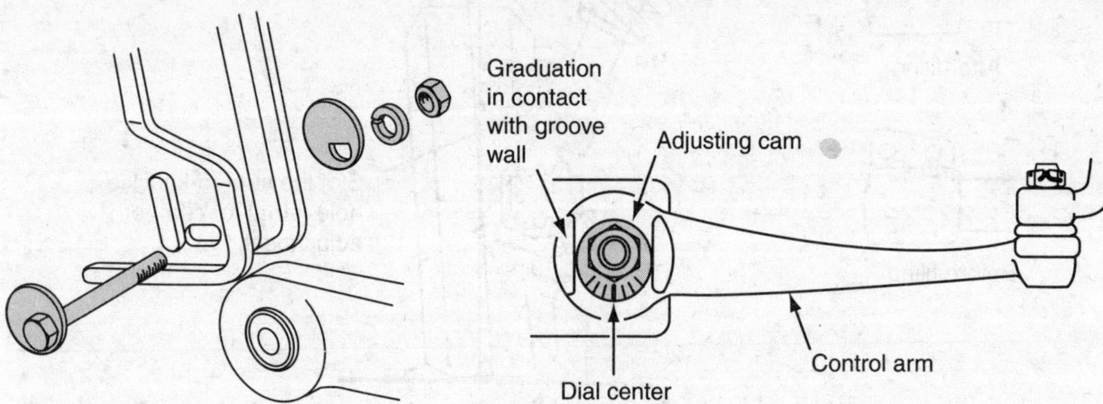

FIGURE 15-50 *Rear wheel camber adjusting kit.*

FIGURE 15-51 *Graduated cam for rear camber adjustment, double wishbone suspension.*

Rear Wheel Toe Adjustment

Improper **rear wheel toe** moves the thrust line away from the geometric centerline, which causes steering pull and feathered tire tread wear. If the left rear wheel has excessive **toe-out**, the **thrust line**

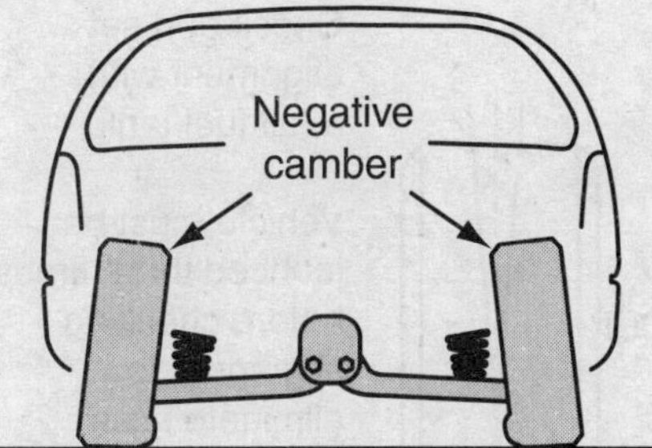

FIGURE 15-52 *Improper rear wheel camber may be caused by sagged rear springs on independent rear suspension systems.*

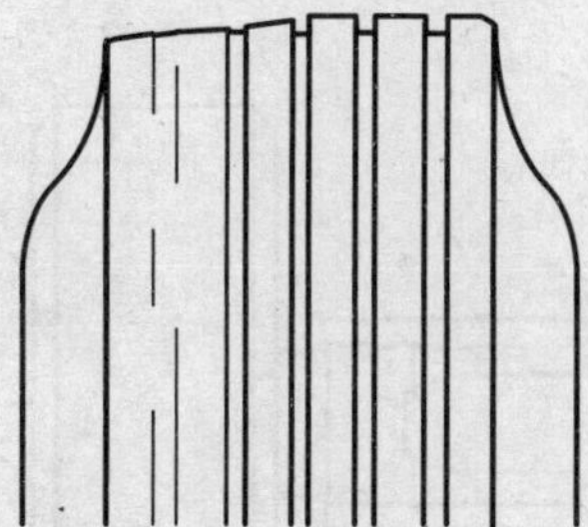

FIGURE 15-53 *Tire tread wear caused by improper rear wheel toe adjustment.*

is moved to the left of the geometric centerline. Excessive toe-in on the left rear wheel moves the thrust line to the right of the geometric centerline. When toe-in or toe-out is excessive on the right rear wheel, it has the opposite effect on the thrust line compared to the left rear wheel. When the thrust line is moved to the left of the geometric centerline, the steering pulls to the right, whereas a thrust line positioned to the right of the **geometric centerline** results in steering pull to the left.

Improper rear wheel toe adjustment on a non-driving rear axle causes feathered tire tread wear (Figure 15-53). The toe may be adjusted on many rear suspension systems used on front-wheel-drive cars by changing the tapered shim thickness between the front and rear edges of the rear spindle mounting flange (Figure 15-54). As mentioned previously, these shims are also used to adjust rear wheel camber.

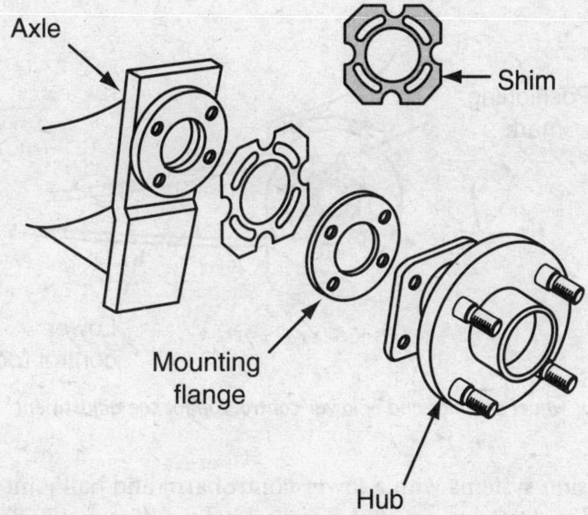

FIGURE 15-54 *Adjusting rear wheel toe by changing shim thickness between rear spindle and mounting flange.*

On some transverse leaf rear suspension systems, a special toe adjusting tool is inserted in openings in the jack pad and the rear lower control rod (Figure 15-55). This tool has a turnbuckle in the center of the tool. When the nut on the inner end of the rear lower control rod is loosened, the turnbuckle is rotated to lengthen or shorten the tool and move the rear lower control rod to adjust the rear wheel

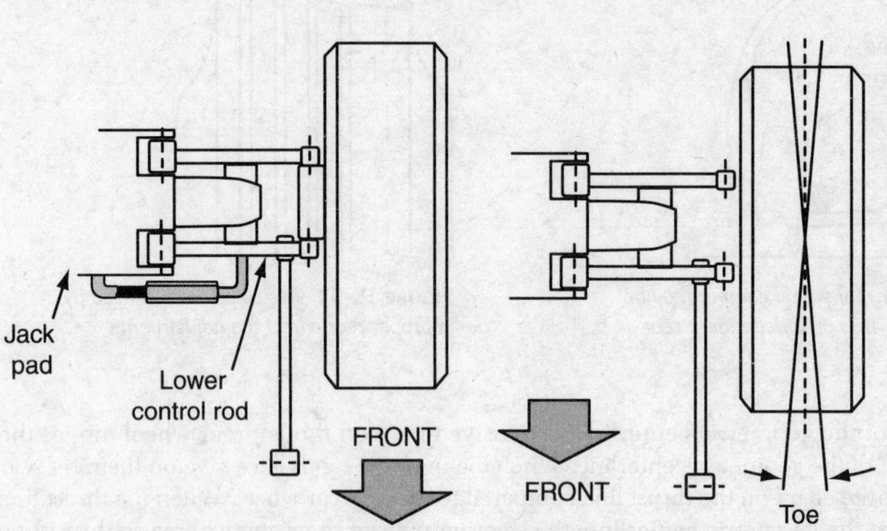

FIGURE 15-55 *Special toe adjusting tool for transverse leaf-spring rear suspension.*

FIGURE 15-56 *Moving lower rear control rod position to adjust rear wheel toe.*

toe (Figure 15-56). After the toe is adjusted to specification, the nut on the rear lower control rod bolt must be tightened to the specified torque.

On some independent rear suspension systems, an eccentric star wheel on the rear lower control rod may be rotated to adjust the rear wheel toe (Figure 15-57).

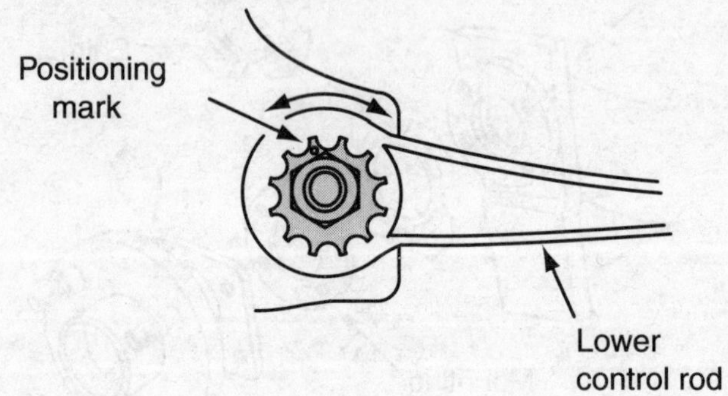

FIGURE 15-57 *Eccentric star wheel on inner end of lower control rod for toe adjustment.*

On some rear suspension systems with a lower control arm and ball joint, the nut on the tie-rod is loosened, and the tie-rod is rotated to adjust the rear wheel toe (Figure 15-58). After the toe is adjusted to specifications, the tie-rod nut must be tightened to the specified torque.

On some front-wheel-drive cars, the rear wheel toe is adjusted by loosening the toe link bolt and moving the wheel in or out to adjust the toe (Figure 15-59). After the rear wheel toe is properly adjusted, the toe link bolt must be tightened to the specified torque. On other front-wheel-drive cars, the rear wheel toe is adjusted by loosening the nut on the inner adjustment link cam nut (Figure 15-60). The cam bolt is rotated to adjust the rear wheel toe. After the rear wheel toe is properly adjusted, the adjustment link cam nut must be tightened to the specified torque.

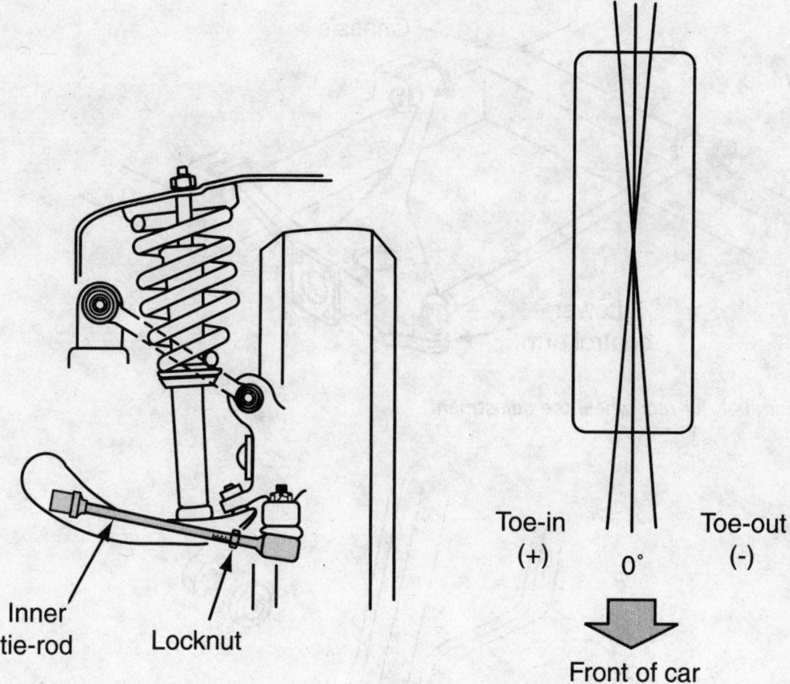

FIGURE 15-58 *Rotating rear tie-rod to change tie-rod length and adjust rear wheel toe.*

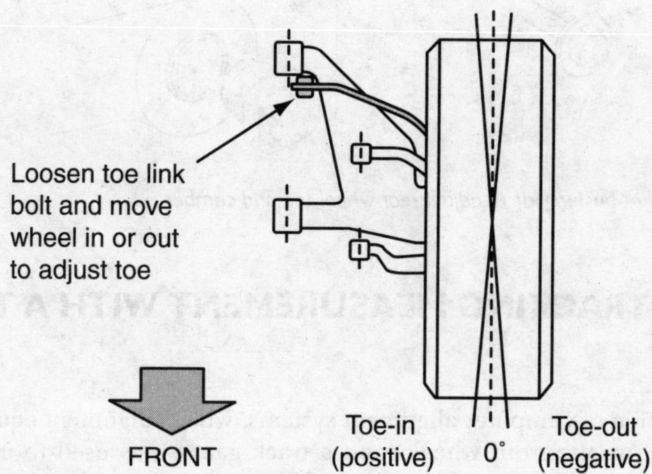

FIGURE 15-59 *Loosening toe link bolt to adjust rear wheel toe.*

A variety of aftermarket bushing kits are available to adjust rear wheel toe. Some of these kits also adjust rear wheel comber (Figure 15-61).

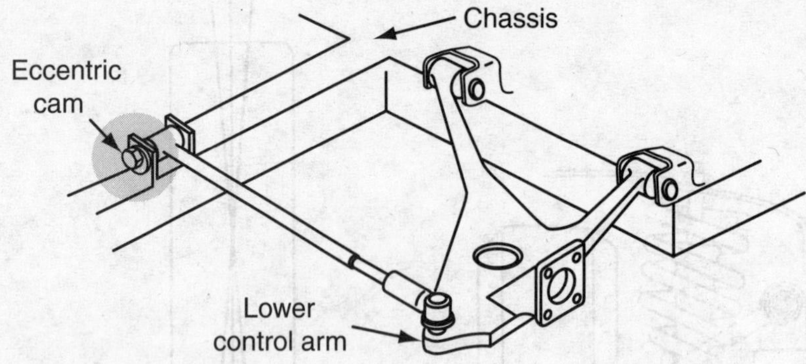

FIGURE 15-60 *Cam bolt for rear wheel toe adjustment.*

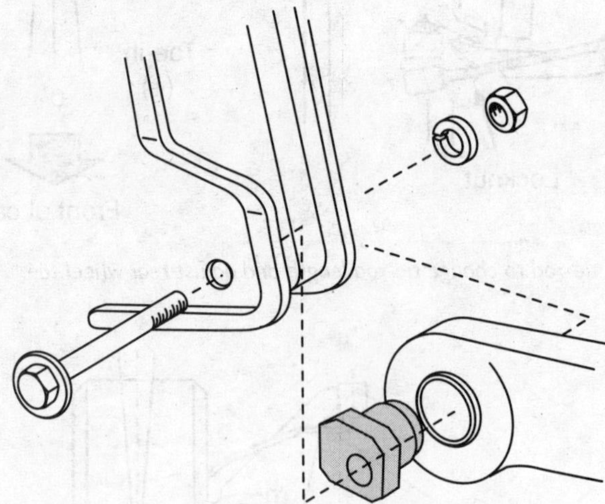

FIGURE 15-61 *Aftermarket bushing kit to adjust rear wheel toe and camber.*

REAR WHEEL TRACKING MEASUREMENT WITH A TRACK GAUGE

Prior to the introduction of computer alignment systems, wheel alignment equipment performed a two-wheel alignment on the front wheels, and a track gauge was used to measure **rear wheel tracking.** A **track gauge** is connected between the front and rear wheels to determine the rear wheel tracking or thrust line. When all four wheels are parallel to the geometric centerline of the vehicle, the thrust line is positioned at the geometric centerline. Under this condition, the rear wheels track directly behind the front wheels (Figure 15-62).

If the left front of the vehicle is involved in a severe collision, the left front wheel may be driven rearward to a setback condition, and the rear wheels may be moved straight sideways. Under this condition, the rear wheels no longer track directly behind the front wheels (Figure 15-63). The term sideset is applied to the condition where the rear axle is moved straight sideways.

A track gauge is a straight metal bar graduated in inches or millimeters. The scale on the outside edge of the track bar is similar to a tape measure. Three straight metal pointers are mounted in

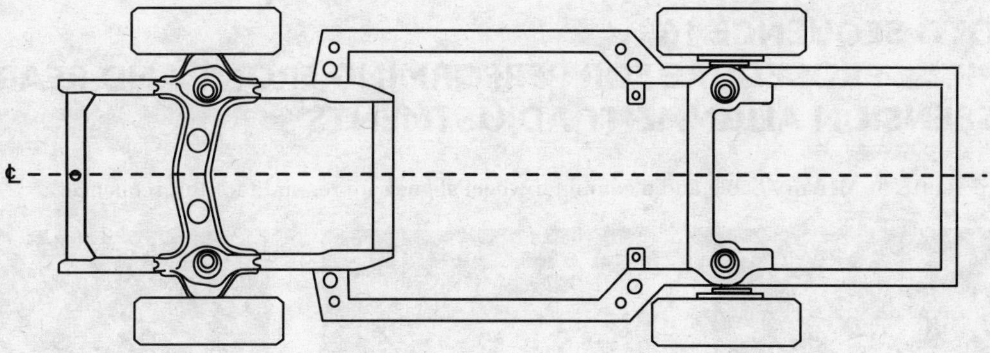

FIGURE 15-62 *When all four wheels are parallel to the geometric centerline, the thrust line is positioned at the geometric centerline and the rear wheels track directly behind the front wheels.*

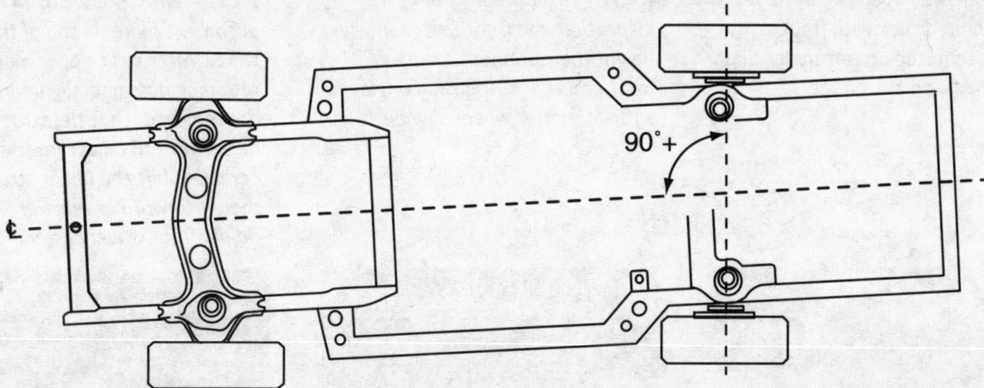

FIGURE 15-63 *Collision damage causes front wheel setback and improper rear wheel tracking with rear wheel offset.*

brackets on the track gauge. These pointers are also graduated much like a tape measure. When the wing nuts in the brackets are loosened, the brackets may be moved lengthwise on the track bar. The metal pointers may be adjusted inward or outward in the brackets.

To inspect rear wheel tracking, one of the track gauge pointers is positioned against the rear outside edge of the front wheel rim at spindle height. The other two pointers are positioned on the outside edges of the rear wheel rim at spindle height. The track gauge must be kept parallel to the side of the vehicle (Figure 15-64).

Rear Wheel Tracking Measurement Procedure

Follow these steps to measure rear wheel tracking:

1. Lift one side of the front suspension with a floor jack and lower the suspension onto a safety stand. Be sure the tire is lifted off the shop floor.
2. Place a lateral runout gauge against the outside edge of the rim lip and rotate the wheel to check wheel runout. (Refer to Chapter 4 for wheel runout measurement.) Place a chalk mark at the location of the maximum wheel runout. If the wheel runout is excessive, replace the wheel.

PHOTO SEQUENCE 16
TYPICAL PROCEDURE FOR PERFORMING FRONT AND REAR SUSPENSION ALIGNMENT ADJUSTMENTS

A Ford Taurus or Mercury Sable and a computer wheel aligner are required for this sequence.

P15-1 *Position vehicle properly on alignment rack with front wheels centered on turntables and rear wheels on slip plates.*

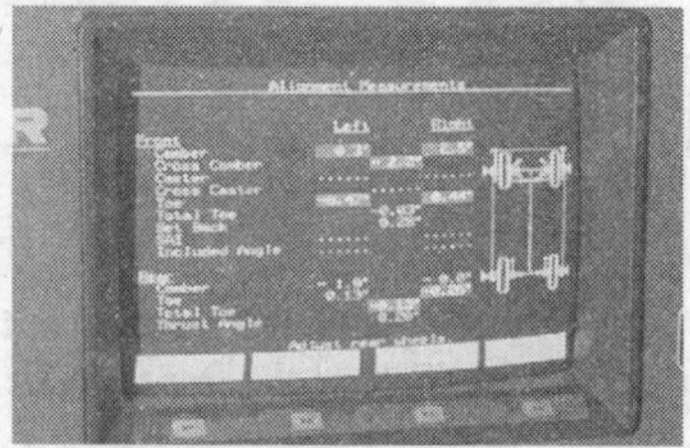

P15-2 *After prealignment inspection and front and rear ride height measurement, measure front and rear suspension angles with computer wheel aligner.*

P15-3 *Drill spot welds to remove alignment plate on top of the strut tower. After strut upper mount retaining nuts and alignment plate are removed, shift the strut inward or outward to adjust front wheel camber. Shift the upper strut mount forward or rearward to adjust front wheel caster.*

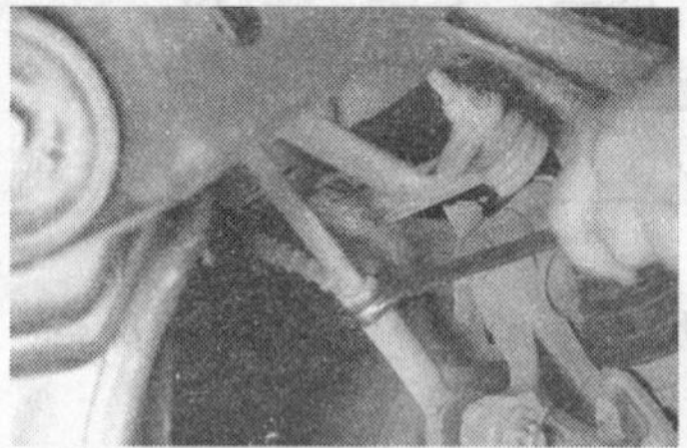

P15-4 *Loosen the locknuts and adjust the tie-rod length to adjust front wheel toe.*

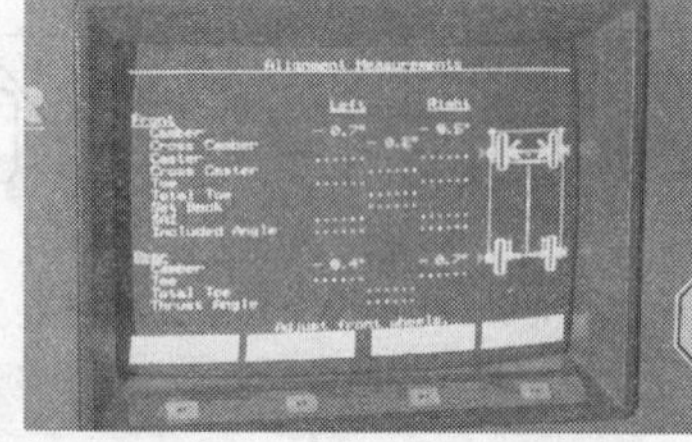

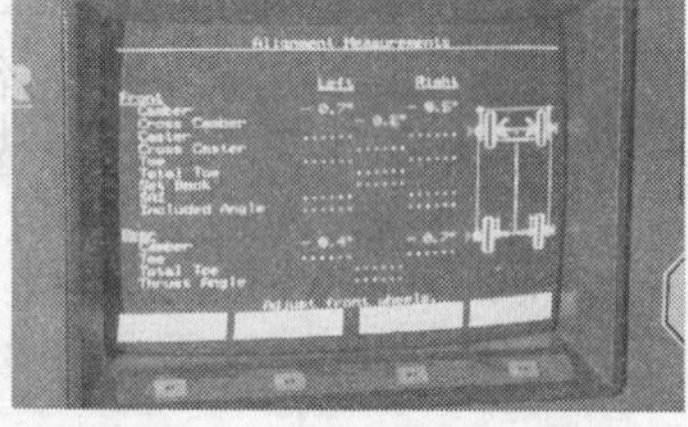

P15-5 *Recheck front suspension alignment readings on the monitor screen.*

P15-6 *Adjust the left rear wheel camber and toe by rotating the cam bolt on the inner end of the lower control arm. If the rear wheel camber and toe have not been adjusted previously, a rear camber adjusting kit may have to be installed in the inner end of the lower control arm.*

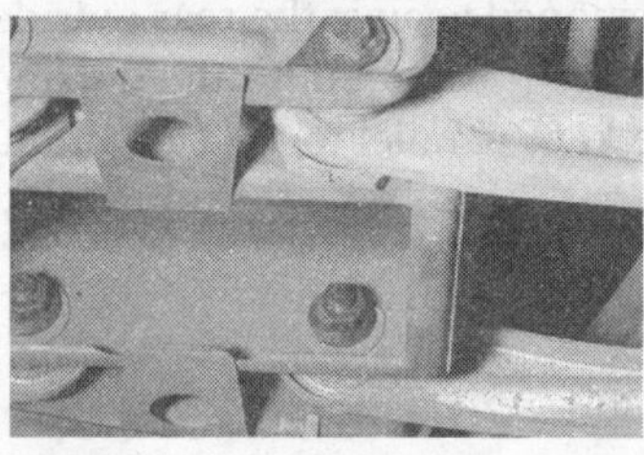

P15-7 *Adjust the right rear wheel camber and toe by rotating the cam bolt on the inner end of the lower control arm. If the rear wheel camber and toe have not been adjusted previously, a rear camber adjusting kit may have to be installed in the inner end of the lower control arm.*

P15-8 *Recheck all front and rear alignment readings on the monitor screen. Be sure all readings are within specifications, including the thrust angle.*

FIGURE 15-64 *Track bar positioned to measure rear wheel tracking.*

3. Rotate the chalk mark to the exact top or bottom of the wheel, and remove the safety stand and floor jack to lower the wheel onto the shop floor.
4. Repeat steps 1, 2, and 3 at the other three wheels.
5. Hold the single pointer on the track gauge so it contacts the rear edge of the front rim.
6. Adjust the other two pointers so they contact the outer edges of the rear wheel rim.
7. Adjust the pointers on the rear wheel so the track gauge is parallel to the side of the vehicle. Be sure all three pointers are clamped securely.
8. Move the track gauge to the opposite side of the vehicle and position the pointers in the same location on these wheels. If the vehicle has proper tracking, all three pointers on the track gauge will contact the front and rear rims at exactly the same location on both sides of the vehicle, and the track gauge will be parallel to the sides of the vehicle.

Examples of Improper Rear Wheel Tracking Measured with a Track Gauge

Rear Axle Offset. When the track gauge is positioned on the left side of the vehicle, the rear pointer on the rear wheel must be moved farther inward compared with the pointer at the front edge of the rear rim. On the right side of the vehicle, the front pointer is positioned forward and ahead of the rim edge when the two pointers are positioned on the edges of the rear rim. This indicates the wheelbase is less between the wheels on the right side of the vehicle compared with the left side. The front pointer on the rear rim is some distance from the rim face (Figure 15-65). These pointer positions indicate the right rear wheel has moved forward and the left rear wheel has moved rearward. This **rear axle offset** condition moves the thrust line to the left of the geometric centerline.

Wheel Setback. If a vehicle has been subjected to a severe right front sideways impact, the left front wheel may be driven outward and rearward. The track gauge and pointers are positioned on the right

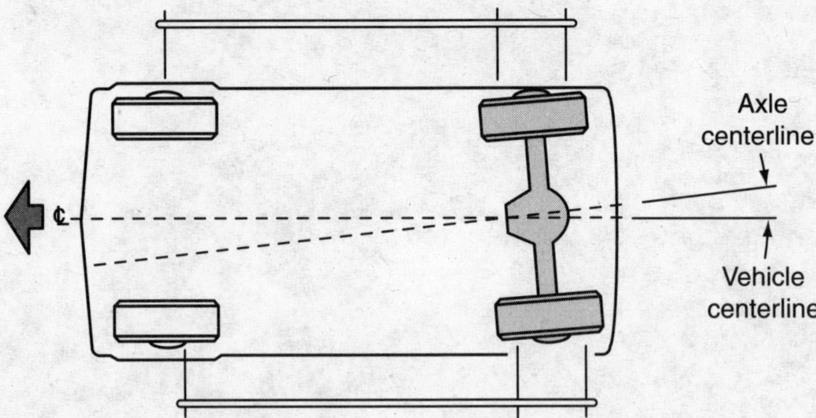

FIGURE 15-65 *Track bar measurement of an offset rear axle.*

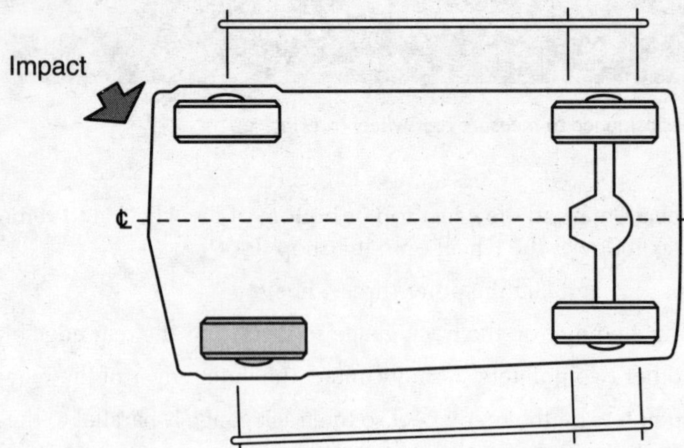

FIGURE 15-66 *Track bar measurement of a left front wheel that is moved rearward to a setback position.*

side of the vehicle and then moved to the left side. The front pointer is positioned ahead of the rim edge on the left side, and the track gauge is not parallel to the side of the vehicle (Figure 15-66).

The track gauge must be moved inward on the front pointer to position the bar parallel to the side of the vehicle. When this adjustment is made, the distance on the front pointer is less on the left side of the vehicle compared with the distance on the right side of the vehicle. These track gauge measurements indicate the left front wheel is moved rearward to a setback position as well as being outward.

Diamond-Shaped Frame Condition. When a vehicle experiences severe collision damage on the left front, the entire left side of the vehicle may be driven rearward in relation to the right side of the chassis. Under this condition, the left front wheel is moved to a setback condition, and the rear axle is offset, which moves the thrust line to the left of the geometric centerline. This particular type of damage is most likely to occur on a rear-wheel-drive vehicle with a frame and a one-piece rear axle.

Since the entire left side of the vehicle is driven rearward, the wheelbase is the same on both sides of the vehicle. Therefore, the track gauge pointers indicate the wheelbase is the same between the front and rear wheels on both sides of the vehicle. However, the two rear track gauge pointers must be

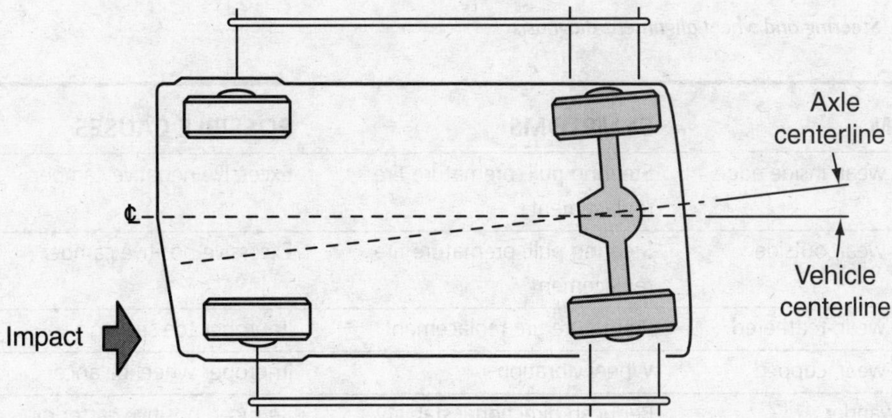

FIGURE 15-67 *A severe left front collision impact moves the entire left side of the vehicle rearward resulting in front wheel setback and rear axle offset, which provides a diamond-shaped chassis.*

adjusted to different lengths to contact the rear rim edges. On the left side of the vehicle, the rear track gauge pointer is some distance from the rear rim edge if these two pointers are set at the same measurement (Figure 15-67).

When the track gauge is positioned on the right side of the vehicle, there is some distance between the front pointer and the edge of the rear rim if both rear pointers are set at the same distance.

Measuring vehicle tracking with a track gauge is a two-person operation and requires a considerable amount of time to perform the wheel runout and track bar measurements. The track gauge also lacks precision accuracy. Computer alignment systems perform the same checks by measuring the thrust line angle, setback, and all the other front and rear suspension alignment angles with speed and accuracy.

CASE STUDY

A customer complained that the left rear tire on his Cutlass Calais had suffered severe tread wear in the last 2,000 miles. The technician examined this tire and found the customer was not exaggerating. All the tread wear indicators were showing and the other tires showed very little wear. The customer indicated that the left rear tire tread looked like the tread on the other tires 2,000 miles previously. While checking the tread wear on the left rear tire, the technician noticed the car had been newly painted. Further discussion with the customer revealed the car had been recently purchased, and there was no warranty on the vehicle. During a road test, the technician found that the steering pulled to the left while driving straight ahead. The technician suggested a thorough prealignment inspection and complete four-wheel alignment with a computer alignment system.

During the prealignment inspection, all the steering and suspension components except the left rear tire appeared to be in normal condition. However, the technician noticed the left rear quarter panel and other body components had been replaced. Apparently the car had suffered severe collision damage in this area.

The four-wheel alignment results were satisfactory except the left rear wheel, which had a 5° toe-in and a thrust angle of 8°. This severe rear toe-in condition had moved the thrust line to the right of the geometric centerline. When the technician referred to the manufacturer's service manual, this information stated the rear wheel toe is not adjustable, and if the rear wheel camber and toe are not

TABLE 15-1 *Steering and wheel alignment diagnosis*

PROBLEM	SYMPTOMS	POSSIBLE CAUSES
Tire tread wear, inside edge	Steering pull, premature tire replacement	Excessive negative camber
Tire tread wear, outside edge	Steering pull, premature tire replacement	Excessive positive camber
Tire tread wear, feathered	Premature tire replacement	Improper toe setting
Tire tread wear, cupped	Wheel vibration	Improper wheel balance
Steering wander	Reduced directional stability	Reduced positive caster or negative caster
Steering pull	Steering pull to the right when driving straight ahead	Reduced positive caster, right-front wheel Excessive positive camber, right-front wheel Excessive toe-out, left-rear wheel
Steering pull	Steering pull to the left when driving straight ahead	Reduced positive caster, right-front wheel Excessive positive camber, right-front wheel Excessive toe-out, right-rear wheel
Steering wheel return	Excessive steering wheel returning force after a turn	Excessive positive caster on front wheels
Steering wheel return	Steering wheel does not return properly after a turn	Binding column or linkage Reduced positive caster on front wheels
Harsh riding	Reduced ride quality when driving on road irregularities	Worn shock absorbers or struts Excessive positive caster, front wheels. Reduced ride height

within specifications, the rear underbody and suspension should be inspected for damage. The technician located the underbody dimension specifications in the service manual (Figure 15-68 and Figure 15-69).

The technician began checking the rear suspension underbody measurements with a tram gauge. When dimension M was measured between the center of the bolt heads in the trailing arm brackets, this measurement was 1 in. (25.4 mm) less than specified. This measurement indicated the left rear subframe had been forced inward toward the center of the vehicle, which resulted in the improper toe and thrust angle. Further inspection of the rear axle channel with a long straightedge indicated this channel was bent rearward in the center. The car was sent to the body shop to pull the rear subframe

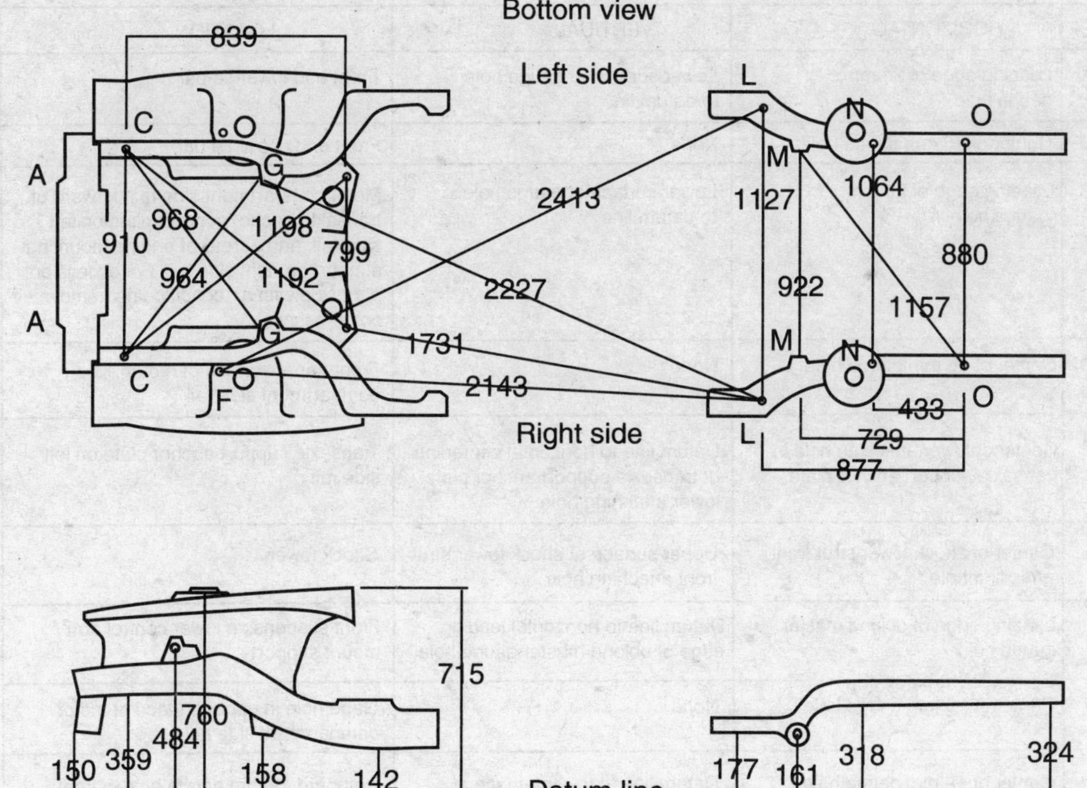

* All dimensions are metric.
* All control points are symmetrical side to side unless otherwise noted.
* All tolerances are +/– 3 mm.

FIGURE 15-68 *Underbody measurement specifications and locations.*

and unitized body back to the original position and provide the specified distance between the center of bolt heads on the trailing arms. Since the rear axle channel is a critical component in providing rear suspension ride quality and alignment, the customer was advised this component should be replaced. A new rear tire was also installed.

When the rear suspension was reassembled, all the alignment angles were rechecked and the rear wheel toe and thrust line were within specifications. During a road test, there was no evidence of steering pull or any other steering problems.

From this experience, the technician learned the importance of four wheel alignment. The technician also discovered that accurate underbody measurement specifications are absolutely essential.

REF	HORIZONTAL	VERTICAL	LOCATION
A	Leading edge of 24 mm gauge hole	Lower surface at gauge hole to datum line	Front end lower tie bar
B	Center of 16 mm gauge hole	None	Front end upper tie bar
C	Leading edge of 20 mm gauge hole	Lower surface at gauge hole to datum line	Motor compartment side rail, forward of transaxle anchor support plate on left side rail, and at rear of engine mounting support on right side rail. For access on right side with air conditioning, remove air compressor.
D	Center of 16 mm gauge hole	None	Front upper surface of motor compartment side rail
E	Center of lower attaching hole in transaxle support anchor plate	Datum line to horizontal centerline of transaxle support anchor plate lower attaching hole	Transaxle support anchor plate on left side rail
F	Center of shock tower strut front attaching hole	Upper surface at shock tower strut front attaching hole	Shock tower
G	Leading edge of oblong master gauge hole	Datum line to horizontal leading edge of oblong master gauge hole	Front suspension lower control arm mount support
H	Center of 16 mm gauge hole	None	Gage hole in upper surface of motor compartment side rail
I	Center of 19 mm gauge hole	Datum line to lower surface at gauge hole	Outboard 19 mm gauge hole in front suspension control arm mounting reinforcement support
J	Center of hood hinge pivot pin head	None	Hood hinge
K	Center of front upper hinge pin hole	Upper surface at hinge pin hole	Front upper door hinge, body side
L	Leading edge of 22 mm gauge hole	Lower surface at leading edge of gauge hole to datum line	Compartment pan longitudinal rail, forward of rear suspension spring seat support
M	Center of attaching bolt head	Datum line to horizontal centerline of attaching bolt head of rear suspension control arm support.	Rear suspension control arm support forward of rear suspension spring seat support
N	Center of 16 mm gauge hole	Datum line to lower surface at gauge hole	Outboard gage hole at rear suspension spring seat support
O	Leading edge of 21 mm gauge hole	Lower surface at gauge hole to datum line	Compartment pan longitudinal rail

FIGURE 15-69 *Explanation of underbody horizontal and vertical measurement locations.*

SERVICE TIPS

- Since rear wheel alignment plays a significant role in aiming or steering the vehicle, the rear wheel alignment should be corrected before adjusting front suspension angles. The rear wheel camber, toe, and thrust line must be within specifications before adjusting the front suspension angles.
- The bolt in the lower control arm bushing must be installed from the rear and the tension strut bushing bolt must be installed from the front to avoid contact with other suspension components.
- The vehicle manufacturer does not recommend bending the I beams to adjust front wheel camber. However, this procedure is suggested by some equipment manufacturers.
- The most accurate check of a properly centered steering wheel is while driving the vehicle straight ahead during a road test.

REVIEW QUESTIONS

1. While discussing camber adjustments on a MacPherson strut front suspension system:
Technician A says an eccentric cam on the strut-to-steering-knuckle bolt may be used to adjust camber. *Technician B* says an eccentric on the lower ball joint stud may be used to adjust camber.
Who is correct?
A. A only **C.** Both A and B
B. B only **D.** Neither A nor B

2. While discussing camber adjustment on a short-and-long arm front suspension system with adjusting shims positioned between the upper control arm mounting shaft and the outside of the frame:
Technician A says adding equal shim thickness on both mounting bolts increases negative camber. *Technician B* says adding more shim thickness on the front bolt decreases positive camber.
Who is correct?
A. A only **C.** Both A and B
B. B only **D.** Neither A nor B

3. While diagnosing and adjusting front wheel camber:
A. Front wheel camber is measured with the front wheels turned 20°.
B. The steering pulls to the side with the least amount of positive camber.
C. The right front wheel may have more positive camber to compensate for road crown.
D. The upper strut mount may be moved inward or outward to adjust camber.

4. When diagnosing and adjusting front wheel caster:
A. On some suspensions, the radius rod should be shortened to decrease positive caster.
B. On some twin I-beam suspensions, the I beams may be bent to adjust caster.
C. On some double-wishbone suspensions, a graduated cam on the pivot adjuster is rotated to adjust caster.
D. The steering pulls to the side of the suspension that has the most positive caster.

5. The camber adjustment is within specifications, but the SAI angle is more than specified on the left side of a MacPherson strut front suspension.
   Technician A says the camber adjustment bolt may be adjusted to correct the problem. *Technician B* says the left front wheel may have a setback condition.
   Who is correct?
   A. A only **C.** Both A and B
   B. B only **D.** Neither A nor B
6. Unequal SAI angles on the left and right sides of the front suspension may cause:
   A. Tread wear on the front tires.
   B. Brake pull during sudden stops.
   C. Bump steer on a rough road.
   D. Steering wander while driving straight ahead.
7. On many front suspension systems, the maximum variation between the left and right SAI is:
   A. 0.75° **C.** 1.5°
   B. 1° **D.** 2.5°
8. All of these statements about adjusting front wheel toe are true EXCEPT:
   A. If the positive caster is increased on the right front wheel, this wheel moves toward a toe-out position.
   B. The tie-rod sleeves may be heated with an acetylene torch to loosen them.
   C. The opening in the sleeve clamp must be positioned away from the slots in the tie-rod sleeve.
   D. The front wheel toe should be measured with the front wheels straight ahead.
9. A rear independent suspension system has a tie-rod connected from the steering knuckle to the lower control arm.
   Technician A says if the tie-rod is lengthened, the rear wheel is moved toward a toe-out position. *Technician B* says if the tie-rod is shortened, the positive camber is increased on the rear wheel.
   Who is correct?
   A. A only **C.** Both A and B
   B. B only **D.** Neither A nor B
10. While discussing a vehicle on which the front suspension alignment angles are within manufacturer's specifications, but the thrust line is 7° to the right of the vehicle centerline:
   Technician A says this problem may be caused by excessive toe-out on the right rear wheel. *Technician B* says this vehicle will tend to steer to the left when driven straight ahead.
   Who is correct?
   A. A only **C.** Both A and B
   B. B only **D.** Neither A nor B

CHALLENGE QUESTIONS

1. A car with a MacPherson strut front suspension has 1.5° positive camber on the left front wheel and 1.5° negative camber on the right front wheel. The most likely cause of this problem is:
   A. Worn upper strut mounts.
   B. Improperly positioned steering gear.
   C. Engine cradle shifted to the right.
   D. Bent strut rods.

2. A pickup truck with a MacPherson strut front suspension pulls to the left. Preliminary inspection shows that the SAI is correct, but the camber of the right front wheel is –1 1/4°. *Technician A* says a bent spindle could be the cause. *Technician B* says the problem may be a worn-out strut.
   Who is correct?
   A. A only **C.** Both A and B
   B. B only **D.** Neither A nor B
3. The nose of a car seems to "push" into the turn when making a right turn.
   Technician A says the probable cause is there is not enough left front wheel toe-out on turns. *Technician B* says the probable cause is too much positive camber on the left rear wheel.
   Who is correct?
   A. A only **C.** Both A and B
   B. B only **D.** Neither A nor B
4. "Feathering" type wear of a rear tire is likely caused by:
   A. Improper rear wheel camber alignment.
   B. Improper rear tire inflation.
   C. Improper rear wheel balance.
   D. Improper rear wheel toe alignment.
5. The owner of an older pickup says the truck has begun to "wander and shimmy" in the past few months, especially when the bed of the truck is empty.
   Technician A says the twin I-beam front suspension caster is probably out of spec. *Technician B* says the eyes of the rear leaf springs are probably worn.
   Who is correct?
   A. A only **C.** Both A and B
   B. B only **D.** Neither A nor B

JOB SHEET 49

Name ______________________________ Date ______________

CENTER STEERING WHEEL

Upon completion of this job sheet, you should be able to center a steering wheel.

ASE Correlation

This job sheet is related to ASE Automotive Suspension and Steering Task: *Center steering wheel.*

Tools and Materials

Tie-rod sleeve adjusting tool

Describe the Vehicle Being Worked On:

Year __________ Make ______________ Model ______________

VIN ______________ Engine type and size ______________

Procedure

Task Completed

1. List the suspension and steering service procedures that may require steering wheel centering after these procedures are completed.

____

____

____

____

2. The steering wheel is centered properly with the front wheels straight ahead in the shop, but the steering wheel is not centered when driving the vehicle straight ahead. List the causes of this problem.

____

____

____

____

3. Lift the front end of the vehicle with a hydraulic jack, and position safety stands under the lower control arms. Lower the vehicle onto the safety stands, and place the front wheels in the straight-ahead position.

Are the lower control arms securely supported on safety stands? ☐ Yes ☐ No

Are the front wheels straight ahead? ☐ Yes ☐ No

Instructor check ______________________________

4. Use a piece of chalk to mark each tie-rod sleeve in relation to the tie-rod, and loosen the sleeve clamps.

Are the tie-rod sleeves marked in relation to the tie-rods? ☐ Yes ☐ No

Instructor check ______________________________

Task Completed

5. Position the steering wheel spoke in the position it was in while driving straight ahead during the road test. Turn the steering wheel to the centered position and note the direction of the front wheels.

   Direction the front wheels are turned with the steering wheel centered:
   right _____ left _____

6. If the steering wheel spoke is low on the left side while driving the vehicle straight ahead, use a tie-rod sleeve rotating tool to shorten the left tie-rod and lengthen the right tie-rod. A one-quarter turn on a tie-rod sleeve moves the steering wheel position approximately one inch. Turn the tie-rod sleeves the proper amount to bring the steering wheel to the centered position. For example, if the steering wheel spoke is two inches off-center, turn each tie-rod sleeve one-half turn.

   Left tie-rod sleeve: lengthened _____ shortened _____

   Right tie-rod sleeve: lengthened _____ shortened _____

   Amount of left tie-rod sleeve rotation _____

   Amount of right tie-rod sleeve rotation _____

   Is the steering wheel centered with front wheel straight ahead? ☐ Yes ☐ No

   Instructor check ____________________

☐ 7. If the steering wheel spoke is low on the right side while driving the vehicle straight ahead, lengthen the left tie-rod and shorten the right tie-rod.

8. Mark each tie-rod sleeve in its new position in relation to the tie-rod. Be sure the sleeve clamp openings are positioned properly, as indicated in this chapter. Tighten the clamp bolts to the specified torque.

   Are the tie-rod sleeves marked in relation to tie-rods? ☐ Yes ☐ No

   Are the tie-rod sleeve clamps properly installed? ☐ Yes ☐ No

   Tie-rod sleeve bolt specified torque _____

   Tie-rod sleeve bolt actual torque _____

   Instructor check ____________________

9. Lift the front chassis with a floor jack, and remove the safety stands. Lower the vehicle onto the shop floor, and check the steering wheel position during a road test.

   Steering wheel position while driving straight ahead during a road test:
   ☐ Satisfactory ☐ Unsatisfactory

Instructor's Response ____________________

____

____

JOB SHEET 50

Name ______________________________ Date ______________

ADJUST FRONT WHEEL ALIGNMENT ANGLES

Upon completion of this job sheet, you should be able to adjust front wheel alignment angles.

ASE Correlation

This job sheet is related to ASE Automotive Suspension and Steering Task: *Inspect and adjust front and rear wheel camber. Inspect and adjust front wheel caster and toe.*

Tools and Materials

A vehicle with improperly adjusted front wheel camber, caster, and toe.

Describe the Vehicle Being Worked On:

Year ________ Make ______________ Model ______________
VIN ______________ Engine type and size ______________

Procedure

Task Completed

1. Position the vehicle properly on the alignment ramp with the front wheels properly positioned on the turntables and the rear wheels on slip plates.

   Are the front wheels properly positioned on turntables? ☐ Yes ☐ No

   Are the rear wheels properly positioned on slip plates? ☐ Yes ☐ No

   Is the parking brake applied? ☐ Yes ☐ No

   Instructor check ______________

2. Perform a prealignment inspection and correct any defective conditions or components found during the inspection. List the defective conditions or components, and explain the reasons for your diagnosis.

   ____

   ____

   ____

3. Measure front and rear ride height and correct it if necessary.

   Specified front suspension ride height ______

   Actual front suspension ride height ______

   Specified rear suspension ride height ______

   Actual rear suspension ride height ______

Task Completed

List the necessary repairs to correct the front and rear suspension ride height and explain the reasons for your diagnosis.

____

____

____

____

4. Measure and adjust front wheel camber.

Specified front wheel camber ______

Actual front wheel camber: left ______ right ______

Front wheel camber after adjustment: left ______ right ______

Camber adjustment method ______

5. Measure SAI and included angle.

Specified SAI ______

Actual SAI: left ______ right ______

Specified included angle ______

Actual included angle: left ______ right ______

If the SAI and/or included angle are not within specifications, state the necessary repairs and explain the reasons for your diagnosis.

____

____

____

____

6. Measure and adjust front wheel caster.

Specified front wheel caster ______

Actual front wheel caster: left ______ right ______

Front wheel caster after adjustment: left ______ right ______

Caster adjustment method ______

7. Inspect camber measurements and adjust if necessary.

Camber adjustment: ☐ Satisfactory ☐ Unsatisfactory

Left front camber readjusted to ______

Right front camber readjusted to ______

8. Measure and adjust front wheel toe.

Specified front wheel toe ______

Actual front wheel toe: left ______ right ______

Total toe ______

Front wheel toe after adjustment: left ______ right ______

Total front wheel toe ______

Task Completed ______

9. Inspect steering wheel centering with front wheels straight ahead and center the wheel if necessary.

Is steering wheel centered? ☐ Yes ☐ No

Instructor check ____________________

10. Measure turning angle.

Specified turning angle ______

Actual turning angle left front wheel ______

Actual turning angle right front wheel ______

Turning angle correction required: ☐ Yes ☐ No

Left front wheel turned inward 20°, turning angle on right front wheel ______

Right front wheel turned inward 20°, turning angle on left front wheel ______

If the turning angle is not within specifications, state the necessary repairs and explain the reasons for your diagnosis.

____

____

____

____

Instructor's Response ____________________

____

____

JOB SHEET 51

Name ____ Date ____________________

ADJUST REAR WHEEL ALIGNMENT ANGLES

Upon completion of this job sheet, you should be able to adjust rear wheel alignment angles.

ASE Correlation

This job sheet is related to ASE Automotive Suspension and Steering Tasks: *Inspect and adjust front and rear wheel camber. Inspect and adjust rear wheel toe.*

Tools and Materials

A vehicle with improperly adjusted rear wheel camber and toe.

Describe the Vehicle Being Worked On:

Year __________ Make ____________________ Model ______________
VIN ____________________ Engine type and size ________________

Procedure

Task Completed

1. Position the vehicle properly on the alignment ramp with the front wheels properly positioned on the turntables and the rear wheels on slip plates.

   Are the front wheels properly positioned on turntables? ☐ Yes ☐ No

   Are the rear wheels properly positioned on slip plates? ☐ Yes ☐ No

   Is the parking brake applied? ☐ Yes ☐ No

   Instructor check ____

2. Perform a prealignment inspection, and correct any defective conditions or components found during the inspection. List the defective conditions or components, and explain the reasons for your diagnosis.

   ____

   ____

   ____

3. Measure front and rear ride height and correct if necessary.

   Specified front suspension ride height ______

   Actual front suspension ride height ______

   Specified rear suspension ride height ______

   Actual rear suspension ride height ______

Task Completed

If the rear ride height is not within specifications, state the necessary repairs and explain the reasons for your diagnosis.

____

____

____

____

4. Measure and adjust camber on left rear wheel.

Specified left rear wheel camber ______

Actual left rear wheel camber ______

Left rear wheel camber after adjustment ______

Camber adjustment method ______________________________

5. Measure left rear wheel toe.

Specified left rear wheel toe ______

Actual left rear wheel toe ______

Left rear wheel toe after adjustment ______

Toe adjustment method ______________________________

6. Measure and adjust camber on right rear wheel.

Specified right rear wheel camber ______

Actual right rear wheel camber ______

Right rear wheel camber after adjustment ______

Camber adjustment method ______________________________

7. Measure right rear wheel toe.

Specified right rear wheel toe ______

Actual right rear wheel toe ______

Right rear wheel toe after adjustment ______

Toe adjustment method ______________________________

8. Measure thrust angle.

Specified thrust angle ______

Actual thrust angle ______

If the thrust angle is not within specifications, state the necessary repairs and explain the reasons for your diagnosis.

____

____

____

____

Task Completed

9. Road-test vehicle for satisfactory steering and suspension operation.

Steering directional control: ☐ Satisfactory ☐ Unsatisfactory

Complete steering operation: ☐ Satisfactory ☐ Unsatisfactory

Suspension operation: ☐ Satisfactory ☐ Unsatisfactory

If the steering or suspension operation is unsatisfactory, state the necessary repairs and explain the reasons for your diagnosis.

____

____

____

____

Instructor's Response ____

____

____

FOUR WHEEL ALIGNMENT PROCEDURE

16

Upon completion and review of this chapter, you should be able to:

- Perform a prealignment inspection.
- Diagnose wheel alignment and tire wear problems.
- Position a vehicle on the alignment rack and connect the wheel units on a computer wheel aligner to the wheel rims.
- Select the specifications in the computer wheel aligner for the vehicle being aligned.
- Perform a preliminary wheel alignment inspection with the preliminary inspection screen.
- Perform a ride height inspection and measurement with the ride height screen.
- Perform an automatic or manual wheel runout compensation procedure.
- Measure front wheel camber and caster.
- Measure front and rear wheel setback.
- Measure steering axis inclination (SAI).
- Measure front wheel toe and turning radius.

- Measure toe change during front wheel jounce and rebound to check steering linkage height.
- Diagnose bent front struts.
- Recognize the symptoms of improper rear wheel alignment.
- Measure rear wheel camber and toe.

WHEEL ALIGNMENT PRELIMINARY DIAGNOSIS AND INSPECTION

Customer Complaints Related to Suspension or Brakes

Drivers may experience a variety of symptoms related to incorrect wheel alignment or defective brakes (Figure 16-1). Not all the symptoms are related to wheel alignment, but the customer may request an alignment to correct these problems. The technician must diagnose and correct the cause of the specific complaint. Wheel alignment angles that affect tire wear are toe and camber. The most likely symptoms of incorrect toe or camber settings are pull to one side while driving, wander, feathered tire wear, or tire wear on one side.

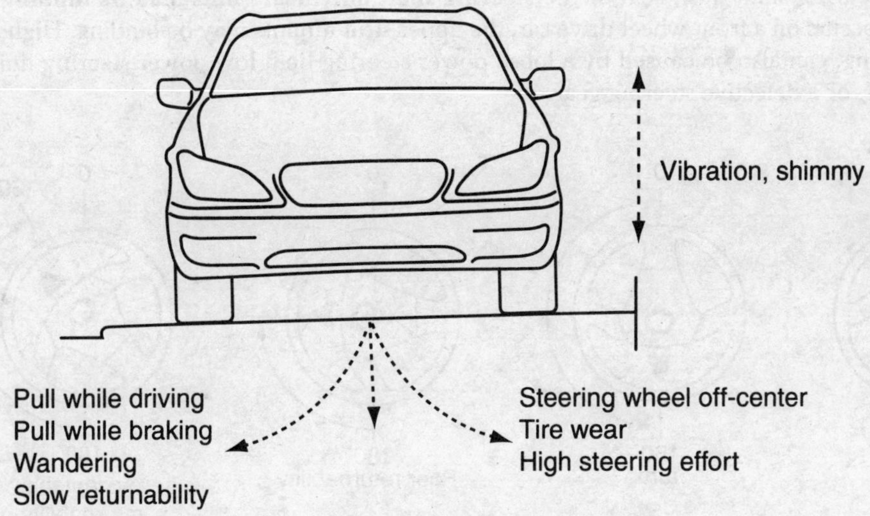

FIGURE 16-1 *Customer complaints related to wheel alignment or brakes.*

Road Test

In many cases, a **road test** is necessary to verify customer complaints. During a road test, the vehicle should be driven under the conditions when the customer complaint occurred. While road-testing the vehicle, the technician should listen for any unusual noises related to suspension and steering.

The technician should check for these steering problems during a road test:

1. Excessive vertical chassis oscillations

2. Chassis waddle
3. Steering wander, pull, or drift
4. High steering effort and binding
5. Tire squeal while cornering
6. Bump steer
7. Torque steer
8. Excessive steering wheel free play
9. Suspension bottoming on rough road surfaces
10. Wheel hop during hard acceleration
11. Nose dive while braking or rear suspension squat when accelerating
12. Excessive body sway when cornering
13. Memory steer
14. Steering wheel return

Chassis waddle may be caused by excessive tire or wheel runout. Excessive vertical chassis oscillations are the result of defective shock absorbers or struts. (Refer to Chapter 4 for tire and wheel runout diagnosis and Chapter 5 for shock absorber and strut diagnosis.)

Most steering systems are designed so the steering wheel returns to within 30° to 60° of center after a 180° turn (Figure 16-2). If the steering wheel returnability is not satisfactory and **memory steer** is evident, the steering shaft dash seal or the steering shaft universal joints may be binding. When memory steer occurs on a front-wheel-drive car, the upper strut mounts may be binding. High steering effort, or binding, can also be caused by a loose power steering belt, low power steering fluid level, worn front tires, or a defective steering gear.

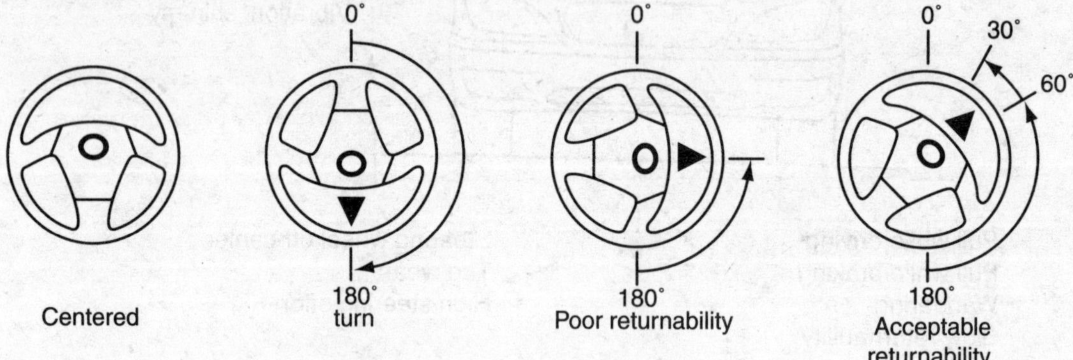

FIGURE 16-2 *Steering wheel returnability.*

A front-wheel-drive vehicle with unequal drive axles produces some **torque steer** on hard acceleration. Some front-wheel-drive vehicles, especially those with higher horsepower, have equal front drive axles to reduce torque steer. On a front-wheel-drive vehicle, torque steer is aggravated by different tire tread designs on the front tires or uneven wear on the front tires.

Bump steer occurs if the tie-rods are not the same height, meaning one of the tie-rods is not parallel to the lower control arm. This condition may be caused by a bent or worn idler arm or pitman arm on a parallelogram steering linkage. On a rack and pinion steering system, worn steering gear mounting bushings may cause this unparallel condition between one of the tie-rods and the lower control arm.

Steering pull may be caused by improper caster or camber adjustments.

During a road test, any of the following symptoms may indicate improper rear wheel alignment:

1. The front wheel **toe-in** is set correctly with the steering wheel centered on the alignment rack, but the steering wheel is not centered when the vehicle is driven straight ahead.
2. When there are no worn suspension parts or defective tires and all front suspension angles are within specifications, but the vehicle wanders or drifts to one side.
3. The vehicle is not overloaded, all front suspension angles are within specifications, and there are no worn suspension parts, but tire wear recurs.

Prealignment Inspection

The technician should identify the exact suspension or steering complaint before a wheel alignment or other suspension work is performed. The technician must diagnose the cause or causes of the complaint and correct this problem during the wheel alignment (Figure 16-3). Since collision damage may affect wheel alignment angles, an inspection for collision damage on the vehicle should be completed prior to a wheel alignment (Figure 16-4).

Worn suspension and steering components must be replaced before a wheel alignment is performed. A wheel alignment should be performed after suspension components such as struts have been replaced.

The following components and measurements should be checked in a prealignment inspection:

1. Curb weight
2. Tires
3. Suspension height
4. Steering wheel free play
5. Shock absorbers or struts
6. Wheel bearing adjustment
7. Ball joint condition
8. Control arms and bushings
9. Steering linkages and tie-rod ends
10. Stabilizers and bushings
11. Full fuel tank

Components to be checked in a **prealignment inspection** and wheel alignment measurements are summarized in Figure 16-5.

These checks should be completed with the car on the floor:

1. Inspect for excessive mud adhered to the chassis. Remove heavy items from the trunk and passenger compartment that are not considered in the vehicle curb weight. If heavy items such as tool display cases or merchandise are normally carried in the vehicle, these items should be left in the car during a wheel alignment.

Condition	Probable Cause
Tire wear:	
Outer shoulder	Too much positive camber
Inner shoulder	Too much negative camber
Sawtooth pattern:	
Sharp edge towards center	Too little toe-in
Sharp edge away from center	Too much toe-in
Both shoulders	Underinflation, high-speed cornering, overloading
Tread roll under	High speed in curves
Cupping, dishing	Wheel imbalance, radial runout
Shimmy:	
With or without vehicle instability	Too much positive caster, unequal caster between wheels
Without instability	Tire imbalance, tire runout, driveline vibration
Vibration: (Caster/camber not a probable cause. The condition is listed because it is sometimes misdiagnosed as shimmy.)	Driveline misalignment, driveline imbalance, vehicle shake (accompanied by a characteristic moan), tire runout, unequal weight distribution between wheels
Steering wander/pull	Incorrect camber Unequal caster Overload, which elevates front end
Brake pull	Too much negative caster Unequal tire pressure, brake line damage that impedes hydraulic action on one side
Hard steering	Incorrect caster Damaged steering linkage, worn steering linkage, damaged spindles, rear-end overload, bent steering arm causing incorrect turning angle

FIGURE 16-3 *Diagnosis of wheel alignment problems.*

2. Inflate tires to the recommended pressure and note any abnormal tread wear or damage on each tire. Be sure all tires are the same size.
3. Check the front tires and wheels for radial runout. (Refer to Chapter 4 for this measurement.)
4. Check the suspension **ride height.** If this measurement is not within specifications, check for broken or sagged springs. On a torsion bar suspension system, check the torsion bar adjustment.

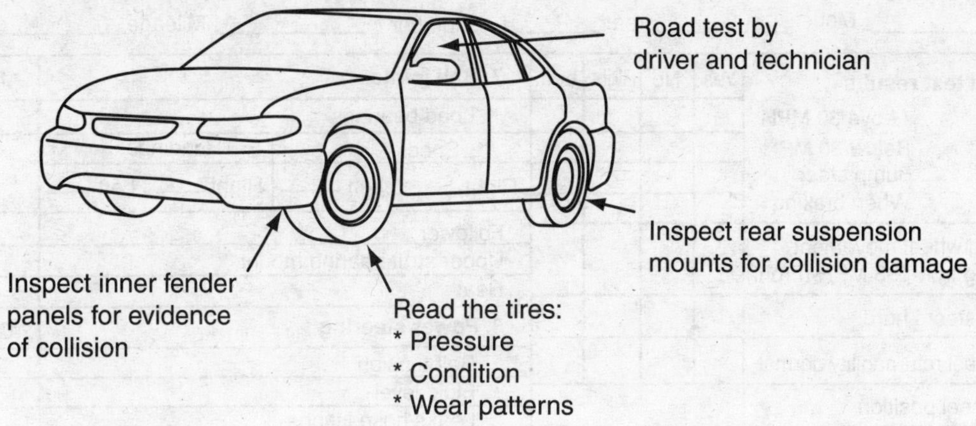

FIGURE 16-4 *Collision damage inspection.*

5. Inspect front and rear suspension bumpers. Worn bumpers may indicate weak springs or worn-out shock absorbers or struts.
6. When the wheels are in the straight-ahead position, rotate the steering wheel back and forth to check for play in the steering column, steering gear, or linkages.
7. Inspect the shock absorbers or struts for loose mounting bushings and bolts. Examine each shock absorber or strut for leakage.
8. Inspect the condition of each shock absorber or strut with a bounce test at each corner of the vehicle. (This test is explained in Chapter 5.)

The following checks should be performed with the vehicle raised and the suspension supported:

1. Inspect the front wheel bearings for lateral movement. (This inspection is described in Chapter 3.) On front-wheel-drive vehicles, perform this inspection on all four wheel bearings. Wheel bearings must be properly adjusted prior to a wheel alignment. Clean, repack, or adjust the wheel bearings as necessary.
2. Measure the ball joint radial and axial movement. If excessive movement exists in either direction, ball joint replacement is required. (Ball joint diagnosis and replacement is explained in Chapter 6.) Be sure the suspension is supported correctly during ball joint diagnosis.
3. Inspect the control arms for damage and inspect the control arm bushings for wear.
4. Inspect all the steering linkages and tie-rod ends for looseness.
5. Inspect for worn stabilizer mounting links and bushings.
6. Inspect for loose steering gear mounting bolts and worn mounting brackets and bushings.

PREALIGNMENT INSPECTION CHECKLIST

Owner ______________ Phone ______ Date ______

Address ______________ VIN ______________

Make ______ Model ______ Year ______ Lic. number ______ Mileage ______

1. Road test results	Yes	No	Right	Left
Above 30 MPH				
Below 30 MPH				
Bump steer				
When braking				
Steering wheel movement				
Stopping from 2-3 MPH (Front)				
Vehicle steers hard				
Strg wheel returnability normal				
Strg wheel position				

Vibration	Yes	No	Frnt	Rear

2. Tire pressure Specs Frnt ____ Rear ____

Record pressure found

RF ______ LF ______ RR ______ LR ______

3. Chassis height Specs Frnt ____ Rear ____

Record height found

RF ______ LF ______ RR ______ LR ______

	Yes	No
Springs sagged		
Torsion bars adjusted		

4. Rubber bushings	OK
Upper control arm	
Lower control arm	
Sway bar / stabilizer link	
Strut rod	
Rear bushing	

5. Shock absorbers/struts	Frnt	Rear

6. Steering linkage	Frnt OK	Rear OK
Tie-rod ends		
Idler arm		
Center link		
Sector shaft		
Pitman arm		
Gearbox/rack adjustment		
Gearbox/rack mounting		

7. Ball joints	OK
Load bearings	
Specs: Right ____ Left ____ / Readings: Right ____ Left ____	
Follower	
Upper strut bearing mount	
Rear	

8. Power steering	OK
Belt tension	
Fluid level	
Leaks/hose fittings	
Spool valve centered	

9. Tires/wheels	OK
Wheel runout	
Condition	
Equal tread depth	
Wheel bearing	
10. Brakes operating properly	

11. Alignment	Spec R	Spec L	Initial reading R	Initial reading L	Adjusted reading R	Adjusted reading L
Camber						
Caster						
Toe						

Bump steer	Toe change right wheel Amount	Toe change right wheel Direction	Toe change left wheel Amount	Toe change left wheel Direction
Chassis down 3"				
Chassis up 3"				

	Spec R	Spec L	Initial reading R	Initial reading L	Adjusted reading R	Adjusted reading L
Toe-out on turns						
SAI						
Rear camber						
Rear total toe						
Rear indiv. toe						
Wheel balance						
Radial tire pull						

FIGURE 16-5 *Prealignment inspection and wheel alignment checklist.*

Tire Wear Diagnosis

Various types of tire tread wear patterns indicate specific alignment or balance defects (Figure 16-6).

Conditions	Rapid wear at shoulders	Rapid wear at center	Cracked treads	Wear on one edge	Feathered edge	Bald spots	Scalloped wear
Effect							
Causes	Underinflation or lack of rotation	Overinflation or lack of rotation	Underinflation or excessive speed	Excessive camber	Incorrect toe	Unbalanced wheel Or tire defect	Lack of rotation of tires or worn or out-of-alignment suspension
Corrections	Adjust pressure to specifications when tires are cool. Rotate tires.			Adjust camber to specs	Adjust toe to specs	Dynamic or static balance wheels	Rotate tires and inspect suspension

FIGURE 16-6 *Tire tread wear patterns and causes.*

FOUR WHEEL ALIGNMENT WITH COMPUTER ALIGNMENT SYSTEMS

Preliminary Procedure

WARNING: When using a computer wheel aligner, always follow the equipment manufacturer's recommended procedures to provide accurate readings and to avoid equipment and vehicle damage or personal injury.

The vehicle should be on an **alignment ramp** with a **turntable** under each front tire and conventional **slip plates** under the rear tires (Figure 16-7). Slip plates under the rear tires allow unrestricted movement of the rear wheels during rear wheel camber and toe adjustments (Figure 16-8). If suspension adjustments are made with the tires contacting the alignment ramp or the shop floor, the tires cannot move when the adjustment is completed. This action causes inaccurate suspension adjustments. The center of the front wheel spindles should be in line with the zero mark on the turning plates. The locking pins must be left in these plates and the parking brake applied.

Mount the **rim clamps** on each wheel. It may be necessary to remove the chrome discs or hub caps before these clamps can be installed. The adjustment knob on the rim clamp should be pointing

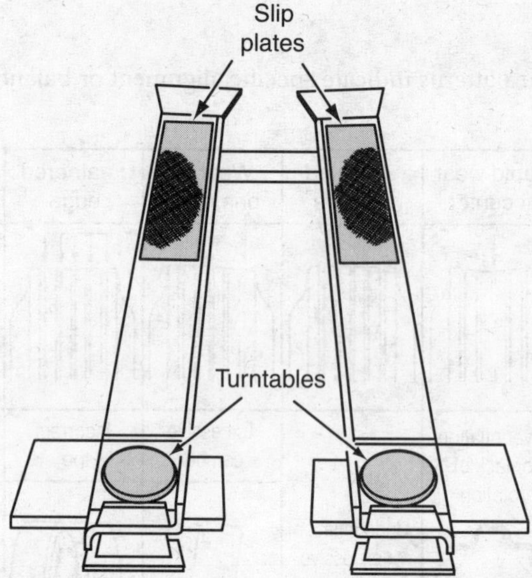

FIGURE 16-7 *Alignment ramp with turntables.*

FIGURE 16-8 *Rear wheel slip plates. (Courtesy of Snap-On Tools Corp.)*

toward the top of the wheel, and the bubble on the wheel unit should be centered (Figure 16-9). A set knob on the wheel unit allows the service technician to lock the wheel unit in this position. Some computer wheel aligners have a display on the monitor that indicates if any of the wheel sensors are not level (Figure 16-10). These sensors may be leveled by pressing a control knob on each wheel sensor. Some **digital signal processor (DSP)** wheel sensors contain a microprocessor and a **high-frequency transmitter** that acquire measurements and process data and then send these data to a **receiver** mounted on top of the wheel alignment monitor. This type of wheel sensor does not require any cables connected between the sensors and the computer wheel aligner. The data from this type of wheel sensor signal are virtually uninterruptible, even by solid objects. When these wheel sensors are

FIGURE 16-9 *Rim clamp and wheel sensor.*

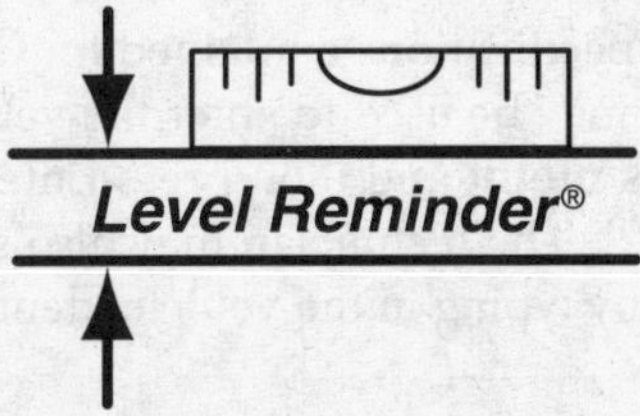

FIGURE 16-10 *Wheel sensor level indicator on the monitor screen.*

stored on the computer wheel aligner, a "docking station" feature charges the batteries in the wheel sensors.

Some wheel sensors contain infrared emitter/detectors or light-emitting diodes (LEDs) between the front and rear wheel sensors to perform alignment measurements. Older wheel sensors have strings between the front and rear wheel sensors. Each wheel sensor contains a microprocessor with a preheat circuit that stabilizes the readings in relation to temperature. Some wheel sensors have touch keypads on the wheel units to allow the entry of commands from each unit. The front wheel units have arms that project toward the front of the vehicle to transmit signals between these units. When a blocked beam prompt appears on any screen, the beam between two wheel units is blocked. This could be caused by a person standing in the beam, an open car door, or a suspension jack. The blocked beam prompt must be eliminated before any tests are completed.

The manufacturers of various types of computer alignment systems publish detailed operator's manuals for their specific equipment. Our objective here is to discuss some of the general screens that a technician uses while measuring wheel alignment angles with a typical computer aligner.

Main Menu

One of the first items displayed on the computer aligner screen is the **main menu** screen. From this screen, the technician makes a selection by touching the desired selection on the monitor screen with

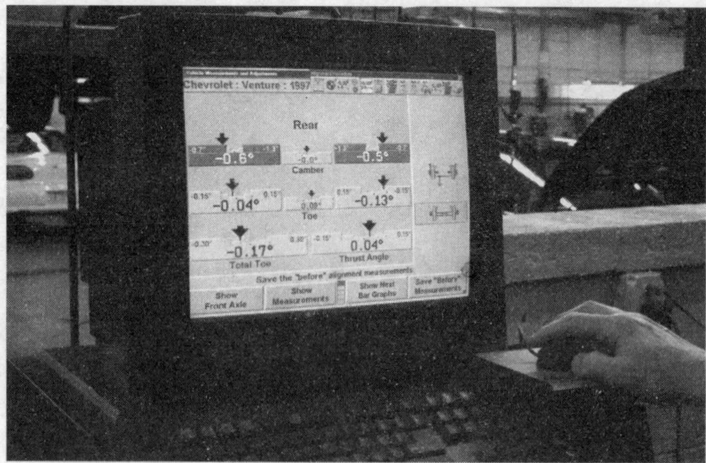

FIGURE 16-11 *Making screen selections with a mouse.*

a mouse (Figure 16-11) or by pressing the number on the keypad that matches the number beside the desired procedure. A cursor may also be used to select the type of alignment.

Specifications Menu

Some computer wheel aligners have specifications contained on CDs. The appropriate CD must be placed in the aligner. Several methods may be used to enter the vehicle specifications. The technician may scroll through the **specifications menu** and then press Enter when the appropriate vehicle is highlighted on the screen (Figure 16-12). The technician may also select the proper vehicle specifications by pointing with the light pen or by typing in the vehicle identification number (VIN) or the first letter in the vehicle make.

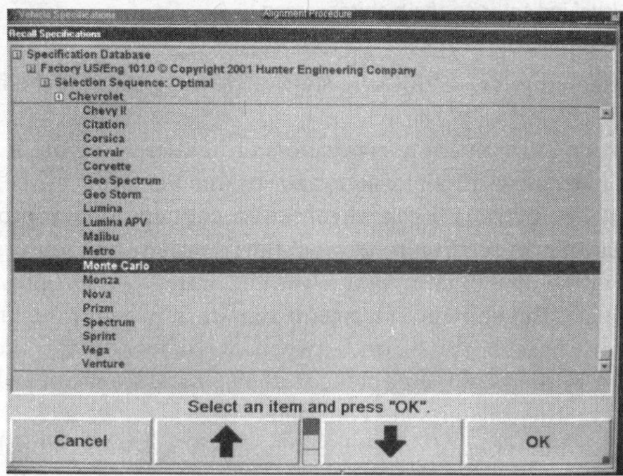

FIGURE 16-12 *Entering vehicle specifications.*

On other computer wheel aligners, the specifications are contained on a floppy disk and the technician selects the appropriate make, model, and year of vehicle with the cursor on the screen.

On early computer alignment systems, the vehicle specifications were contained on bar graphs. The technician moved a wand across the appropriate bar graph to enter the specifications for the vehicle being aligned.

Preliminary Inspection Screen

The **preliminary inspection screen** allows the technician to enter the condition of all front and rear suspension components that must be checked during a prealignment inspection. On some computer alignment systems, the technician may enter checked, marginal, and repair or replace for each component (Figure 16-13). These entered conditions may be printed out at any time or with the complete wheel alignment results.

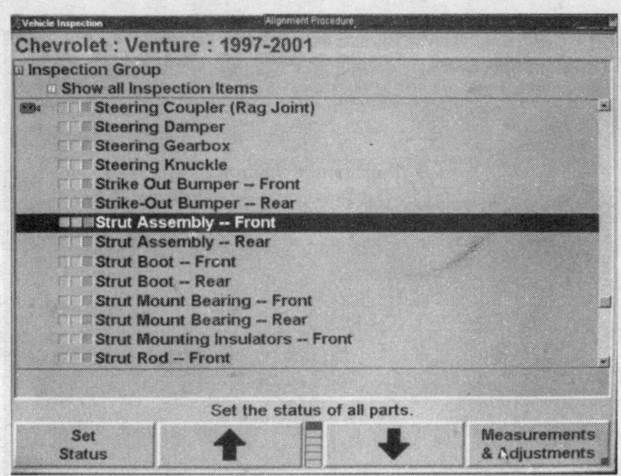

FIGURE 16-13 *Preliminary inspection screen.*

Ride Height Screen

Some computer wheel aligners have optical encoders in the wheel sensors that measure ride height when this selection is displayed on the screen and the ride height attachment on each wheel sensor is lifted until it touches the lower edge of the fender (Figure 16-14). The ride height measurement is

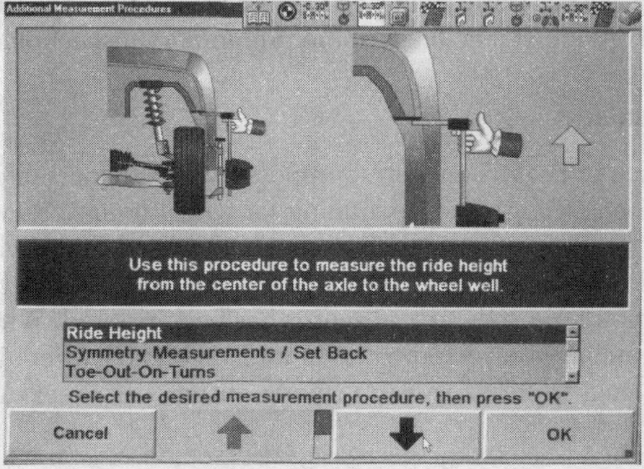

FIGURE 16-14 *Ride height screen and ride height attachment in wheel sensor.*

displayed on the screen. If the screen display is green, the ride height is within specifications. A red ride height display indicates this measurement is not within specifications. Improper ride height may be caused by sagged or broken springs, bent components such as control arms, or worn components such as control arm bushings.

CAUTION: The ride height must be within specifications before proceeding with the wheel alignment. Improper curb riding height affects many of the other suspension angles.

Some computer wheel aligners provide a **ride height screen** with a graphic display indicating the exact location where the ride height should be measured (Figure 16-15). The computer aligner compares the ride height measurements entered by the technician to the specifications.

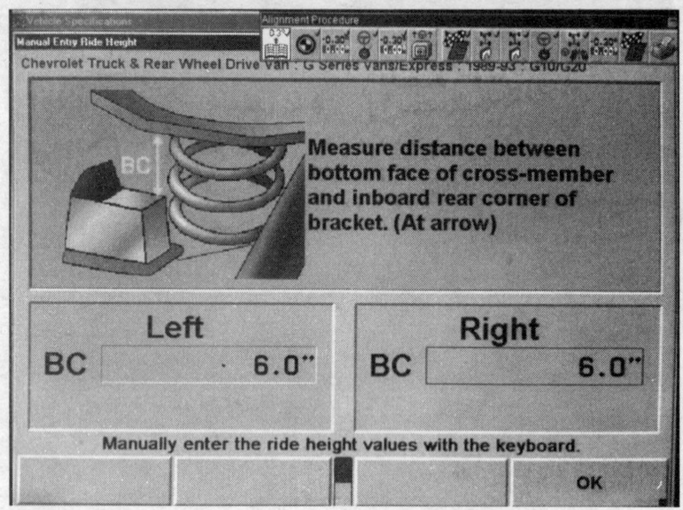

FIGURE 16-15 *Ride height screen.*

Tire Condition Screen

When the **tire inspection screen** is displayed, the technician may enter various tire wear conditions for each tire (Figure 16-16). The cursor on the screen is moved to the tire being inspected. The tire conditions are printed out with the preliminary inspection results and the alignment report. On other computer wheel aligners, tire condition is included in the preliminary inspection screens.

Wheel Runout Compensation

As mentioned previously, screen indicators on some computer wheel aligners inform the technician if any of the wheel sensors require leveling or compensating for wheel runout. Runout compensation is accomplished by pressing the appropriate button on each wheel sensor. Some wheel sensors provide continuous compensation. This feature provides accurate alignment angles even when a wheel is rotated after the compensation button on the wheel sensor has been pressed. When the wheel runout screen is displayed, the technician is directed to level and lock each wheel unit and then press the compensation button on each wheel sensor to provide automatic wheel runout compensation (Figure 16-17).

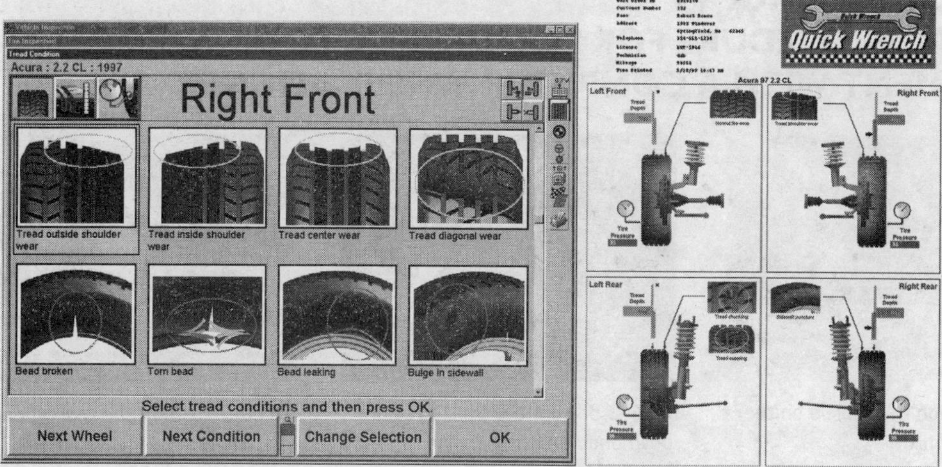

FIGURE 16-16 *Tire inspection screen.*

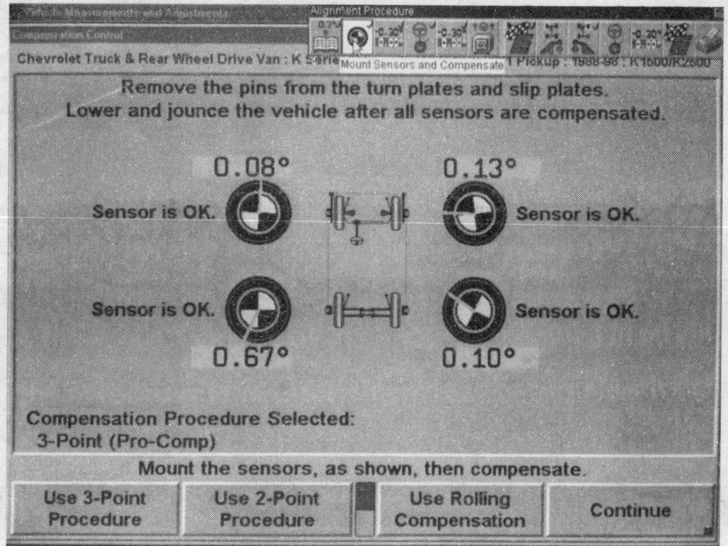

FIGURE 16-17 *Wheel runout compensation screen.*

If the computer aligner does not have automatic wheel runout compensation, a manual wheel runout procedure must be followed. This type of computer aligner displays a wheel runout measurement screen. During this procedure, the wheel being checked for runout is lifted with the hydraulic jack on the alignment rack and the wheel is rotated until the rim clamp knob faces downward. Level and lock the wheel unit in this position; then push Yes on the wheel unit as instructed on the screen. Rotate the wheel until the rim clamp knob faces upward; then level and lock the wheel unit. After this procedure, press Yes on the wheel unit. This same basic procedure is followed at each wheel.

PHOTO SEQUENCE 15
TYPICAL PROCEDURE FOR PERFORMING FOUR-WHEEL ALIGNMENT WITH A COMPUTER WHEEL ALIGNER

P16-1 *Position the vehicle on the alignment ramp.*

P16-2 *Be sure the front tires are positioned properly on the turntables.*

P16-3 *Position the rear wheels on slip plates.*

P16-4 *Attach the wheel units.*

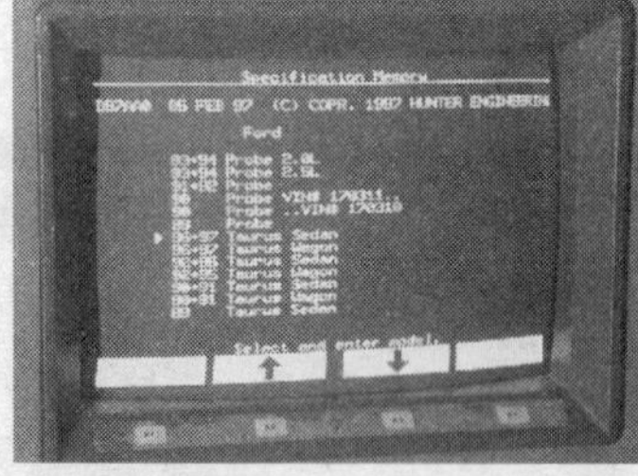

P16-5 *Select the vehicle make and model year.*

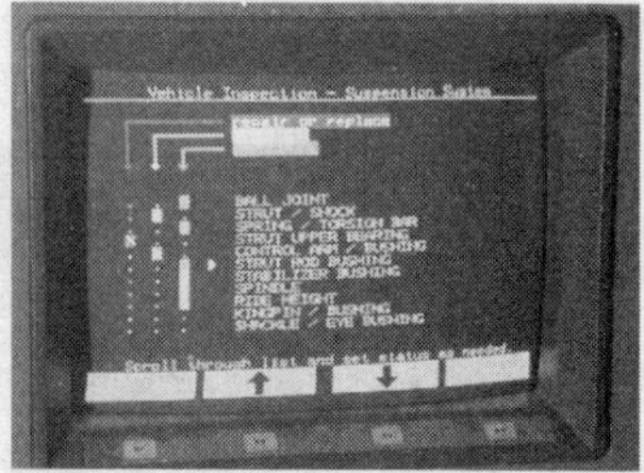

P16-6 *Check items on the screen during preliminary inspection.*

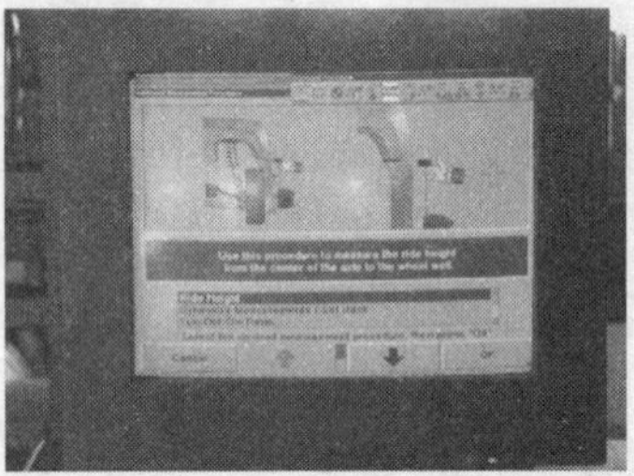

P16-7 *Display the ride height screen.*

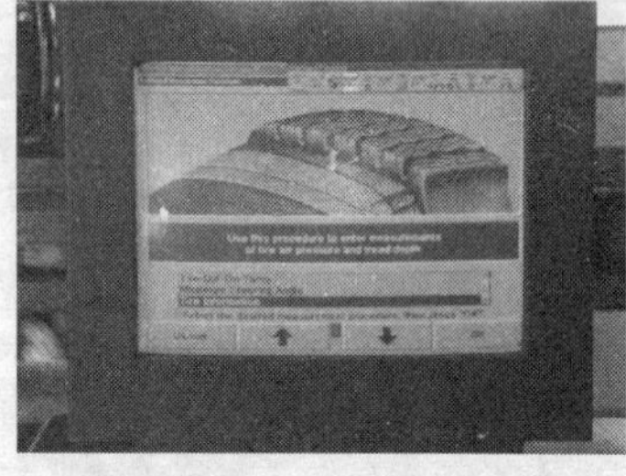

P16-8 *Check the tire condition for each tire on the tire condition screen.*

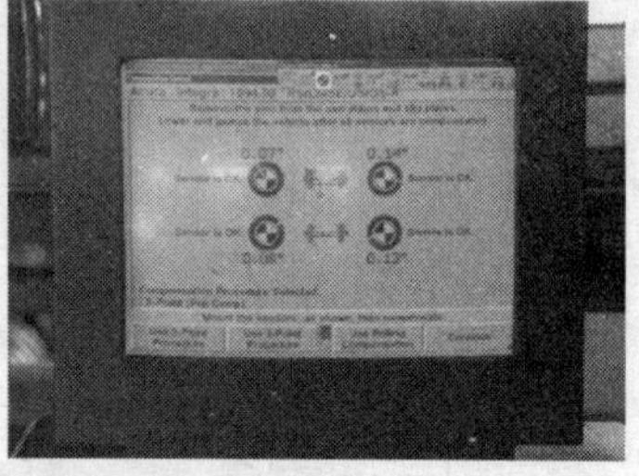

P16-9 *Display the wheel runout compensation screen.*

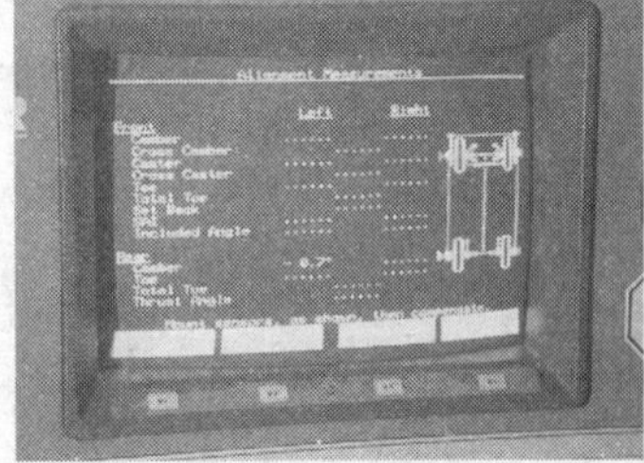

P16-10 *Display the front and rear wheel alignment angle screen.*

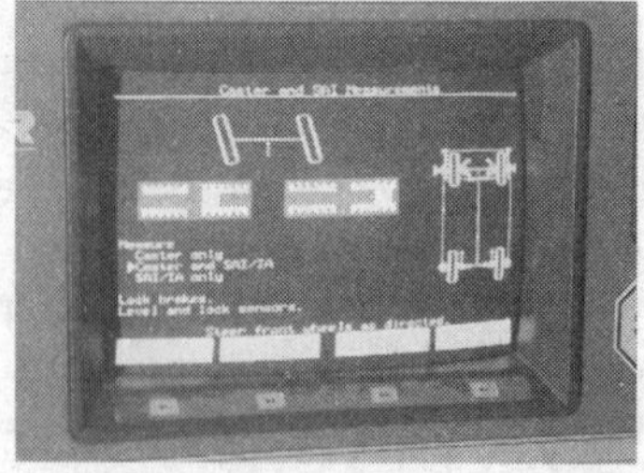

P16-11 *Display the turning angle screen and perform the turning angle check.*

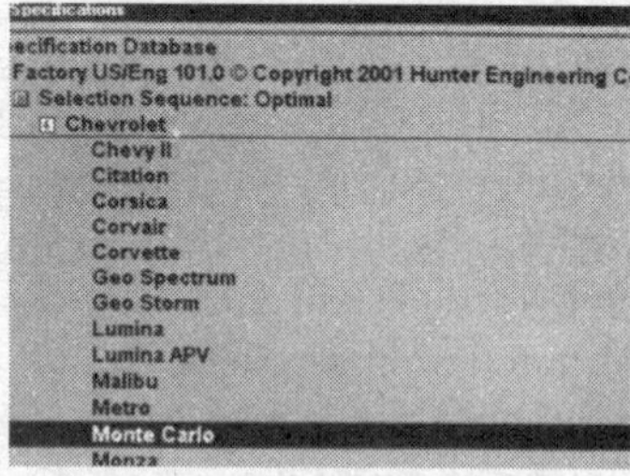

P16-12 *Display the adjustment screens.*

WHEEL ALIGNMENT SCREENS

Front and Rear Wheel Alignment Angle Screen

Prior to a display of the **front and rear wheel alignment angle screen** on some computer wheel aligners, the screen display directs the technician to position the front wheels straight ahead, lock the steering wheel, apply the **brake pedal depressor,** and level and lock the wheel units. See Photo Sequence 15. The brake pedal depressor is an adjustable rod installed between the front edge of the front seat and the brake pedal (Figure 16-18). If the vehicle has power brakes, the engine should be running when the depressor is used to apply the brakes. Some steering wheel holders are installed between the steering wheel and the top of the front seat (Figure 16-19). A ratchet and handle on the steering wheel holder allow extension of this holder.

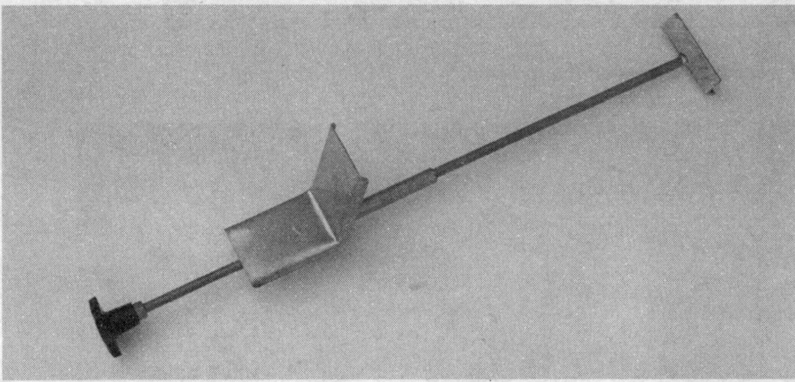

FIGURE 16-18 *Brake pedal depressor.*

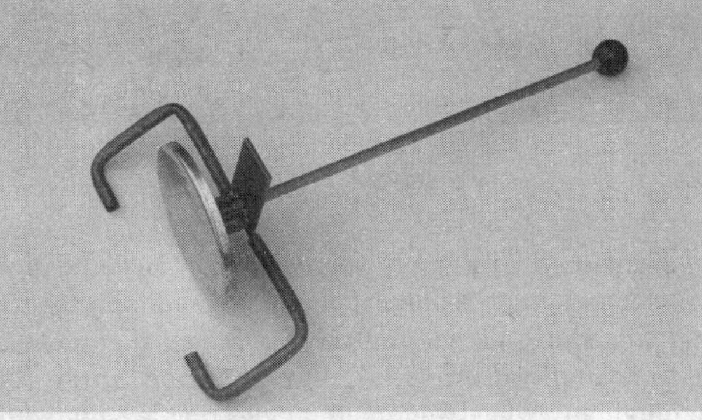

FIGURE 16-19 *Steering wheel holder.*

After the wheel runout compensation procedure is completed at each wheel sensor, some computer wheel aligners automatically display **camber**, toe-in or **toe-out**, **total toe**, **setback,** and **thrust line** measurements on the front and rear suspension. After this procedure, the screen directs the technician to swing the front wheels outward a specific amount (Figure 16-20). The steering wheel holder must be released and the lock pins removed from the front turntables before the wheel swing procedure. This front wheel swing may be referred to as a caster/SAI swing. The amount of front wheel swing varies depending on the make of the computer aligner. Older computer wheel aligners required the technician

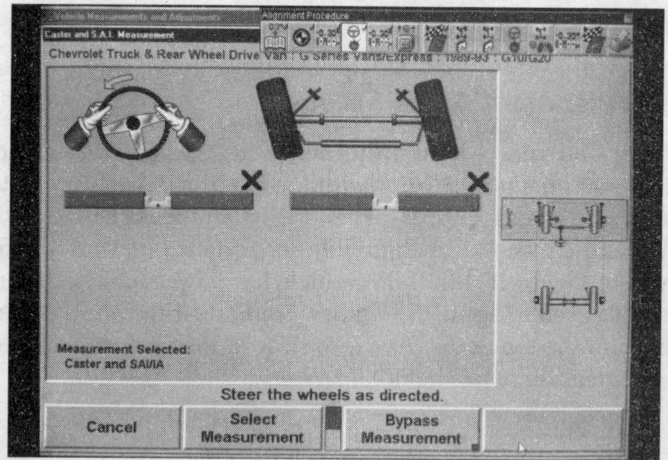

FIGURE 16-20 *Wheel swing instructions on the screen.*

FIGURE 16-21 *Wheel swing procedure illustrated on the screen.*

to read the degrees of wheel swing on the turntable degree scales. On some newer computer wheel aligners, the required amount of wheel swing is illustrated on the screen (Figure 16-21).

After the front wheel swing procedure, all the front and rear wheel alignment angles are displayed, including **caster, steering axis inclination (SAI),** and **included angle** (Figure 16-22). Some computer wheel aligners highlight any wheel alignment angles that are not within specifications. If cross camber and cross caster are displayed on the screen, these readings indicate the maximum difference allowed between the right and left side readings. Alignment angles within specifications are highlighted in green; alignment angles that are not within specifications are highlighted in red.

Turning Angle Screen

Some computer wheel aligners have a turning angle screen. When this screen is displayed, the technician removes the locking pins from the turntables. Each front wheel must be turned outward a specified amount, and the turning angle on the opposite front wheel must be entered with the keypad as directed on the screen (Figure 16-23). A toe-out on turns option is available on some DSP

Vehicle Measurements and Adjustments

Chevrolet Truck & Rear Wheel Drive Van : K Series/Silverado (4X4) 1972-2001 Pickup : 1999-2000 : Silverado (GMT800) : 1500

Front	Left		Right
Camber	0.4°		-0.2°
Cross Camber		0.6°	
Caster	4.0°		4.3°
Cross Caster		-0.4°	
SAI	10.3°		11.2°
Cross SAI		-0.9°	
Toe	0.01°		0.06°
Total Toe		0.07°	
Rear	**Left**		**Right**
Camber	-0.1°		-0.5°
Cross Camber		0.3°	
Toe	0.15°		-0.05°
Total Toe		0.10°	
Thrust Angle		0.10°	

Save the "before" alignment measurements.

Show Virtual View | Show Secondary Measurements | Save "Before" Measurements

FIGURE 16-22 *Front and rear wheel alignment screen.*

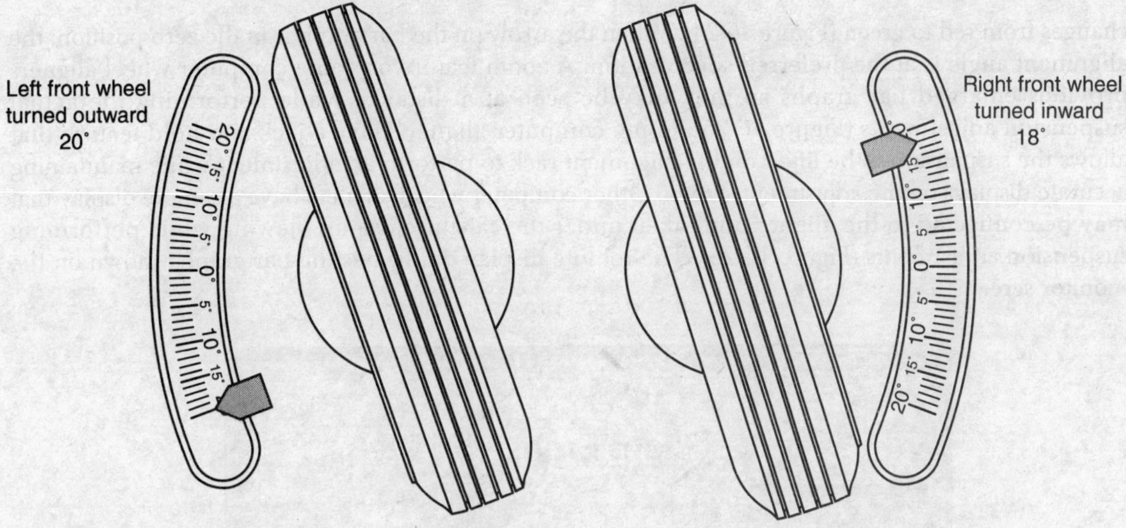

FIGURE 16-23 *Turning angle screen.*

wheel sensors. This option has optical encoders in the wheel sensors that measure the turning angle electronically rather than reading the degree scales on the front turntables.

ADJUSTMENT SCREENS

The technician may select adjustment screens that provide bar graph readings of camber, caster, and toe. An arrow on the bar graph shows the amount and direction the actual measurement is from the preferred specification. As the alignment angle is adjusted, the arrow moves. If an alignment angle moves from out of the specification range to within the specification range, the bar graph color

FIGURE 16-24 *Alignment angle adjustment screens. (Courtesy of Hunter Engineering Company.)*

changes from red to green (Figure 16-24). When the arrow on the bar graph is in the zero position, the alignment angle is at the preferred specification. A zoom feature on some computer wheel aligners provides enlarged bar graphs so they may be seen at a distance while performing the actual suspension adjustments (Figure 16-25). Some computer aligners have a jack and hold feature that allows the suspension to be lifted on the alignment rack to perform an adjustment while maintaining accurate displays on the adjustment screen. Other computer wheel aligners have a remote display that may be connected to the aligner and taken under the car for close-up viewing while performing suspension adjustments (Figure 16-26). The remote display duplicates the bar graphs shown on the monitor screen.

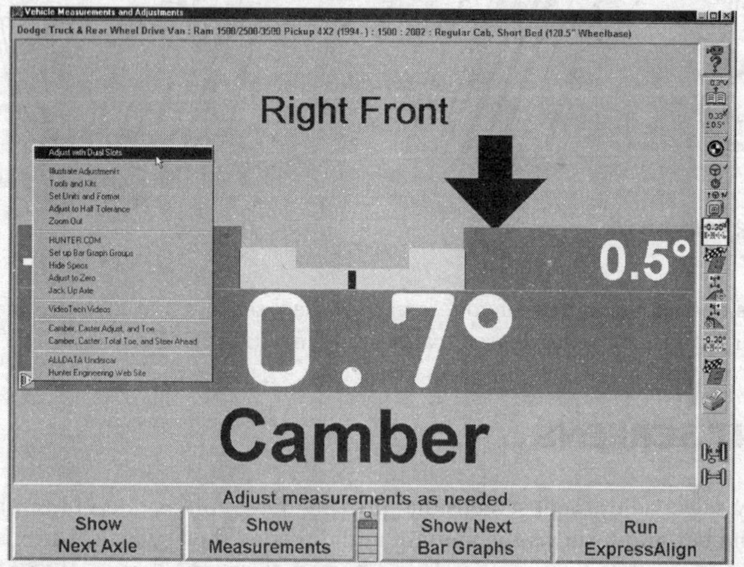

FIGURE 16-25 *Zoom feature on adjustment screens. (Courtesy of Hunter Engineering Company.)*

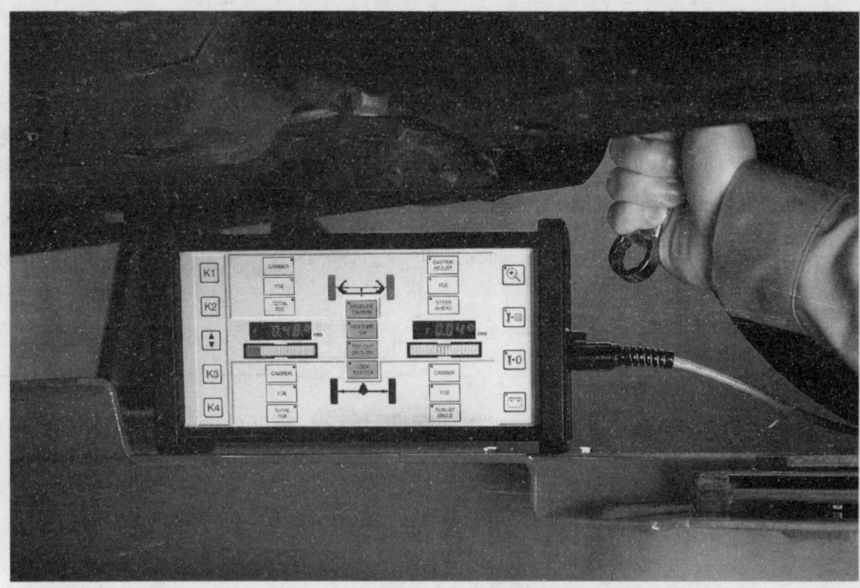

FIGURE 16-26 *Remote display for computer wheel aligner. (Courtesy of Hunter Engineering Company.)*

Some computer wheel aligners provide **symmetry angle measurements** that help the technician determine if out-of-specification readings may have been caused by collision or frame damage. These symmetry angle measurements display **axle offset,** right or left **lateral axle sideset** and track-width difference, front and rear wheel setback, and wheelbase difference (Figure 16-27). Setback is an angle formed by a line drawn at a 90° angle to the centerline and a line connecting the centers of the front or rear wheels (Figure 16-28). Wheelbase difference is an angle created by a line through the rear wheel centers and a line through the front wheel centers (Figure 16-29). Right or left lateral offset is an angle between the thrust line and a line connecting the centers of the left front and left rear wheels or right front and right rear wheels (Figure 16-30). Track-width difference is an angle created by the line connecting the centers of the right rear and right front wheels and the line connecting the centers of the left rear and left front wheels (Figure 16-31). Axle offset is an angle formed by the line that is projected forward at 90° in relation to the center of the rear axle and the thrust line (Figure 16-32).

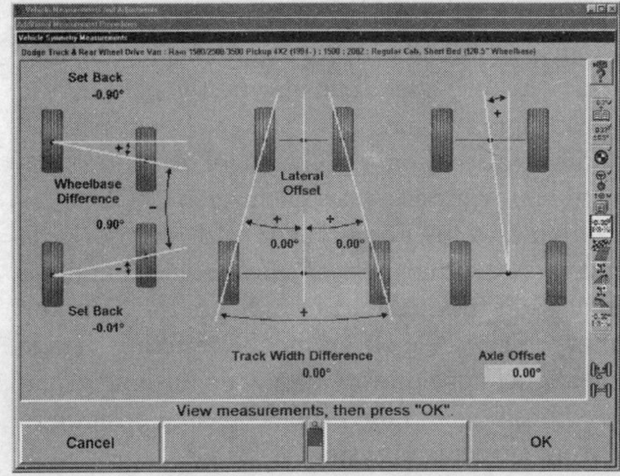

FIGURE 16-27 *Symmetry angle measurements. (Courtesy of Hunter Engineering Company.)*

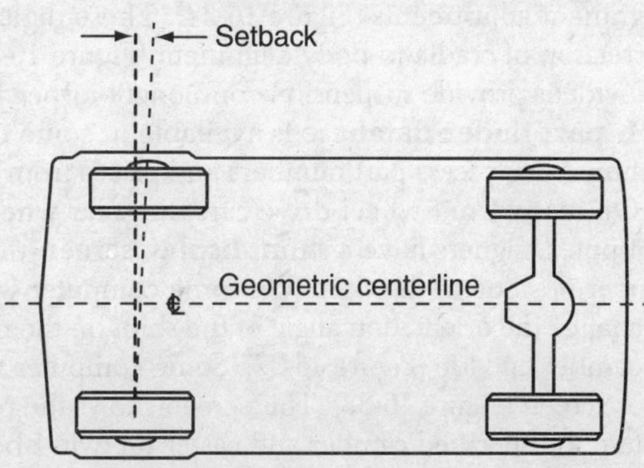

FIGURE 16-28 *Front or rear wheel setback.*

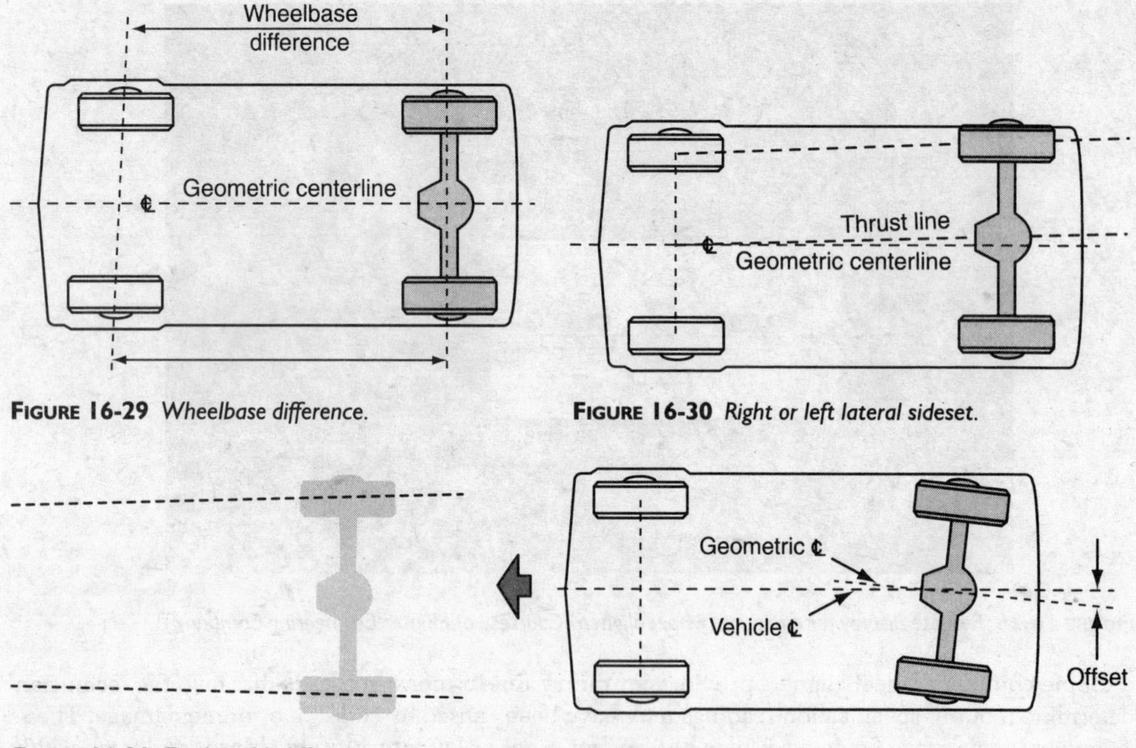

FIGURE 16-29 *Wheelbase difference.*

FIGURE 16-30 *Right or left lateral sideset.*

FIGURE 16-31 *Track-width difference.*

FIGURE 16-32 *Axle offset.*

DIAGNOSTIC DRAWING AND TEXT SCREENS

The technician may select tools and kits for the vehicle being serviced from the tools and kits database. When this feature is selected, the monitor screen displays the necessary wheel alignment adjustment tools for the vehicle selected at the beginning of the alignment (Figure 16-33). The kits displayed on the monitor screen are special components such as adjustment shims that are available for alignment adjustments on the car being serviced.

The technician may select **digital adjustment photos** that indicate how to perform wheel alignment adjustments (Figure 16-34). These digital photos include photos for cradle inspection and correction of cradle-to-body alignment (Figure 16-35). Live-action videos can also be selected. These CD videos provide suspension component inspection procedures (Figure 16-36).

A **part-finder database** is available in some computer wheel aligners. This database allows the technician to access part numbers and prices from many under-car parts manufacturers.

On many front-wheel-drive cars, the rear wheel camber and toe are adjusted with shims. Some computer aligners have a **shim display screen** that indicates the thickness of shim required and the proper position of the shim. On some computer wheel aligners, the technician may use the light pen to change the orientation angle of the shim on the monitor screen while observing the resulting change in camber and toe (Figure 16-37). Some computer wheel aligners provide an automatic bushing calculator screen (Figure 16-38). This screen shows the required bushing and the proper bushing position to obtain the specified camber and caster on twin I-beam front suspension systems.

A **control arm movement monitor** is available on some computer wheel aligners. On short-and-long arm front suspensions, this feature indicates the required shim thickness to provide the specified camber and caster (Figure 16-39).

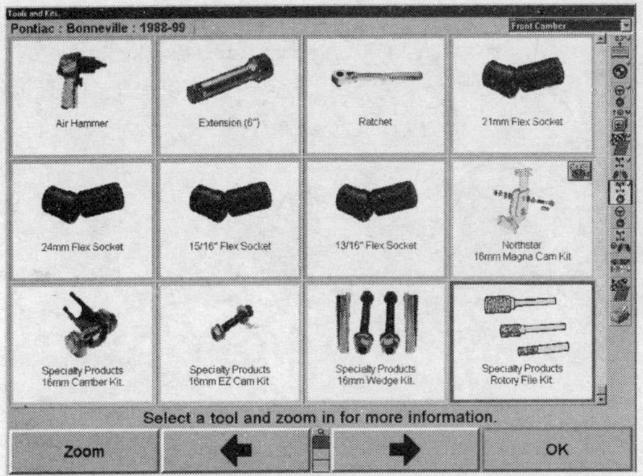

FIGURE 16-33 *Wheel alignment tools and kits display. (Courtesy of Hunter Engineering Company.)*

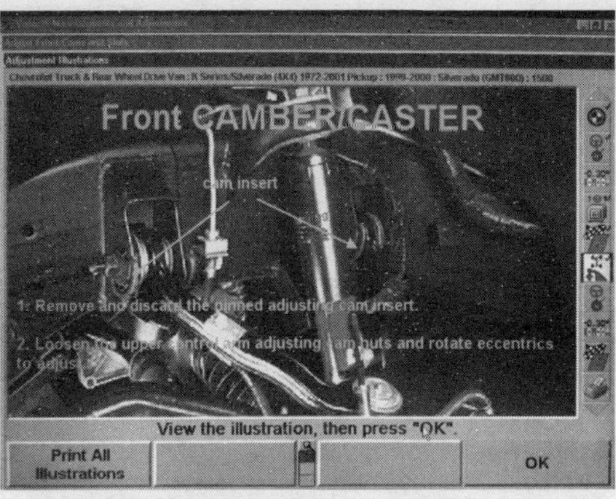

FIGURE 16-34 *Wheel alignment adjustment photos.*

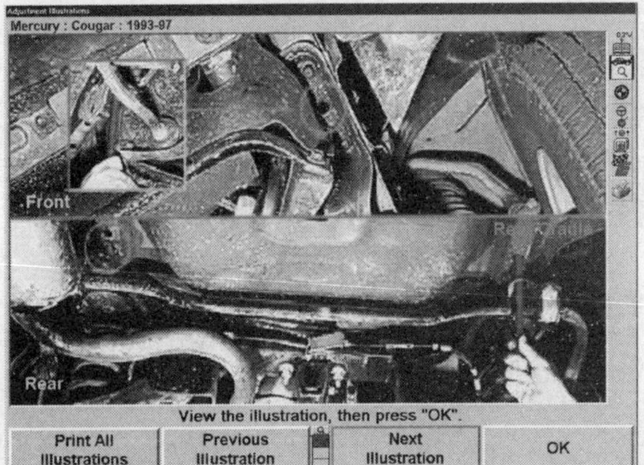

FIGURE 16-35 *Cradle inspection and correction photos. (Courtesy of Hunter Engineering Company.)*

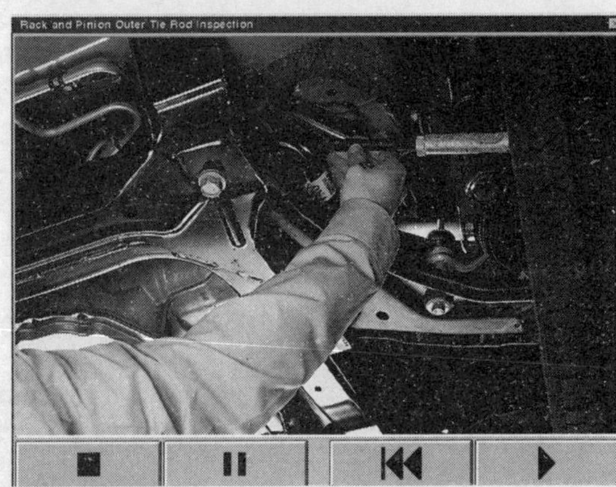

FIGURE 16-36 *Live-action videos of suspension inspection and service. (Courtesy of Hunter Engineering Company.)*

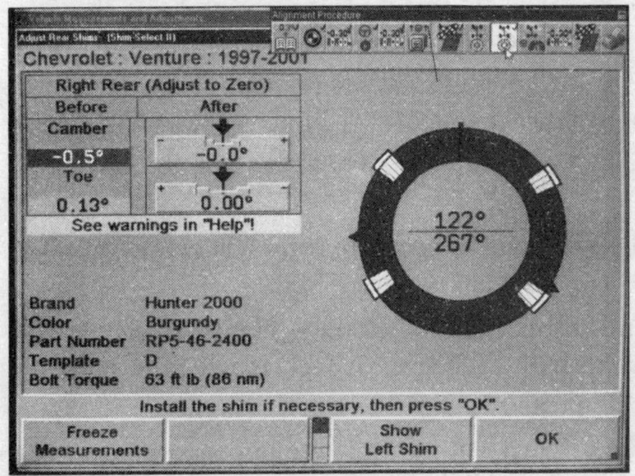

FIGURE 16-37 *Shim selection screen.*

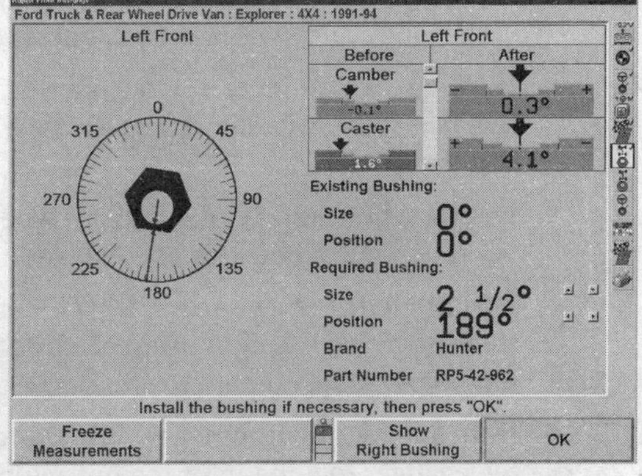

FIGURE 16-38 *Automatic bushing calculation screen. (Courtesy of Hunter Engineering Company.)*

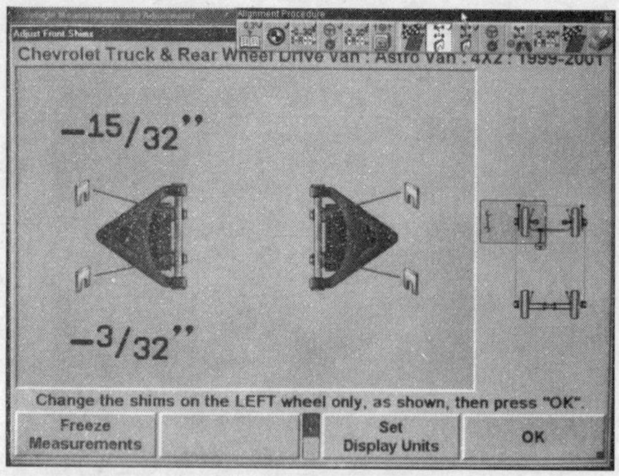

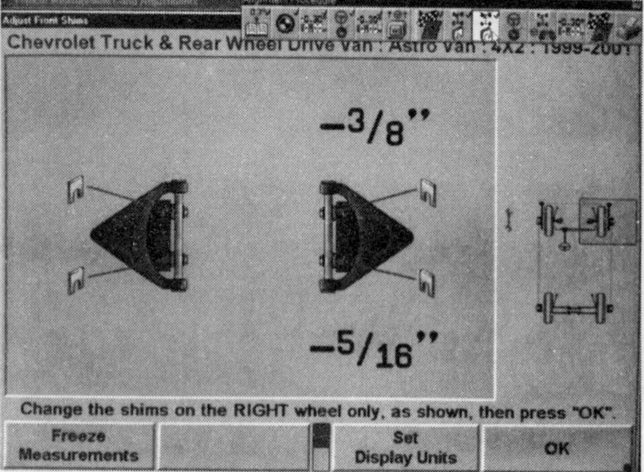

FIGURE 16-39 *Control arm movement monitor indicates the required shim thickness to provide specified camber and caster.*

On some computer wheel aligners, the technician may select Print at any time, and print out the displayed screen, including diagnostic drawings. Another optional procedure is to print out the wheel alignment report before and after the adjustment of wheel alignment angles.

CHECKING TOE CHANGE AND STEERING LINKAGE HEIGHT

If the steering linkage on each side is not the same height, a condition called bump steer may occur. When bump steer occurs, the steering suddenly swerves to one side when one of the front wheels strikes a road irregularity. When this steering linkage condition is present, abnormal toe changes occur during wheel jounce and rebound.

Follow this procedure to check for abnormal toe changes during wheel jounce and rebound:

1. Be sure the toe is adjusted to specifications with the front wheels centered and the steering wheel locked.
2. Pull the chassis downward approximately 3 in. (7.6 cm) and observe the toe change. It is acceptable if the toe setting on each front wheel remains at the original reading or if each front wheel toes in or toes out an equal small amount (Figure 16-40).
3. During wheel jounce, if one front wheel toes inward or outward while the opposite wheel remains at the original setting, the steering linkage height is not equal and must be corrected (Figure 16-41).
4. During wheel jounce, if one front wheel toes in and the opposite front wheel toes out, the steering linkage height is unequal and must be corrected (Figure 16-42).
5. Push the chassis upward 3 in. (7.6 cm) and inspect the toe change (Figure 16-43). If the steering linkage height is equal, the toe setting on each front wheel remains the same or moves the same amount to a toe-in or toe-out position.
6. If the toe on one front wheel remains at the original setting while the opposite front wheel toe changes to a toe-in or toe-out setting, the steering linkage height is unequal. When one front wheel moves to a toe-in position, and the opposite front wheel moves to a toe-out setting, unequal steering linkages are indicated.

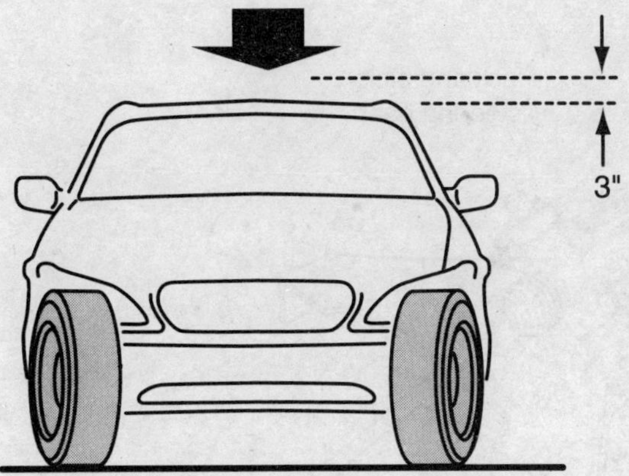

FIGURE 16-40 *Normal toe change during wheel jounce.*

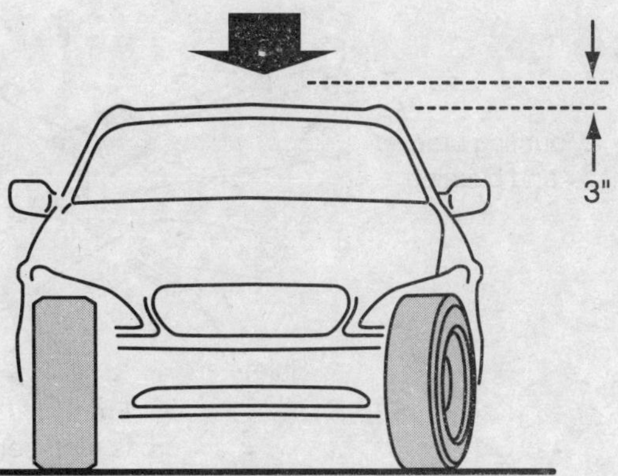

FIGURE 16-41 *If the toe change on one front wheel remains at the original setting while the toe on the opposite wheel toes in or out during wheel jounce, unequal steering linkage height is indicated.*

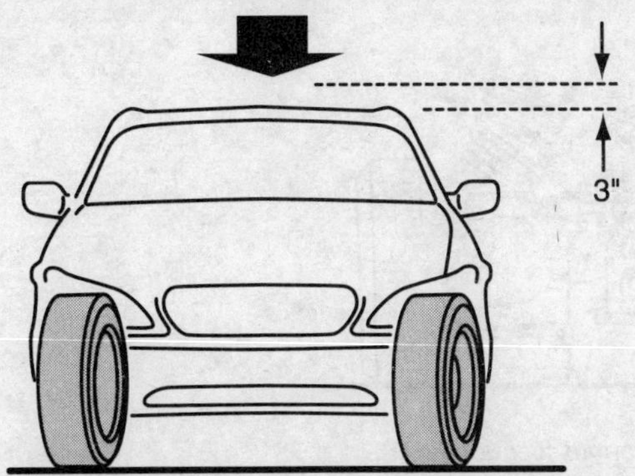

FIGURE 16-42 *If the toe on one front wheel toes in and the toe on the opposite front wheel toes out during wheel jounce, unequal steering linkage height is indicated.*

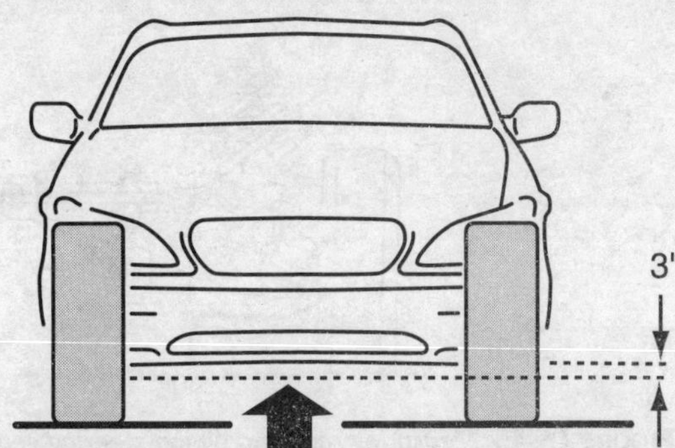

FIGURE 16-43 *Pull the chassis upward 3 in. (7.6 cm) to check for improper toe change indicating unequal steering linkage height.*

On some imported vehicles, the steering linkage height can be adjusted with shims between the rack and pinion steering gear and the chassis (Figure 16-44). The idler arm may be moved upward or downward on some domestic vehicles to adjust the steering linkage height. On other vehicles, if the steering linkage height is unequal, steering components are worn or bent. These components include tie-rods, tie-rod ends, idler arms, pitman arms, and rack and pinion steering gear mounting bushings.

Another method of inspecting for equal tie-rod height on rack and pinion steering gears is to measure the distance from the center of the inner retaining bolt on the lower control arm to the alignment ramp on each side of the front suspension (distances A and B in Figure 16-45). If this distance is not equal on each side of the front suspension, one of the front springs may be sagged or such components as control arm bushings may be worn. When distances A and B are not equal, this problem must be corrected before performing the steering gear measurements. If distances A and B are equal, measure from the outer ends of the rack and pinion steering gear to the alignment ramp (distances C and D). If these distances are not equal, the rack and pinion steering gear mountings may be worn or distorted.

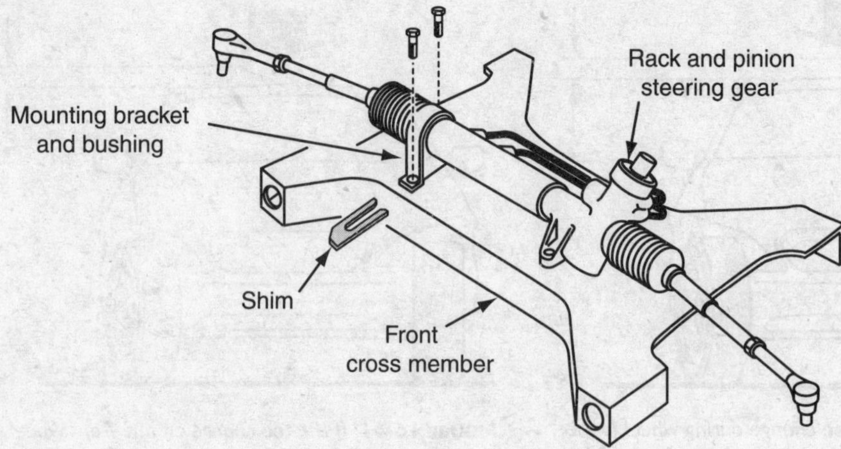

FIGURE 16-44 *On some imported vehicles, shims between the rack and pinion steering gear and the chassis adjust the steering linkage height.*

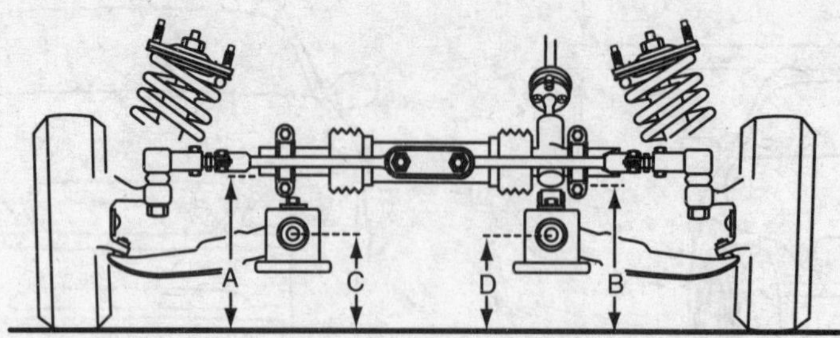

FIGURE 16-45 *Measuring rack and pinion steering gear height at various locations.*

BENT FRONT STRUT DIAGNOSIS

Diagnostic Procedure

Front struts that are bent forward or rearward may be diagnosed as follows:

1. With the vehicle on the aligning rack and the magnetic gauges in position for the camber measurement, swing one front wheel out 10° and read the camber.
2. Turn the same wheel inward 10° and read the camber. The difference between the two readings is usually less than 4 1/2°. If the strut is bent forward or rearward, the difference in the camber readings will be excessive. A 10° difference is not uncommon.
3. Repeat steps 1 and 2 on the other front wheel.

Front struts could also be bent inward or outward. To diagnose this condition, use the following procedure:

1. With the wheel aligner in operation, sit on the front fender to load the suspension downward, and then read the camber.

2. Unload the suspension and lift up on the vehicle while the camber is recorded. The two camber readings should be within 1/2°. If the strut is bent inward or outward, the difference in the two camber readings will be excessive. A 4° to 6° camber change is not uncommon.
3. Repeat steps 1 and 2 on the other front wheel.

CASE STUDY

A customer complained about erratic steering on a front-wheel-drive Dodge Intrepid. A road test revealed the car steered reasonably well on a smooth road surface, but while driving on irregular road surfaces, the steering would suddenly swerve to the right or left.

The technician performed a preliminary wheel alignment inspection and found the right tie-rod end was loose; all the other suspension and steering components were in satisfactory condition. The technician replaced the loose tie-rod end, but a second road test indicated that the bump steer problem was still present. After advising the customer that a complete wheel alignment was necessary, the technician drove the vehicle on the wheel aligner and carefully checked all front and rear alignment angles. Each front and rear wheel alignment angle was within specifications. The technician realized that somehow he had not diagnosed this problem correctly.

While thinking about this problem, the technician remembered a general diagnostic procedure he learned while studying automotive technology. This procedure stated: Listen to the customer complaints, be sure the complaint is identified, think of the possible causes, test to locate the exact problem, and be sure the complaint is eliminated. The technician realized he had not thought much about the causes of the problem, and so he began to recall the wheel alignment theory he learned in college. He remembered that the tie-rods must be parallel to the lower control arms, and if the tie-rod height is unequal, this parallel condition no longer exists. The technician also recalled that unequal tie-rod height causes improper toe changes during wheel jounce and rebound, which result in bump steer.

An inspection of the toe during front wheel jounce and rebound indicated the toe on the right front wheel remained the same during wheel jounce and rebound, but the toe on the left front wheel moved to a toe-out position. Since the tie-rods had been inspected during the preliminary alignment inspection, the technician turned his attention to the rack and pinion steering gear mounting. He found the bushing on the right end of the steering gear was worn and loose. This bushing was replaced and all the steering gear mounting bolts were tightened to the specified torque. An inspection of the toe change during wheel jounce and rebound revealed a normal toe change.

From this experience the technician learned the following two things:

1. His understanding of wheel alignment theory was very important in diagnosing steering problems.
2. Always be thorough! During a prealignment inspection, check all suspension and steering components, including rack and pinion steering gear mountings.

SERVICE TIPS

- If steering pull or drift is evident during the road test, drive the vehicle on the same road in the opposite direction to determine if a crosswind is causing the steering pull.
- Decreasing the rear ride height 1 in. (25.4 mm) moves the front wheel caster 1° more positive.

- Many computer wheel aligners can print out any single screen. It may be helpful to print out the wheel alignment angle screen before and after the alignment angles are adjusted to the vehicle manufacturer's specifications. These printouts may be presented to the customer; many customers appreciate this service.

REVIEW QUESTIONS

1. While discussing a front suspension height that is 1 in. (2.54 cm) less than specified:
   Technician A says the suspension height must be correct before a wheel alignment is performed.
   Technician B says the lower front suspension height may be caused by worn lower control arm bushings.
   Who is correct?
   A. A only **C.** Both A and B
   B. B only **D.** Neither A nor B
2. While performing a prealignment inspection:
   Technician A says improper front wheel bearing adjustment may affect wheel alignment angles.
   Technician B says worn ball joints have no effect on wheel alignment angles.
   Who is correct?
   A. A only **C.** Both A and B
   B. B only **D.** Neither A nor B
3. While discussing a front suspension system in which the right front wheel has 2° positive camber and the left front wheel has 1/2° positive camber:
   Technician A says when the vehicle is driven straight ahead, the steering will pull to the left.
   Technician B says there will be excessive wear on the inside edge of the left front tire tread.
   Who is correct?
   A. A only **C.** Both A and B
   B. B only **D.** Neither A nor B
4. When discussing unsatisfactory steering wheel returnability:
   Technician A says the rack and pinion steering gear mounts may be worn. *Technician B* says this problem may be caused by interference between the dash seal and the steering shaft.
   Who is correct?
   A. A only **C.** Both A and B
   B. B only **D.** Neither A nor B
5. While discussing turning radius measurement:
   Technician A says a bent steering arm will cause the turning radius to be out-of-specification.
   Technician B says if the turning radius is not within specification, tire tread wear is excessive while cornering.
   Who is correct?
   A. A only **C.** Both A and B
   B. B only **D.** Neither A nor B
6. While measuring and adjusting front wheel toe:
   A. If the positive caster is increased on the right front wheel, this wheel moves toward a toe-in position.
   B. Improper front wheel toe setting causes steering wander and drift.
   C. The front wheel toe should be checked with the front wheels straight ahead.
   D. Improper front wheel toe setting causes wear on the inside edge of the tire tread.

7. All of these statements about front wheel toe change during wheel jounce and rebound are true EXCEPT:
   A. If one front wheel toes in and the opposite front wheel toes out during front wheel jounce and rebound, the tie-rod height is unequal.
   B. If both front wheels toe in or toe out a small, equal amount during front wheel jounce and rebound, the tie-rods are parallel to the lower control arms.
   C. The improper toe change during front wheel jounce and rebound may cause bump steer.
   D. Improper toe change during front wheel jounce and rebound may be caused by a worn upper strut mount.
8. While using a computer wheel aligner:
   A. The technician may select defective suspension components from a list on the screen.
   B. It is not necessary to check or compensate for wheel runout.
   C. If the camber bar graph is red, the camber setting is within specifications.
   D. A wheel sensor containing a high-frequency transmitter requires a cable connected to the aligner computer.
9. While using computer wheel aligners:
   A. On many computer wheel aligners, the technician may only print out the four-wheel alignment results.
   B. Some wheel sensors have the capability to measure ride height and display this reading on the screen.
   C. A front wheel swing is necessary before reading the front wheel camber.
   D. If the computer aligner contains a control arm movement monitor, the technician has to estimate the necessary shim thickness.
10. While using computer wheel aligners:
    A. Symmetry angle measurements display thrust angle, rear wheel toe, and rear wheel camber.
    B. Setback is the angle formed by a line at 90° to the vehicle centerline at the axle attachment point and a line through the left and right wheel centers.
    C. Wheelbase difference is an angle created by a line through the rear wheel centers and the thrust line.
    D. Right or left lateral offset is an angle between a line through the left front and left rear tires and a line between the right front and right rear tires.

CHALLENGE QUESTIONS

1. While discussing turning radius:
   Technician A says incorrect turning radius may often be noted by tire squeal while cornering.
   Technician B says to adjust turning radius toe-out on turns, turn the inner wheel to stop.
   Who is correct?
   A. A only
   B. B only
   C. Both A and B
   D. Neither A nor B
2. The customer says that sometimes her car suddenly swerves to one side on a bump. All of the following could cause this problem EXCEPT:
   A. Loose steering gear.
   B. Worn tie-rods.
   C. Sagging front springs.
   D. Steering gear lash adjustment.

3. While discussing steering diagnosis:
Technician A says uneven half-shaft axle lengths may cause a vehicle to pull to one side when accelerating. *Technician B* says abnormal toe changes can cause a vehicle to pull to one side on road irregularities.
Who is correct?
A. A only **C.** Both A and B
B. B only **D.** Neither A nor B

4. After you have completed a front end alignment, a customer returns to your shop and complains of continued vehicle drift. To correct this problem, you should:
A. Inspect the manual steering gear for possible miscentering of the sector gear.
B. Inspect rear wheel alignment.
C. Ask the customer to fill the fuel tank.
D. Inspect the steering column flex coupling.

5. While performing a prealignment inspection:
Technician A says a prealignment inspection should include checking the vehicle interior for heavy items. *Technician B* says tools and other items normally carried in the vehicle should be included during an alignment.
Who is correct?
A. A only **C.** Both A and B
B. B only **D.** Neither A nor B

Job Sheet 46

Name ______________________________ Date ______________

ROAD-TEST VEHICLE AND DIAGNOSE STEERING OPERATION

Upon completion of this job sheet, you should be able to road-test a vehicle and diagnose steering operation.

ASE Correlation

This job sheet is related to ASE Automotive Suspension and Steering Task: *Diagnose all types of steering complaints and determine the necessary repairs.*

Describe the Vehicle Being Worked On:

Year __________ Make ______________ Model ______________
VIN ______________ Engine type and size ______________

Procedure

Task Completed

1. Road-test vehicle under such driving conditions as slow-speed driving, cornering, and normal cruising speed while driving on a straight, level road surface. Check for the following abnormal steering conditions: ☐
2. Vertical chassis oscillations: ☐ Satisfactory ☐ Unsatisfactory
3. Chassis lateral waddle: ☐ Satisfactory ☐ Unsatisfactory
4. Steering pull to right: ☐ Satisfactory ☐ Unsatisfactory
5. Steering pull to left: ☐ Satisfactory ☐ Unsatisfactory
6. Steering effort: ☐ Satisfactory ☐ Unsatisfactory
7. Tire squeal while cornering: ☐ Satisfactory ☐ Unsatisfactory
8. Bump steer: ☐ Satisfactory ☐ Unsatisfactory
9. Torque steer: ☐ Satisfactory ☐ Unsatisfactory
10. Memory steer: ☐ Satisfactory ☐ Unsatisfactory
11. Steering wheel return: ☐ Satisfactory ☐ Unsatisfactory
12. Steering wheel free play: ☐ Satisfactory ☐ Unsatisfactory
13. Return the vehicle to the shop and inspect suspension and steering to determine the cause of abnormal conditions. List the necessary repairs and/or adjustments to correct all abnormal conditions that occurred during the road test.

____

____

Instructor's Response ______________________________

____

____

JOB SHEET 47

Name ______________________________ Date ______________

MEASURE FRONT AND REAR WHEEL ALIGNMENT ANGLES WITH A COMPUTER WHEEL ALIGNER

Upon completion of this job sheet, you should be able to measure front and rear wheel alignment with a computer wheel aligner.

ASE Correlation

This job sheet is related to ASE Automotive Suspension and Steering Tasks:

1. *Measure vehicle ride height and determine the necessary repairs.*
2. *Inspect and adjust front and rear wheel camber on adjustable and nonadjustable front and rear suspension systems and determine the necessary repairs.*
3. *Inspect and adjust front wheel caster on adjustable and nonadjustable suspension systems.*
4. *Inspect and adjust front wheel toe.*
5. *Inspect toe-out on turns and determine the necessary repairs.*
6. *Inspect steering axis inclination (SAI) and kingpin inclination (KPI), and determine the necessary repairs.*
7. *Inspect the included angle and determine the necessary repairs.*
8. *Inspect rear wheel toe and adjust or repair as necessary.*
9. *Inspect rear wheel thrust line and adjust or repair as necessary.*
10. *Inspect front wheel setback and repair as necessary.*

Tools and Materials

Computer wheel aligner

Describe the Vehicle Being Worked On:

Year __________ Make ________________ Model ____________

VIN ____________________ Engine type and size ________________

Procedure

Task Completed

WARNING: When you drive a vehicle onto an alignment ramp, be sure no one is standing in front of the vehicle to avoid causing personal injury.

1. Lock the front turntables and drive the vehicle onto the alignment ramp. Apply the parking brake.

   Are the front tires properly positioned on the front turntables? ☐ Yes ☐ No

   Are the rear tires properly positioned on the slip plates? ☐ Yes ☐ No

   Instructor check ________________________________

Task Completed

2. Install the rim clamps and wheel sensors. Perform wheel sensor leveling and wheel runout compensation procedures.

   Are the wheel sensors level? ☐ Yes ☐ No

   Is the wheel runout compensation procedure completed? ☐ Yes ☐ No

   Instructor check ____

3. Select the specifications for the vehicle being aligned.

   Are the specifications selected? ☐ Yes ☐ No

   Instructor check ____

4. Perform a prealignment inspection using the checklist in the computer wheel aligner. List any components that must be repaired or replaced, and explain the reasons for your diagnosis.

   ____

   ____

   ____

   ____

   ____

5. Measure the ride height.

   Left front ride height ______ Specified ride height ______

   Right front ride height ______ Specified ride height ______

   Left rear ride height ______ Specified ride height ______

   Right rear ride height ______ Specified ride height ______

   State the necessary repairs to correct ride height and explain the reasons for your diagnosis.

   ____

   ____

   ____

   ____

6. Measure the front and rear suspension alignment angles following the prompts on the computer wheel aligner screen.

   Left front camber ______ Right front camber ______

   Cross camber ______ Specified front wheel camber ______

   Specified cross camber ______

   Left front caster ______ Right front caster ______

   Cross caster ______ Specified front wheel caster ______

   Specified cross caster ______

   Left front SAI ______ Right front SAI ______

   Specified SAI ______ Included angle ______

Task Completed ______

Thrust angle ______

Specified thrust angle ______

Left front toe ______ Right front toe ______

Total toe ______ Specified front wheel toe ______

Left rear camber ______ Right rear camber ______

Specified camber ______

Left rear toe______ Right rear toe ______

Total toe ______ Specified rear wheel toe ______

State the necessary adjustments and repairs to correct front and rear suspension alignment angles and explain the reasons for your diagnosis.

______
______
______
______
______

7. Measure the turning radius.

Left turn: Turning radius right front wheel ______
Turning radius left front wheel ______

Specified turning radius ______

Right turn: Turning radius left front wheel ______
Turning radius right front wheel ______

Specified turning radius ______

State the necessary repairs to correct the turning radius, and explain the reasons for your diagnosis.

______
______
______
______
______
______

Instructor's Response ______
______
______

JOB SHEET 48

Name ______________________________ Date ______________

CHECK PROPER STEERING LINKAGE HEIGHT BY MEASURING TOE CHANGE

Upon completion of this job sheet, you should be able to check steering linkage height by measuring toe change.

ASE Correlation

This job sheet is related to ASE Automotive Suspension and Steering Task: *Diagnose all types of steering complaints and determine the necessary repairs.*

Tools and Materials

Computer wheel aligner

Describe the Vehicle Being Worked On:

Year __________ Make ______________ Model ______________
VIN ______________ Engine type and size ______________

Procedure

Task Completed

1. Be sure the toe is adjusted to specifications with the front wheels centered and the steering wheel locked.

   Toe, left front __________

   Toe, right front __________

   Total toe, front wheels __________

2. Pull the chassis downward approximately 3 in. (7.6 cm) and record the toe change.

   Toe change left front from __________ to __________

   Toe change right front from __________ to __________

3. During the wheel jounce in step 2, did the toe remain at the original setting on the left front? Amount of toe change from the original setting on the left front wheel

   ____

   During the wheel jounce in step 2, did the toe remain at the original setting on the right front? Amount of toe change from the original setting on the right front wheel

   ____

4. During the wheel jounce in step 2, did the right and the left front wheels move an equal amount toward a toe-in position? Amount of toe change toward a toe-in position on both front wheels __________

5. During the wheel jounce in step 2, did one front wheel move toward a toe-in or toe-out position while the opposite front wheel remained at the original position? Amount that one front wheel moved toward a toe-in or toe-out position while the opposite front wheel remained at the original position __________

Task Completed

6. During the wheel jounce in step 2, did one front wheel move toward a toe-in and the opposite front wheel move toward a toe-out position?
   Amount that one front wheel moved toward a toe-in position __________
   Amount the opposite front wheel moved toward a toe-out position __________
7. Push the chassis upward 3 in. (7.6 cm) and inspect the toe change.
   Left front toe change: from __________ to __________
   Right front toe change: from __________ to __________
8. During the wheel rebound in step 7, did one front wheel remain at the original setting and the opposite front wheel move toward a toe-in or toe-out position?
   Amount that one front wheel moved toward a toe-in or toe-out position while the opposite front wheel remained at the original setting __________
9. During the wheel rebound in step 7, did one front wheel move toward a toe-in position while the opposite front wheel moved toward a toe-out position?
   Amount that one front wheel moved toward a toe-in position, and the amount the opposite front wheel moved toward a toe-out position __________
10. List all the abnormal conditions that indicate unequal steering arm height.
   ____
   ____
   ____
   ____
11. Inspect the front steering linkages and steering gear mountings, and list the necessary repairs to correct the improper toe change during wheel jounce and rebound. Explain the reasons for your diagnosis.
   ____
   ____
   ____

Instructor's Response ____
____
____

APPENDIX

METRIC CONVERSIONS A

	to convert these	to these,	multiply by:
TEMPERATURE	Centigrade Degrees	Fahrenheit Degrees	1.8 then + 32
	Fahrenheit Degrees	Centigrade Degrees	0.556 after – 32
LENGTH	Millimeters	Inches	0.03937
	Inches	Millimeters	25.4
	Meters	Feet	3.28084
	Feet	Meters	0.3048
	Kilometers	Miles	0.62137
	Miles	Kilometers	1.60935
AREA	Square Centimeters	Square Inches	0.155
	Square Inches	Square Centimeters	6.45159
VOLUME	Cubic Centimeters	Cubic Inches	0.06103
	Cubic Inches	Cubic Centimeters	16.38703
	Cubic Centimeters	Liters	0.001
	Liters	Cubic Centimeters	1000
	Liters	Cubic Inches	61.025
	Cubic Inches	Liters	0.01639
	Liters	Quarts	1.05672
	Quarts	Liters	0.94633
	Liters	Pints	2.11344
	Pints	Liters	0.47317
	Liters	Ounces	33.81497
	Ounces	Liters	0.02957
WEIGHT	Grams	Ounces	0.03527
	Ounces	Grams	28.34953
	Kilograms	Pounds	2.20462
	Pounds	Kilograms	0.45359
WORK	Centimeter-Kilograms	Inch-Pounds	0.8676
	Inch-Pounds	Centimeter-Kilograms	1.15262
	Meter-Kilograms	Foot-Pounds	7.23301
	Foot-Pounds	Newton-Meters	1.3558
PRESSURE	Kilograms/Square Centimeter	Pounds/Square Inch	14.22334
	Pounds/Square Inch	Kilograms/Square Centimeter	0.07031
	Bar	Pounds/Square Inch	14.504
	Pounds/Square Inch	Bar	0.06895

Automotive Suspension and Steering Systems Special Tool Suppliers

Appendix

B

Automotive Group
Kent-Moore Division, SPX Corporation
Roseville, MI

Bear Automotive Service Equipment Company
Milwaukee, WI

Easco/KD Tools
Lancaster, PA

Hennessy Industries, Inc.
LaVerge, TN

Hunter Engineering Company
Bridgeton, MO

Mac Tools, Inc.
Washington Courthouse, OH

OTC Division, SPX Corporation
Owatonna, MN

Sears Industrial Sales
Cincinnati, OH

Snap-On Tools Corporation
Kenosha, WI

Specialty Products Company
Longmont, CO

Sun Electric Corporation
Crystal Lake, IL

INDEX